SILVER BURDETT & GINN
LIFE SCIENCE

Series Authors

Peter Alexander, Ph.D.
Professor of Biology and Computer Science
St. Peter's College
Jersey City, New Jersey

Marilyn Fiegel, Ed.D.
District Science Coordinator
West Seneca Central Schools
West Seneca, New York

Steven K. Foehr
Teacher of Science
Wickford Middle School
North Kingston, Rhode Island

Anne F. Harris
Environmental Scientist
Black and Veatch, Engineers/Architects
Kansas City, Missouri

Joseph G. Krajkovich, Ed.D.
Supervisor of Science
Edison Twp. Board of Education
Edison, New Jersey

Kenneth W. May
Chairperson, Science Department
Camden Central School
Camden, New York

Nicholas Tzimopoulos, Ph.D.
Director of Science
Sleepy Hollow High School
North Tarrytown, New York

Rita K. Voltmer, Ph.D.
Assistant Professor of Science Education
Miami University
Oxford, Ohio

SILVER BURDETT & GINN
MORRISTOWN, NJ • NEEDHAM, MA
Atlanta, GA • Cincinnati, OH • Dallas, TX • Menlo Park, CA • Northfield, IL

Content Reviewers

Clyde D. Barbour, Ph.D.
Associate Professor
Department of Biological Sciences
Wright State University
Dayton, Ohio

C. Ritchie Bell, Ph.D.
Professor of Botany
University of North Carolina
Director, North Carolina
Botanical Garden
Chapel Hill, North Carolina

Penny L. Bernstein, Ph.D.
Research Associate
Rutgers University
New Brunswick, New Jersey

Herndon G. Dowling, Ph.D.
Professor of Biology
New York University
New York, New York

Margaret J. Hartman, Ph.D.
Professor of Biology
California State University
Los Angeles, California

Ivan Huber, Ph.D.
Professor of Biology
Fairleigh Dickinson University
Madison, New Jersey

Cynthia A. Needham, Ph.D.
Associate Professor, Microbiology
Boston University School of Medicine
Boston, Massachusetts

Teacher Reviewers

Kathy Arterburn
Life Science Teacher
Socorro Middle School
Socorro, New Mexico

Kevin M. Averill
Assistant Principal for Academics
Neumann Prep
Wayne, New Jersey

William T. Conn, Jr.
Science Supervisor
Memphis City Schools
Memphis, Tennessee

Donald L. Cooper, Ph.D.
Chairperson, Science Department
Morrow Junior High School
Morrow, Georgia

Howard B. Fisher
Biology Teacher
Binghamton High School
Binghamton, New York

Marguerite L. Hart
Curriculum Coordinator
Metropolitan School District of
Washington Township
Indianapolis, Indiana

Douglas K. Kugler
Science Teacher
Abilene Middle School
Abilene, Kansas

Brother James W. Lent
Chairperson, Science
St. Charles School
Albuquerque, New Mexico

Peggy Leonard, M.T.
Former Biology and Medical
Science Teacher
Parkway West High School
Ballwin, Missouri

Sherrie Martin
Assistant Principal
Ferndale High School
Ferndale, Washington

William M. Persky
Science Teacher
Munich International School
Munich, Germany

Robert A. Rhinehart
Science Curriculum Coordinator
Our Lady of Wayside
Arlington Heights, Illinois

Susan Seal
Science Teacher
Westlane Middle School
Indianapolis, Indiana

Constance W. Skelton
Science Coordinator
Little Flower School
Bethesda, Maryland

Donald Steinberg
Director of Science Education
School District of Philadelphia
Philadelphia, Pennsylvania

Patricia S. Whitfield
Chairperson, Science Department
Stone Middle School
Melbourne, Florida

About the Cover
The front cover shows a male wood duck, *Aix spónsa*, in flight. This North American species is commonly found around lakes and along streams. The internal structures of the wood duck, showing the respiratory, skeletal, and muscular systems, are shown on the back cover. See Chapter 13, sections 13-1 and 13-2, for more information about birds.

Contents

UNIT ONE   THE STUDY OF LIFE SCIENCE   *viii*

■ **Chapter 1   INTRODUCTION TO LIFE SCIENCE 2**
  1–1 What Is Life Science?   *3*   **1–3** Measurement   *11*
  1–2 Scientific Method   *7*   **1–4** Tools and Techniques of Life
                                                         Science   *18*

■ **Chapter 2   CLASSIFICATION – A SKILL IN LIFE SCIENCE 26**
  2–1 The Need for Classification *27*   **2–3** The Modern Classification
  2–2 Classification in the Life   System   *33*
          Sciences   *30*   **2–4** Five-Kingdom System   *36*
                                                2–5 Identifying Living Things *39*

Science in Careers/People in Science   *44*   Issues and Technology   *45*

UNIT TWO   CELLS AND LIVING THINGS   *48*

■ **Chapter 3   THE CHARACTERISTICS OF LIFE 50**
  3–1 Traits of Living Things   *51*   **3–4** Reproduction   *60*
  3–2 Nutrition and Metabolism   *54*   **3–5** The Nature of Matter   *63*
  3–3 Growth and Response   *57*   **3–6** Chemicals of Life   *66*

■ **Chapter 4   THE CELL 74**
  4–1 The Cell Theory   *75*   **4–4** Energy for Cells   *88*
  4–2 Structure of Cells   *77*   **4–5** Cell Division   *91*
  4–3 Cell Transport   *83*

■ **Chapter 5   VIRUSES AND BACTERIA 98**
  5–1 Viruses   *99*   **5–4** Reproduction and Growth of
  5–2 Kingdom Monera   *104*   Bacteria   *109*
  5–3 Bacteria   *107*   **5–5** Bacteria: Harmful and Helpful *111*

■ **Chapter 6   PROTISTS AND FUNGI 118**
  6–1 Traits of Protists   *119*   **6–4** Fungi   *128*
  6–2 Plantlike Protists   *121*   **6–5** Relatives of Fungi   *134*
  6–3 Animallike Protists   *124*

Science in Careers/People in Science   *140*   Issues and Technology   *141*

UNIT THREE   PLANTS   144

■ **Chapter 7   NONSEED PLANTS**   *146*

7–1	Traits of Nonseed Plants	147	7–4 Bryophytes	156
7–2	Green Algae	150	7–5 Tracheophytes	160
7–3	Brown Algae and Red Algae	153		

■ **Chapter 8   SEED PLANTS**   *168*

8–1	Traits of Seed Plants	169	8–4 Roots of Seed Plants	177
8–2	Gymnosperms	172	8–5 Stems of Seed Plants	182
8–3	Angiosperms	174	8–6 Leaves of Seed Plants	185

■ **Chapter 9   LIFE PROCESSES OF PLANTS**   *190*

9–1	Food Making and Energy Release	191	9–4 Reproduction in Angiosperms	201
9–2	Transport of Materials	196	9–5 Reproduction from Plant Parts	206
9–3	Reproduction in Gymnosperms	199	9–6 Plant Growth and Behavior	208

Science in Careers/People in Science   214   Issues and Technology   215

UNIT FOUR   ANIMALS   218

■ **Chapter 10   SIMPLE INVERTEBRATES**   *220*

10–1	Traits of Invertebrates	221	10–5 Roundworms	233
10–2	Sponges	224	10–6 Segmented Worms	235
10–3	Coelenterates	227	10–7 Mollusks	238
10–4	Flatworms	230		

■ **Chapter 11   COMPLEX INVERTEBRATES**   *244*

11–1	Traits of Arthropods	245	11–4 Crustaceans	257
11–2	Insects	248	11–5 Other Arthropods	259
11–3	Success of Insects	253	11–6 Echinoderms	262

■ **Chapter 12   COLD-BLOODED VERTEBRATES**   *268*

12–1	Phylum Chordata	269	12–5 Bony Fish	278
12–2	Traits of Vertebrates	272	12–6 Traits of Amphibians	281
12–3	Traits of Fish	274	12–7 Traits of Reptiles	285
12–4	Jawless Fish and Cartilage Fish	276		

■ **Chapter 13   WARM-BLOODED VERTEBRATES**   *292*

13–1	Traits of Birds	293	13–3 Traits of Mammals	300
13–2	Reproduction in Birds	298	13–4 Types of Mammals	303

■ **Chapter 14   COMPARING ANIMALS**   *312*

14–1	Support and Movement	313	14–4 Excretion	326
14–2	Digestion	316	14–5 Nervous Control	328
14–3	Respiration and Circulation	320	14–6 Reproduction	331

Science in Careers/People in Science   336   Issues and Technology   337

UNIT FIVE   HEREDITY AND CHANGE   340

■ **Chapter 15   GENETICS** *342*
15—1 Heredity   *343*   15—4 Sex Chromosomes   *355*
15—2 Inheritance of Traits   *348*   15—5 Applications of Genetics   *359*
15—3 Chromosomes, Genes,
          and Heredity   *353*

■ **Chapter 16   CHANGE OVER TIME** *364*
16—1 Change and Mutation   *365*   16—4 Theories of Evolution   *377*
16—2 Evidence of Change Over   16—5 Modern Views of Evolution   *381*
          Time   *369*
16—3 History of the Earth   *374*

Science in Careers/People in Science   *386*   Issues and Technology   *387*

UNIT SIX   THE HUMAN BODY   390

■ **Chapter 17   SUPPORT, MOVEMENT, AND BODY COVERING** *392*
17—1 Organization of the   17—4 The Muscular System   *403*
          Human Body   *393*   17—5 Body Movement and Disorders *406*
17—2 The Human Skeleton   *396*   17—6 Skin   *409*
17—3 Structure and Growth
          of Bone   *400*

■ **Chapter 18   NUTRITION AND DIGESTION** *414*
18—1 Nutrition   *415*   18—3 The Balanced Diet   *422*
18—2 Vitamins, Minerals, and   18—4 The Digestive System   *426*
          Water   *419*   18—5 Digestion and Absorption   *430*

■ **Chapter 19   TRANSPORT, RESPIRATION, AND EXCRETION** *436*
19—1 The Blood   *437*   19—4 Disorders of the Circulatory
19—2 Blood Vessels and   System   *449*
          Lymph   *442*   19—5 The Respiratory System   *452*
19—3 The Heart and   19—6 The Excretory System   *457*
          Circulation   *445*

■ **Chapter 20   CONTROL SYSTEMS** *464*
20—1 Sending Electrical   20—3 The Senses   *473*
          Messages   *465*   20—4 Chemical Regulation   *478*
20—2 The Nervous System   *468*   20—5 Drugs and the Body   *482*

■ **Chapter 21   REPRODUCTION** *490*
21—1 Reproductive Systems   *491*   21—4 Human Heredity   *502*
21—2 Producing Sex Cells   *495*   21—5 Genetic Disorders   *506*
21—3 Fertilization and
          Development   *498*

Science in Careers/People in Science   *514*   Issues and Technology   *515*

UNIT SEVEN   ECOLOGY
518

■ Chapter 22   THE ENVIRONMENT   520
  22—1 The Biosphere   521
  22—2 Populations and Communities   524
  22—3 Energy Flow in the Biosphere   527
  22—4 Symbiotic Relationships   532
  22—5 Cycles in Nature   534

■ Chapter 23   CHANGES IN THE ENVIRONMENT   540
  23—1 Changes in Populations   541
  23—2 Succession   546
  23—3 Land Biomes   550
  23—4 Water Biomes   558

■ Chapter 24   PRESERVING THE ENVIRONMENT   564
  24—1 Matter Resources   565
  24—2 Protecting Wildlife   571
  24—3 Energy Resources   573
  24—4 Problems of Pollution   578
  24—5 A Look to the Future   583

Science in Careers/People in Science   588   Issues and Technology   589

APPENDIX 1 Taxonomic Tree   592
APPENDIX 2 Safety   594
LIFE SCIENCE SKILLS HANDBOOK   595
GLOSSARY   606
INDEX   617

Activities

Chapter 1   INTRODUCTION TO LIFE SCIENCE
• How Is Mass Measured Using a Balance?   15
• How Is Temperature Measured?   17
• How Is a Microscope Used?   20

Chapter 2   CLASSIFICATION — A SKILL IN LIFE SCIENCE
• How Is a System of Classification Designed?   29
• How Can Animals Be Classified?   32
• How Is a Key Used to Identify a Living Thing?   40

Chapter 3   THE CHARACTERISTICS OF LIFE
• How Do Plants Respond to Different Stimuli?   59
• Which Foods Contain Protein?   67

Chapter 4   THE CELL
• How Does Folding Change Surface Area?   79
• How Do Animal and Plant Cells Differ?   81
• How Does Temperature Affect the Spreading of Food Coloring in Water?   85

Chapter 5   VIRUSES AND BACTERIA
• How Do Blue-green Bacteria Differ?   106
• Where Are Bacteria Found in the Environment?   108
• How Do Disinfectants Affect Bacterial Growth?   112

Chapter 6   PROTISTS AND FUNGI
• What Are the Characteristics of a Paramecium?   126
• What Substances Do Yeasts Need for Growth?   131
• What Is the Structure of a Fungus?   133

Chapter 7   NONSEED PLANTS
• What Is the Structure of Green Algae?   152
• What Is the Structure of a Moss?   159
• What Is the Structure of a Fern?   163

Chapter 8   SEED PLANTS
- How Do Monocots
  and Dicots Differ?   *176*
- Where Do Root Hairs Develop?   *181*

Chapter 9   LIFE PROCESSES OF PLANTS
- How Do Stomates Function?   *193*
- What Is the Structure of a Flower?   *202*
- What Is the Effect of
  Water on Bean Growth?   *210*

Chapter 10   SIMPLE INVERTEBRATES
- What Is the Structure of a Sponge?   *226*
- How Does a Hydra
  Respond to Stimuli?   *229*
- How Does an Earthworm
  Respond to Stimuli?   *237*

Chapter 11   COMPLEX INVERTEBRATES
- What Is the Structure of an Insect?   *254*
- What Is the Structure of a Crayfish?   *258*
- What Is the Structure of a Starfish?   *264*

Chapter 12   COLD-BLOODED
                    VERTEBRATES
- How Does Temperature Affect the
  Respiration Rate of
  Cold-blooded Animals?   *273*
- What Is the Structure
  of a Bony Fish?   *280*
- What Is the Structure of a Frog?   *283*

Chapter 13   WARM-BLOODED
                    VERTEBRATES
- How Do Contour and
  Down Feathers Differ?   *295*
- What Is the Structure
  of a Mammal Heart?   *301*

Chapter 14   COMPARING ANIMALS
- What Makes Up a
  Frog's Digestive System?   *318*
- What Are the Organs of a
  Transport System?   *325*
- How Do Animals
  Respond to Vinegar?   *330*

Chapter 15   GENETICS
- How Is a Punnett Square Used?   *351*
- How Can Incomplete
  Dominance Be Shown?   *352*
- How Do Chromosomes
  Determine Sex?   *357*

Chapter 16   CHANGE OVER TIME
- What Materials Are
  Best for Fossil Formation?   *371*
- How Can Natural Selection
  Be Shown?   *379*

- How Do Traits Vary
  Within a Species?   *382*

Chapter 17   SUPPORT, MOVEMENT,
                    AND BODY COVERING
- What Is the Structure of a Bone?   *401*
- How Can the Composition
  of Bone Be Tested?   *402*
- How Does a Chicken Wing Move?   *406*

Chapter 18   NUTRITION AND DIGESTION
- How Can Food Be
  Tested for Starch?   *417*
- How Can Food Be Tested for Fats?   *418*
- What Nutrition Information
  Is on Food Labels?   *423*

Chapter 19   TRANSPORT, RESPIRATION,
                    AND EXCRETION
- How Does the Pulse Vary?   *448*
- How Can You Use a Model
  to Show Breathing?   *455*
- How Can You Make a
  Model of a Nephron?   *459*

Chapter 20   CONTROL SYSTEMS
- What Are Some Reflex
  Responses to Stimuli?   *471*
- How Can Learning Be Measured?   *472*
- How Do Sounds Reach the Ear?   *476*

Chapter 21   REPRODUCTION
- What Are the Events in Meiosis?   *496*
- Are Human Traits Related?   *503*
- How Is the Gene for
  Left-handedness Inherited?   *510*

Chapter 22   THE ENVIRONMENT
- What Are Some Biotic
  and Abiotic Factors?   *523*
- What Interactions Occur in a
  Plot of Land?   *525*
- How Does Energy Move
  in a Food Chain?   *530*

Chapter 23   CHANGES IN THE
                    ENVIRONMENT
- Does Precipitation Affect a
  Bird Population?   *544*
- What Evidence of Succession
  Can Be Observed?   *549*

Chapter 24   PRESERVING THE
                    ENVIRONMENT
- What Is the Composition of Soil?   *567*
- What Is the Cost of a Leaky Faucet?   *568*
- How Much Pollution
  Is in Water and Air?   *582*

THE STUDY OF LIFE SCIENCE

T here are several million kinds of living things. Life science is the study of all varieties of living things. Some living things are invisible to the unaided eye and can only be studied by using devices such as microscopes. In their work, life scientists use many tools and many skills. As you read this unit, you will learn about the tools and skills of life scientists. You will also find out how life scientists group the living things they study. ■

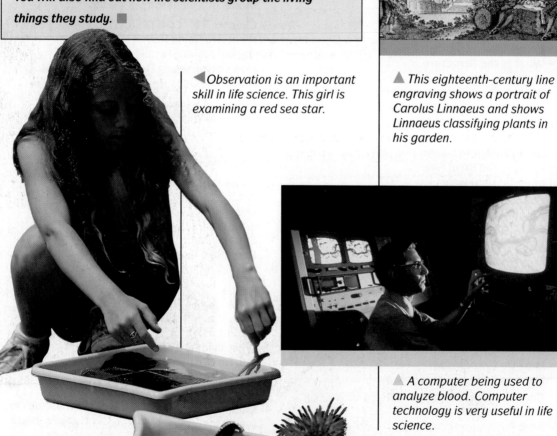

◀ *Observation is an important skill in life science. This girl is examining a red sea star.*

▲ *This eighteenth-century line engraving shows a portrait of Carolus Linnaeus and shows Linnaeus classifying plants in his garden.*

▲ *A computer being used to analyze blood. Computer technology is very useful in life science.*

▶ This drawing shows the French scientist Louis Pasteur working in his laboratory during the late 1800s.

◀European barberry plant infected with a fungus. The drawing was done by a German artist during the late nineteenth century.

▼ This photograph showing a spider mite on a leaf was made possible by the use of a scanning electron microscope.

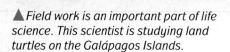

▲ Field work is an important part of life science. This scientist is studying land turtles on the Galápagos Islands.

INTRODUCTION TO LIFE SCIENCE

What do you see when you look at a "picture postcard" scene such as the one in the photograph? What might a scientist see? What questions might a scientist ask about such a scene? A scientist might want to know why some trees still have their leaves while other trees have lost all their leaves. A scientist might also want to know what kinds of plants and animals live in the lake and along its shore. The scientist might be curious about the living things that are in the forest. Questions about how the houses around the lake affect the quality of the lake water might also occur to the scientist. Scientists look at the world in a special way and ask many questions about what they see.

- *What is a scientist?*
- *How do scientists study the world around them?*
- *What tools do scientists use in their studies?*

1-1 WHAT IS LIFE SCIENCE?

Curiosity is a desire to know. What things are you curious about? Perhaps you have wondered about some of the many living things around you. What causes a caterpillar to change into a butterfly? What happens to fish and frogs when the pond they live in freezes over for the winter? Why do trees live for many years but some other types of plants die after only one year? What causes the striped pattern of a zebra's fur? All of these questions are concerned with things in nature. Finding the answers to such questions is what science is all about.

Science is a method of obtaining knowledge about nature. Nature includes the earth, space, living things, and nonliving things. *Scientists* are people who study nature and try to find explanations for things they observe in nature. How scientists study nature will be explained in the next section.

There are many branches of science and many types of scientists. **Life science** is the branch of science that studies living things. Life science is also known as *biology*.

After completing this section, you will be able to

- **define** the term *science*.
- **define** the term *life science* and **give examples** of fields of life science.
- **distinguish** between science and technology and **give examples** of technology from life science.

The key terms in this section are
life science   technology
science

scientia (knowledge)

NOTE

Many terms in science have their origins in other languages, including Latin and Greek. The foreign word parts and their meanings are listed in the margin for many of the science terms in this book. Use the word parts to help you understand the meanings of the science terms.

People who study living things are called *life scientists* or *biologists*. Life scientists seek answers to many questions about nature. How does space travel affect humans and other living things? How does an ancient Chinese technique called acupuncture reduce pain? What changes in cells can result in cancer? Why did the dinosaurs die out millions of years ago? These are just a few of the diverse topics that are part of life science.

Life science is divided into a number of fields. *Zoology* (zoh AHL uh jee) is the study of animals. The term *zoology* comes from the Greek word *zoios*, which means "animal." What other words come from this Greek word? What kind of living thing is the zoologist in Figure 1-1 studying?

Figure 1-1

A zoologist (*left*) studies animals, and a botanist (*right*) studies plants. Both are life scientists, or biologists.

Botany (BAHT uh nee), another field of life science, is the study of plants. The botanist in Figure 1-1 is checking plants for insect pests. Botany and zoology are the oldest fields of life science. The study of animals and plants as a science began over 2000 years ago. Many fields of life science began in more recent times. *Microbiology* is the study of life forms that are so small they can be seen only through a microscope. Why did this study begin more recently than did either zoology or botany? *Ecology* (ee-KAHL uh jee) is the study of relationships between living things and their surroundings. The surroundings include other living things, as well as nonliving things such as water and air. What might the ecologists in Figure 1-2 be studying?

Life science is also divided into fields based on the study of the structure or function of living things. *Anatomy*

4

Figure 1-2

Ecologists study relationships among living things and their nonliving sur-roundings.

(uh NAHT uh mee) is the study of the structure, or form, of living things. *Physiology* (fihz ee AHL uh jee) is the study of how living things function.

Knowledge from life science is useful in many ways. For example, life scientists learn about the causes of heart attacks and how to prevent them. Knowledge of how plants grow helps people produce crops that will yield the most food from the least land. The knowledge from life science is often used to make people's lives better or easier. **Technology** (tehk NAHL uh jee) is the use of scientific knowledge in an effort to improve the quality of human life. As you have learned, science is a way of obtaining knowledge. Technology is using or applying that knowledge. There are many examples of technology in life science.

One example of technology results from the study of trees that are used for lumber. Lumber is used in building homes, in making paper, and for many other purposes. Fir trees are used for lumber. Some fir trees grow faster and taller than other fir trees. There are many factors that affect the way a tree grows. Through many years of work, botanists have learned what many of these factors are. This knowledge has been put to practical use. Lumber companies now plant specially bred fir trees. These trees grow faster and taller than average fir trees. As more of these fast- and tall-growing fir trees are planted, more lumber becomes available more quickly. Also, fewer natural forests need to be cut down to be used as sources of lumber. The use of scientific knowledge about tree growth to produce more lumber more rapidly is an example of technology.

Figure 1-3

Kidney machines save the lives of many people whose own kidneys do not function.

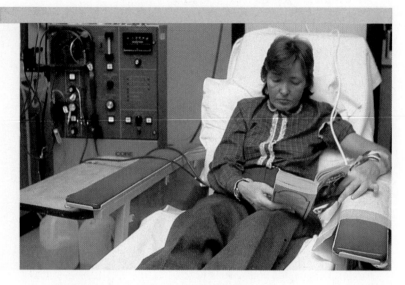

Another example of technology is based on studies of the physiology, or function, of kidneys in animals. The kidneys are natural filters in an animal's body. They remove wastes from the blood. Knowledge of how the kidneys work has been applied to the design of kidney machines, such as the one shown in Figure 1-3. These machines can filter wastes from the blood of a person whose own kidneys are diseased or damaged.

Technology is intended to improve the quality of people's lives. However, technology sometimes has unwanted side effects. For example, weedkillers are a technology intended to improve farming. But the overuse of weedkillers damages soil. Crops do not grow well in soil that has been damaged. In this case the careless use of technology creates an effect opposite to what was intended. Less food is grown, instead of more.

REVIEW

1. What is science?
2. What is life science?
3. Name and describe three fields of life science.
4. What is the relationship between science and technology?

CHALLENGE Two kinds of tiny living things live in the soil. Research finds that one of these living things produces a chemical that kills the other. Further studies show that this chemical is useful as a medicine in treating certain diseases. What part of this example represents science? What part represents technology? What drawbacks do some medicines have?

1-2 SCIENTIFIC METHOD

Scientists search for answers to many questions about nature. There is a certain method used by all scientists as they seek these answers. The special way in which a scientist gathers information and tests ideas is called the **scientific method**. The scientific method is a logical way of solving problems. It does not always occur in the same order for each problem that scientists attempt to solve. The scientific method can be divided into four key processes. By using these processes, scientists are able to test their ideas in a logical way.

The scientific method often begins with the curiosity of one scientist. Suppose a life scientist is aware that different kinds of plants produce flowers at different times of the year. The scientist sees that chrysanthemums, or mums, growing outdoors do not produce flowers until autumn. This is an observation—often the first process in the scientific method. An **observation** is an examination of some part of nature. The senses of sight, smell, touch, taste, and hearing are used in making observations. What senses are the scientists in Figure 1-4 using?

After completing this section, you will be able to

- **define** the term *scientific method.*
- **identify** the processes in the scientific method.

The key terms in this section are

conclusion	observation
experiment	scientific method
hypothesis	theory

Figure 1-4

These scientists are using different senses as they examine various parts of nature.

Observations may be recorded in the form of written notes or as drawings. The life scientist who is curious about mums may make many observations of mums growing in different areas over a period of time. Observations often lead scientists to ask questions. One question that the life scientist might ask is "What factor causes mums to flower in autumn?"

Part of the scientific method is to research what is already known about a subject. Scientists usually look for such information in a library. Suppose the life scientist finds out that many factors can affect flowering in plants. These factors might include temperature, amount of light, type of soil, and amount of rainfall. The scientist might also research the topic of weather. It would be helpful to know what the average weather conditions are during autumn in the regions where mums grow.

A second process of the scientific method is to form a hypothesis (hī PAHTH uh sihs). A **hypothesis** is a proposed answer to a question about nature. Hypotheses are based on observations and research. A hypothesis is often described as a "best guess" or an "educated guess." The life scientist in the example forms a hypothesis that mums flower in autumn because of the lower temperatures at that time of year. This is a proposed answer to the question, "What factor causes mums to flower in autumn?"

A hypothesis must be tested to see if it is correct. This is a third process of the scientific method. A test of a hypothesis is called an **experiment**. The life scientist designs an experiment to test the hypothesis about the flowering of mums. Experiments usually have two parts, or groups. One group is called the control, or the *control group*. The other is called the *experimental group*. The experimental group differs from the control group in only one factor or condition. The condition that makes the experimental group different from the control is called the *variable*.

At the end of the experiment, the two groups are compared with one another. The scientist must then determine if the variable affected the experimental group. If it did, the scientist notes how it affected this group. It is best to have only one variable in an experiment. Experiments that have more than one variable may produce confusing results. It may be hard to know which one of the variables affected the experimental group.

The following experiment might be used to test the hypothesis that mums flower in autumn because of the lower temperatures at that time of year. Refer to Figure

Figure 1-5

These mums flower in autumn, after many other kinds of flowering plants have died. What clue suggests that the picture was taken in autumn?

experiri (to test)
-ment (act of)

1-6 as you read about the experiment. A large number of potted mum plants are divided into two groups. The mums in the control group are grown in the laboratory. They are grown under conditions that are the same as those during summer months in regions where mums grow.

The variable in the experiment is temperature. The mums in the experimental group are also grown in the laboratory. The conditions of light and water are the same as those for the control group. But the temperature for the experimental group is different. Over the course of the experiment, the temperature for this group is lowered. This is like the drop in temperature that occurs during the autumn months.

CONTROL GROUP

Temperature: constant 27°C
Light: 16 hours per day
Water: 50 mL per day

EXPERIMENTAL GROUP

Temperature: lowered from 27°C to 17°C
Light: 16 hours per day
Water: 50 mL per day

Figure 1-6

An experiment usually has a control group and an experimental group. Why is it important that the plants in both groups be very much alike?

During the experiment the life scientist observes both groups of plants. The number of flowers produced, if any, is recorded for each group. Information from observations and measurements, along with information from research, is called *data*.

A fourth process of the scientific method is to make a conclusion. A **conclusion** is a statement of whether or not the data from an experiment support the hypothesis. Suppose the data show that neither the experimental group nor the control group produces flowers. The life scientist then concludes that the data do not support the hypothesis. When such a conclusion is reached, scientists may form a new hypothesis.

The life scientist may now hypothesize that mums flower in autumn because of the shorter daylight period

con- (with)
claudere (closing)

at that time of year. A new experiment is designed to test this hypothesis. What is the variable now? The data show that the experimental group produces flowers but the control group does not. The life scientist concludes that the data support the new hypothesis.

Part of the scientific method is to publish the results of experiments. The results are printed in a scientific magazine, or journal. Other scientists can then learn about the experiment. Some scientists might repeat the experiment. They want to be sure that the conclusion is accurate.

Figure 1-7

In addition to publishing the results of experiments, scientists may present their results at scientific meetings, or conferences.

Scientists accept a hypothesis only after it has been tested many times and is supported by results. A hypothesis may become a theory (THIHR ee). A **theory** is a hypothesis that has been tested many times and that is supported by data. A theory may be used to explain other related events in nature. For example, the shorter daylight period in autumn might also explain why leaves fall at that time of year. Theories usually explain a broader range of events than do hypotheses. Scientific theories may be changed over time. New information or new ways of making observations may cause scientists to later alter theories. Sometimes a new theory replaces an older one.

REVIEW

1. What is the scientific method?
2. Describe the four main processes of the scientific method.
3. Why is it important that the results of experiments be published?

CHALLENGE Design an experiment to test the hypothesis that mushrooms do not grow well in bright light.

1-3 MEASUREMENT

THE NEED FOR MEASUREMENT

Suppose your neighbor is moving and offers to give you a large dresser. You have need for the dresser, but you do not know if there is enough space for it in your room. The dresser is very heavy, and you would have to carry it up two flights of stairs to reach your room. Without taking the dresser upstairs, how would you determine whether it will fit?

Scientists measure and record the properties of the things they study. Measurements are important because they help scientists make accurate observations. Measurements also allow data to be compared. By recording measurements, scientists have data that can be referred to in the future. When studying the factors that cause mums to bloom, the life scientist measures the growth of mum plants. This data is then referred to when the scientist makes conclusions about the experiment.

Scientists often need to measure things precisely. Look at Figure 1-8. What is being measured in each photograph? In science it is usually not very helpful to say that objects are large or small, light or heavy, hot or cold. Consider the following statement: The red blood cells of humans are larger than those of mice. A scientist would want to know exactly how much larger the red blood cells of humans are than those of mice. A more helpful statement would be the following: Red blood cells of humans have a diameter of 7 micrometers; the red blood cells of mice have a diameter of 6 micrometers.

> After completing this section, you will be able to
>
> - **recognize** the need for standard units of measurement in science.
> - **identify** the standard units of measurement used in science.
> - **identify** the devices used in measuring length, mass, volume, and temperature.
>
> The key terms in this section are
>
> | | |
> |---|---|
> | degree Celsius | mass |
> | kilogram | meter |
> | liter | volume |

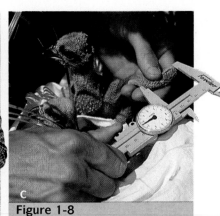

Figure 1-8

Measurements are important in many areas of life science.

The statement giving numbers and units provides precise information. For the statement to have meaning, however, scientists must know what a micrometer is. To use any system of measurement, you must know the values of units in that system. A system of measurement has *standards*. A standard is a unit that serves as a basis for making certain measurements. A foot is a standard of length. If the dresser in the earlier example measures five feet in length, then its length is five times the standard. Standards are set and agreed upon so that people can easily and accurately communicate ideas about size with each other.

Different systems of measurement have been used in the past. Some standards were based on the length of different parts of the body, such as arms and hands. In ancient Egypt, distance was measured in cubits. Figure 1-9 shows how a cubit was determined. A cubit was the distance along a bent forearm, from the elbow to the tip of the middle finger. The cubit was later standardized at what is now 18.24 inches or 46.32 centimeters. Using body parts as standards is convenient. Measurements can be made quickly since the standard is attached to the person who is measuring. What problems occur using a system of measurement based on standards that are body parts?

Figure 1-9

How did ancient Egyptians determine the length of a cubit?

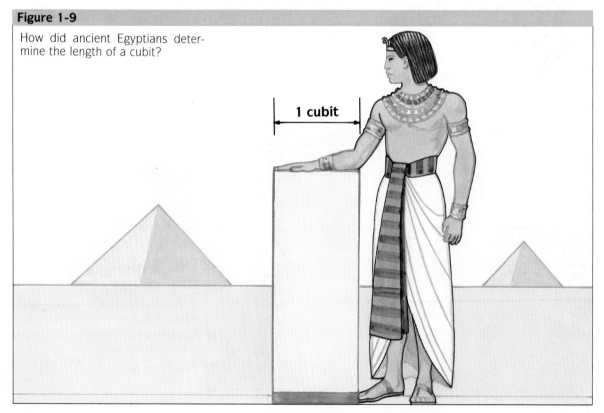

1 cubit

METRIC SYSTEM

Scientists must be able to report their results to other scientists around the world. For this reason, measurements must have the same meaning in all countries. In France during the 1790s, a new system of measurement was introduced. This system is called the *metric system*. Its modern version, called the International System of Measurement (SI), is used by scientists all over the world. When a scientist in North America reports measurements in SI units, they are understood by scientists everywhere in the world. SI units are also used in everyday life in most countries. You may have noticed that the labels on some packaged foods, such as canned vegetables, show quantities in grams.

Five important units are the meter (m), kilogram (kg), liter (L), degree Celsius (°C), and second (s). Table 1-1 lists these units and their symbols. The units listed can be made larger or smaller by multiplying or dividing them by ten and multiples of ten.

SI units use prefixes to describe the size of a unit. For example, *kilo-* means "one thousand." There are 1000 meters in a kilometer. Table 1-2 lists some common SI prefixes and their values. In general these prefixes are added to the unit names without changing the spelling of either the basic unit or the prefix. For example, 1/1000 of a gram is called a milligram (*milli-* + gram). How many liters are in a kiloliter? What fraction of a meter is a centimeter? What fraction of a meter is the diameter of a human red blood cell?

Table 1-1
Units of Measurement

Measurement	Unit	Symbol
length	meter	m
mass	kilogram	kg
volume	liter	L
temperature	degree Celsius	°C
time	second	s

Table 1-2 *Common Prefixes for SI Units*

Prefix	Meaning	Symbol	Example
kilo-	one thousand	k	1 km, or 1 kilometer, is 1000 meters.
centi-	one hundredth	c	1 cm, or 1 centimeter, is 1/100 (.01) of 1 meter.
milli-	one thousandth	m	1 mm, or 1 millimeter, is 1/1000 (.001) of 1 meter.
micro-	one millionth	μ	1 μm, or 1 micrometer, is 1/1,000,000 (.000001) of 1 meter.

The **meter** (m) is the SI unit used when measuring length or distance. A meter is slightly longer than a yard. Length is often measured with a meterstick or with a metric ruler. The numbers on a meterstick and metric ruler indicate centimeters (cm). The smallest spaces between lines show millimeters (mm). A dime is a little over 1 mm in thickness. There are 10 mm in 1 cm. The diameter of a nickel is almost 2 cm. Use a metric ruler to determine the length of the salamander shown in Figure 1-10.

The **kilogram** (kg) is the SI unit used when measuring mass. **Mass** is a measure of the amount of matter in an object. Mass is different from weight. Weight is a measure of the force of gravity on something. Gravity is not constant from place to place. For example, the force of gravity is less on the moon than on the earth. Thus, an object weighs less on the moon than on the earth. But the object's mass is the same in both places.

Mass is measured with an instrument called a balance. There are several types of balances. A double-pan balance is shown in Figure 1-11. This balance works like a seesaw. The material to be measured is placed on one pan. Objects of known mass are added, one at a time, to the other pan until the pans balance. When the pans balance, the total mass of the objects is equal to the mass of the material on the other pan.

Figure 1-10

What is the length of this painted salamander in millimeters? In centimeters?

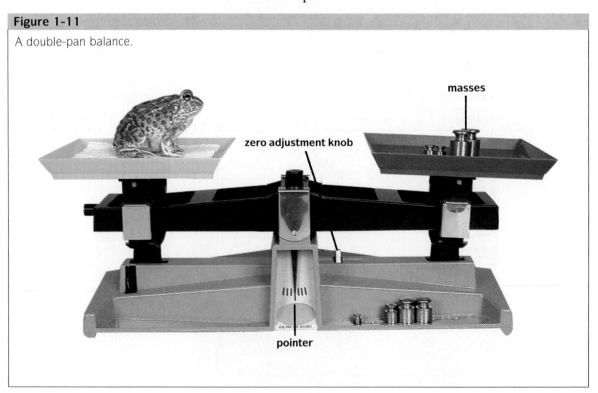

Figure 1-11

A double-pan balance.

masses

zero adjustment knob

pointer

OBJECTIVE
Measure the mass of various objects in metric units, using a balance.

MATERIALS
balance, variety of small objects (coins, paper clips, earthworm or other small animal), masses, forceps

PROCEDURE
A. Study Figure 1-11, which shows the labeled parts of a balance. Find each part on your balance.
B. Notice the pointer and the scale in the center of your balance. The long line at the center of the scale is the zero point. When the pans are empty, the pointer should line up with the zero point. This means the balance is zeroed. If your balance is not zeroed, use the adjustment knob to zero the balance.
C. Place a small object on the left pan. Use a forceps to pick up and place masses on the right pan. Continue adding masses until the balance is again zeroed. When the balance is zeroed, the mass of the object is equal to the total of the masses on the right pan. Record the mass of the object.
D. Repeat step **C** to determine the masses of other objects.

RESULTS AND CONCLUSIONS
1. For each object whose mass you determined, give the mass in grams and in milligrams.
2. Would the results of this activity be affected if it were done on the moon? Explain why or why not.

The **liter** (L) is a unit of volume. **Volume** is a measure of the amount of space something occupies. The volume of a liquid is usually measured with an instrument called a graduated cylinder, or graduate. A graduate is marked in milliliters. Notice in Figure 1-12 that the surface of the liquid curves upward at the sides of the graduate. This curved surface is called a *meniscus*. To read a graduate, view it with the liquid's surface at eye level. Read the mark that lines up with the lowest point of the meniscus. What volume of liquid is shown in Figure 1-12?

Figure 1-12

Always read the volume of a liquid at the lowest point of the meniscus.

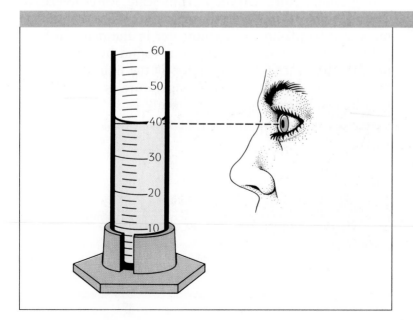

15

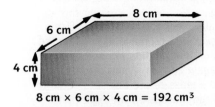

8 cm × 6 cm × 4 cm = 192 cm³

Figure 1-13

The volume of this regular solid is found by multiplying its length, width, and height.

The volume of a solid can be measured in two ways. If the solid has a regular shape, its dimensions can be used. The volume of a box, for example, can be measured by multiplying its three dimensions (Volume = length × width × height). A box that is 8 cm by 6 cm by 4 cm has a volume of 192 cubic centimeters (cm³), as shown in Figure 1-13. A volume of 1 cm³ is equal to 1 mL. What is the volume of a box that is 5 cm by 4 cm by 3 cm?

If a small solid object does not have a regular shape, its volume can still be measured. The object is placed in a graduate that is partly filled with water. The amount of water that the object displaces equals its volume. What is the volume of the rock in Figure 1-14?

Figure 1-14

The amount of water displaced by the rock is equal to the volume of the rock.

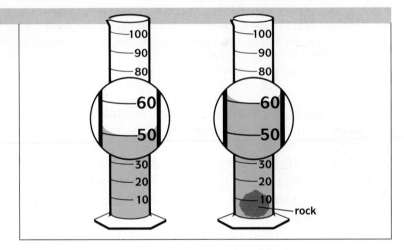

The **degree Celsius** (°C) is a unit used when measuring temperature. On the Celsius scale, water freezes at 0° and boils at 100°. The temperature of a material is measured by placing a thermometer in the material for a period of time. The temperature is found by reading the number that lines up with the top of the liquid inside the thermometer. Normal room temperature is about 21°C. In humans, normal body temperature is 37°C.

SCIENCE PUZZLER

In the Fahrenheit temperature scale, water freezes at 32° and boils at 212°. How many units (degrees) are there between the freezing and boiling points? Compare Fahrenheit and Celsius units. How many Fahrenheit units equal one Celsius unit?

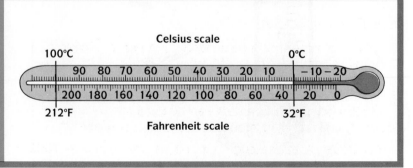

ACTIVITY   How Is Temperature Measured?

OBJECTIVES
Measure the temperature of air and water, using a Celsius thermometer.
Estimate the temperature of cold water.

MATERIALS
Celsius thermometer, masking tape, window pole or other long pole, clock or watch, cold water, hot water, 500-mL beaker

PROCEDURE
A. Examine a Celsius thermometer. Look for the divisions, or scale, marked on the thermometer. **Caution:** Handle a thermometer carefully. Never hold a thermometer by its bulb.
   1. What unit does each division represent?
B. Read and record the air temperature at the height of the top of your desk. Allow the thermometer to remain on your desk for 5 minutes. To read the temperature, hold the thermometer at eye level. Turn the thermometer until you see the column of liquid at its widest position. The number that lines up with the top edge of the liquid is the temperature. Be sure to include the proper unit with the number.
C. Use masking tape to attach the thermometer to the end of a long pole.

Place the pole in a corner, leaning against a wall. The thermometer should be at the top of the pole, as close to the ceiling as possible. Allow the pole to remain in place for 5 minutes. After 5 minutes, read and record the air temperature near the ceiling.
D. Fill a beaker with cold water. Put your hand in the water and estimate the water temperature. Record your estimate. Place the thermometer in the water, wait 1 minute, and then read and record the temperature of the cold water.
   2. How close was your estimate to the actual temperature of the water?
E. Repeat step **D**, but substitute hot water for the cold water and do not put your hand in the hot water.

RESULTS AND CONCLUSIONS
1. How do the air temperatures at desk height and ceiling height differ? Hypothesize about why they differ.
2. What is the difference in temperature between the hot water and the cold water?
3. Why is using the sense of touch not an accurate way of determining temperature? What factor would affect how hot or cold something feels to your hand?

The *second* (s) is the SI unit for time. In the present system there are 60 seconds in a minute, 60 minutes in an hour, and 24 hours in a day. This system is used everywhere on the earth. In science the prefix *milli-* is sometimes used with the unit *second* for certain types of measurement. The time it takes a message to travel along nerves from one part of the body to another might be given in milliseconds.

REVIEW

1. Why is it important for scientists to measure things?
2. What is the advantage of having standard units of measurement in science?
3. Identify four common units of measurement, and explain what type of measurement each is used for.
4. List the meaning of prefixes used in SI measurement.

CHALLENGE   A millisecond is a unit of time equal to 1000 microseconds. How many microseconds are in 1 second?

1-4 TOOLS AND TECHNIQUES OF LIFE SCIENCE

micro- (small)
-scope (observation)

SCIENTIFIC TOOLS

All around you there are living things that are so tiny your eyes cannot see them. Scientists use many tools to help them observe objects and events that their senses cannot otherwise detect. One of the most important tools used in life science is the microscope. A **microscope** is a device used to observe objects that are too small to be seen with the unaided eye. An object this small is called microscopic. What is seen when an object is viewed through a microscope is called an *image*.

There are several types of microscopes. A *simple microscope* is made up of a single lens. A hand lens or magnifying glass, shown in Figure 1-15, is a simple microscope. The type of microscope most commonly used is the *compound microscope*—a microscope that contains two lenses. One lens produces an enlarged or magnified image of an object. The second lens further magnifies the image. Figure 1-16 shows a compound microscope. Notice that the function of each labeled part is given. What is the function of the fine adjustment? What does the diaphragm control?

Simple and compound microscopes are often called *light microscopes* because they use light to produce an enlarged image. The lenses in a light microscope cause light rays to bend. It is the bending of light rays that results in the magnified image of an object. A powerful light microscope can produce an image that is 1000 times larger than the object being viewed. The amount of magnification is often shown as a number followed by an ×. Thus, 1000× means that an image is 1000 times larger than the object being viewed.

In the early 1930s another kind of microscope, called the electron microscope, was invented. An **electron microscope** uses beams of electrons, instead of beams of light, to produce an enlarged image. Some electron microscopes can magnify objects up to 300,000 times.

There are two kinds of electron microscopes in use today. In a *transmission electron microscope* (TEM), an electron beam is passed through the object to be magnified. A TEM is shown in Figure 1-17. A specimen to be observed with a TEM must be very thin. If the specimen is not thin enough, the electron beam will not be able to pass through it. A TEM cannot be used to examine things that are alive. Life scientists often use a TEM to examine very thin slices taken from living things.

Figure 1-15

A hand lens is a simple microscope.

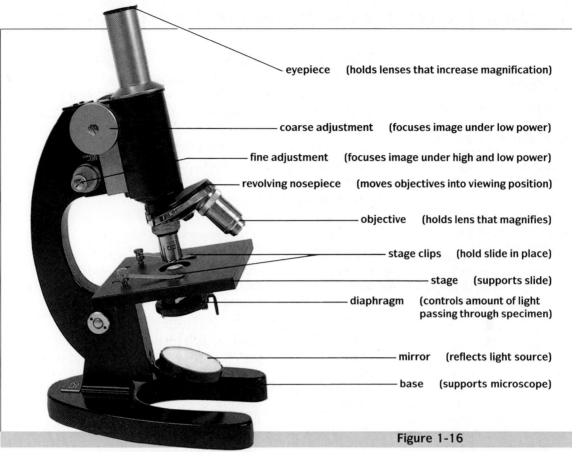

eyepiece   (holds lenses that increase magnification)

coarse adjustment   (focuses image under low power)

fine adjustment   (focuses image under high and low power)

revolving nosepiece   (moves objectives into viewing position)

objective   (holds lens that magnifies)

stage clips   (hold slide in place)

stage   (supports slide)

diaphragm   (controls amount of light passing through specimen)

mirror   (reflects light source)

base   (supports microscope)

Figure 1-16

A compound light microscope.

In a *scanning electron microscope* (SEM), an electron beam is bounced off the surface of the object to be magnified. Figure 1-17 shows an SEM. The SEM produces a magnified image of only the surface of an object. An SEM cannot magnify as much as a TEM, but the SEM produces a more three-dimensional image. With an SEM it is also possible to examine things that are alive.

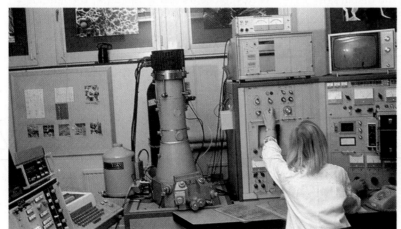

Figure 1-17

A scanning electron microscope (*left*) and a transmission electron microscope (*right*).

How Is a Microscope Used?

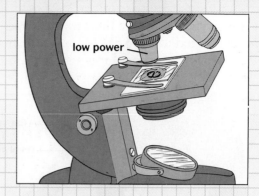

low power

OBJECTIVE
Demonstrate the correct use of a microscope.

MATERIALS
microscope, newspaper, scissors, microscope slide, dropper, water, coverslip

PROCEDURE

A. Study Figure 1-16, which shows the labeled parts of a compound microscope. Find each part on your microscope.

B. Notice the numbers on each objective and on the eyepiece. Multiply the number on the low-power objective by the number on the eyepiece. This will give you the total magnification of the microscope when the low-power objective is used. Determine what the total magnification is when the high power objective is used.

C. Turn the revolving nosepiece to line up the low-power objective with the eyepiece. The objective will click into place when it is properly lined up. Then carefully turn the coarse adjustment knob until the objective is at its lowest point. Always watch the objective as it is lowered. In some microscopes it is possible to lower the objective onto the slide, breaking the slide and damaging the objective.

D. Aim the mirror at your light source. Then look into the eyepiece, using one eye. To avoid eyestrain, keep both eyes open when looking through the eyepiece. Tilt the mirror until you can see a circle of light through the eyepiece. **Caution:** Never use direct sunlight as a light source. This strong light could damage your eye. Turn the diaphragm in both directions, and observe what happens to the light.

E. Look through a newspaper for the smallest letter e you can find. Use scissors to cut out the letter. Place the letter in the center of a microscope slide. Use a dropper to place one drop of water on the piece of newspaper. Slowly lower a coverslip onto the wet newspaper. The type of slide you have just made is called a *wet mount.*

F. Place the slide on the center of the stage of the microscope. Then use the clips to hold the slide in place. Be sure the letter e is directly over the hole in the stage.

G. Look into the eyepiece. Slowly turn the coarse adjustment knob until the letter e comes into focus. When focusing using the low-power objective, always begin by turning the coarse adjustment knob to raise the objective. Now turn the fine adjustment knob to bring the letter e into sharper focus. Draw the letter e as it looks under low power. Indicate the magnification on your drawing.

H. Move the slide to the right, and observe the direction of movement of the letter e. Move the slide to the left, and again note the direction of movement of the letter e. Now move the slide away from you and then toward you, and observe the direction of movement of the letter e.

I. Turn the revolving nosepiece to the high-power objective. Watch as you turn the nosepiece to be sure that the lens does not hit the slide. When going to a higher magnification, never use the coarse adjustment knob to focus. Use only the fine adjustment knob on high power. Look into the eyepiece as you focus. Draw the letter e as it appears under high power. Indicate the magnification on your drawing.

RESULTS AND CONCLUSIONS
1. How does the letter e move when the slide is moved to the right? To the left?
2. How does the letter e move when the slide is moved away from you? Toward you?
3. Compare the drawings you made in step **G** and step **I**. Suppose you were using the microscope to observe a living thing that is the same size as the letter e. What aspects of the living thing would be best observed under low power? Under high power?

Look at Figure 1-18. Compare the images from a compound light microscope, a TEM, and an SEM. Notice that the picture from the light microscope is in color. The color was added to the SEM picture. A picture from a TEM is black and white, but color is sometimes added. Compare the three-dimensional image produced by the SEM with the flat image produced by the TEM.

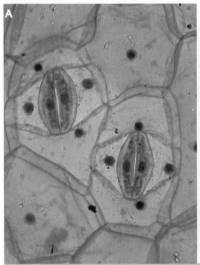
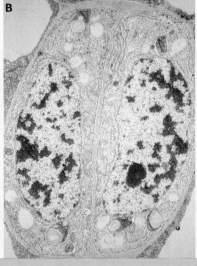

Figure 1-18

The underside of a leaf as it appears when viewed with a compound light microscope (A), a TEM (B), and an SEM (C).

Sometimes life scientists work outdoors, in natural areas. This is called field work. Field work allows a scientist to study living things in their natural surroundings. A life scientist doing field work may use a hand lens to help identify living things. *Binoculars* may be used to view living things at a distance when doing field work. Most wild animals will run from humans. Binoculars allow a scientist to go unnoticed by such animals while they are being viewed.

In recent years, computers have become an important tool in life science. Computers can analyze large amounts of data in a short time. There are many different ways that computers are used in science. One use of computers is to store and analyze the data from experiments.

Some of the actions of living things can be described by mathematical equations. Computers can solve such equations far more quickly than can humans. Computers can also use measurements to make pictures of things. Computers have been used to make pictures of things so small that they cannot be seen with an electron microscope. You can see such a computer-made picture in Figure 1-19.

Figure 1-19

A computer-made picture of a tiny unit of matter—a molecule.

SCIENCE & TECHNOLOGY

Some of the newest computers in use have been called supercomputers. They can process data hundreds of times faster than most ordinary computers.

Computers solve a problem step by step. Data travels from the memory part of the computer through a connection to the processor. The processor is the part of the computer that does the mathematical computation. The answer or solution to a computation is then sent back to the memory. Even though a problem might involve many steps, the computer cannot work on more than one step at a time.

New technology has been used to shorten the distance that signals have to travel between the parts of the computer. This speeds up computations. Speed is the advantage of the new supercomputers. In the CRAY-2, the supercomputer shown, circuits are packed so closely that they need to be kept in a liquid coolant that keeps the circuits from overheating.

Researchers are designing a new line of computers that will perform even faster than the supercomputers. These new computers will have several processors that will work as a team to decrease the total time it takes to find a solution to a problem.

SCIENTIFIC TECHNIQUES

Experiments in life science often require that living things be grown and studied outside their natural surroundings. These living things may be microscopic in size. Such living things may be studied in the laboratory by providing the conditions needed for their growth. Growing microscopic living things under controlled conditions in a laboratory is called *culturing*. The treatment and cure for many diseases have been made possible by the use of culturing.

Anatomy, the study of the structure of living things, sometimes requires *dissection*. When something is dissected, it is cut apart. Dissection allows life scientists to learn about the internal structure of living things. Figure 1-20 shows some of the tools used in dissection.

The tools used by scientists allow them to go beyond the limits of their senses. Throughout this book you will see photographs that were taken with the use of microscopes. You will learn about breakthroughs in technology that were made possible by the use of computers and other tools. You will also learn how the tools of scientists are a vital part of the study of living things.

dissecting pan

scissors

scalpel

dissecting needle

forceps

pins

Figure 1-20

These are some of the tools used in dissection.

REVIEW

1. Why are tools useful in science?
2. Explain how a compound light microscope differs from an electron microscope. How are the images produced by a TEM and an SEM different.
3. How are computers useful in life science?

CHALLENGE Suppose a life scientist wanted to find out how a microscopic living thing moves. Should the scientist use a compound light microscope or an electron microscope to study this living thing? Explain your answer.

CHAPTER SUMMARY

The main ideas in this chapter are listed below. Read these statements before you answer the Chapter Review questions.

- Science is a method of obtaining knowledge about nature. Life science, or biology, is the branch of science that involves the study of living things. Life science includes the fields of zoology, botany, microbiology, ecology, anatomy, and physiology. (1-1)

- Technology is the use of scientific knowledge in an effort to improve the quality of human life. (1-1)

- The scientific method is the special way in which a scientist gathers information and tests ideas. There are four main processes in this method: observation, hypothesis, experiment, and conclusion. (1-2)

- A hypothesis may become a theory if it has been tested many times and has been supported by data. A theory may be used to explain related events in nature. (1-2)

- Measurements allow scientists to make and record precise observations. SI is the system of measurement that is used by scientists. (1-3)

- The meter, liter, kilogram, degree Celsius, and second are important units in scientific measurement. (1-3)

- Scientists use many different tools to observe objects and events that their senses could not otherwise detect. (1-4)

- Microscopes, such as the compound light microscope and the electron microscope, are used in order to observe objects that are too small to be seen with the unaided eye. (1-4)

- Computers are helpful tools in science because they can analyze large amounts of data in a short time. (1-4)

The key terms in this chapter are listed below. Use each term in a sentence that shows the meaning of the term.

conclusion	kilogram	meter	scientific method
degree Celsius	life science	microscope	technology
electron microscope	liter	observation	theory
experiment	mass	science	volume
hypothesis			

Chapter Review

Use the key terms from this chapter to complete the following sentences correctly.

1. A method of obtaining knowledge about nature is called _____.

2. A measure of the amount of space something occupies is called _____.

3. A proposed answer to a scientific question about nature is called a/an _____.

4. A measure of the amount of matter in an object is called _____.

5. The unit used when measuring temperature is the _____.

6. The test of a hypothesis is a/an _____.

7. The use of scientific knowledge in an effort to improve the quality of human life is called _____.

8. An SI unit used when measuring length is the _____.

9. A device that uses beams of electrons to produce an enlarged image of an object is called a/an _____.

10. A hypothesis that has been tested many times and that is supported by data is a/an _____.

CONCEPTS

1. What is a scientist? (1-1)

2. What field of life science involves the study of animals? What field involves the study of plants? (1-1)

3. Describe two examples of technology from life science. (1-1)

4. Why is a hypothesis sometimes described as an educated guess? (1-2)

5. What is an experiment? (1-2)

6. Explain how the two groups used in an experiment differ from each other. (1-2)

7. Why is it best that there be only one variable in an experiment? (1-2)

8. How does a hypothesis differ from a theory? (1-2)

9. What is a conclusion? (1-2)

10. Why is it important for scientists to measure and record their observations? (1-3)

11. List four prefixes used with SI units, and explain what they mean. (1-3)

12. What unit would you use in measuring the length of a microscopic object? Explain why you chose that unit. (1-3)

13. What device is used to measure liquid volume? What is a meniscus, and what part of it is used when measuring liquid volume? (1-3)

14. A solid with a regular shape is 10 cm by 8 cm by 4 cm. What is its volume? (1-3)

15. Why do scientists use tools in their work? (1-4)

16. How do simple and compound microscopes differ? (1-4)

17. How do light and electron microscopes differ? (1-4)

18. What is culturing? (1-4)

19. What can scientists learn from dissection? (1-4)

20. How might binoculars be useful in field work? (1-4)

APPLICATION/ CRITICAL THINKING

1. Scientists have learned much about how the human heart works. Give an example of technology that has come from this knowledge.

2. Design an experiment to test the hypothesis that a frog's heart beats faster as the water temperature rises.

3. If a large number of living things are used in an experiment, they must be as alike as possible. Explain why.

4. An object 20 μm in length is viewed with a microscope that has 100X magnification. What is the length of the image?

5. An idea or an opinion that influences an observation is called a bias. How do you think a bias might affect the accuracy of an observation?

EXTENSION

1. Use reference books to find out about phase-contrast microscopes and stereomicroscopes. What is each type of microscope used for? What are the greatest magnifications of each type?

2. Write a report about several technological applications of science in the areas of farming and the raising of food animals such as cattle and poultry.

3. Find out how these early units of measurement were defined: digit, palm, span, fathom, foot, and pace. Then measure various objects or distances using some of these units. Record your measurements.

READINGS

Asimov, Isaac. *Asimov's Biographical Encyclopedia of Science and Technology*. New York: Doubleday and Co., 1982.

Dempsey, Michael. *Illustrated Fact Book of Science*. New York: Arco Publishing, 1983.

The Diagram Group. *Comparisons*. New York: St. Martin's Press, 1980.

BEAR'S PAW CLAM
Hippopus hippopus

ABALONE
Haliotus fulgens

ANGEL'S WING
Cyrtopleura costata

RADIX MUREX
Murex radix

CHAMBERED NAUTILUS
Nautilus pompilius

TOP SHELL
Trochus niloticus

ATLANTIC DEER COWRIE
Cypraea cervus

HUMP-BACKED COWRIE
Cypraea mauritiana

CUBAN TREE SNAILS
Liguus fasciatus

LION'S PAW SCALLOP
Lyropecten nodusus

LEOPARD CONE
Conus leopardus

CAPTAIN CONE
Conus captaneus

CLASSIFICATION — A SKILL IN LIFE SCIENCE

Have you ever walked along a beach and collected shells? Many beautiful varieties of shells wash up along the ocean's edge. You may have found fan-shaped scallop shells. Perhaps you have picked up the long, narrow bluish-black shells of a mussel. Or you may have seen some silvery oyster shells with bumpy surfaces. Maybe you have opened these shells, hoping to find a pearl inside.

What would you do with a shell collection? Would you sort the shells? Would you group together those shells with the prettiest colors or the most unusual shapes? Perhaps you would try to identify the shells by using a guide to shells.

- *How are living things named?*
- *How do scientists classify living things?*

2-1 THE NEED FOR CLASSIFICATION

People love to collect things. Some people collect antiques. Others collect rocks, shells, stamps, coins, comic books, baseball cards, dolls, or records. There are as many types of collections as there are types of objects to collect. What other types of objects are collected? How do people organize the objects in their collections?

Many people who collect things develop a system to organize their collections. Figure 2-1, on the next page, shows several different coins. How would you organize a coin collection? What feature of each coin could be used in grouping or classifying them so that you could easily find a certain coin? You could group the coins according to the year in which they were made. You could also group them according to their face value. For example, you could place all pennies together, all nickels together, and all dimes together. To make order out of a collection of objects, you must have a method of classification (klas uh-fuh KAY shuhn). **Classification** is the grouping or arranging of things according to a system.

After completing this section, you will be able to

- **describe** the need for classification systems.
- **define** the terms *taxonomy* and *classification*.

The key terms in this section are
classification
taxonomy

27

Figure 2-1

How can these coins be organized?

Besides organizing the objects in a collection, you would want to be able to talk about your collection. To talk about the collection, you must use the same terms that other collectors understand. For example, suppose two coin collectors want to trade coins. One collector may be looking for a 1917 quarter minted in Denver. Suppose this collector says, "I want *two bits* minted in Denver in 1917." The other collector might be confused. What is meant by *two bits*? Two bits is a slang term for a quarter. To understand each other, the collectors must use terms they both know and agree upon.

In classifying living things, it is helpful to use names that everyone agrees upon. It is confusing if many different names are used for the same thing. For example, look at the animal in Figure 2-2. What is the name of this animal? If you live in the eastern United States, you probably call it a mountain lion. If you live in the western United States, you may call it a cougar or puma. Another name is a panther. Mountain lion, cougar, puma, and panther are common names. These names all refer to the same animal.

Figure 2-2

What do you call this animal?

OBJECTIVE

Design a system for classifying several different kinds of objects.

MATERIALS

assortment of objects supplied by your teacher

PROCEDURE

A. Look at all the objects supplied by your teacher. Decide how the objects are related to each other. Look for ways in which the objects are alike: shape, color, function, and material.

B. Design a system for classifying the objects. Divide the objects into two main groups. Then divide each of these main groups into subgroups.

C. Give a name to each of the groups. The names should be based on how the objects look, how they are used, and what materials they are made of.

D. Other students in your class have been given similar objects to classify. Compare your system of classification with the systems of other students. Find out how the systems are alike and how they differ.

RESULTS AND CONCLUSIONS

1. What trait or traits did you use to classify the objects into two main groups? What names did you give the two groups?
2. What trait or traits did you use to classify the objects into subgroups?
3. Describe another way to classify the objects.
4. How does your system of classification compare with the systems of other students in your class? Were any of the systems the same?
5. Which classification system designed by students in your class was the best? Give reasons for your answer.

There is one name that all scientists have agreed upon for this animal. This name is *Felis concolor*. In the next section you will learn how scientists name living things.

Did you know that a koala bear is not a bear? A jellyfish is not a fish? A horseshoe crab is not a crab? You can see from these examples that common names can be very confusing. Sometimes they can give you misinformation. Is there any way to solve this problem of confusing names?

Scientists all over the world classify living things according to a system. They have agreed upon a system for naming organisms. All organisms are named according to this system. The science of classifying living things is called **taxonomy** (tak SAHN uh mee). Scientists who classify living things are called *taxonomists*.

taxis- (arrangement)

REVIEW

1. Why are classification systems needed?
2. Why is it confusing to use common names for living things?
3. What is taxonomy?

CHALLENGE Suppose each of the scientists at a meeting speaks a different language. The scientists want to discuss the traits of the mountain lion/cougar/puma/panther. When they discuss this animal, what would be the best name for them to use?

2-2 CLASSIFICATION IN THE LIFE SCIENCES

After completing this section, you will be able to

- **describe** the history of classification.
- **describe** Linnaeus's system of classification.
- **explain** why Latin is used to name organisms.

People have long realized the need for a system of classification of organisms. One of the most famous people to classify plants and animals was Aristotle (AR ihs taht-uhl). Aristotle was a Greek philosopher who lived from 384 to 322 B.C. He grouped animals according to where they lived. His system had three main groups of animals: those that lived on land, those that lived in water, and those that lived in air. This system was used as late as the seventeenth century.

In the eighteenth century a Swedish scientist named Carolus Linnaeus (lih NEE uhs) developed a classification system. A system that is based on his ideas is still used by scientists to classify living things today. In his system of classification, Linnaeus placed living things into one of two large groups—the plant kingdom and the animal kingdom. He divided these two kingdoms into smaller groups. All of the living things in each of these groups appeared to be related. Each group was called a *genus* (JEE-nuhs). Each genus contains one or more smaller groups, each called a *species* (SPEE sheez).

In Linnaeus's system of classification, each living thing is given a two-part Latin name. The first part of the name is the genus. The second part of the name is the species. Sometimes the two-part name gives information about a trait or traits of a living thing. For example, in Linnaeus's system a hog-nosed snake, shown in Figure 2-3, is known as *Heterodon platyrhinos* (HEHT er uh dahn   plat uh RĪN-uhs). *Heterodon* is the genus name and *platyrhinos* is the species name. In Latin the species name means "flat nose."

Figure 2-3

Hog-nosed snake. What trait of this snake is described by its species name?

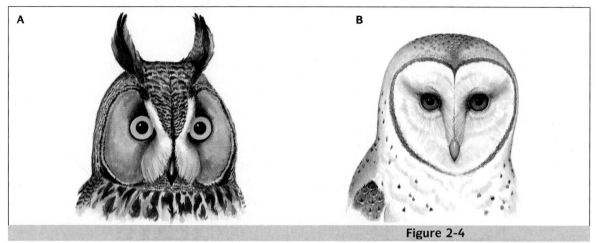

Figure 2-4

Long-eared owl (*A*) and barn owl (*B*). What are their scientific names?

Figure 2-4 shows two owls. What traits might scientists have used in naming these two birds? The owl on the left looks as though it has ears. Its common name is long-eared owl. Scientists call it *Asio otus*. *Asio* is the genus name of one group of owls. *Otus* is a word meaning "ear." The owl on the right has a face that looks like a large white heart. Its common name is barn owl. Its scientific name is *Tyto alba*. *Tyto* is the genus name for another group of owls. *Alba* means "white." Note that in the scientific name of each owl, the species name describes a trait of that bird.

SCIENCE & TECHNOLOGY

New living things are always being discovered, sometimes in very unusual places. The names given to these new living things sometimes honor their discoverer or new technology.

Scientists have found new species of worms, clams, crabs, and fish near the bottom of the ocean. These animals live in groups around hot-water vents, or openings, in the ocean floor.

The water around the vents remains warm—as high as 23°C. Some of the animals feed on tiny living things called bacteria, which live around the vents. The bacteria, in turn, feed on sulfur-containing compounds that spurt out of the ocean vents.

A research submarine called *Alvin* has traveled down to some of these deep-sea vents. Scientists on *Alvin* discovered a worm, which was later named *Alvinella pomejana*. This scientific name honors the submarine used in the discovery of the worm. Another worm discovered around the vents has been named *Paralvinella grasslei*. This name honors both the submarine and the scientist, Dr. Grassle, who explored the ocean bottom.

How Can Animals Be Classified?

Design a system for classifying animals.
Classify animals into groups, according to similar traits.

MATERIALS
an assortment of preserved animals or an assortment of photographs of animals

PROCEDURE
A. Look at the animals provided. Decide what traits the animals have in common.
B. Place the animals into two main groups, according to similar traits. Then divide the main groups into subgroups.
C. Give names to the animal groups and subgroups, based on similar traits.
D. Compare your system of classifying animals with the systems of other students in your class. Find out how your system is like theirs and how it is different.

RESULTS AND CONCLUSIONS
1. What were the main groups into which you divided the animals in step **B**? What were the subgroups?
2. What animals did you put in the main groups? What trait or traits do these animals have in common? What animals did you put in the subgroups? What trait or traits do these animals have in common?
3. Describe any problems you had in selecting animals for placement into the groups and subgroups.
4. Describe the major traits of any animals you know of that would fit into the subgroups of your classification system.
5. How did your classification system compare with the systems designed by other students in your class?

Sometimes the species name is taken from the person who first described a living thing. Other times the species name is used to honor a famous person. One such example is the *Rhea darwinii* (REE uh   dar WIHN ee ee). This ostrichlike bird was named for Charles Darwin, who is famous for his theory on the origin of species.

Linnaeus had several reasons for choosing Latin as the language for naming living things. He chose Latin because it was used by scientists all over the world. In addition, Latin was no longer used as an everyday language. Since Latin was not used in daily life, it was no longer subject to change.

REVIEW

1. Name one of the first people to classify living things. Describe the system that person used.
2. Describe Linnaeus's system of classification.
3. Give examples of information that might be given in the second part of a scientific name.
4. Why did Linnaeus choose Latin as the language for naming living things?

CHALLENGE The following are scientific names of trees: *Salix alba, Quercus bicolor, Quercus rubra,* and *Viburnum dentatum.* From these names, list some important traits of the plants. You may use a dictionary to help you.

2-3 THE MODERN CLASSIFICATION SYSTEM

Linnaeus published his classification systems in the 1750s. At that time, structure was the main basis for the way a living thing was classified. Even today, structure is important in classification. However, problems arise if structure alone is used. For example, since a bat has wings and can fly, scientists might group bats with birds. However, a closer study of bat behavior and internal structure shows that bats are quite different from birds. Bats have more traits in common with mammals, such as rabbits and mice, than with birds. Thus, bats are classified as mammals, not birds. Behavior and internal structure must be thought about when classifying living things.

In classifying living things, scientists also look at fossils. Fossils are the preserved remains of once-living things. Scientists look for ways in which modern and ancient living things are alike. Likenesses can show how modern living things are related to each other and to once-living things. In Figure 2-5, compare the model of the woolly mammoth with the modern elephant.

Figure 2-5

The adult and baby woolly mammoths are models that were made based on fossil remains (*left*). A modern elephant (*right*).

Scientists have also looked more closely at the chemical structure of the *cell*. The cell is the basic unit of living things. Scientists have looked, too, at the contents of the *nucleus* (NOO klee uhs) of the cell. The nucleus is the cell structure containing substances that control the cell's functions. Scientists have found that many living things show likenesses in the substances in the nucleus. These likenesses give information important in classifying living things. Living things with like nuclear substances are often closely related.

In the modern classification system, large groups are broken down into smaller and still smaller groups. Figure 2-5 is a drawing that shows the seven main classification groups. The group in the top row of the triangle contains the greatest number of living things. All the living things in this row are animals. The fact that they are animals is a trait that all living things in this group have in common. The group in the bottom row of the triangle contains the fewest number of living things. But these organisms are most closely related and have a great number of traits in common. The group at the top of the triangle is called a kingdom. A **kingdom** is the largest classification division. It consists of several related phyla (FĪ luh) (sing., *phylum*). The kingdom shown in Figure 2-6 is kingdom Animalia (an uh MAYL yuh). It is one of five kingdoms. All the living

Figure 2-6

The main classification groups.

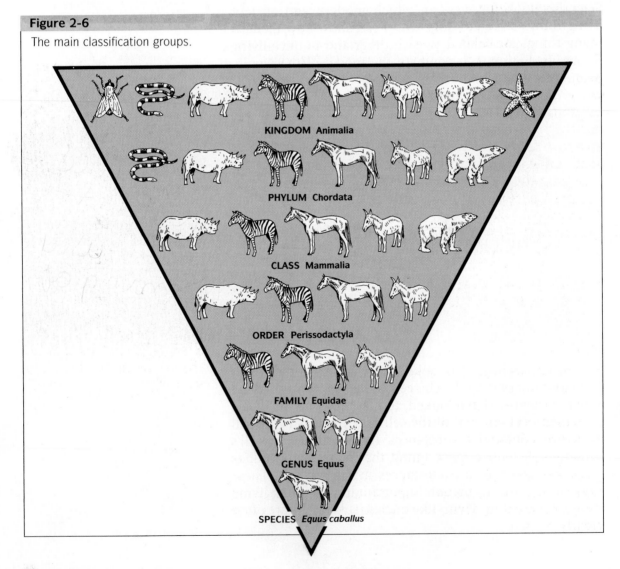

KINGDOM Animalia

PHYLUM Chordata

CLASS Mammalia

ORDER Perissodactyla

FAMILY Equidae

GENUS Equus

SPECIES *Equus caballus*

things that have been named can be placed in one of these five kingdoms.

Refer to Figure 2-6 as you read about the modern classification system. Locate the group just below kingdom. This group is called a phylum (FĪ luhm). A **phylum** is a group of closely related classes. The group below phylum is called a class. A **class** is a group of closely related orders. The five animals in the class in Figure 2-6 are all mammals. They share many traits. Below the group called class are four animals belonging to the same order. An **order** is a group of closely related families. A **family** is a group of closely related genera (sing., *genus*). A **genus** is a group of closely related species. A **species** (pl., *species*) is a group of living things that can mate with each other and whose young can also mate and produce offspring. Members of the same species are the most closely related living things.

Figure 2-6 shows more than the seven main classification groups. It also shows how a horse is classified. The top row shows that a horse belongs to kingdom Animalia. This kingdom includes all animals. A few of the many kinds of animals that exist are shown in this row. As you look down the rows of the triangle, you will see that each row has fewer members. But the animals in each lower row have more and more traits in common. What living things are shown in the row marked *class*? How are these animals alike? How are they different? Look at the row marked *genus*. Notice that the horse and the donkey are more like each other than they are like the other animals in the row marked *class*. Look at the lowest point in the triangle. What is the two-part name for a horse? Look at Figure 2-7, which shows the classification of a tiger lily. To what order does the tiger lily belong? The calla lily and the star lily also belong to this order.

REVIEW

1. What are the traits used in the classification of living things?
2. Explain why a single trait, such as the ability to fly, can lead to confusion in classifying. Use a flying insect, such as a butterfly, in your explanation.
3. List and define the seven main classification groups.

CHALLENGE Use a reference book to find the genus and species names for a house cat and an ocelot. What do these names tell you about whether a cat and an ocelot can mate and produce young that can also mate and produce offspring?

Figure 2-7

Tiger lily. Kingdom: Plantae; Phylum: Tracheophyta; Class: Angiospermae; Order: Liliales; Family: Liliaceae; Genus: *Lilium;* Species: *tigrinum.*

2-4 FIVE-KINGDOM SYSTEM

When Linnaeus developed his system of classification, scientists grouped living things into one of two kingdoms. Living things were either plants or animals. A living thing was placed into kingdom Plantae (PLAN tee) if it produced its own food and could not move from one place to another. Today, kingdom **Plantae** is a major classification group that contains all plants. Trees, shrubs, ferns, and grasses are some of the plants in kingdom Plantae.

A living thing was placed into kingdom Animalia if it could not make its own food and could move from place to place. Today, kingdom **Animalia** is a major classification group that contains all animals. Fish, birds, snakes, cats, insects, and humans are some of the animals in kingdom Animalia.

Scientists later found that not all living things fit into one of these two kingdoms. Figure 2-8 shows a tiny living thing called a *euglena.* Is it a plant or an animal? The euglena moves like an animal. It has a taillike structure that it whips back and forth, causing it to move. Like a plant, the euglena contains a green coloring material and can make its own food. Scientists did not know how to classify the euglena. They also discovered other living things that were not clearly plants or animals.

As new living things were discovered, scientists could not find proper places for them in the two-kingdom system. A third kingdom was added. Living things such as the euglena fit better into this new kingdom. The new

Figure 2-8

Euglena. Is it a plant or an animal?

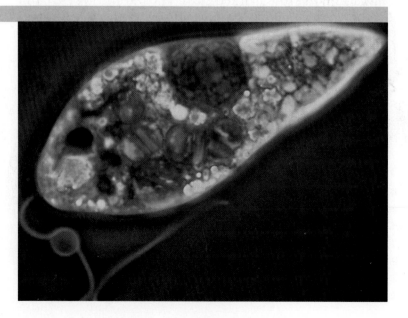

36

kingdom was called kingdom Protista (proh TIHS tuh). Kingdom **Protista** is a major classification group that contains living things that are made up of a single cell that has a nucleus. Some of these living things have traits that are like those of animals and like those of plants. Living things in kingdom Protista are called *protists*.

protistos (the very first)

The microscope is an important tool in the study of living things. It shows details that cannot be seen with the unaided eye. Viewing living things through the microscope helped show scientists the need for kingdom Protista. Scientists soon found that a fourth kingdom was also needed.

Scientists carefully studied certain simple living things, such as *bacteria*. They found that the cells of bacteria do not have a nucleus. Most other living things have this structure. Figure 2-9 shows a bacterial cell. Material that is usually found in the nucleus is scattered throughout the cell. Most scientists today agree that living things that do not have a nucleus should be placed in a kingdom of their own. Kingdom **Monera** (muh NIHR uh) is a major classification group containing living things that are made up of a single cell that lacks a nucleus. Living things in kingdom Monera are called *monerans*.

monos (alone, single)

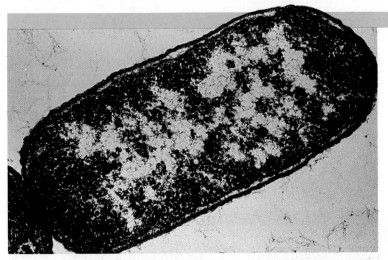

Figure 2-9

A typical moneran.

Mushrooms and molds are types of *fungi* (FUHN jī). Fungi cannot make their own food. They absorb their food from living things or decaying material. Most scientists think that fungi should be placed in a kingdom of their own. Thus, a fifth kingdom was added to the classification system. Kingdom **Fungi** is a major classification group that contains living things that are not green and do not make their own food.

Table 2-1 lists the five-kingdom classification system. Look at the traits and examples of living things in each kingdom. What are some living things in kingdom Plantae? In which kingdom is the amoeba placed? Which kingdom contains living things that lack a nucleus?

Table 2-1 *The Five Kingdoms*

	Kingdom Monera	Kingdom Protista	Kingdom Fungi	Kingdom Plantae	Kingdom Animalia
Major traits	Single-celled; absence of nucleus; nuclear material scattered	Most are single-celled; some make own food; some cannot make own food	Most are many-celled; cannot make own food	Single-celled and many-celled; make own food; cannot move from place to place	Many-celled; cannot make own food; can move from place to place
Examples	Bacteria, blue-green bacteria	Paramecium, amoeba, euglena	Mushroom, mold, yeast	Tree, small flowering plant, fern, algae	Sponge, insect, clam, fish, bird, snake, human

Systems of classification are always changing. Some scientists argue that there should be only three or four kingdoms. Some believe that a sixth kingdom is needed. The rules for classifying living things will continue to change as new living things are discovered. The classification system will also keep changing as new knowledge about the relationships among living things is obtained.

REVIEW

1. Use an example of a living thing to show a problem with the two-kingdom classification system.
2. How did the microscope affect the classification of living things?
3. List and briefly describe the five kingdoms presently used in classification.
4. Why does the classification system keep changing?

CHALLENGE Suppose that while looking through a microscope at a soil sample, you find a living thing that has not been classified. What are some traits that you would look for to help you classify the living thing?

2-5 IDENTIFYING LIVING THINGS

FIELD GUIDES

There may be as many as 10 million different species of living things on the earth. No one person could recognize all these living things. There are aids, however, that are helpful in identifying living things. One very useful aid is a field guide. A **field guide** is a book that contains facts about identifying certain groups of things. For example, there are field guides to birds, flowers, trees, insects, and mammals. There are also field guides to nonliving things, such as rocks and minerals. These books are called field guides because they are small enough to be easily carried when doing field work. Many people take a field guide along when they are on a camping trip.

Figure 2-10 shows you some drawings of woodpeckers as they might appear in a field guide. Notice the arrows that point to different parts of the birds. These arrows highlight *field marks*. Field marks are important features used to identify living things in the field. Notice that one arrow points to the crest on the head of one of the birds. A crest is a cluster of feathers that sticks up from the top of the bird's head. Such a field mark may help to distinguish one species of bird from another.

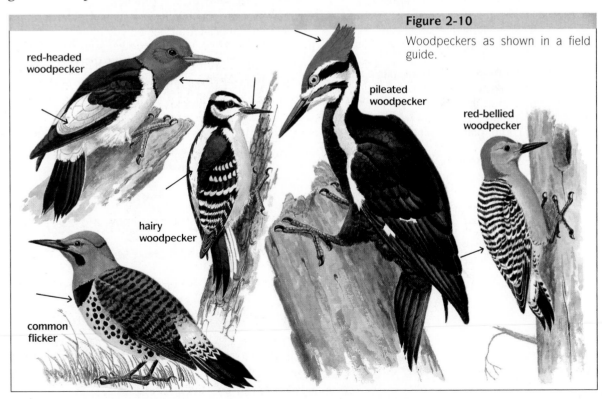

Figure 2-10

Woodpeckers as shown in a field guide.

red-headed woodpecker

hairy woodpecker

pileated woodpecker

red-bellied woodpecker

common flicker

TAXONOMIC KEYS

Besides field guides, there are other aids to identifying living things. A **taxonomic** (tak suh NAHM ihk) **key** is a guide to identifying living things, based on certain traits. A taxonomic key is made up of a list of paired statements. Each pair of statements describes specific traits of living things. Only one of the statements in each pair will be true of the living thing you are trying to identify. Thus,

ACTIVITY   How Is a Key Used to Identify a Living Thing?

OBJECTIVE
Identify various reptiles through the use of a taxonomic key.

MATERIALS
taxonomic key on this page

PROCEDURE
A. Study the drawings of the three reptiles labeled *A* through *C*.
B. Use the taxonomic key below to identify each reptile.
   1. a. Scaly, long, narrow reptile having no limbs .... Snakes
      b. Scaly, long, narrow reptile having narrow tail and two pairs of legs .... Go to **2**.
   2. a. Skin can change color; has a flap of skin attached to throat .... Anole
      b. Skin cannot change color; throat flap absent .... Go to **3**.
   3. a. Large, pointed spines all over body .... Go to **4**.
      b. Scales on body very rough but having no distinct spines .... Go to **5**.

4. a. Two large horns on top of head; body beige and brown .... Texas horned lizard
   b. Small horns on head; red, yellow, and brown spots on body .... Mountain short-horned lizard
5. a. Body color pale; nearly same color all over .... Sand dune lizard
   b. Row of dark spots next to light stripe on back; large pink patch on each side of belly .... Rose-bellied lizard

RESULTS AND CONCLUSIONS
1. What are the names of reptiles *A*, *B*, and *C*?
2. What specific trait helped you identify reptile *A*?
3. What trait does an anole have that the other reptiles shown do not have?
4. Explain how the taxonomic key helped you identify the reptiles shown.

each pair of statements offers you a choice. The statement you choose directs you to another pair of statements. You keep reading pairs of statements and choosing the one that describes the living thing. Finally you make a choice that leads to the name of the living thing that you have been trying to identify.

A taxonomic key is often long and complex. For example, a key could help you to find out which of ten different lizards you have found. Branches of the key could also help you to identify snakes. Like a field guide, a taxonomic key is helpful to have along when you are doing field work.

REVIEW

1. Explain how a field guide helps in identifying a living thing.
2. Explain how a taxonomic key is used.

CHALLENGE Develop your own taxonomic key. It can be used to identify anything you choose. Try it with members of your class.

SCIENCE PUZZLER

While visiting a farm, you see a bird with a sleek body. The upper part of its body is blue-black. The lower part is the color of cinnamon. The feathers at the throat are a rosy brown. Its tail divides into two parts, forming a V. The bird makes a sound like *vit-vit*. Use a field guide to identify the bird.

CHAPTER SUMMARY

The main ideas in this chapter are listed below. Read these statements before you answer the Chapter Review questions.

- Taxonomy is the science of classifying living things. A system of classification provides an orderly arrangement of living things. (2-1)

- The basis for the modern system of classification was developed by Linnaeus. In this system all living things have a two-part name developed from Latin words. (2-2)

- The classification of a living thing is based on structure, behavior, fossil studies, the chemical structure of the cell, and the kinds of chemical substances in the nucleus. The seven major categories in the classification system are kingdom, phylum, class, order, family, genus, and species. (2-3)

- Most scientists believe that living things should be classified according to a five-kingdom system. The five kingdoms in this system are Monera, Protista, Fungi, Plantae, and Animalia. (2-4)

- Living things may be identified with a field guide and a taxonomic key. (2-5)

The key terms in this chapter are listed below. Use each term in a sentence that shows the meaning of the term.

Animalia	field guide	Monera	Protista
class	Fungi	order	species
classification	genus	phylum	taxonomic key
family	kingdom	Plantae	taxonomy

Chapter Review

VOCABULARY

Use the key terms from this chapter to complete the following sentences correctly.

1. A classification group that contains several related phyla is a/an _____ .

2. Kingdom _____ contains living things whose cells lack a nucleus.

3. A book that contains facts that help in identifying living things is a/an _____ .

4. The science of the classification of living things is _____ .

5. The classification group that contains several closely related orders is called a/an _____ .

6. Kingdom _____ contains living things that have many cells, produce their own food, and do not move from place to place.

7. A list of paired statements that helps in identifying living things is a/an _____ .

8. Kingdom _____ contains living things that have many cells, do not produce their own food, and can move from one place to another.

9. The classification group that contains several closely related species is called a/an _____ .

10. Kingdom _____ contains organisms that include mushrooms, molds, and yeasts.

CONCEPTS

1. Explain why scientists developed the science of taxonomy. (2-1)

2. Why is the use of the names cougar, puma, mountain lion, and panther confusing? (2-1)

3. Explain the system Aristotle used for dividing animals into major groups. (2-2)

4. Who developed a classification system that is the basis for the system used today? Explain the two-part name used in this system. (2-2)

5. Explain why a name such as *Asio otus* is useful to a scientist. (2-2)

6. Give two reasons why Latin is the language used by taxonomists. (2-2)

7. What are some traits that may be used in the scientific name of a living thing? (2-3)

8. List the seven major categories in the modern system of classification. (2-3)

9. What kinds of information are used in the classification of a living thing? (2-3)

10. Compare the relationship between the members of a species with that between the members of a phylum. (2-3)

11. Explain why knowledge about the euglena and similar living things caused scientists to change the two-kingdom system of classification. (2-4)

12. Describe the most important traits of living things in each of the five kingdoms. (2-4)

13. Explain how the microscope is related to the development of kingdom Monera. (2-4)

14. Name some living things in kingdom Fungi. Explain why these living things are not part of kingdom Plantae. (2-4)

15. Describe how a field guide may be used to identify living things. (2-5)

16. What are field marks? How are they helpful in the identification of an animal? (2-5)

1. Using a field guide for the identification of insects, list the field marks for these insects: luna moth, bumblebee, and field cricket.

2. Develop a taxonomic key for the identification of leaves from various maple trees. Use a reference book to find the names and descriptions of several types of maple trees before you begin.

3. Suggest a development or discovery that could lead to the need for a sixth kingdom.

1. Make a list of all the animals that you have ever seen or that you know about through magazines, television, and books. Compare your list with other lists developed by your classmates. Based on these lists, explain why a classification system is important.

2. Research the life and write a biography of Carolus Linnaeus.

3. Collect a leaf from each of ten different plants. **Caution:** Certain leaves are poisonous to the touch or poisonous when eaten. Find out which leaves are poisonous. Get the permission of a responsible adult before you collect any leaves. Place the leaves on a poster or in a booklet. Label each leaf with its proper classification from kingdom through species.

Dudd, Margaret B. *Collections for Kids*. San Diego, Calif.: Oak Tree Publications, Inc., 1982.

Gilbert, L. "The Obscure Fame of Carl Linnaeus." *Audubon*, September 1984, p. 102.

Gutrick, Martin J. *Science of Classification: Finding Order Among Living and Nonliving Things*. New York: Franklin Watts, Inc., 1980.

When you have visited a doctor's office, have you ever noticed that the doctor has records about your health? Keeping medical information in order and up to date is the job of a medical records clerk.

Information about past illnesses, allergies, and family medical history is kept in the patient's records. Also included are test results for any illnesses being treated. Medical records clerks must keep files accurately so that no mistakes in patient care occur.

Medical records clerks type and file records. The clerks add new information as it is learned. Many medical records clerks use computers to do their work.

Medical records clerks have a high school diploma and have good office skills. A two-year certificate may be required. If you are interested in this career, you should take typing and other business courses in high school.■

Medical Records Clerk

What kind of information were you seeking the last time you asked a librarian for help? A librarian must be familiar with all the resources of the library.

Some libraries are specialized for science resources. These libraries contain science journals, books, and other references. Often they contain science magazines. A science library usually is used by doctors, researchers, and students. A science librarian helps to make the resources of a science library available. An important part of the job is helping people find needed information.

Science librarians usually have a four-year college degree in science. They often have an additional degree in library science. If you are interested in this career, you should take science courses in high school.■

Science Librarian

Dr. Stephen J. Gould, Paleontologist

Dr. Stephen J. Gould is a paleontologist (pay lee ahn TAHL-uh jihst). He studies the history of life. He uses the scientific method in learning about animals and plants. Dr. Gould investigates how different kinds of organisms have changed over time.

Many scientists have gathered evidence that shows living things change. A lot of the scientists believe that most changes among organisms are slow and gradual. Dr. Gould's studies indicated that organisms change quickly. He and another scientist formed a hypothesis from the data. They hypothesized that many organisms change very little for many years and then undergo periods of rapid change in spurts. Dr. Gould's work may change scientists' ideas about how new kinds of living things develop.

Dr. Gould is also a writer and a teacher. He has written several books and articles about his ideas. He teaches at Harvard University.■

Medicine has made great advances in the last few decades. Vaccines against many diseases have been produced. Surgical procedures have been developed for problems such as eye disorders, bone and joint injuries, and heart disease. Many new drugs are used to treat diseases that were fatal only a few years ago. All of these medical advances have come with the help of research done on animals.

Some people object to such research. In some research projects, animals are killed or subjected to painful conditions. People who support animal rights say that animals should not be subjected to such cruelty. These people say that experiments using animals should be stopped.

Opponents of this view believe that research must be allowed to continue. They say that many human lives have been saved as a result of such research. They claim that there is often no other way to test new treatments for people.

When a new drug or a new treatment procedure is developed, it is tested on laboratory animals. If the drug or procedure is successful on animals, it is then tested on humans. Sometimes, college students or medical students volunteer to be test subjects. Sometimes, prisoners volunteer to be tested.

In some cases a new drug or procedure is tried on a person who has a fatal medical problem for which there is no cure or treatment. For example, Barney Clarke, the first human to have the Jarvik-7 artificial heart, would have died without this device. As a result of using the artificial heart, Clarke lived about 3 months longer than he otherwise would have lived.

Clarke was not the first recipient of an artificial heart. Before doctors were ready to try out the device on a human, they tested it thoroughly on various animals.

Figure 1 shows the total number of animals used in experiments in the United States over a 3-year period. In addition to testing high-tech devices like the artificial heart, these animals were used for testing drugs, artificial flavorings in new foods, and cosmetics.

APPLYING CRITICAL THINKING SKILLS

1. How many animals were used in experiments in 1985? How does this number compare with the number of animals used in previous years? What conclusions can you draw from this?

2. People are sometimes surprised to learn that cosmetics are tested on animals before being used on people. What do you think cosmetics are tested for? Do you think animals are needed for this? What alternatives would you suggest?

3. What reasons might college students or medical students have for taking part in testing programs? What reasons might prisoners have?

4. If your doctor wanted you to try a new medication, would you want to know how it had been tested? Would you agree to take the medication if you knew it had not been tested? Explain your answer.

You may have heard a person who was taking part in a testing program being referred to as a "guinea pig." This expression

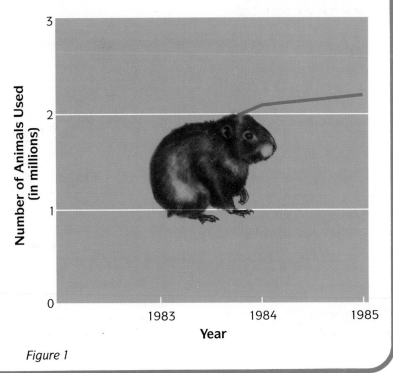

Figure 1

comes from the fact that many of these animals are used in research. However, the guinea pig is not the only species used. Rats and mice are used, too.

There are several reasons for using small animals like these. They take up little space in a laboratory. They are inexpensive to buy and to care for. Thus a researcher can have many test subjects to work with.

One disadvantage in using rats and mice is that these animals are very different from humans. Sometimes, larger animals are needed. For example, one test on the Jarvik-7 heart used cattle. It was important to see if the artificial heart was strong enough to pump blood through a large body. A small animal would not be useful in such a test.

Sometimes an experiment must use animals that are similar to humans. Much of the research conducted to find a vaccine against polio used monkeys. In the 1950s over a million monkeys were used for this purpose. As a result of these experiments,

there are very few cases of polio in the world today. Polio is a disease of the nervous system. Monkeys were used in polio research because the nervous system of a monkey is similar to that of a human.

One researcher duplicated some of the effects of a stroke by destroying much of the sense of touch in some monkeys. The point of this experiment was to see if there was a way that the monkeys could learn to move around without using the sense of touch. When someone complained that this was cruel, the experiment was investigated. As a result, the researcher's government grant was taken away.

The United States Department of Agriculture regulates the use of some animals. Rats and mice make up about 95 percent of all animals used in laboratories. These animals are not under government control. Only 5 percent of the animals used in research are under government control. Figure 2 shows which animals make up this small group.

APPLYING CRITICAL THINKING SKILLS

1. What are the three most commonly used animals under government regulation?
2. Mice and rats are commonly bred for use in the laboratory. Where do researchers get some of the other kinds of animals that are used?
3. Why, do you think, is the use of rats and mice not regulated by the government? Do you think it should be? Explain your answer.
4. Do you think that animals under government regulation are better off than those that are not? Explain your answer.

Supporters of animal experiments say that there is enough protection for animals. The Animal Welfare Act requires American scientists to adequately feed, water, and house research animals. There also are periodic inspections of research facilities. These inspections are carried out by the government agencies that fund animal research.

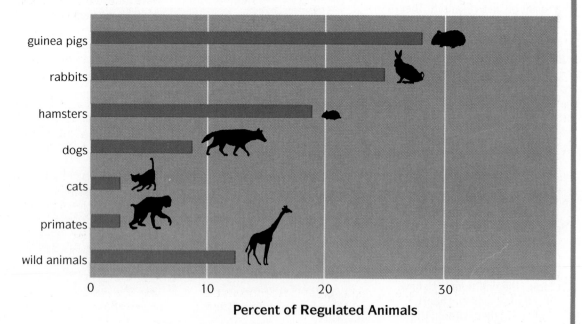

Figure 2

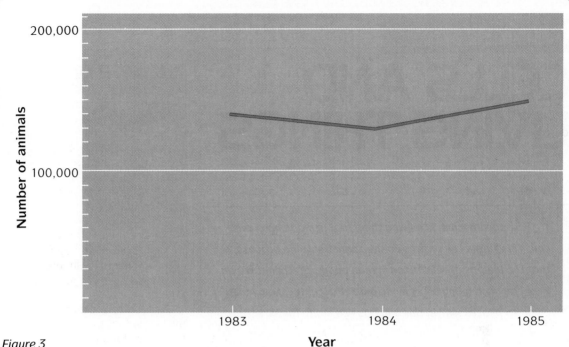

Figure 3

Year

Information on animal care is made available to researchers. The *Guide to the Care and Use of Laboratory Animals* is published by the National Academy of Science. Most universities and scientific organizations whose members conduct animal research distribute guidelines and have animal-care committees.

However, some people believe that experimentation done in the cosmetic industry is needlessly painful. In the Draize eye test, makeup is put into the eyes of rabbits to see if it irritates the eyes. The results may range from swollen eyes to blindness.

Some scientists are trying to take a middle course between those who say that all animal experimentation is bad and those who say that none of it is bad. These scientists still support the use of animals in experiments. However, they say these tests should be done more carefully. In the Draize eye test, for example, only a small amount of the substance to be tested is used. If a substance is found to injure an animal, no more of it is tested.

There are some alternatives to animal testing. Sometimes, tissue cultures can be used. Tissues are surgically removed from an animal and grown in the laboratory. The effect of chemicals on the cells of the tissue culture can be studied.

Computers are also being used to test drugs and other chemicals. Computer programs have been designed to predict how animals will react to certain chemicals. So far, the computers have been accurate 80 percent of the time.

Even with these developments, there are still some tests that require the use of live animals. Some scientists say there is no alternative. Many human lives have been saved by the treatments that have come from some of these experiments.

However, some experiments subject animals to pain and death. In some experiments the researchers determined that the use of painkillers would interfere with the results of the experi-

ment. Figure 3 shows how many animals have been used in experiments that involve pain.

APPLYING CRITICAL THINKING SKILLS

1. How many research animals were reported to be in pain in 1985? Look back to Figure 1 to find out how many animals were used in research in 1985. What percent of the total animals used were in pain?

2. Do you think cosmetics, like makeup or hair dye, should be tested? What would happen if these substances were not tested?

3. Sometimes, animals have to be subjected to pain in experiments. It would be difficult to test painkillers any other way. Do you think this pain is justified? Explain your answer.

4. Which kinds of animal research do you think are necessary? Which do you think are not necessary? Explain your answers.

CELLS AND LIVING THINGS

A paramecium is a living thing that is made up of one cell. This single cell carries on the same basic life processes that the billions of cells in the human body together carry on. How can such a tiny bit of living matter accomplish so many complex processes? In this unit you will study the structure and function of cells. You will also learn about the great variation among simple living things that are neither plants nor animals. ■

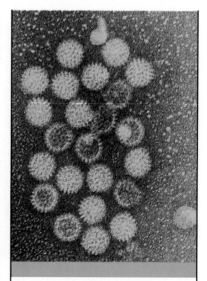

▲ *This type of virus, magnified tens of thousands of times, causes an inflammation of the stomach and intestines.*

▼ *Some living things, such as these golden wands, feed off decaying matter.*

▼ *Anton van Leeuwenhoek's drawing of a flea. Leeuwenhoek was the first person to see tiny living things with a microscope he built in the seventeenth century.*

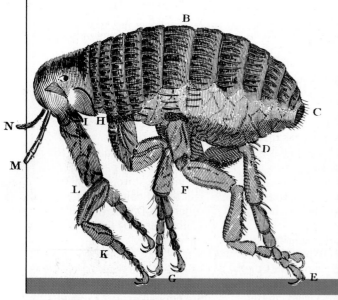

▼ Cells vary in shape and size. These are human cheek cells. The cells were stained with purple dye to make them easier to see.

► This compound microscope was designed by John Marshall in England in the 1690s. It was the first microscope that could be raised and lowered over the specimen.

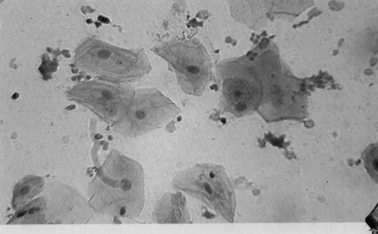

▼ These paramecia are single cells. Notice the tiny hairlike parts that are used to move the paramecia through liquid.

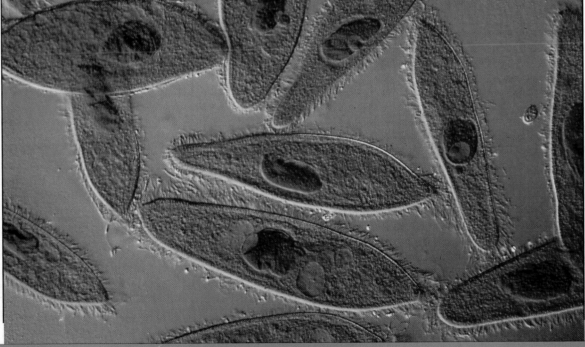

THE CHARACTERISTICS OF LIFE

The forest fire in the photograph has characteristics that resemble those of living things. The flames seem to jump from one tree to another. Animals such as squirrels might behave in this way. The flames consume the leaves and wood of the trees. Beavers and some insects are living things that feed on trees. Gases are given off as the fire burns the tree. Some of them are the same gases given off by living things. But despite these many similarities to living things, the fire is not alive.

- *What are the special characteristics that make something alive?*
- *What materials make up living things?*
- *How are new living things produced?*

3-1 TRAITS OF LIVING THINGS

LIFE PROCESSES

Have you ever wondered whether something is alive or not? How can you tell the difference between living and nonliving things? This question is not easy to answer because living things come in so many different forms. An oak tree and a blade of grass are different in form, but they are both plants. An elephant, a sponge, and a mosquito do not look alike, but they are all animals. Many living things are neither plants nor animals, but they too are alive. A complete, individual living thing is called an **organism** (AWR guh nihz uhm). Despite their many differences, all organisms have many features in common. These features together are what make something a living thing.

Although organisms may look very different from each other, they all do similar things to stay alive. The things that organisms do to maintain life are called **life processes**. The life processes are described in the following statements.

> *After completing this section, you will be able to*
>
> - **distinguish** between living and nonliving things.
> - **identify** the life processes common to all living things.
> - **recognize** the cell as the basic unit of life.
>
> *The key terms in this section are*
> cell   organism
> life processes

51

Taking In Materials　An organism takes in materials, such as food and gases, from its surroundings. These materials provide energy.

Releasing Energy　An organism releases the energy in food. Energy is used in carrying on life processes.

Growing　An organism grows, or increases in size, during its *life cycle*. Each species has its own life cycle during which it passes through a series of changes.

Responding　An organism reacts, or responds, to changes in its surroundings.

Releasing Wastes　An organism releases waste materials into its surroundings. These wastes are formed as organisms carry out other life processes.

Producing New Organisms　An organism produces others of its own kind.

A living organism carries on all of these life processes. A nonliving thing may carry on some of these processes but not all of them. A car engine takes materials—fuel and oxygen—from its surroundings. It gives off wastes in the form of exhaust gases. But a car engine cannot make others of its own kind. A thermostat responds to changes in temperature, but it cannot grow. What life processes are shown in Figure 3-1?

Figure 3-1

A young horse, or foal, with its parent (*left*). The wild pig is running from a leopard (*right*). How does this response aid the wild pig's survival?

CELLS

In addition to carrying on life processes, organisms are alike in another way. Organisms are made of one or more cells. A **cell** is the smallest unit in which all of the life processes can be carried on. It is the basic unit of life and the smallest unit in which life can exist. A complex organism, such as a human, may consist of trillions of cells. Many microscopic life forms, such as the one shown in Figure 3-2, are made up of a single cell. You will learn about cells, and how they function, in Chapter 4.

NEEDS OF LIVING THINGS

All living things have basic needs. These needs must be met in order for organisms to carry on life processes. Table 3-1 summarizes the needs of living things. Energy is one of the needs that all organisms have. A source of water or moisture is another need. Organisms also require certain gases from their surroundings. A certain range of temperatures to carry on the life processes is another need.

Just as organisms vary in their appearance, they also vary in their specific needs. Some organisms, such as the orchid in Figure 3-3, need high temperatures to survive; others require much lower temperatures. Animals need oxygen. However, some kinds of organisms are poisoned by oxygen. These living things require other kinds of gases. Whatever needs an organism has, these needs must be met in order for the life processes to continue.

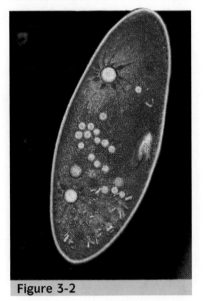

Figure 3-2

A paramecium is an organism that is made up of just one cell. Why is a cell called the basic unit of life?

Figure 3-3

A parrot and an orchid live in tropical places. These organisms would die if they were exposed to cold temperatures for too long a time.

Table 3-1 *Needs of Living Things*

Need	Example
Energy	Animals get energy from the food they eat.
Water	Humans drink water. The human body is about 70 percent water.
Gases	Animals take in oxygen from the air.
Temperature	A tropical bird, such as a parrot, needs warm temperatures to survive.

REVIEW

1. What are the life processes carried on by all organisms?
2. What do all living things have in common?
3. How do organisms differ from nonliving things?
4. What are the basic needs of living things?

CHALLENGE What are the stages in the human life cycle? Which stage of the life cycle are you in?

3-2 NUTRITION AND METABOLISM

nutrire (nourish)
-tion (process)

NEED FOR FOOD

The need for food is common to all living things. An organism needs food for at least two reasons. One reason is that substances in food are used during growth to add new material to an organism. The substances in food are also used to repair parts of an organism that have been damaged or worn out. A second reason that an organism needs food is as a source of energy. Energy is the ability to do work. Many kinds of work occur within an organism. Growing new cells and pumping blood are examples of work that occur in the human body. Food provides the energy that makes this work possible.

Consider a machine such as a car. Steel, plastic, and rubber are some of the building materials needed to make a car. Fuel in the form of gasoline is needed to run the car. The fuel provides energy. A living thing can be thought of as a living machine. A living thing needs both building materials and energy. It gets both materials and energy from food. **Nutrition** (noo TRIHSH uhn) is the process by which organisms obtain and use the food they need. Organisms differ in their methods of nutrition, as can be seen in Figure 3-4. Animals get food by eating other organisms or by eating parts or products of other organisms. Plants use sunlight, gases, and water to make their own food. Other kinds of organisms, such as the mushroom in Figure 3-4, absorb food substances from soil.

An animal *eats* food.

Figure 3-4

Three methods of nutrition.

light energy

SUGAR

water

carbon dioxide gas

A plant *makes* food.

A mushroom *absorbs* food.

USE OF FOOD

Exactly how do organisms use food after they make it or otherwise obtain it? There are several chemical processes involved in using food as a source of building materials and energy. **Metabolism** (muh TAB uh lihz uhm) is the sum of all the chemical processes that occur in an organism.

metabole (change)
-ism (act of)

The first part of metabolism in many organisms is the process of digestion. **Digestion** (duh JEHS chuhn) is a series of steps in which large complex food substances are broken into smaller, simpler forms. Look at Figure 3-5A to get an idea of what happens in digestion. Food substances are often in a form that is too large or too complex to be used directly by an organism. Digestion breaks down food into forms that are usable by the organism.

dis- (apart)
gerere (carry)

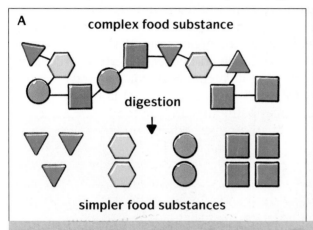

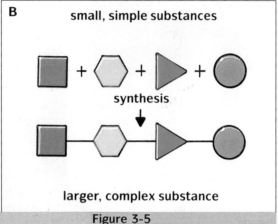

Figure 3-5

Digestion breaks down complex food substances (A). Synthesis joins together simple substances (B).

re- (back, again)
spirare (breathe)

Many of the foods broken down by digestion are used as a source of energy. The process of releasing energy from food is called **respiration** (rehs puh RAY shuhn). In this process, food is combined with oxygen. Water and other waste products are given off. Energy is the most important product of respiration. The energy released from food is used to carry on the life processes.

Some of the products of digestion are used by the organism in building new living materials. New materials are used in growth and in the replacement of parts that are damaged or worn out. Organisms build new materials by a process called *synthesis* (SIHN thuh sihs). In synthesis, small simple substances are joined together to form a larger, more complex substance. You can see what occurs in this process by looking at Figure 3-5B. Compare this process with digestion. You can see why synthesis can be thought of as the opposite of digestion.

Why do organisms first break down food substances in digestion and then join substances together in synthesis? One reason is that the smaller pieces produced by digestion can be easily moved about within an organism. A second reason is that each species has its own special chemical makeup. Think of an animal that eats plants. The substances in a plant are not the same as those in the muscles of the animal. The animal must first digest the plant materials. Then, through synthesis, the small parts may be built up again into the types of substances needed to form the muscles of the animal.

Many processes of metabolism result in the formation of waste products. Some wastes are poisons. Organisms need a way to get rid of such wastes. **Excretion** (ehk-SKREE shuhn) is the process by which the waste products of metabolism are removed from an organism.

You can see that metabolism involves an exchange of materials between an organism and its surroundings. Raw materials are taken in and wastes are excreted. All organisms carry on such exchanges of materials.

Figure 3-6

When you perspire, some of the waste products of metabolism are removed from your body. What is this process called?

REVIEW

1. Give two reasons why organisms need food.
2. What two processes of metabolism can be thought of as the opposites of each other? Explain why.
3. What occurs during respiration?

CHALLENGE Water is a nonpoisonous waste product of metabolism. Why is its excretion necessary to life?

56

3-3 GROWTH AND RESPONSE

Organisms usually increase in size during one or more parts of their life cycle. Recall that living things are made up of basic units called cells. **Growth**, or an increase in size, usually results from an increase in the number of cells in a living thing. A single-celled organism can grow only by increasing the size of its cell. But there is a limit to how big any cell can grow.

In most other living things, growth is usually not caused by an increase in the size of cells. Cells sometimes do change size, but such changes are usually only temporary. The size of the cells in most many-celled organisms usually remains fairly constant. Many-celled organisms grow by producing new cells and thus increasing the total number of their cells. Compare the growth of the two kinds of organisms in Figure 3-7.

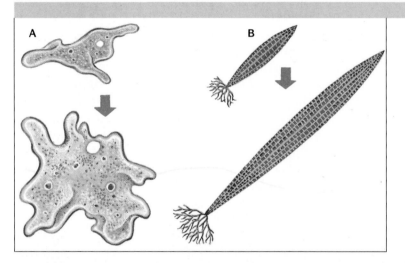

Figure 3-7

A single-celled organism grows by increasing the size of its cell (*A*). A many-celled organism, such as a grass plant, grows by producing more cells (*B*).

Have you ever seen a cat with its back arched and its fur raised, as shown in Figure 3-8? What causes cats to act in this way? Cats sometimes react this way when frightened by a dog or other larger animal. An event or a condition which causes an organism to react is known as a **stimulus** (STIHM yuh luhs) (pl., *stimuli*). The reaction of an organism to a stimulus is called a **response**. In the case of the cat, the presence of a dog served as a stimulus. The arching of the cat's back and the raising of its fur were the responses to this stimulus.

The surroundings of an organism are its *environment* (ehn vī ruhn muhnt). The environment of an organism includes living and nonliving things. An organism receives many stimuli from its environment. Some stimuli come

Figure 3-8

Besides the one shown, what other responses might a frightened cat have to the stimulus of a dog or other larger animal?

from other living things. Stimuli can also come from non-living things. Receiving and responding to stimuli help a living thing survive in its environment.

Many stimuli come from changes in an organism's environment. It is important that an organism be able to respond to these changes. Such responses may be needed for survival. Some changes in the environment act as danger signals. To survive, the organism must respond by preparing to defend itself against a danger or to escape it. For example, many kinds of organisms will die if they become too dry. A reduced amount of moisture in the environment acts as a stimulus to such organisms. They may respond with a defensive action. Some single-celled organisms respond to this stimulus by forming a waterproof coating. The waterproof coating keeps the organism from drying out until more water is available. How might a many-celled organism, such as a frog, respond to dryness in its environment?

Some changes in the environment may signal the presence of something that is useful to an organism. A stimulus may mean the presence of food or other needed materials. An organism must respond often to such stimuli in order to survive. The spiders shown in Figure 3-9 responded to the shaking of their web. The shaking usually means that an insect has been caught in the web. The spiders eat the fly, which provides energy for their life processes. A plant placed in front of a window may respond to light by growing toward it. Leaves that face the light can make more food than those that do not. This response helps the plant survive.

Figure 3-9

These orb-weaver spiders have poor vision. They locate insects caught in their web by feeling the vibrations of the threads.

ACTIVITY   How Do Plants Respond to Different Stimuli?

OBJECTIVE
Identify the responses of plants to different stimuli.

MATERIALS
small potted plants, black construction paper, scissors, transparent tape, marking crayon, newspapers

PROCEDURE

A. Obtain three small potted plants. Label the side of each pot. Label them *A*, *B*, and *C*.

B. Cut a circle from construction paper so that the circle has the same diameter as the top of the pots. Cut the circle in half. Cut a rectangular piece from a sheet of construction paper. The long sides of the rectangle should be the same length as the height of plant *B*. Use transparent tape to attach the rectangular piece to the two circle halves, as shown. You have made a light shield.

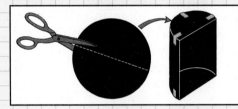

C. Place plant *A* near a sunny window so that the letter *A* on the pot faces the window. Turn the plant one-half turn each day. You can use the letter on the pot to help you keep track of the position of the pot. Plant *A* is the control.

D. Place plant *B* near the same window, so that the letter *B* faces the window. Place the paper light shield around the pot so it is on the side opposite the letter *B*. Do not turn this plant.

E. Place plant *C* on its side near the same window. The letter *C* should always face the ceiling except when the plant is being watered. Turn the plant each day so that one day the bottom of the pot faces the window and the next day the bottom of the pot faces away from the window.

F. Water the plants each day for 2 weeks. Observe the plants, and record any differences in the way they grow.

G. Carefully remove each plant from its pot. To do this, tap the edge of the pot while holding it upside down over sheets of newspaper. Be sure to note which pot each plant came from. Gently wash the soil off the roots under running tap water.

RESULTS AND CONCLUSIONS

1. Why is plant *A* called the control? As you answer the following questions, compare plants *B* and *C* with plant *A*.
2. How did the stems and leaves of plant *B* respond to the stimulus of light received from only one direction? Were the roots affected? Try to explain why or why not.
3. How did the stems and leaves of plant *C* respond to the stimulus of the plant being on its side? Were the roots affected? Try to explain why or why not.
4. Why, do you think, was it necessary to turn plant *C* each day?

REVIEW

1. How does growth in a single-celled organism differ from growth in a many-celled organism? How is growth alike in both types of organisms?
2. Give an example of one stimulus that you experienced to-day. Describe your response.
3. How does responding to stimuli help an organism survive in its environment?

CHALLENGE When food decays, acids are produced. If a drop of weak acid is placed in water containing certain single-celled organisms, the organisms will move toward the acid. How does this response benefit the organism?

3-4 REPRODUCTION

After completing this section, you will be able to

- **recognize** that living things come only from other living things.
- **distinguish** between sexual and asexual reproduction.
- **compare** organisms that are produced by each form of reproduction.

The key terms in this section are
asexual reproduction
reproduction
sexual reproduction

REDI'S EXPERIMENTS

Throughout much of human history, people believed that living things could come from nonliving things. The following is a "recipe" for making mice that was accepted by people who lived during the seventeenth century. *Place a pile of wheat or other grain in a dark corner. Cover with old rags. In a few days, mice will be formed by this mixture.* Do you believe that this recipe actually makes mice? What do you think causes mice to appear?

Another old belief was that flies are produced from rotting meat or from dead animals. People often saw maggots on rotting meat. Maggots are a wormlike stage in the life cycle of a fly. The maggots on the meat later changed into flies. Francesco Redi, a seventeenth-century Italian doctor, did not believe that rotting meat produced flies. Redi set out to show that maggots and flies come only from other flies and not from rotting meat. Refer to Figure 3-10 as you read about Redi's experiments.

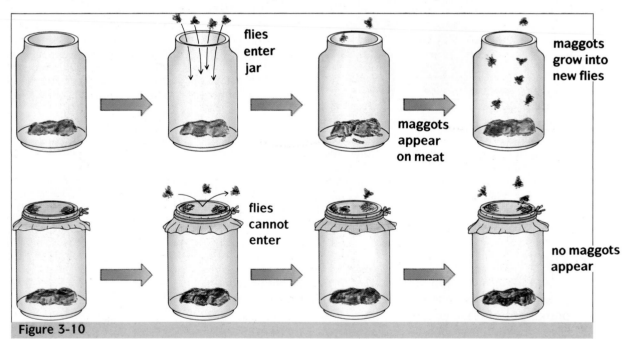

Figure 3-10

Francesco Redi's experiments showed that maggots grow from eggs laid by flies.

Redi placed pieces of meat into jars. He left some of the jars open. Other jars were covered with gauze, a fine netlike cloth. Redi observed that flies entered the open jars and laid eggs on the meat. After a few days, maggots appeared on the rotting meat in these open jars. The maggots later grew into new flies.

Flies were unable to enter the jars covered with gauze. But air, dust, and microscopic life forms were able to pass through the gauze over the covered jars. So although the meat in the covered jars continued to rot, no maggots appeared on it. Redi concluded that maggots can only appear where flies have laid eggs. In other words, flies come only from other flies. Redi's idea has been tested many times by others. The results are always the same. Life cannot arise, or come, from nonliving things. Life comes only from other life.

TYPES OF REPRODUCTION

Biologists today believe that living things can arise only from other organisms of the same kind. **Reproduction** (ree pruh DUHK shuhn) is the process by which organisms produce other organisms of the same kind. Oak trees produce other oak trees. Flies cannot be produced by rotting meat. Only flies can produce other flies.

The ability of organisms to reproduce others of their kind is one of the most basic features of life. Reproduction must occur if a species is to survive. Any species that fails to reproduce will pass out of existence.

There are two very different ways in which organisms reproduce. **Asexual** (ay SEHK shoo uhl) **reproduction** is a form of reproduction that involves only one parent. **Sexual reproduction** is a form of reproduction that involves two cells, usually from two parents.

Asexual reproduction is the simpler of the two forms of reproduction. In one type of asexual reproduction, the organism simply divides, or splits, into two new organisms. In another type a part of a parent organism breaks away and grows into a new adult organism. Both of these methods of asexual reproduction are shown in Figure 3-11. A new organism produced by either method always resembles its parent. Since only one parent is involved, the new organism has the same features as that parent.

Most microscopic life forms reproduce by asexual means. Figure 3-11A shows reproduction in a single-celled organism. Many plants and some simple animals also reproduce by this method. Figure 3-11B shows asexual reproduction in a hydra, a simple animal. More complex animals, such as humans, cannot reproduce asexually.

Most often, two parents are involved in sexual reproduction. Each parent contributes a cell. The two cells join to form a new organism. Since it gets cells from each parent, the new organism usually has a blend of the traits of its two parents. The new organism is usually different

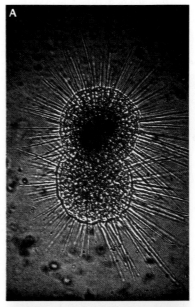

Figure 3-11

Two types of asexual reproduction.

from either parent. Compare the kittens in Figure 3-12 with their parents. How are they like each parent? How are they different from each parent?

Sexual reproduction causes a mixing of the traits of organisms. For this reason, sexual reproduction tends to increase variety among living things. Consider the great variety that can be seen among humans. Sexual reproduction is an important cause of the great variety we see among humans and other species.

Most organisms, except for the simplest forms, can reproduce sexually. Nearly all animals and plants reproduce by this method. Many of the more complex animals can reproduce only by sexual reproduction.

Figure 3-12

The kittens have traits of both parents: the father (*left*) and the mother (*right*).

REVIEW

1. What past belief did Redi's experiments disprove? What do scientists today believe about the origin of new living things?
2. How do sexual reproduction and asexual reproduction differ? How do new organisms that result from each form of reproduction differ?
3. Which form of reproduction results in an increase in variety among living things? Explain your answer.

CHALLENGE Two one-celled organisms of the same species join together. A thick wall encloses the two cells. At a later time the wall breaks open, and many new organisms are released. What type of reproduction is this? Explain your answer. Then describe the appearance of the new organisms in relation to their parents.

3-5 THE NATURE OF MATTER

All things in the natural world, both living and non-living, are made up of matter. **Matter** is anything that has mass and takes up space. Matter exists in different states or phases—as solids, liquids, and gases.

Matter, together with energy, accounts for all the things that exist and all the events that occur in the universe. Recall that energy is the ability to do work. Anything you can think of can be classified as either matter or energy. A piece of wood is matter. If the wood is burned, energy in the form of heat and light is given off.

All matter is composed of tiny particles called atoms. An **atom** is the smallest unit of matter that can exist and still be recognized as a particular kind of matter. Atoms are so small that they cannot be seen, using even the most powerful microscopes. Based on the results of many experiments, scientists have formed *models* of atoms. A model is a way of showing how something looks or how it acts.

Scientists have learned that there are many types of atoms. An **element** is a substance that is made up of only one type of atom. There are 92 elements that are known to exist naturally on the earth. Another 16 elements have been produced artificially by scientists. All things on the earth are made up of one or more of these 92 elements. You are familiar with some elements that exist in pure form, uncombined with other kinds of elements. How many of the elements in use in Figure 3-13 can you find in your classroom?

After completing this section, you will be able to

- **recognize** the atomic nature of matter.
- **distinguish** between elements and compounds.
- **describe** the use of chemical symbols, formulas, and equations to represent chemical change.

The key terms in this section are

atom	matter
compound	molecule
element	

a- (without)
tomos (a cutting)

Figure 3-13

Elements in use: iron in railing (*left*); mercury in thermometer (*middle top*); helium in blimp (*middle bottom*); and silver in jewelry (*right*).

63

Scientists all over the world use the same *chemical symbols* to represent the elements. A symbol is a shorthand way of writing the name of an element. Symbols for 12 elements found in living things are shown in Table 3-2.

Table 3-2 *Elements in Living Things*

Element	Symbol	Source of Symbol
Carbon	C	English name
Hydrogen	H	English name
Oxygen	O	English name
Nitrogen	N	English name
Phosphorus	P	English name
Sulfur	S	English name
Potassium	K	Latin name (*kalium*)
Magnesium	Mg	English name
Calcium	Ca	English name
Iron	Fe	Latin name (*ferrum*)
Sodium	Na	Latin name (*natrium*)
Chlorine	Cl	English name

com- (together)
ponere (put)

Different types of elements can combine. A **compound** is a substance that contains atoms of two or more elements joined together. Look at Figure 3-14. You can see that water is a compound formed when 2 hydrogen atoms and 1 oxygen atom join. Table sugar is a compound made up of 12 carbon atoms, 22 hydrogen atoms, and 11 oxygen atoms. The nature of a compound is determined by two factors. One factor is the types of elements that the compound contains. The other factor is the number of atoms of each element that make up the compound. Many compounds other than table sugar are made up of carbon, hydrogen, and oxygen atoms. These other compounds are different because they contain different numbers of atoms of the same three elements.

The smallest unit of an element is an atom. Similarly, the smallest unit of many compounds is a **molecule** (MAHL-uh kyool). Molecules are composed of atoms. A molecule of water is the smallest particle of water that can exist. If a molecule of water was split into smaller units, it would no longer be water. It would be the elements hydrogen and oxygen.

Scientists use symbols and numbers to represent the *chemical formula* of a compound. A chemical formula shows the types and number of atoms in a compound or a molecule. The chemical formula for water is H_2O. The formula shows that there are 2 hydrogen atoms and 1 oxygen atom.

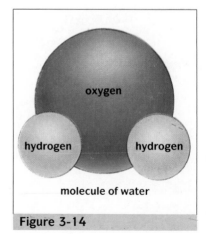

oxygen

hydrogen hydrogen

molecule of water

Figure 3-14

The compound water forms when 2 hydrogen atoms combine with 1 oxygen atom.

When two or more elements combine to form a compound, a *chemical change* occurs. A chemical change is a change in matter in which a new substance or substances form. There are many kinds of chemical changes that can occur. One kind of chemical change occurs when two compounds combine to form a new compound or compounds. Figure 3-15 shows an example of this kind of chemical change. The breakdown of a compound into individual elements is another kind of chemical change. A large compound may break down into smaller compounds. This is still another kind of chemical change. In each case, new substances form.

Figure 3-15

A chemical change occurs when sulfuric acid combines with sugar. New compounds are formed.

Scientists use chemical formulas in a *chemical equation* to describe what happens in a chemical change. For example, the joining of hydrogen and oxygen to form water could be shown by the following chemical equation.

$$2H + O \rightarrow H_2O$$

The equation shows that 2 atoms of hydrogen join with 1 atom of oxygen to produce one molecule of water. Formulas and equations allow scientists to communicate easily and quickly about chemical changes.

REVIEW

1. What is matter?
2. What are all forms of matter made up of?
3. Distinguish between an atom and a molecule.
4. Is H_2O an element or a compound? Explain your answer.
5. What information does a chemical formula give?

CHALLENGE Write an equation to describe the following chemical change: 1 atom of carbon combines with 2 atoms of oxygen to form one molecule of carbon dioxide.

3-6 CHEMICALS OF LIFE

Chemists classify compounds into two major types. An **organic** (awr GAN ihk) **compound** is a compound that contains the element carbon. An *inorganic compound* is a compound that does not contain carbon. Organic compounds are found mainly in living things and in the remains of once-living things. Inorganic compounds are found chiefly in nonliving matter, such as rocks and ocean water. Although water is an inorganic compound, it makes up a large part of the matter in living things.

ORGANIC COMPOUNDS

Sugars are organic compounds with which you are already familiar. Sugars are found in many different foods, especially fruits. There are many kinds of sugar. Glucose (GLOO kohs) is one kind of sugar. It is found in most living things, including humans. *Starches* are another type of organic compound. Starches consist of many sugar molecules joined together to form long chains. Figure 3-16 shows how a starch is formed. Starches are found in foods such as bread, spaghetti, and potatoes.

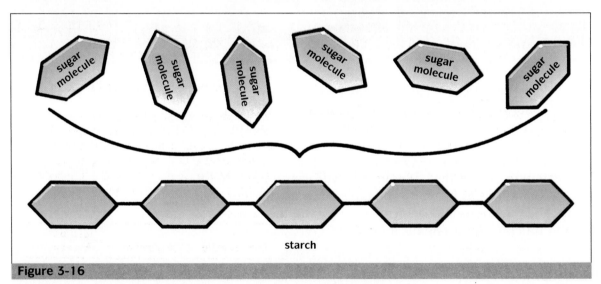

Figure 3-16

Starches are formed from sugar molecules joined in long chains.

carbo- (carbon)
hydr- (water)
-ate (having, containing)

Sugars and starches are carbohydrates (kahr boh HĪ-drayts). **Carbohydrates** are a group of organic compounds that are the main source of energy for living things. All carbohydrates are made up of carbon, hydrogen, and oxygen atoms. Carbohydrates can be thought of as fuel for the life processes. When you eat these compounds, you provide your body with energy needed for muscles to move and for brain cells to function.

Another group of organic compounds includes fats, oils, and waxes. These compounds are all lipids (LIH pihds). **Lipids** are organic compounds that store energy. They are found in meat, butter, and vegetable oils. Like carbohydrates, lipids are made up of carbon, hydrogen, and oxygen atoms. But the proportion of the three types of atoms is quite different in these two groups of compounds.

Lipids are like carbohydrates in another way. Lipids can be used as an energy source. But they are often stored by living things for long periods of time. The energy in carbohydrates is often used right away. The energy stored in lipids can act as a reserve supply for future use.

Proteins (PROH teenz) are organic compounds that form the structure and control the function of living things. Proteins are the building materials of life. They are used in making new cells and in repairing cells. Proteins also make up other parts of living things. For example, your hair and fingernails are made up of proteins. Proteins are important in the function of living things. *Enzymes* (EHN-zīmz) are proteins that control the rate of chemical changes that occur in living things. Many of these chemical changes can occur only if enzymes are present. A protein in blood

Figure 3-17

A thick layer of lipid under its skin helps keep body heat inside this walrus.

ACTIVITY Which Foods Contain Protein?

OBJECTIVES
Predict which foods contain protein.
Test for the presence of protein in different foods.

MATERIALS
safety goggles, lab apron, food samples, waxed paper, spoon, test tube, dropper, Biuret solution

PROCEDURE
A. Wear safety goggles and a lab apron during this activity.
B. Test a food sample for the presence of protein. Place a small piece of the food to be tested on a piece of waxed paper. Use the back of a spoon to crush the food.
C. Place the crushed food in a test tube.
D. Use a dropper to add 6 drops of Biuret solution to the test tube. Gently shake the test tube from side to side after adding each drop. Observe the color of the solution in the test tube. If the solution turns from blue to pink or purple, protein is present.
E. Test a variety of food samples for the presence of protein by repeating steps **B** through **D**. Use clean equipment each time. Before testing each sample, predict the result. Record your predictions and results in a data table such as the one shown.

Food Sample	Prediction	Test for Protein

RESULTS AND CONCLUSIONS
1. Which food samples did you predict would contain protein? Why?
2. Which food samples contained protein?
3. Suppose you tested a sugar cube and a piece of canned tuna for the presence of protein. What results would you predict? Explain the reasoning you used in making your prediction.

carries oxygen to all parts of the body. Other proteins help to defend the body against disease. Some proteins act as chemical messengers. They carry chemical control signals from one part of an organism to another.

Proteins are very complex substances. They are made up of many smaller units. **Amino** (uh MEE noh) **acids** are the building blocks from which proteins are formed. There are thousands of different proteins in a living cell. But these many kinds of proteins are made from only 20 different amino acids. You can see in Figure 3-18 how amino acids are linked to form a protein. Proteins differ from one another in the number and kinds of amino acids they contain. They also differ in the way the amino acids are arranged. Each amino acid is made up of carbon, hydrogen, oxygen, and nitrogen atoms. Which of these four elements is not found in either carbohydrates or lipids?

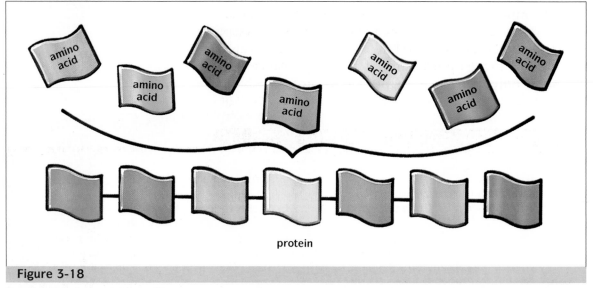

protein

Figure 3-18

Proteins are formed from different amino acids joined together in various arrangements.

Proteins are found in large amounts in meats. They are also plentiful in certain vegetables, such as soybeans. But most fruits and vegetables contain little protein.

Living things contain another group of organic compounds called nucleic (noo KLEE ihk) acids. **Nucleic acids** are organic compounds that control the activities of cells. **DNA** is a nucleic acid that stores all of the information needed for a cell to function. DNA contains instructions for making proteins. **RNA** is a nucleic acid that puts into use the information stored in DNA. RNA carries the instructions of DNA to structures that make proteins in a cell. Another function of RNA is to carry the needed amino acids to these structures. Why are amino acids needed?

LIFE FROM CHEMICALS?

You have learned that living things come from other living things. If this is so, how did the first living things arise? There are many hypotheses about the origin of life. Most scientists believe that the first living things arose from nonliving chemicals. They think that simple compounds on the early earth combined to form more complex compounds, such as proteins, found in living things. But how could living things arise from nonliving chemicals? This question has become the focus of scientific research and experiment.

Because of the belief that life began billions of years ago, scientists have tried to find out what the earth was like in the past. There is much evidence showing that the early earth was quite different from the planet we know today. It is believed that the atmosphere of the earth has changed over time. In the past it may have been made up of a mixture of gases different from that which makes up the air we breathe. The oceans of the past are also thought to have differed chemically from the oceans today.

In experiments, scientists have tried to duplicate the conditions that might have existed on the early earth. In these experiments, electric current was used as an energy

SCIENCE & TECHNOLOGY

Is there life elsewhere in the universe? If there is, are the life forms similar to those on the earth?

Life on the earth is based on long chains of carbon atoms. Life based on carbon is sometimes called organic life.

As far as scientists can tell, there is some organic matter on other planets in our solar system. But the environments of these planets are very different from the environment of the earth. The presence of organic life elsewhere in our solar system therefore seems very unlikely.

Scientists hope someday to find other earthlike worlds in other solar systems.

Devices such as the radio telescope shown may help in the search for organic life in the universe. Matter in the universe gives off energy in the form of radio waves.

Modern radio telescopes can detect these waves. Forty different molecules, many of them organic, have been detected beyond our solar system.

Figure 3-19

Many scientists believe that the earth might have looked like this before there were living things.

source. The current is much like lightning discharges that might have occurred during storms on the early earth. The current was passed through a mixture of gases thought to have made up the atmosphere of the past. In other studies, electric current was passed through solutions. The solutions were made to resemble the mixture of chemicals that might have formed the oceans of the past. The results of these experiments were that several different complex organic compounds were formed. Some of these compounds include those that make up living things. Some scientists think that these complex organic compounds might have come together, under certain conditions, to produce the first living things.

REVIEW

1. How are all organic compounds alike?
2. Which two groups of organic compounds serve as energy sources? How do these groups differ?
3. What are three functions of proteins in living things? How are proteins and nucleic acids related?
4. Briefly describe one hypothesis that scientists have formed about the origin of the first living things.

CHALLENGE Suppose there were just three amino acids, *A*, *B*, and *C*. If all three are needed to make a protein, how many different proteins could be made? A letter may appear only once in each protein. Show the arrangement of the letters for each protein.

CHAPTER SUMMARY

The main ideas in this chapter are listed below. Read these statements before you answer the Chapter Review questions.

- The life processes carried on by all organisms include taking in materials, releasing wastes, growing, responding, and producing new organisms. All living things are made up of cells and have certain basic needs. (3-1)

- Organisms use food as both a source of building materials and a source of energy. Through nutrition, organisms obtain and use food. (3-2)

- Metabolism is the sum of all the chemical processes that occur in an organism. Metabolism includes digestion, respiration, and synthesis. Waste products of metabolism are removed by excretion. (3-2)

- In many-celled organisms, growth usually results from an increase in the number of cells. In single-celled organisms, growth results from an increase in the size of the cell. (3-3)

- A stimulus is an event or condition that causes an organism to respond. Often the responses of an organism to stimuli help it survive. (3-3)

- Reproduction is the process by which organisms produce other organisms of the same kind. Asexual reproduction involves only one parent. Sexual reproduction usually involves two parents. (3-4)

- All matter is made up of atoms. An atom is the smallest unit of an element. Two or more elements can combine to form a compound. A molecule is the smallest unit of many compounds. A chemical change is a change in which a new substance or substances form. (3-5)

- Organic compounds contain carbon. Carbohydrates and lipids are organic compounds that supply organisms with energy. Proteins, which are made up of amino acids, are organic compounds that are the building materials of life. DNA and RNA are nucleic acids. These organic compounds control the activities of cells. (3-6)

- Some scientists believe that complex organic compounds on the early earth might have come together to produce the first living things. (3-6)

The key terms in this chapter are listed below. Use each term in a sentence that shows the meaning of the term.

amino acids	excretion	organic compound
asexual reproduction	growth	organism
atom	life processes	proteins
carbohydrates	lipids	reproduction
cell	matter	respiration
compound	metabolism	response
digestion	molecule	RNA
DNA	nucleic acids	sexual reproduction
element	nutrition	stimulus

Chapter Review

VOCABULARY

Use the key terms from this chapter to complete the following sentences correctly.

1. The sum of all the chemical processes that occur in an organism is called _____.
2. An event or condition that causes an organism to react is a/an _____.
3. The smallest unit in which all the life processes can be carried on is a/an _____.
4. A substance containing atoms of two or more elements is a/an _____.
5. A complete, individual living thing is a/an _____.
6. _____ results from an increase in the number of cells.
7. Reproduction that involves only one parent is called _____.
8. The process by which wastes of metabolism are removed is called _____.
9. The process by which an organism obtains and uses food is called _____.
10. Reproduction that involves two parents is called _____.

CONCEPTS

1. What five life processes are carried on by all organisms? (3-1)
2. What are the basic needs of organisms? (3-1)
3. What are two reasons why organisms need food? (3-2)
4. What are three ways in which organisms get food? (3-2)
5. Compare the processes of digestion and synthesis. (3-2)
6. What occurs during respiration? (3-2)
7. Why is excretion needed to maintain life? (3-2)
8. How do many-celled organisms grow? (3-3)
9. Why is responding to stimuli necessary to an organism's survival? (3-3)
10. What did Redi's experiments help to prove? (3-4)
11. Name the process that is necessary for the survival of any species. (3-4)
12. How do organisms produced by sexual reproduction differ from those produced by asexual reproduction? (3-4)
13. What is matter, and what is the smallest unit of matter? (3-5)
14. How do an element and a compound differ? (3-5)
15. What does a chemical formula show? (3-5)
16. What do all organic compounds have in common? (3-6)

17. How does the chemical makeup of proteins differ from that of lipids and carbohydrates? (3-6)

18. What are the building blocks of proteins? (3-6)

19. Describe two functions of proteins. (3-6)

20. Compare the functions of DNA and RNA. (3-6)

1. Explain this poem in terms of life processes.
   It's a very strange thing,
   As strange as can be.
   Whatever I eat,
   Turns into me.

2. In what way is the building of a brick wall similar to the growth of an organism?

3. Glucose is put directly into the bloodstream of some hospital patients. What part of metabolism is bypassed by this procedure? Why might this be done?

4. Redi performed early experiments in which he sealed several jars containing pieces of fresh meat. Unlike a gauze covering, the covering on these jars did not allow air to pass through. No maggots or flies appeared on the meat in these airtight jars. Redi's opponents criticized his method in these experiments. What might have been their objection?

1. Find out how much water there is in living things. Determine the mass of a piece of uncooked, chopped fruit, vegetable, or meat. Have a parent or other adult bake the food at 135°C (275°F) for about 3 hours. When the food has cooled, determine its mass again. Subtract this figure from the mass of the food before drying. The result is the mass of the water in that food.

2. Make a model of a simple molecule, using clay balls and toothpicks. Label each atom in your molecule model. You may wish to make a model of water (H_2O), carbon dioxide (CO_2), or hydrogen peroxide (H_2O_2). Consult a reference book to help you arrange the atoms correctly.

3. Collect ingredient labels from different kinds of packaged foods. Read the nutrition information. What foods contain the greatest amount of carbohydrates? What foods are good sources of protein? What foods are high in lipids?

Asimov, Isaac. *How Did We Find Out About the Beginning of Life?* New York: Walker & Co., 1982.

Hutchins, Ross E. *Nature Invented It First.* New York: Dodd, Mead & Co., 1980.

Pines, Maya. *Inside the Cell: New Frontiers of Medical Science.* Hillside, N.J.: Enslow Publishers, 1980.

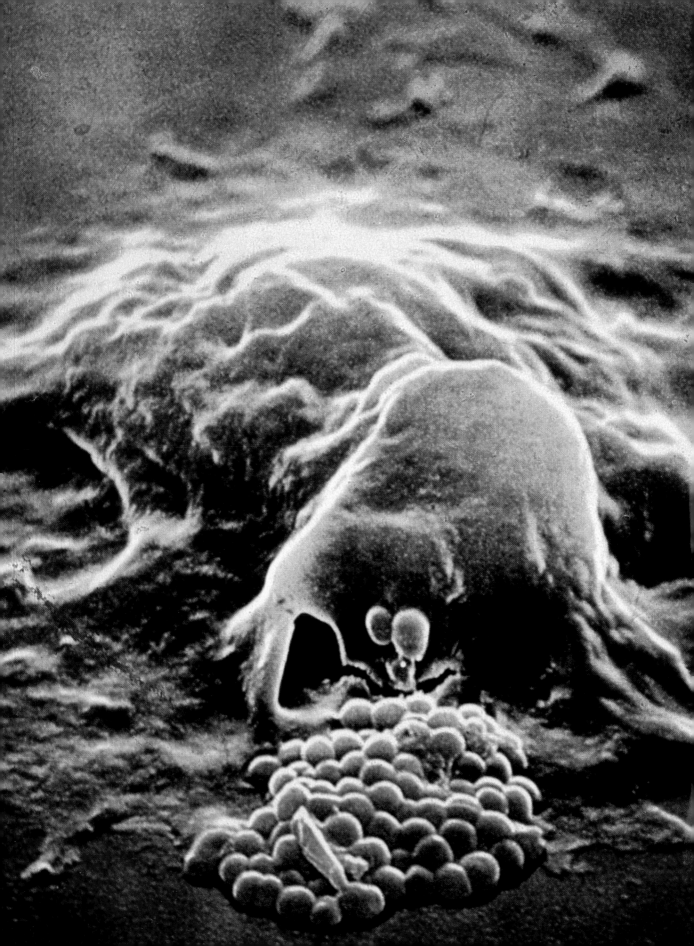

THE CELL

Like all living things, the human body is made up of cells. Many different types of cells are found in the body. The cell shown in the photograph is a macrophage. The word macrophage *means "big eater." This type of cell helps to protect the body against disease. It can destroy some types of harmful organisms that enter the body, such as the green-colored bacteria shown. The harmful organism is surrounded and then taken in by the macrophage. While macrophages function in protecting the body, they also carry on life processes. The structure of cells enables them to carry on these processes.*

- *How did scientists first learn about cells?*
- *How do cells carry on life processes?*
- *How do cells differ from one another?*

4-1 THE CELL THEORY

You have learned that organisms are made up of one or more cells. Most cells are too small to be seen with the unaided eye. For this reason, no one knew about cells before the microscope was invented.

The first microscopes were simple. A simple microscope, like a hand lens, has only one lens. The most common microscope now in use is the compound light microscope, which has two lenses.

In the 1660s Robert Hooke, an English scientist, designed his own compound microscope. He used it to examine many kinds of objects. One of the things Hooke observed was a thin slice of cork. Figure 4-1, on the next page, shows the drawing Hooke made of cork as he saw it through his microscope. Notice that there are many small boxlike spaces in the cork. These spaces reminded Hooke of the rooms, or cells, in which monks lived. So he gave the name *cell* to the spaces in the cork. Cork, which comes from the bark of a tree, is made up of cells that were once living. What Hooke saw were actually the outer walls that remained after the cells had died. Today the word *cell* is used as the term for the basic unit of living things.

> After completing this section, you will be able to
>
> - **summarize** historical developments which led to the cell theory.
> - **restate** the cell theory.
>
> The key term in this section is
> **cell theory**

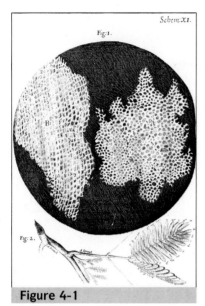

Figure 4-1

Cork cells as drawn by Robert Hooke.

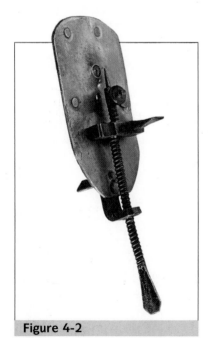

Figure 4-2

Anton van Leeuwenhoek's simple microscope.

At about the same time that Hooke was working in England, Anton van Leeuwenhoek (LAY vehn hook) built his own simple microscopes in Holland. You can see one of Leeuwenhoek's microscopes in Figure 4-2. This type of microscope can enlarge objects about 200 times. Leeuwenhoek used his microscope to examine many natural substances, including blood, scrapings from his teeth, and rain water. In many of the things that Leeuwenhoek examined, he found living cells. He discovered that even a drop of water can hold thousands of tiny one-celled organisms. Leeuwenhoek's observations of cells soon became well known.

Microscopes were greatly improved during the next 200 years. Better microscopes led scientists to new finds in nineteenth-century Germany. Matthew Schleiden (SHLĪ-dehn), a botanist, used a microscope to observe many types of plant parts. All of the structures that he saw were made up of cells. Schleiden proposed that cells are the basis of all plant life. Theodor Schwann (shwahn) made observations of animal parts. He concluded that cells are the basis of animal life. Schwann also stated that life processes take place within the cells. A short time later, Rudolf Virchow (VIHR koh) discovered that cells divide, forming new cells.

The work of Schleiden, Schwann, and Virchow became the basis for the work of many other biologists. All of this research led to the cell theory. The **cell theory** states that

- All living things are made up of one or more cells.
- Cells are the basic unit of structure and function of all living things.
- New cells come only from other cells.

The cell theory is a basic theory in biology. Biologists continue to study cells. Powerful new microscopes reveal a variety of structures within the cell. As methods and equipment for cell study continue to improve, more is learned about the structure and function of cells.

REVIEW

1. Why was the invention of the microscope so important to the study of living things?
2. Name three scientists whose work led to the cell theory. What were their contributions?
3. Describe the cell theory.

CHALLENGE What kinds of living things might Leeuwenhoek have observed in rain water?

4-2 STRUCTURE OF CELLS

ANIMAL CELLS

Since the cell was discovered, microscopes have been greatly improved. Improved microscopes revealed *organelles* (awr guh NEHLZ) within cells. Organelles are cell structures that carry out the work of the cell. If you looked at an animal cell through a microscope, there is one organelle you would probably notice first. It is a rounded structure usually found near the center of the cell. This structure is the nucleus (NOO klee uhs). Find the nucleus in the animal cell in Figure 4-3. The **nucleus** is the organelle that controls the activities of the cell.

A cell is often compared to a factory. Like a factory, a cell has many parts, and each part has a special job. The nucleus can be compared to the main office, where the manager works and the files are kept. Like the main office, the nucleus controls activities and stores information. The nucleus controls cell reproduction and the making of many kinds of materials, especially proteins.

After completing this section, you will be able to

- **identify** the functions of organelles in animal cells.
- **identify** the functions of organelles in plant cells.

The key terms in this section are

cell membrane   nucleus
cell wall   ribosomes
chloroplast   vacuoles
cytoplasm
endoplasmic reticulum (ER)
mitochondria
nuclear membrane

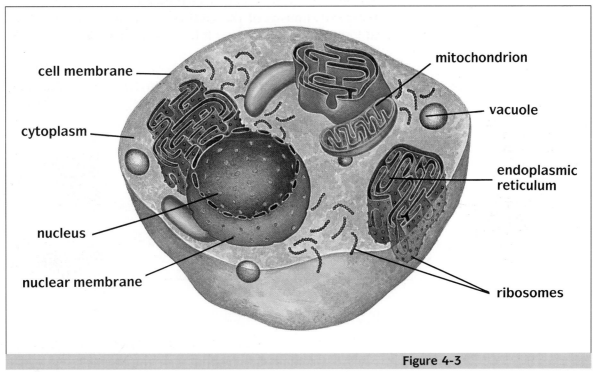

Figure 4-3

A typical animal cell.

The nucleus contains the nucleic acid DNA. As you have learned, information stored in DNA is used to control activities in the cell. The nucleus also contains the nucleic acid RNA. Recall that RNA is used in making proteins.

Structures called *chromosomes* (KROH muh sohmz) can be seen in the nucleus when the cell reproduces. You will learn more about chromosomes in Section 4-5.

Like the partitions around the main office, the nuclear membrane encloses the nucleus. The **nuclear membrane** is a membrane that surrounds the nucleus and separates it from the other parts of the cell. This membrane controls the movement of substances into and out of the nucleus. There are tiny openings in the nuclear membrane. What function might these openings serve?

cyto- (cell)
plasm (to form)

The jellylike substance that surrounds the nucleus is the **cytoplasm** (SĪ tuh plaz uhm). Notice that most of the cell is filled with cytoplasm. The cytoplasm can be compared to the factory building. The factory building contains many separate areas where work is performed. In the same way, organelles within the cytoplasm carry on the work of the cell.

Mitochondria (mī tuh KAHN dree uh) (sing., *mitochondrion*) are organelles that release energy from food. These structures are like the power plant that supplies energy to the factory. In fact they are often referred to as the powerhouses of the cell. Look at the mitochondrion in Figure 4-4. Notice that it has a smooth outer membrane and folded inner membranes. The folds of the membranes hold enzymes that are used in the release of energy. Folding provides extra surface area. Thus, more enzymes can be packed in the structure than would be possible without folds. How does increased surface area affect the amount of energy this organelle supplies?

Figure 4-4

The folded inner membranes of the mitochondrion contain enzymes used in the release of energy.

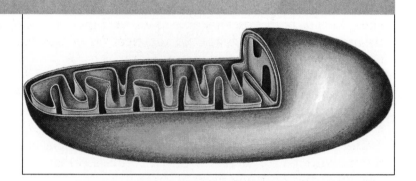

Ribosomes (RĪ buh sohmz) are the organelles on which new proteins are formed. The ribosomes can be compared to the machines that put parts together to make the products of the factory. RNA from the nucleus is sent to the ribosomes. Amino acids, which are found in the cytoplasm, are also brought to the ribosomes. The RNA directs

ACTIVITY   How Does Folding Change Surface Area?

OBJECTIVE
Determine the effect of the folding of a structure on surface area.

MATERIALS
scissors, construction paper, pencil, metric ruler

PROCEDURE

A. Use scissors to cut a sheet of construction paper in half to form two rectangular pieces. Label one piece A. Label the other piece B.

B. Use a metric ruler to measure the length and width of piece A. Find the area of A by multiplying its length by its width. Record this number as the total surface area.

C. Fold piece A as shown.

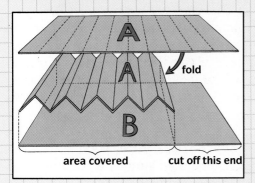

fold

area covered   cut off this end

D. Lay the folded piece A on top of piece B. On piece B mark the position of piece A as shown.

E. Cut off and discard the part of piece B that was not covered by piece A.

F. Measure the length and width of the remaining piece B. Find the area of the remaining piece B. Record this number as the area covered. This is the space taken up by A after it was folded.

RESULTS AND CONCLUSIONS

1. Which is greater, the total surface area of the folded piece or the area covered? What is the difference? What causes this difference?

2. How could the difference between the area covered and the total surface area be made even greater?

3. The enzymes that do the work in mitochondria only function if they are attached to membranes. Suppose that pieces A and B represent inner membranes of two mitochondria. Which mitochondrion—A or B—could probably supply more energy to a cell? Explain your answer.

---

the amino acids to combine to form proteins. Ribosomes may be free in the cytoplasm or attached to other organelles. Locate both types of ribosomes in Figure 4-3. Ribosomes are so small that even the electron microscope does not show details of their structure.

The **endoplasmic reticulum** (ehn doh PLAZ mihk reh TIHK yuh luhm), or **ER**, is a network of membranes that runs throughout the cytoplasm. The ER forms tubes through which materials move to all parts of the cell. Think of the ER as pipelines through which supplies are moved through the factory. Note in Figure 4-3 that there are ribosomes on some parts of the ER.

endo (inner)
rete (net)

Vacuoles (VAK yoo ohlz) are fluid-filled sacs in a cell. They are like the storage areas of the factory. Find a vacuole in Figure 4-3. Vacuoles store a variety of substances. The vacuoles of some cells may store lipids or carbohydrates. In organisms made up of a single cell, vacuoles may also have other functions.

vacuus (empty)

Notice in Figure 4-3 that the cell is enclosed by a cell membrane. The **cell membrane** is the organelle that controls the movement of substances into and out of the cell. The membrane can be compared to the fence around the factory. The fence has many gates. The opening and closing of the gates control the movement of materials into and out of the factory.

PLANT CELLS

You have just read about many of the organelles in animal cells. These organelles are also found in plant cells. But some of these structures look different in the plant cell. Look at the typical plant cell shown in Figure 4-5.

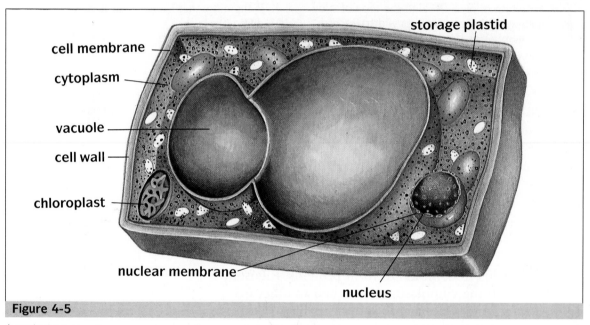

Figure 4-5

A typical plant cell.

The vacuole is very large compared with the other organelles in this cell. As in an animal cell, the vacuole in a plant cell is used for storage.

The plant cell has some structures that are not found in animal cells. Notice that the plant cell in Figure 4-5 is enclosed by a cell wall. The **cell wall** is a nonliving structure that surrounds the plant cell. The cell wall lies outside the cell membrane and gives the cell shape and support. The cell membrane is part of the living cell; the cell wall is not. Some cell walls are very strong and rigid.

Plants, unlike most other organisms, can make their own food. A **chloroplast** (KLAWR uh plast) is an organelle in which food is made in a plant cell. Find the chloroplasts, the small green structures, in Figure 4-5. The process by

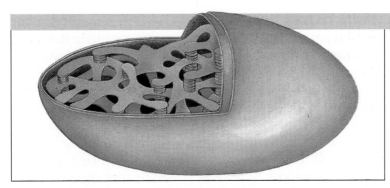

Figure 4-6

A chloroplast can be compared to a food factory.

which plants use energy from the sun to make food is called *photosynthesis* (foh tuh SIHN thuh sihs). *Chlorophyll* (KLAWR uh fihl) and enzymes are found in the chloroplasts and are used in this process. Chlorophyll is a green pigment that absorbs energy from sunlight. Pigments are coloring matter. Chlorophyll is needed for food making.

Chloroplasts are one kind of *plastid*. Plastids are organelles that serve as food factories or as storage places. Which function does a chloroplast have? Some kinds of plant cells store starches in plastids. These plastids are white or colorless. Other plastids contain pigments. A carrot has plastids filled with orange pigment.

ACTIVITY How Do Animal and Plant Cells Differ?

OBJECTIVE
Compare the organelles of an animal cell with those of a plant cell.

MATERIALS
iodine stain, 2 droppers, 2 microscope slides, toothpicks, coverslips, microscope, *Elodea*, scissors, forceps

PROCEDURE
A. Use a dropper to place a small drop of iodine stain on a microscope slide.
B. Use the flat side of a clean toothpick to gently scrape the inside of your cheek.
C. Place the end of the toothpick with the cells in the drop of iodine, and mix thoroughly. The iodine stain makes the structures of the cell easier to see. Cover the mixture with a coverslip.
D. Observe the cheek cells under the low power of a microscope. Then switch to high power. Notice that the iodine has stained some structures of the cells.

E. Make a drawing of a cheek cell as it appears under high power. Label the cell and any parts of it that you can identify.
F. Use a dropper to place a drop of water on a clean microscope slide.
G. Cut the tip off an *Elodea* (uh LOH dee uh) leaf. Use forceps to place the leaf tip in the water on the slide. Cover the leaf tip with a coverslip.
H. Observe the *Elodea* under low power.
I. Make a drawing of an *Elodea* cell under low power. Label the cell and any structures that you can identify.

RESULTS AND CONCLUSIONS
1. What structures did you find in both cheek cells and *Elodea* cells?
2. What structures did you find only in *Elodea* cells?
3. Identify each of the structures that you observed, and give its function.

VARIATIONS AMONG CELLS

Figure 4-3 is a drawing of a typical animal cell. Figure 4-5 shows a typical plant cell. The drawings show many of the structures that may be present in animal and plant cells, but no real cells look just like these. The organelles present in a cell depend upon the function of that cell. A muscle cell uses a great amount of energy to cause movement. It has many more mitochondria than the typical animal cell that you have studied. How do a large number of mitochondria help a muscle cell to function?

You have seen that the kinds of organelles in a cell depend upon the function of the cell. Note the shape of the nerve cell in Figure 4-7. The nerve cell carries messages from other nerve cells to muscle cells. A single nerve cell may connect to several other cells. How does the shape of the nerve cell serve this function?

Figure 4-7

A typical nerve cell has many extensions.

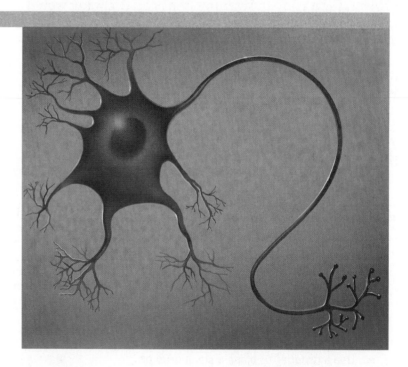

REVIEW

1. What are the functions of the nucleus of a cell?
2. Why are mitochondria called the powerhouses of the cell?
3. Distinguish between a cell membrane and a cell wall.
4. Which organelles are found only in plant cells? What are their functions?

CHALLENGE The cells in a potato have no chloroplasts. If you saw such cells under a microscope, how could you identify them as plant cells?

4-3 CELL TRANSPORT

Cells get many substances from their surroundings. These substances include water, gases, and food. All cells have a constant need for water. Water forms a large part of the cytoplasm and is used in many of the chemical changes in cells. Most cells need oxygen. Some cells also need carbon dioxide or other gases. Cells that do not make food must take in food. Substances also move out of cells. Waste products and excess water pass out of cells. There is a constant movement of substances into and out of cells. The cell membrane controls this movement.

THE NATURE OF THE CELL MEMBRANE

Compare a cell to a mesh bag. Look at Figure 4-8. The mesh bag can easily hold the oranges. But what would happen if you poured water into the bag? The water would move through the holes in the mesh. The mesh is *permeable* (PER mee uh buhl) to water. A permeable material allows other materials to flow through it. But the mesh does not allow the oranges to pass through it. The mesh is *semipermeable*; it allows some materials to flow through it but not others. A cell membrane is semipermeable because only some substances can pass through it. Cell membranes are permeable to oxygen and water. Most cell membranes are not permeable to many kinds of large organic molecules, such as proteins.

After completing this section, you will be able to

- **describe** the nature of the cell membrane.
- **describe** the processes of diffusion and osmosis.
- **distinguish** between the processes of passive and active transport.

The key terms in this section are
active transport
diffusion
osmosis
passive transport

Figure 4-8

How is this mesh bag similar to a cell membrane?

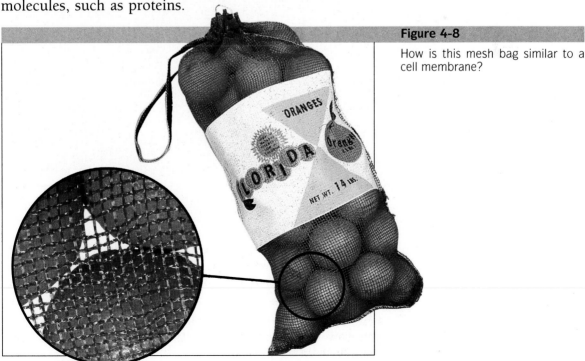

PASSIVE TRANSPORT

Some substances can move freely through the cell membrane. This free movement is an example of passive transport. **Passive transport** is the movement of a substance through the cell membrane without the use of energy by the cell. Most often, water, oxygen, and other gases move through the cell membrane by passive transport. Pores, or small holes, in the cell membrane allow small molecules to pass into or out of the cell.

As you have learned, matter is made up of particles. These particles are atoms and molecules. Air, your desk, even the cells of your body are made up of these particles. In solids the particles move back and forth, or vibrate in place. But particles in liquids and gases move from one place to another. They move in many directions, without a pattern. Their motion is random.

The movement of particles in liquids and gases can be compared to the movement of the balls used in a game of pool. Each pool ball moves in a straight line. When a moving ball hits the side of the pool table or another ball, its direction changes. Look at Figure 4-9. Like the pool balls, each particle of matter moves in a straight line. When one particle bumps into another, the direction of each particle changes.

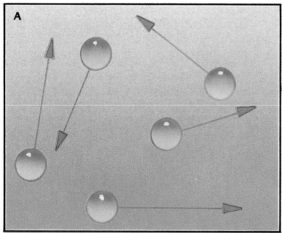
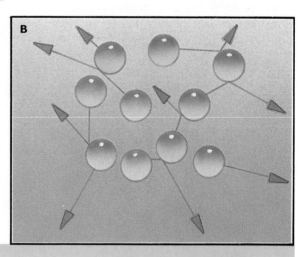

Figure 4-9

Particles of matter move in random directions (A). When particles of matter are crowded, they often bump into each other and move apart (B).

When particles of matter are crowded, they are likely to bump into each other. As they bump into each other, they tend to move apart. As a result, they move from an area where many particles are crowded together to an area where they are less crowded. The movement of atoms or molecules from a crowded area to a less crowded area is called **diffusion** (dih FYOO zhuhn).

Although the term *diffusion* may be new to you, it is likely that you are familiar with this process. Think about what happens when a piece of toast burns. Even if you are not near the toaster, you can smell the smoke from the burnt toast. The odor of the burnt toast moves from the kitchen to the rest of the house. The atoms and molecules that make up the smoke move away from an area where they are crowded, inside the toaster. They move toward a less crowded area, the rest of the house.

In Figure 4-10A you can see a cube of sugar at the bottom of a glass of water. The sugar molecules are packed, or crowded together, in the cube. In Figure 4-10B you can see that some of the sugar molecules have moved away from the cube. They have spread out in the water to areas where they are less crowded. Figure 4-10C shows the sugar molecules spread evenly throughout the water. The sugar molecules have diffused through the water.

Diffusion is a type of passive transport. When a substance moves through a cell membrane by diffusion, the cell does not use energy to move that substance. In the same way that sugar diffuses through water, gases diffuse from cell to cell through the cell membranes.

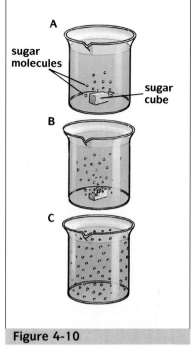

Figure 4-10

Sugar molecules diffusing in water.

ACTIVITY How Does Temperature Affect the Spreading of Food Coloring in Water?

OBJECTIVE
Identify the process by which food coloring spreads out in water.
Determine how temperature affects this process.

MATERIALS
lab apron, glass-marking pencil, 2 250-mL beakers, cold water, hot water, dropper, red food coloring

PROCEDURE
A. Wear a lab apron during this activity. With a glass-marking pencil, label two beakers. Label one beaker *cold* and the other one *hot*.
B. Fill the beaker labeled *cold* with cold water.
C. Fill the beaker labeled *hot* with hot water.
   Caution: Do not splash the hot water on your skin.
D. Place both beakers where they will not be disturbed.

E. Add one drop of red food coloring to each beaker. Release the drop just above the surface of the water to avoid splashing.
F. Observe the two beakers immediately after adding the food color. Record your observations.
G. Observe the beakers again after 10 minutes. Record your observations.

RESULTS AND CONCLUSIONS
1. Describe what happens to the red food coloring in each beaker in step **F**.
2. Describe what happens to the red food coloring in each beaker in step **G**.
3. What process did you observe in this activity?
4. How does temperature affect the rate at which this process occurs?
5. Predict what the contents of each beaker would look like after 24 hours. Explain your predictions.

Figure 4-11

By the process of osmosis, a type of passive transport, water molecules move into the cell.

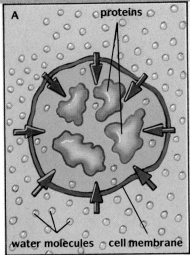
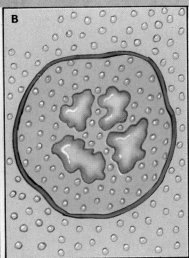

Recall that a cell membrane is semipermeable. **Osmosis** (ahz MOH sihz) is the diffusion of water through a semipermeable membrane. Figure 4-11 shows the process of osmosis through a cell membrane. This semipermeable membrane allows water molecules to pass into or out of the cell. But some molecules, such as proteins, are too large to pass through the cell membrane. In Figure 4-11A, notice that the water molecules are more crowded outside the cell than inside it. Through osmosis, the water molecules move from an area where they are crowded to an area where they are less crowded, as can be seen in Figure 4-11B.

ACTIVE TRANSPORT

Diffusion and osmosis are forms of passive transport. Water, gases, and other small molecules may pass through the cell membrane by these processes. But sometimes, molecules cannot enter cells by passive transport. This is the case when molecules of a substance are more crowded inside the cell than they are outside that cell. For example, root cells of plants need minerals from the soil. But the minerals are more crowded in the root cells than in the water of the soil around the roots. So the minerals cannot diffuse into the cells. The cells must use energy to move the minerals. **Active transport** is the process by which a cell uses energy to move molecules of a substance from an area where the molecules are less crowded to an area where they are more crowded.

Figure 4-12 is a model that shows one way in which active transport may occur. *Carrier molecules* are thought

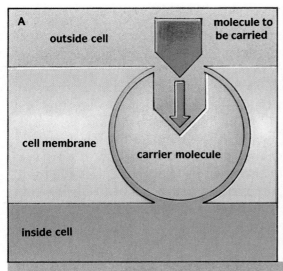
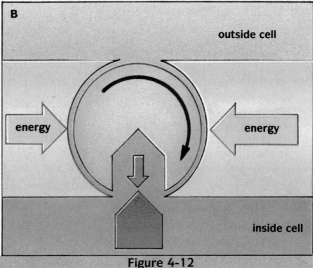

Figure 4-12

A model of active transport. The molecule to be carried fits into the slot of a carrier molecule (A). The carrier molecule rotates and releases the molecule (B).

to be part of the cell membrane. Notice in part *A* that a molecule to be carried through the membrane, into the cell, fits in a slot in the carrier molecule. In part *B* you can see that the carrier molecule has turned, or rotated, in the membrane. The molecule being carried is now released into the cell. The carrier molecule then rotates back to its first position and may repeat the process. Energy is required to rotate the carrier molecule.

Both passive transport and active transport can be compared to riding a bicycle. Look at Figure 4-13*A* and imagine that you are coasting downhill on the bicycle. You would not need to use energy in order to move the bicycle downhill. The movement of the bicycle without the use of your energy can be likened to passive transport. A cell does not use energy to move substances by passive transport. Look at Figure 4-13*B* and imagine riding the bicycle uphill. You would need to pedal to move uphill. When you pedal, you use energy. The use of energy to move the bicycle can be compared to active transport. A cell uses energy to move substances by active transport.

Figure 4-13

Passive transport and active transport can be compared to riding a bicycle.

REVIEW

1. What is a semipermeable membrane?
2. Distinguish between osmosis and diffusion.
3. How do passive transport and active transport differ?

CHALLENGE A smoke detector sounds an alarm when smoke fills the air. Explain why it may be several minutes after a fire starts before the smoke detector emits a sound.

4-4 ENERGY FOR CELLS

Many forms of work occur in cells. Work requires energy. Cells must have a steady supply of energy to do work. In Chapter 3 you learned that organisms get energy from food. Lipids, such as fats and oils, are one source of energy. Carbohydrates—especially sugars—are the best source of energy. Carbohydrates are changed to the simple sugar glucose. Glucose is the main source of energy for cells. But cells cannot use glucose directly to do work. The energy in glucose must be changed to a usable form. Through a complex process that occurs in cells, glucose is broken down. When glucose is broken down, energy is released. Most of the energy that is given off is stored in the compound *ATP*.

ATP is a substance in cells that stores energy. The energy in ATP can be used directly to do work in cells. The breakdown of glucose to form ATP is part of respiration. In Chapter 3 you learned that respiration is the process of releasing energy from food. Respiration takes place within the mitochondria of cells and can be shown by this equation.

glucose + oxygen → carbon dioxide + water + ATP (energy)

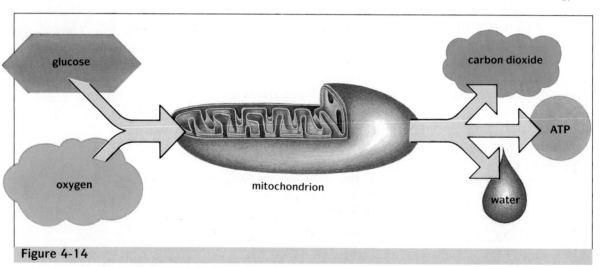

Figure 4-14

In respiration, glucose and oxygen are used by the mitochondrion. ATP is the energy product. What other products are given off?

Glucose and oxygen are used in this chemical change. Carbon dioxide and water are given off. ATP is the energy product of this chemical change. The process of respiration is shown in Figure 4-14.

The energy in ATP comes from the energy in glucose. But where does the glucose come from? Directly or indirectly, plants provide food for living things. Animals get food by eating plants or by eating other animals that have eaten plants. You know that plants make food. The food that plants make is glucose. As you have learned, photosynthesis is the process by which plants make food. Photosynthesis can be shown by this equation.

carbon dioxide + water + light (energy) → glucose + oxygen

Chlorophyll, found in chloroplasts, absorbs light energy from the sun. This provides the energy needed for food making to occur. Figure 4-15 shows that water and carbon dioxide are used to make glucose. Oxygen is given off as a waste product.

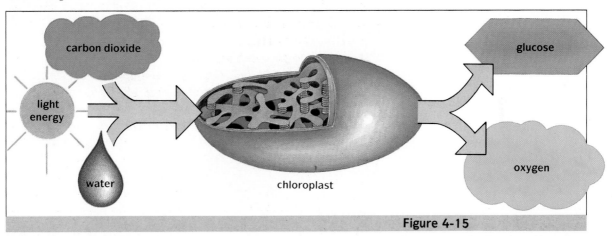

Figure 4-15

In photosynthesis, the chloroplast uses carbon dioxide, water, and energy from sunlight. Glucose is made and oxygen is given off.

Compare the equations for respiration and photosynthesis, shown in Table 4-1. Notice that the two equations are opposites. In respiration, glucose combines with oxygen. Energy, carbon dioxide, and water are produced. In photosynthesis, energy from sunlight is used to join carbon dioxide and water. Oxygen and glucose are produced. Respiration releases energy. Photosynthesis uses energy.

Table 4-1 *Respiration and Photosynthesis Compared*

Respiration	Photosynthesis
glucose + oxygen → carbon dioxide + water + ATP (energy)	carbon dioxide + water + light (energy) → glucose + oxygen
Takes place in most cells.	Takes place only in cells that contain chlorophyll.
Glucose is broken down.	Glucose is made.
Energy in glucose is released.	Energy is stored in glucose.
Carbon dioxide is given off.	Carbon dioxide is taken in.
Water is given off.	Water is used.
Oxygen is used.	Oxygen is given off.

DO YOU KNOW?

Special cells in a firefly use ATP for an unusual activity — producing light. The giving-off of light by a living thing is called bioluminescence.

In fireflies, special cells are grouped together to form a structure called a lantern. Many lanterns are found on the underside of the firefly. Within the cells of the lanterns, a chemical change occurs. ATP is combined with oxygen and a substance called luciferin. During the change, luciferin molecules absorb energy from ATP and release this energy as light.

There are other organisms that are also bioluminescent. The processes that produce light in these organisms are basically the same as in the firefly.

Most light-producing organisms live in the ocean. These include some types of clams, snails, squid, and fish. At the surface of warm ocean water, there is a very common single-celled organism that is bioluminescent. The cells of this organism give off light when disturbed.

All cells carry on respiration. Plant cells carry on both respiration and photosynthesis. Plant cells often produce more oxygen in photosynthesis than they use in respiration. The extra oxygen is given off into the air. This oxygen can then be used by animal cells, in respiration.

REVIEW

1. Why do cells need energy?
2. Describe the process of respiration.
3. Explain the process of photosynthesis.

CHALLENGE You may have heard the process of breathing referred to as respiration. In this lesson you have learned that respiration is a process that cells use to obtain energy from food. Explain why the same word is used for both processes.

4-5 CELL DIVISION

How much have you grown in the last year? Perhaps your height has increased by 3 or 4 cm. Recall that growth results from an increase in the total number of cells. Your growth represents the addition of millions of new cells to your body. Each of these new cells was formed by *cell division*. Cell division is the process by which a cell divides, forming two new cells.

Growth and reproduction are based on cell division. Organisms grow by making more cells. Organisms reproduce by making more organisms. In both cases, cell division is necessary. Cells that have been damaged or worn out are replaced through cell division. How did cell division produce the changes shown in Figure 4-16?

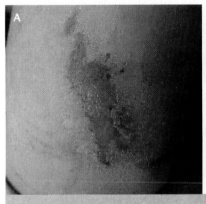
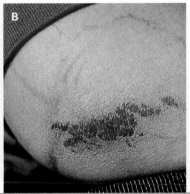
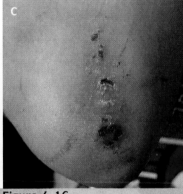

Figure 4-16

A cut on the arm, the next day (*A*). The cut after 10 days (*B*). After 20 days, the cut is nearly healed (*C*).

MITOSIS

Cell division is more complex than simply dividing a cell in half. When a cell divides, two new cells are formed that are just like the one that divided. The cell that divides is the parent cell. The two new cells that form are called daughter cells. **Mitosis** (mī TOH sihs) is cell division in which daughter cells are formed that are just like the parent cell. Each daughter cell carries a copy of the DNA of the parent cell. Where in the cell is DNA found? The daughter cells can perform all of the functions of the parent cell.

After mitosis most cells have a period of growth. A new cell first grows in size and many of the cell parts double. This time of growth between cell divisions is called *interphase*. All life processes except mitosis occur during this time. During interphase the nucleic acid DNA makes

91

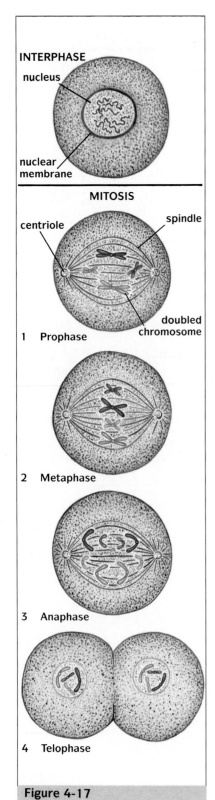

INTERPHASE
nucleus

nuclear membrane

MITOSIS

centriole   spindle

doubled chromosome

1   Prophase

2   Metaphase

3   Anaphase

4   Telophase

Figure 4-17

Interphase and mitosis of a cell.

copies of itself, or doubles. You can see a cell in interphase in Figure 4-17.

Mitosis may be shown as a series of four stages. Though mitosis is a continuous process, dividing it into stages makes it easier to understand. Refer to the numbered pictures in Figure 4-17 as you read about the stages of mitosis in an animal cell.

1. *Prophase* is the first stage of mitosis. Many changes occur within the nucleus during prophase. As you have learned, chromosomes are found in the nucleus. A **chromosome** is a threadlike structure that is made up of DNA and protein. The DNA molecules, which doubled during interphase, shorten during prophase. Doubled chromosomes can now be seen in the nucleus. The shortening and thickening of the DNA molecules make the chromosomes visible.

There are other changes that occur in the cell during prophase. The nuclear membrane disappears. A football-shaped structure, called the *spindle,* appears. The spindle is a group of fibers that guide the movement of the chromosomes during mitosis. In Figure 4-17 you can see that many of the spindle fibers connect to the centrioles (SEHN-tree ohlz). The **centrioles** are organelles that seem to control the spindle in animal cells. Though plant cells form spindles, they do not have centrioles.

2. *Metaphase* is the second stage of mitosis. The doubled chromosomes continue to shorten and thicken. Notice that all of the chromosomes are lined up across the middle of the cell.

3. *Anaphase* is the third stage of mitosis. In this stage the spindle fibers seem to pull apart the doubled chromosomes. Each doubled chromosome separates and forms two single chromosomes. Two identical sets of chromosomes are now visible in the cell. The two sets of chromosomes move apart. They move to opposite sides of the cell. This stage ends when each set of chromosomes has reached a centriole.

4. *Telophase* is the fourth stage of mitosis. The spindle disappears. A nuclear membrane forms around each set of chromosomes. Note that the cell membrane and cytoplasm pinch inward. Two new cells form, each with a set of chromosomes. The same information that was in the nucleus of the parent cell is now in the nucleus of each daughter cell.

THE ROLE OF DNA

DNA has been called the master molecule of life because it controls so many life processes. DNA molecules are large and complex. A single molecule of DNA may contain millions of atoms. This great size allows DNA to store a vast amount of information. You have learned that the information in DNA is used to build proteins. The proteins then carry out the work of the cell. By directing the cell to start or stop making proteins, DNA controls cell division and other life processes.

As you have learned, the DNA in a cell doubles before the cell divides. When the cell divides, each of the two daughter cells gets a complete set of chromosomes. Recall that chromosomes contain DNA. But how does the DNA molecule make copies of itself?

Notice in Figure 4-18 that a DNA molecule has the form of a twisted ladder. The ladder is made up of two long sides or rails that hold the DNA molecule together. Between the rails are steps or rungs. The rungs are made up of compounds called *bases*. There are four different bases. The letters *A, C, G,* and *T* are symbols for the bases.

Notice in Figure 4-18 that two different bases combine to form each rung. But the bases can combine in only a few ways, as you can see in Figure 4-19. Notice that A fits only with T, and that C fits only with G. The pairs of bases form four types of rungs in the DNA ladder. A-T and T-A form two different rungs, even though they contain the same bases. In the same way, C-G and G-C form two types of rungs.

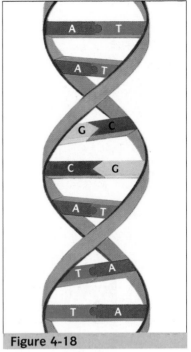

Figure 4-18

A DNA molecule has the form of a twisted ladder.

Figure 4-19

DNA base pairs. Can base T pair with base G?

Base C always pairs with base G.

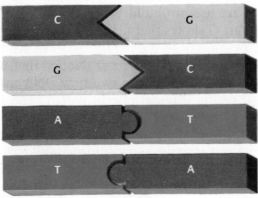

Base A always pairs with base T.

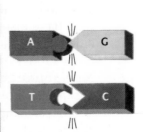

Other pairings are not possible.

The order in which the four types of rungs appear in the DNA molecule is a code. This code has been called the code of life because it carries the information needed to control life processes.

Scientists have proposed a model of the way in which the DNA molecule copies itself. This model is called the zipper model because it shows the DNA ladder opening like a zipper. To make the zipper model easier to understand, the DNA ladder is shown untwisted in Figure 4-20. Part *A* shows the DNA before it copies itself. In part *B* the ladder is splitting down the center. This process can be compared to opening a zipper. Notice that each pair of bases separates.

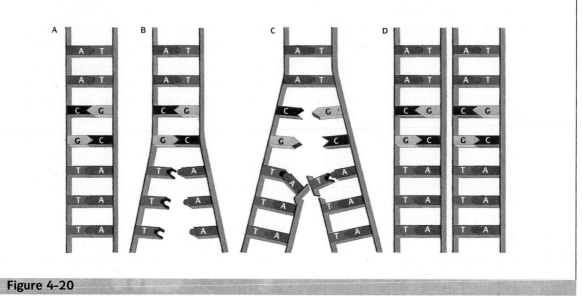

Figure 4-20

The zipper model shows how the DNA molecule makes copies of itself.

A supply of bases is found in the cytoplasm of the cell. These bases are used to build two new halves of the DNA molecule. Part *C* shows that new bases pair with the bases that are on each half of the ladder. You can see two fully formed DNA molecules in part *D*. Notice that new rails have also formed. Each of the two new DNA molecules is identical to the original one in part *A*. The two DNA ladders have the same pairs of bases in the same order. Since the order of the base pairs is a code, the two new DNA molecules carry the same information.

How can the daughter cells formed by mitosis have all the features of the parent cell? The information that controls cell activities is in DNA. Identical sets of DNA molecules in the chromosomes go to each daughter cell. Thus each daughter cell contains the same information.

REVIEW

1. What occurs during interphase?
2. Describe what occurs during each stage of mitosis.
3. Describe the process by which DNA copies itself.

CHALLENGE Knowing the order of bases on one side of a DNA molecule would enable you to predict the order of bases on the other side. Explain why this is so.

CHAPTER SUMMARY

The main ideas in this chapter are listed below. Read these statements before you answer the Chapter Review questions.

- The use of microscopes led to the naming of the cell by Robert Hooke. The work of three scientists, Matthew Schleiden, Theodor Schwann, and Rudolf Virchow, led to the cell theory. (4-1)

- Animal cells contain a nucleus surrounded by cytoplasm. Within the cytoplasm are many organelles. The cell membrane encloses the cell. (4-2)

- Plant cells contain most of the organelles found in animal cells. In addition, chloroplasts, other plastids, and cell walls are found in plant cells. The organelles present in a cell and the shape of the cell depend on the function of the cell. (4-2)

- Cell membranes are semipermeable. Substances can move through cell membranes by passive or active transport. Dif-

fusion and osmosis are types of passive transport and do not require the use of energy by the cell. Active transport requires the use of energy by the cell. (4-3)

- Respiration is the process of obtaining energy from food. The energy is stored in ATP. Photosynthesis is the process by which plants make glucose. (4-4)

- Mitosis is a type of cell division that forms two daughter cells that are just like the parent cell. The four stages of mitosis are prophase, metaphase, anaphase, and telophase. (4-5)

- Chromosomes contain DNA. DNA controls cell activities. The DNA molecule can copy itself, forming identical DNA molecules. (4-5)

The key terms in this chapter are listed below. Use each term in a sentence that shows the meaning of the term.

active transport	chromosome	nuclear membrane
cell membrane	cytoplasm	nucleus
cell theory	diffusion	osmosis
cell wall	endoplasmic reticulum (ER)	passive transport
centrioles	mitochondria	ribosomes
chloroplast	mitosis	vacuoles

VOCABULARY

Use the key terms from this chapter to complete the following sentences correctly.

1. The _____ controls the flow of materials into and out of a cell.
2. A plant cell gets shape and support from the _____ .
3. In a plant cell photosynthesis occurs in the _____ .
4. The nucleus of a cell is surrounded by a _____ .
5. Fluid-filled sacs that are usually much larger in a plant cell than in an animal cell are called _____ .
6. The jellylike substance that surrounds the nucleus of a cell is called _____ .
7. Organelles called the powerhouses of the cell are the _____ .
8. Cell division that results in two identical daughter cells is called _____ .
9. The _____ controls the activities of the cell.
10. The diffusion of water through a semipermeable membrane is called _____ .
11. Diffusion is an example of the type of process called _____ .
12. The organelles on which new proteins are formed are the _____ .

CONCEPTS

1. How did the word *cell* become the name of the basic unit of structure of living things? (4-1)
2. What does the cell theory state? (4-1)
3. Describe the function of ribosomes. (4-2)
4. What is the function of the endoplasmic reticulum? (4-2)
5. What is the function of mitochondria? (4-2)
6. In which organelle of plant cells is food made? (4-2)
7. Which structure of plant cells is nonliving? What is the function of this structure? (4-2)
8. Explain why a cell membrane is said to be semipermeable. (4-3)
9. Name and describe the process by which water moves into and out of a cell. (4-3)
10. Define the term *active transport*. Under what conditions does this process occur? (4-3)
11. Describe the carrier molecule model of active transport. (4-3)

12. Write the equation for respiration in a cell. (4-4)

13. What is ATP, and how do cells use it? (4-4)

14. Compare the processes of respiration and photosynthesis. (4-4)

15. What is the relationship between growth and cell division? (4-5)

16. What is interphase? (4-5)

17. Briefly describe the changes that occur during each of the four stages of mitosis. (4-5)

18. Why is DNA called the master molecule of life? (4-5)

19. The pairs of bases in DNA are arranged in a certain order. Why is the order of bases important? (4-5)

20. Describe how the DNA molecule copies itself. (4-5)

APPLICATION/ CRITICAL THINKING

1. Suppose you examine something with the aid of an electron microscope. You find no evidence of cells or cell parts. Could this object be a living thing? Explain your answer.

2. Before mitosis the DNA molecule separates and forms a copy of itself. Suppose a DNA molecule within a cell made an error when it copied itself. Suggest some possible effects on the daughter cells that would result from mitosis of that cell.

3. Do mitochondria make energy? Explain your answer.

4. You have learned that glucose, a sugar, is used by cells in respiration. Does that mean that animals need to eat a lot of foods containing sugar? Explain your answer.

5. A volume of seawater has more salt in it than the same volume of water from a cell. Suppose a shipwrecked person drank only seawater. What would happen to that person's body cells?

EXTENSION

1. Use reference books to help you write a report about the cell wall of plants. What material makes up the cell wall? What uses have been found for this material?

2. James Watson and Francis Crick were the first scientists to write about the twisted ladderlike structure of DNA. Read about their research and report on it to your class.

3. Make a three-dimensional model of a plant cell or an animal cell. You might use a shoebox, Styrofoam balls, balsa wood, clay, and paper to build the structures. Label each structure.

READINGS

Curry, Allan, and others. *Under the Microscope.* New York: Van Nostrand Reinhold Co., Inc., 1982.

Johnson, Gaylord, and Maurice Bleifield. *Hunting with a Microscope.* New York: Arco Publishing Co., Inc., 1980.

Pines, Maya. *Inside the Cell.* Hillside, N.J.: Enslow Publishers, 1980.

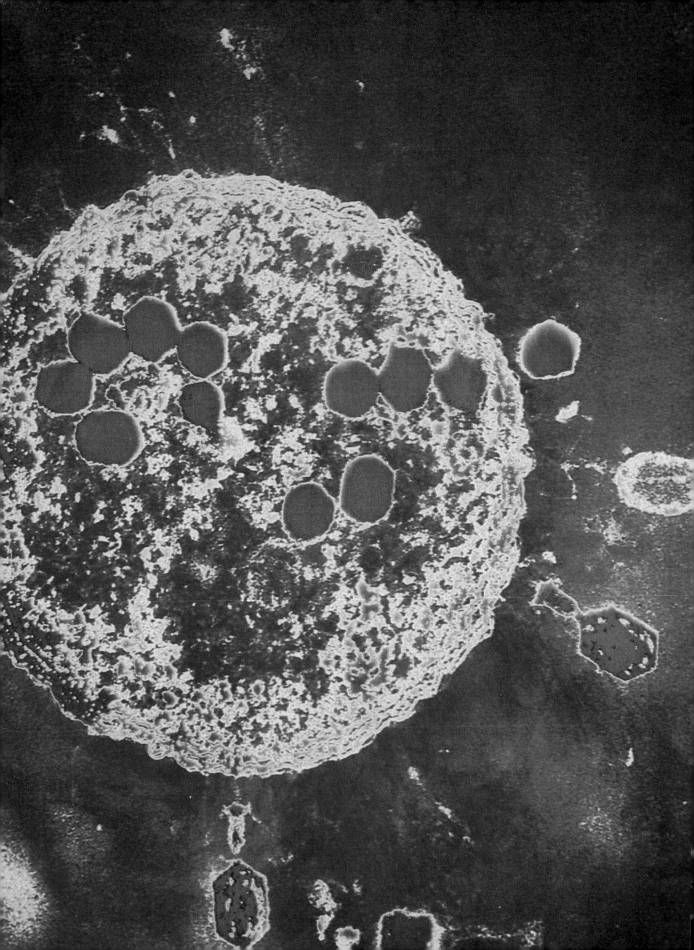

VIRUSES AND BACTERIA

What is happening in the photograph? It might be an aerial view of an attacking army. Many invaders appear to be closing in on a single structure. In reality a microscopic invasion is taking place. The round structure under attack is a living thing. It is a single-celled organism called a bacterium. And what are the tiny invaders that surround the cell? Scientists have not yet classified them as either living or nonliving things. They are viruses. A single virus "soldier" in this invading army could cause the destruction of the bacterium.

- *How do viruses destroy living cells?*
- *Where do bacteria live and what do they need for growth?*
- *How are some bacteria helpful and others harmful?*
- *How can disease-causing bacteria be killed?*

5-1 VIRUSES

TRAITS OF VIRUSES

Have you ever had mumps or chicken pox? If so, you have had a disease caused by a virus. A **virus** is a very small particle made up of a core of nucleic acid with a protein covering, or protein coat. The nucleic acid contains directions for making more viruses. The protein coat protects the virus. The structure of a typical virus is shown in Figure 5-1 on the next page.

Viruses seem to be on the borderline between living and nonliving things. Viruses are made of some of the compounds found in living cells. But like nonliving things, viruses are not cells, nor are they made of cells. They do not have a nucleus or other cell parts. Viruses do not grow. They also cannot reproduce unless they are inside a living cell. They are unable to carry out the other life processes that living cells carry out. Because they are so unlike living things, scientists have not been able to classify viruses into any of the kingdoms of living things.

After completing this section, you will be able to

- **describe** the basic structure of a virus.
- **list** ways in which viruses are like both living and nonliving things.
- **describe** how viruses reproduce, and explain how they cause disease.

The key terms in this section are
vaccine   virus

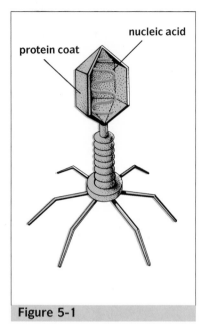

Figure 5-1

Structure of a typical virus.

When it is inside a cell, a virus acts like a computer program for making new viruses. A single virus has all the information needed to make thousands of new viruses. But the virus lacks the machinery, the raw materials, and the energy needed to make even one new virus. A virus enters a living cell and "programs" it. The cell then produces the protein and nucleic acid needed to make new viruses.

There are many kinds of viruses. They may infect plant, animal, and other types of cells. In general each kind of virus infects only the cells of one species. For example, a virus that infects tobacco will not usually infect wheat or corn. Some viruses infect only the cells of a specific kind of tissue. The virus that causes rabies invades only nerve tissue.

Viruses have different shapes, as can be seen in Figure 5-2. Some viruses have simple shapes, such as rods, spheres, and cubes. Other viruses, such as those that infect bacteria (sing., *bacterium*), have distinct head and tail regions. The shapes of viruses are used to help to identify and classify them. What is the shape of the virus that infects tobacco?

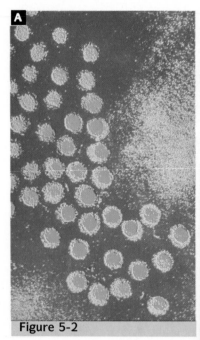

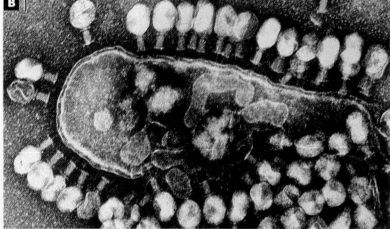

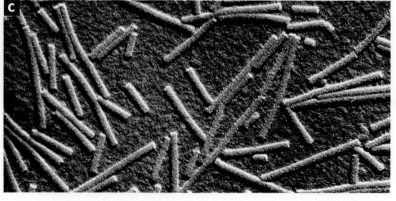

Figure 5-2

Compare the shapes of these viruses. Hepatitus virus (*A*), virus that infects bacteria (*B*), and tobacco mosaic virus (*C*).

HOW VIRUSES REPRODUCE

Viruses are so small that thousands of them can be produced inside a single cell. Because of their small size, only the largest viruses could be seen until the electron microscope was invented. By studying viruses that infect bacteria, scientists have learned much about how viruses reproduce. Look at Figure 5-3 as you read the steps in the reproduction of this kind of virus. Similar steps occur in viruses that infect plants and animals.

1. The protein coat of the virus attaches to the surface of a bacterial cell.
2. The nucleic acid of the virus is injected into the cell. The protein coat is left outside the cell.
3. The nucleic acid of the virus directs the cell to make new virus parts—protein coats and nucleic acid.
4. The protein coats and nucleic acid form new viruses.
5. After many new viruses are made, the bacterial cell bursts open and dies. Hundreds or thousands of new viruses, able to infect other cells, are released.

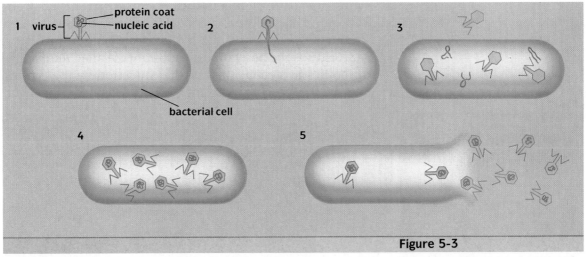

Figure 5-3

Reproduction of a virus that infects bacteria.

Some viruses do not reproduce right after they infect a cell. The type of virus that behaves in this way is called a *latent* (LAY tuhnt) *virus*. The latent virus invades the cell but does not take control of it. The nucleic acid of the virus is injected into the cell and is copied each time the cell divides. After a while, many cells have copies of the nucleic acid of the virus. The nucleic acid of the virus may or may not harm the cell. But at some later time, conditions in or around the cell may cause the latent virus to become active. If this happens, the process shown in Figure 5-3 occurs.

HOW VIRUSES CAUSE DISEASE

Disease may result when viruses damage or destroy cells. Viruses can harm a cell in two ways. A virus can destroy a cell by causing it to burst when new viruses are made and released. A latent virus can also damage a cell. The nucleic acid of the latent virus may block some of the cell's normal functions. This can damage or even kill the cell.

Viruses cause disease in plants and animals and are a major cause of disease in humans. In addition to mumps and chicken pox, viruses cause polio, smallpox, flu, the common cold, and many other diseases. Viruses have also been found to cause some types of cancer. Acquired Immune Deficiency Syndrome (AIDS) is an often-fatal disease caused by a virus. A person who has AIDS is more likely to get other kinds of disease. The ability to fight infection is reduced or absent in a person who has AIDS.

The drugs used to kill bacteria usually have no effect on viruses. Some virus-caused diseases can be prevented by the use of a vaccine. A **vaccine** is a substance that contains viruses or other disease-causing agents that are dead or weakened and can no longer cause disease. The vaccine is injected into the body as can be seen in Figure 5-4. It causes the body to form substances called *antibodies*. Antibodies protect against further infection by the type of virus in the vaccine. Vaccines have been made for some

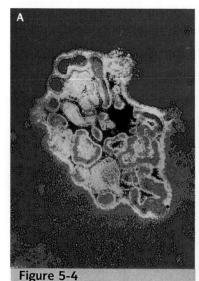
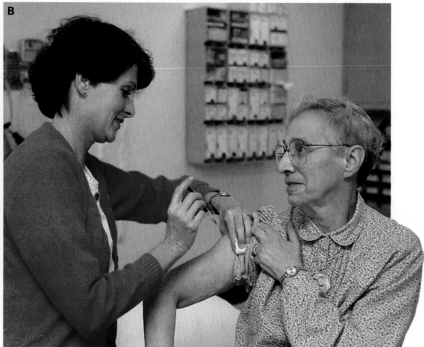

Figure 5-4

One type of virus that causes flu (A). Viruses are not affected by bacteria-killing drugs. Doctors may advise that older people get a flu vaccine to prevent infection by flu viruses (B).

For the first time in history, scientists have been able to see the detailed structure of a virus that infects animals. The new technology of supercomputers has made this scientific breakthrough possible. Supercomputers process information up to 200 times faster than other types of computers. Using X rays with supercomputers, researchers have made models of one of the viruses that cause the common cold. Since a cold may be caused by one of more than a hundred related viruses, this research may not lead to an immediate cure for the common cold. However, the knowledge gained may have far-reaching benefits.

Pictures produced by the supercomputer show areas on the virus's surface that allow the virus to attach to the cell membrane of a human cell. Using this information, scientists may be able to prevent viruses from attaching to cells and beginning their reproductive cycle. Other structures on the surface of the virus show how human antibodies attach to the virus as the body fights the infection. It is hoped that this information will lead to the development of effective treatments for virus-caused diseases.

diseases caused by viruses, including polio, measles, and some types of flu. You probably had to receive vaccines against some virus-caused diseases before you could start school.

The body does have some natural defenses against viruses. A protein called *interferon* (ihn ter FIHR ahn) helps to fight disease caused by viruses. It is not yet known just how interferon works. One theory says that interferon works in the following way. Cells that have been infected by a virus produce interferon. It is then carried to cells that have not yet been infected. The interferon protects the uninfected cells from the virus by interfering in the reproduction of the virus. Some scientists believe that interferon might be used in the future to treat diseases caused by viruses.

REVIEW

1. What is the structure of a virus?
2. How are viruses like living things? How are they like non-living things?
3. Describe how a virus reproduces in a bacterial cell.
4. How does a vaccine prevent an infection by a virus?

CHALLENGE Some people get virus-caused fever blisters on the lip or chin. These blisters may recur each time the person remains in strong sunlight for a long time. How can a virus cause a recurring condition such as this?

5-2 KINGDOM MONERA

The organisms that have the simplest cell structure are the **monerans** (muh NIHR uhnz). All monerans are single-celled. The cell of a moneran is unlike the cell of any other organism. For this reason the monerans are placed in their own kingdom—kingdom Monera. There are two major groups of monerans: the *blue-green bacteria* and the *bacteria*.

Unlike all other cells, moneran cells lack a nucleus. A typical moneran cell is shown in Figure 5-5. The cells contain the nucleic acid DNA, but it is found in the cytoplasm of the cell, not in a nucleus. Moneran cells lack most organelles found in other types of cells. Notice that a cell wall and a cell membrane surround a moneran cell. The simple structure of the moneran cell is believed to resemble the earth's first life forms.

Figure 5-5

Structure of a typical moneran cell.

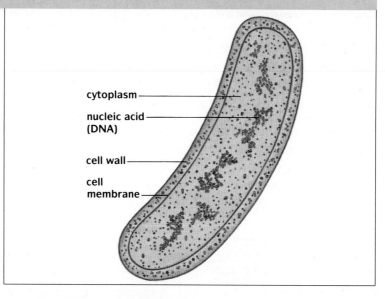

BLUE-GREEN BACTERIA

Blue-green bacteria are monerans that are able to make their own food by photosynthesis. Most are sphere-shaped cells that are large enough to be seen with the aid of a compound microscope. The cells may exist alone or in clusters that form *colonies*. A colony is a group of similar cells that are attached to each other. Many colonies of blue-green bacteria may form a mass large enough to be seen without the use of a microscope. You may have seen colonies of these bacteria on a pond, where they form a bluish-green scum on the surface. Figure 5-6 shows blue-green bacteria that form colonies.

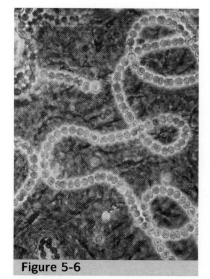

Figure 5-6

These blue-green bacteria, called *Nostoc*, form colonies.

Figure 5-7

Colorful blue-green bacteria grow-ing in and around a hot spring in Yellowstone National Park. What two pigments do all blue-green bacteria have?

Two pigments present in all blue-green bacteria give them their characteristic color. They are the green pigment chlorophyll and a blue pigment called *phycocyanin* (fī koh-sī uh nihn). Despite their name, not all of these bacteria are blue-green in color. Many contain other pigments in large amounts. These blue-green bacteria may appear yel-low, red, brown, or violet, as can be seen in Figure 5-7. At times the Red Sea appears red due to the presence of large numbers of blue-green bacteria.

There are more than 1500 species of blue-green bac-teria. They live in a wide variety of places and are common wherever there is moisture. Blue-green bacteria can live in both fresh and salt water. They grow on the sides of damp rocks, in the moist soil at the edges of streams and rivers, and on the bark of trees. A few species can survive in very harsh environments. Some blue-green bacteria can live in hot springs, at temperatures as high as 80°C. Others can survive below-zero temperatures.

Most blue-green bacteria are useful organisms. They are a food source for many animals that live in water. It has been found that blue-green bacteria can be used to determine water quality. They are among the first living things to react to the presence of human wastes or house-hold detergents in water. These substances cause blue-green bacteria to grow and reproduce at a rapid rate. The presence of a large number of blue-green bacteria is often a sign that water is polluted by sewage.

How Do Blue-green Bacteria Differ?

OBJECTIVE
Compare two types of blue-green bacteria.

MATERIALS
culture of *Oscillatoria,* dropper, microscope slide, coverslip, microscope, prepared slide of *Gloeocapsa*

PROCEDURE
A. Observe *Oscillatoria* (ahs uh luh TAWR ee-uh), which appears as a dark green scum on the surface of the water. Using a dropper, put one drop of *Oscillatoria* on the center of a microscope slide. Carefully place a coverslip on the drop. Observe the slide under low power of the microscope. Notice the long filaments, or strands. Make a drawing of the *Oscillatoria* filaments.

B. Observe a few cells under high power. Observe the cell walls and the pigments within the cells. Draw several cells and label the structures that you see. If the cells appear to be joined together, show this arrangement in your drawing.

C. Observe a prepared slide of *Gloeocapsa* (glee oh KAP suh) under low power. Notice the sheath, or covering, surrounding the cells. Make a drawing of the cells as you observe them under low power. Now examine the slide under high power and make another drawing.

RESULTS AND CONCLUSIONS
1. What color are the pigments of *Oscillatoria*?
2. What color is the sheath of the *Gloeocapsa*?
3. How does the arrangement of cells differ in the two types of blue-green bacteria that you observed?

BACTERIA OR ALGAE?
Blue-green bacteria are like plants in two ways. They make their own food, and they have cell walls. For many years blue-green bacteria were classified as algae (AL jee), the simplest plants. But blue-green bacteria are now classified as monerans. There are a number of reasons for this change in classification. Like algae, blue-green bacteria contain chlorophyll and other pigments used in making food. But unlike algae, the chlorophyll in blue-green bacteria is not contained in chloroplasts.

Another difference between blue-green bacteria and algae is in their cell walls. The cell wall of blue-green bacteria is made of very different compounds from those in the cell wall of algae and other plants. These differences, plus their simple cell structure, make blue-green bacteria more like other monerans than like algae.

REVIEW
1. What are the two major groups in kingdom Monera?
2. How does a moneran cell differ from an animal cell?
3. What are two ways in which blue-green bacteria are like algae and two ways in which they differ from algae?

CHALLENGE Suggest a reason for the rapid growth of blue-green bacteria in polluted water.

5-3 BACTERIA

The other major group of monerans are the bacteria. **Bacteria** are a group of many kinds of monerans. Most bacteria cannot make food. They must get food from other sources. How does this trait make bacteria different from blue-green bacteria? Bacteria are almost everywhere. They live in and on your body. They are in air, soil, and water, and they live in and on plants and animals.

Figure 5-8 shows the three basic shapes of bacterial cells. **Cocci** (KAHK sī) (sing., *coccus*) are sphere-shaped bacteria. They may occur as single cells, in pairs, in chains, or in grapelike clusters. Bacterial pneumonia (noo MOHN-yuh) and strep throat are diseases that are caused by cocci bacteria. **Bacilli** (buh SIHL ī) (sing., *bacillus*) are rod-shaped

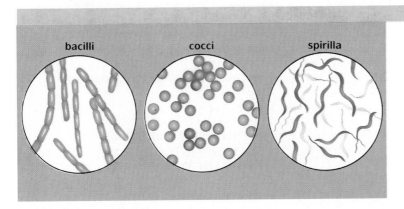

Figure 5-8

Three basic shapes of bacterial cells.

bacteria. Some grow in chains. *Escherichia coli* (ehsh uh-RIHK ee uh   KOH lī) (*E. coli*), which live in the intestines of humans, are rod-shaped bacteria. **Spirilla** (spī RIHL uh) (sing., *spirillum*) are bacteria that are shaped like spirals or corkscrews. Unlike other bacteria, spirilla live only as single cells. Some species of spirilla enrich soil.

All bacterial cells have a similar structure. Like other monerans, bacteria lack a nucleus. Note in Figure 5-9 that the DNA is located in the central part of the cell, but it is not enclosed by a nuclear membrane. The cytoplasm contains ribosomes and stored food. Some bacterial cells also contain vacuoles. Outside the cell membrane is a tough cell wall that gives the cell its shape. In some bacteria a layer called the *capsule* is found outside the cell wall. The capsule is usually a thick, jellylike substance that protects the cell. It also allows the cell to stick to surfaces. How might this trait be useful?

Many bacteria move by means of flagella (fluh JEHL-luh) (sing., *flagellum*). **Flagella** are whiplike structures

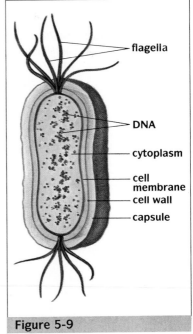

Figure 5-9

Structure of a typical bacterial cell.

ACTIVITY   Where Are Bacteria Found in the Environment?

OBJECTIVES

Predict where the most bacteria can be found in the environment.
Test for the presence of bacteria in the environment.

MATERIALS

6 sterile covered petri dishes containing agar, 3 sterile cotton-tipped swabs, glass-marking pencil, transparent tape

PROCEDURE

A. Make a data table with headings as shown. On your table, list three areas that you would like to test for the presence of bacteria in the air. Then list three surfaces that you would like to test for the presence of bacteria. Predict which air or surface sample has the most bacteria.

Air or Surface Sample	Observations		
	Day 1	Day 2	Day 3

B. Obtain 6 sterile, covered petri dishes containing agar. Label the bottom of each dish with the area or the surface to which it will be exposed and with your name.

C. To expose the agar to air, remove the cover of one petri dish and leave the agar exposed for 10 minutes. Replace the cover and set the dish aside. Repeat this procedure for the other two air samples.

D. To expose the agar to a surface, use sterile, cotton-tipped swabs. Remove each swab from its package only when you are ready to use it. Rub the cotton-tipped end of a swab on a surface you have chosen to test. With one hand, tilt open the petri dish cover. With the other hand, quickly wipe the cotton-tipped end of the swab over the agar. Then remove the swab and close the dish at once. Repeat this procedure for the other two surface samples.

E. After you have exposed the agar in all of the dishes, tape each one closed.

F. Turn each petri dish upside down. Store the dishes in a dark, warm (about 37°C) place for 3 days. Observe the dishes every day. **Caution:** Do not open the petri dishes. Wash your hands after handling the dishes. Record your observations on your data table. At the end of the 3-day period, draw what you see in each dish. Label your drawings. Your teacher will dispose of the dishes.

RESULTS AND CONCLUSIONS

1. Where did you find the most bacteria? How do you know?
2. Where did you find the fewest bacteria? Do your results agree with the prediction you made in step **A**?
3. Do you think that *all* of the colonies you observed in the dishes exposed to surfaces (step **D**) represent bacteria that came only from those surfaces? Explain your answer.

that extend out from the cytoplasm. A bacterial cell may have one or many flagella. Some bacteria have none. The number and location of the flagella are used to help classify bacteria. How many flagella does the cell in Figure 5-9 have? The lack of flagella in blue-green bacteria is another difference between these monerans and bacteria.

REVIEW

1. What are two ways in which blue-green bacteria are different from other bacteria?
2. Make labeled drawings of cocci, bacilli, and spirilli.
3. What structure do some bacteria use in movement?

CHALLENGE   Find out what the word part *diplo-* means. Using this information, make a drawing of diplococci bacteria.

5-4 REPRODUCTION AND GROWTH OF BACTERIA

Bacteria reproduce asexually by splitting into two cells through a process called **fission** (FIHSH uhn). Fission is a simpler process than mitosis. Unlike mitosis, there are no spindle fibers, centrioles, or visible chromosomes in fission. Refer to Figure 5-10 as you read about fission.

1. The DNA molecule makes a copy of itself.
2. The cell membrane and cell wall grow inward, dividing the cell into two daughter cells.
3. A new cell wall forms between the two daughter cells. Each new cell contains an identical strand of DNA.

Under ideal conditions, bacteria reproduce rapidly. Some species can divide as often as once every 20 minutes. After 6 hours, there would be more than 200,000 descendants from a single cell! If bacteria reproduce so quickly, why have they not crowded out all other forms of life? The reason is that conditions for the growth of bacteria are not always favorable.

After completing this section, you will be able to

- **compare** the processes of fission and mitosis.
- **identify** conditions for the growth of bacteria.
- **distinguish** between aerobic and anaerobic bacteria.
- **explain** how an endospore helps a bacterium survive.

The key terms in this section are
aerobic bacteria
anaerobic bacteria
endospore
fission

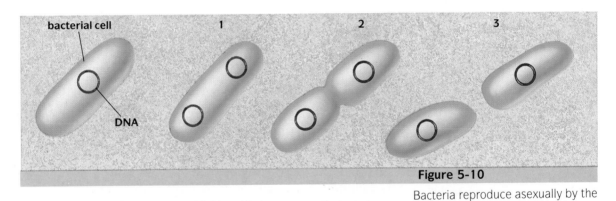

bacterial cell

DNA

1   2   3

Figure 5-10

Bacteria reproduce asexually by the process of fission. How is this process simpler than mitosis?

Bacteria must have certain conditions in order to grow and reproduce. Bacteria must have moisture. Over 90 percent of the volume of a bacterial cell is water. When there is too little moisture, bacteria are inactive. Temperature is another condition. Each type of bacteria has its own ideal temperature range. Most bacteria grow best in the range of 25°C to 40°C. But there are some species that can grow at very high or very low temperatures. The amount of light may also affect growth. Bacteria grow best in darkness. Sunlight kills many kinds of bacteria.

Another factor in the growth of bacteria is the presence or absence of oxygen. Bacteria that need oxygen in order to grow are called **aerobic** (air OH bihk) **bacteria**. The bacteria that cause tuberculosis are aerobic bacteria.

Figure 5-11

Tuberculosis bacilli.

These bacteria, shown in Figure 5-11, live in the lungs. Why would the lungs be a suitable place for these bacteria to grow? Bacteria that can grow only in the absence of oxygen are called **anaerobic bacteria.** Many species of bacteria that live in soil are anaerobic. Most kinds of bacteria can grow either in the presence of oxygen or in its absence. Bacteria also need food. Since most bacteria cannot make their own food, they need a food source.

When conditions are not right for growth, some bacteria form endospores. An **endospore** is a structure that contains bacterial DNA and a small amount of cytoplasm surrounded by a tough protective coat. The endospore forms inside the bacterial cell, as shown in Figure 5-12. After the endospore forms, the bacterial cell breaks open and the endospore is released. An endospore can survive harsh conditions. Some endospores can withstand poisons, freezing, drying, or boiling for a long time. When conditions are once again right for growth, the endospore coat breaks open and a bacterium is released.

Figure 5-12

An endospore inside a bacterial cell. Under what conditions might endospores form?

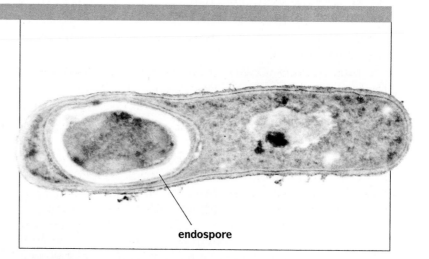

endospore

REVIEW

1. Name and describe the process by which bacterial cells reproduce asexually. How is this process different from mitosis?
2. Identify four conditions needed for the growth of most bacteria.
3. How do aerobic and anaerobic bacteria differ?
4. Describe one way in which bacteria survive harsh conditions.

CHALLENGE Why must food be specially treated before it is canned? Devise a technique for destroying endospores in food that is being canned for long-term storage.

5-5 BACTERIA: HARMFUL AND HELPFUL

HARMFUL BACTERIA

Some bacteria are harmful. They use the tissues of living plants and animals as food. These bacteria are parasites. A **parasite** is an organism that lives in or on another organism and harms it. The organism that the parasite feeds on is the *host*. Bacterial parasites cause diseases such as tetanus, scarlet fever, and whooping cough. They can cause disease in one of two ways. Some bacteria destroy the host's tissues directly, by feeding on them. Others produce wastes that are poisons called *toxins,* which harm the host.

Most bacterial diseases can be cured by the use of *antibiotics.* Antibiotics are drugs that limit or stop the growth of bacteria, as can be seen in Figure 5-13. After a few days of treatment with these drugs, fewer and fewer bacterial cells can survive. Two often-used antibiotics are penicillin (pehn uh SIHL ihn) and streptomycin (strehp-tuh MĪ sihn). Many bacterial diseases can be prevented by the use of vaccines. You probably received a vaccine against whooping cough when you were younger. Whooping cough is caused by bacilli.

Many foods used by humans are also a food source for bacteria. Some bacteria can cause food to spoil. They give the food an unpleasant taste, odor, or appearance. Although these bacteria spoil food, they may not be harmful to humans. Other bacteria can cause serious illness when they are in food eaten by humans. There are two kinds of food poisoning. One kind results from toxins in food. The toxins are waste products of bacteria in the food. Botulism (BAHCH uh lihz uhm) is this kind of food poisoning. Botulism is rare but often fatal. Its victims are

After completing this section, you will be able to

- **describe** how some bacteria are harmful.
- **describe** how some bacteria are helpful.

The key terms in this section are
nitrogen-fixing bacteria
parasite
saprobe

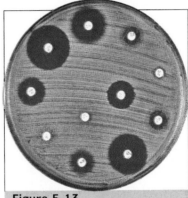

Figure 5-13

Disks containing different antibiotics are placed on a bacterial culture. A clear area around a disk means that the growth of bacteria has been stopped.

SCIENCE PUZZLER

One of the sealed cans in the picture has food in it that contains the bacteria that causes botulism. Would you be willing to eat the food in can *A* or can *B*? How do you know which can to choose? What might have caused the change in one of the cans?

ACTIVITY — How Do Disinfectants Affect Bacterial Growth?

OBJECTIVE
Test the effect of several disinfectants on the growth of bacteria.

MATERIALS
2 covered petri dishes containing bacteria, glass-marking pencil, 7 forceps, 8 paper disks, 6 numbered and labeled beakers of disinfectants (with forceps in each), transparent tape, metric ruler, safety goggles

PROCEDURE
A. Make a data table like the one shown.

	Section	Number and Name of Disinfectant	Diameter of Clear Area
DISH A	1	1	
	2	2	
	3	3	
	Control A	None used	
DISH B	4	4	
	5	5	
	6	6	
	Control B	None used	

B. Firmly hold the cover on a petri dish containing bacteria as you turn the dish upside down. Use a glass-marking pencil to draw lines that divide the bottom of the dish into fourths. Label the sections *1, 2, 3,* and *control A.* Label this dish *A.*

C. Repeat step **B**, using a second petri dish. Label the sections *4, 5, 6,* and *control B.* Label this dish *B.*

D. Use clean forceps to pick up an untreated paper disk. Lift up the cover of dish *A* just enough to place the disk on the section marked *control A.* Repeat this procedure for dish *B,* using the same forceps to place an untreated disk on *control B.* **Caution:** Do not allow your skin or clothing to touch the contents of the dishes.

E. Use the forceps in disinfectant *1* to pick up a paper disk and soak the disk in disinfectant *1.* Place this disk on section *1.* Record the name of disinfectant *1* on your data table.

F. Repeat the procedure described in step **E** for each of the remaining five disinfectants. Put each of the disinfectant-treated disks on the section that has the same number as the disinfectant being used.

G. Tape both dishes closed with transparent tape and turn them upside down. Place the dishes in a dark, warm (about 37°C) place for 3 days. Observe the dishes daily. Look for a clear area around each disk. Record what you see. At the end of 3 days, measure and record the diameter of each clear area *without opening the dishes.* Your teacher will dispose of the dishes in the proper way.

RESULTS AND CONCLUSIONS

1. What does a clear area indicate?
2. Which disinfectants slowed or stopped the growth of bacteria?
3. How can you determine which disinfectant was the most effective in killing the bacteria? Which one was most effective?
4. What was the purpose of using untreated disks?
5. Describe the bacterial growth around the untreated disks (control *A* and control *B*).

most often poisoned by eating food that has been improperly treated during home canning. The other kind of food poisoning is caused by eating food containing certain kinds of bacteria. These are bacteria that reproduce inside the human body and give off toxins in the intestines. *Salmonella* (sal muh NEHL uh) are bacilli that cause this kind of food poisoning. It usually takes a few days to recover from *Salmonella* poisoning.

There are many ways to preserve food and prevent it from spoiling. *Pasteurization* (pas chuhr uh ZAY shuhn) is a method that prevents the growth of bacteria in milk. The milk is heated to 72°C for 15 seconds and then cooled quickly. The heat kills most of the bacteria. Chilling slows the growth of any bacteria that may remain. Food can also be preserved by salt curing or by drying. These methods remove water from the food, making the food too dry to allow the growth of bacteria. Chemicals can also be added to food to keep it from spoiling. The chemicals change the amount of oxygen or moisture in the food, so that bacteria cannot grow in it.

Figure 5-14

Pasteurization of milk. Other foods that are pasteurized include cheeses and fruit juices.

HELPFUL BACTERIA

Since some kinds of bacteria cause disease or spoil food, you may think that all bacteria are harmful. But most bacteria are helpful to other living things. Some kinds of bacteria play an important role in recycling matter in the environment. Bacteria that are saprobes decay, or break down, matter that was once living. A **saprobe** is an organism that uses the remains of dead plants and animals as food. Saprobes break down the cells of dead organisms into elements and compounds that can be used by plants and animals. Without saprobes, other living things would not have these useful materials. How are saprobes affecting the leaves in Figure 5-15?

Bacteria are also helpful in other ways. **Nitrogen-fixing bacteria** combine nitrogen in the air with other elements to form compounds that other living things can use. Some of these bacteria live in the roots of certain

Figure 5-15

Over time the action of saprobes on fallen leaves returns important elements and compounds to the soil. How were these substances removed from the soil?

Figure 5-16

The roots of a pea plant. The swellings are nodules.

plants, such as bean and pea plants. Notice the swellings in the roots shown in Figure 5-16. These swellings are *nodules*. They contain nitrogen-fixing bacteria. Some of these bacteria also live in the soil. They form nitrogen compounds that plants use to make proteins.

Bacteria also play a part in the digestion process in humans. Grazing animals, such as cows and sheep, have bacteria that digest cellulose. Without bacteria, these animals would not be able to digest plants.

Many foods are made using the action of bacteria. Sauerkraut is made by using bacteria to change the sugar in cabbage leaves to a weak acid. Similar methods are used to make cheese and yogurt.

Scientists are now working with bacteria that help control water pollution. Bacteria are used to break down sewage at many water treatment plants. Other kinds of bacteria feed on oil and oil products. These bacteria have been used to help clean up oil spills.

Scientists have also found that bacteria can be used to make proteins that are normally made in the human body. Interferon and insulin are two proteins that can now be made by bacteria. Insulin is used to treat the disease diabetes. For many years insulin from cows or pigs had been used to treat this disease. But animal insulin can cause unwanted side effects in humans. The insulin from bacteria is made by putting human DNA into bacteria. The insulin produced by these treated bacteria is exactly the same as the insulin made by the human body. So this insulin has no side effects. The process used to change the DNA of the bacteria is known as *genetic engineering*.

Figure 5-17

Yogurt is made using the action of these bacilli bacteria (*top*). Many people enjoy the sour taste of yogurt (*bottom*).

REVIEW

1. Name two ways in which bacterial parasites cause disease.
2. Name and describe the process used to prevent bacterial growth in milk.
3. How are nitrogen-fixing bacteria helpful to other organisms?
4. What are two substances that are produced by bacteria that have been changed through genetic engineering?

CHALLENGE Smoked meats do not spoil as quickly as fresh meats. Suggest a reason why.

CHAPTER SUMMARY

The main ideas in this chapter are listed below. Read these statements before you answer the Chapter Review questions.

- A virus is a small particle with a core of nucleic acid and a protein coat. A virus can reproduce only inside a living cell. Some viruses cause disease in plants and animals. (5-1)

- Blue-green bacteria and bacteria make up kingdom Monera. Monerans are simple, one-celled organisms that have a cell wall but lack a nucleus and most other cell organelles. (5-2)

- Blue-green bacteria are monerans that produce their own food by photosynthesis. (5-2)

- Bacteria are monerans that in most cases cannot perform photosynthesis. They occur as cocci, bacilli, and spirilla. (5-3)

- Bacteria reproduce by fission. Bacteria need moisture and grow best in darkness within certain temperature ranges. Bacteria vary in their need for oxygen. (5-4)

- Bacteria that are parasites live in or on other organisms and harm them. Bacterial parasites cause some diseases in humans. (5-5)

- Bacteria can spoil food and can cause food poisoning. Pasteurizing, salt curing, drying, and adding chemicals are methods used to preserve food. (5-5)

- Bacteria that are saprobes recycle organic matter in the environment by decaying plants and animals. Nitrogen in air is made available to plants by nitrogen-fixing bacteria. (5-5)

- Bacteria are used in producing food, in controlling water pollution, and in producing useful substances through genetic engineering. (5-5)

The key terms in this chapter are listed below. Use each term in a sentence that shows the meaning of the term.

aerobic bacteria	blue-green bacteria	flagella	saprobe
anaerobic bacteria	cocci	monerans	spirilla
bacilli	endospore	nitrogen-fixing bacteria	vaccine
bacteria	fission	parasite	virus

Chapter Review

VOCABULARY

Write the letter of the term that best matches the definition. Not all the terms will be used.

1. Whiplike structures used in movement by some bacteria
2. Bacteria that need oxygen in order to grow
3. Rod-shaped bacteria
4. Organisms that live in or on other organisms and harm them
5. Substances that contain dead or weakened viruses that can no longer cause disease
6. Asexual reproduction in bacteria
7. Organisms that use the remains of dead plants and animals as food
8. Bacteria that can manufacture food by photosynthesis
9. Corkscrew-shaped bacteria
10. Small particles made up of a core of nucleic acid with a protein coat
11. Structures that enable bacteria to survive harsh conditions
12. Sphere-shaped bacteria

a. aerobic bacteria
b. anaerobic bacteria
c. bacilli
d. blue-green bacteria
e. cocci
f. endospores
g. fission
h. flagella
i. monerans
j. parasites
k. saprobes
l. spirilla
m. vaccines
n. viruses

CONCEPTS

1. Describe the structure of a virus. (5-1)
2. Why are viruses described as being on the borderline between living and nonliving things? (5-1)
3. How does a virus reproduce in a bacterial cell? (5-1)
4. What is a latent virus? (5-1)
5. How can a virus damage a cell? (5-1)
6. Identify five diseases caused by viruses. (5-1)
7. How can some virus-caused diseases be prevented? (5-1)
8. How does the cell of a moneran differ from the cells of other living things? (5-2)
9. How do blue-green bacteria differ from algae? (5-2)
10. What is the function of pigments in blue-green bacteria? (5-2)
11. Identify and describe the three shapes of bacterial cells. (5-3)
12. Describe the structure of a bacterial cell. (5-3)
13. Describe two functions of the capsule of a bacterial cell. (5-3)

14. How does fission differ from mitosis? (5-4)
15. List four conditions needed for the growth of bacteria. (5-4)
16. Describe the structure and function of an endospore. (5-4)
17. Identify three diseases caused by bacteria. (5-5)
18. How can many bacterial diseases be treated? (5-5)
19. Describe the two kinds of food poisoning. (5-5)
20. Identify three methods of preserving foods. (5-5)
21. What do saprobes use as a food source? (5-5)
22. Identify six ways in which bacteria are helpful. (5-5)
23. How does insulin made through genetic engineering of bacteria differ from insulin obtained from cows? (5-5)

APPLICATION/ CRITICAL THINKING

1. In the past, blue-green bacteria were classified as algae. Based on their cell structure, these organisms are now classified as bacteria. The organisms have not changed. Why do you think their classification has now changed?
2. The lack of a nucleus and other cell structures is the basis for placing monerans in a separate kingdom. Explain why.
3. *E. coli* are bacteria that live in the intestines of humans and produce vitamins. Do you think that these *E. coli* are parasites? Explain your answer.
4. When milk is pasteurized it is heated briefly and then quickly cooled. Why is it important to cool the milk quickly?
5. Nitrogen is an important part of fertilizers. Suggest a method that would reduce the use of commercial fertilizers.

EXTENSION

1. During the fourteenth century, bubonic plague killed about 25 million people. Find out what organism causes this disease and how it kills those who are infected with it.
2. How was penicillin discovered? How is it produced today? Use reference books and write a report on your findings.
3. Do research to learn what new products are being produced using bacteria that have been changed through genetic engineering. Present your results to the class.

READINGS

Asimov, Isaac. *How Did We Find Out About Germs?* New York: Avon Books, 1981.

Blakeslee, A. "Interferon Makes a Comeback." *Science Digest*, January 1985, p. 21.

Simpson, Lance L. "Deadly Botulism." *Natural History,* January 1980, p. 12.

Teasdale, Jim. *Visual Science: Microbes.* Morristown, N.J.: Silver Burdett Co., 1984.

PROTISTS AND FUNGI

Have you ever walked through a forest? Did you look down at the forest floor? If you did, you might have seen this strange-looking organism. It looks a little like a flower vase. The organism is found in several colors—brown, red, or orange-yellow. What is it? This organism is a chanterelle, which is a kind of mushroom. A mushroom is a type of fungus. Perhaps you asked yourself questions about this strange living thing.

- *Is a mushroom a plant?*
- *How does a mushroom get food?*
- *What other small organisms are found on the forest floor?*
- *What kinds of simple living things are found in the streams that run through a forest?*
- *Are the simple organisms living in water classified as plants, animals, or something else?*

6-1 TRAITS OF PROTISTS

You learned that Anton van Leeuwenhoek made some simple microscopes in the late seventeenth century. He used his microscopes to look at samples of water. His studies showed that the water was filled with tiny living things. The creatures that Leeuwenhoek saw have come to be known as protists (PROH tihsts). **Protists** are mostly single-celled microscopic organisms that are found living in fresh water, salt water, and moist places. These organisms make up kingdom Protista.

In Chapter 5 you studied monerans, another group of one-celled organisms. The cells of monerans are simpler in structure than those of protists. Unlike monerans, the cells of protists contain a nucleus and other cell organelles, such as chloroplasts. The organelles of protists allow them to carry out various cell functions. These functions include food making, food getting, and reproduction.

Both protists and monerans exist either as single cells or as colonies. Colonies are groups of similar cells that

protistos (the very first)

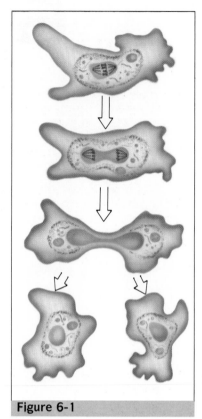

Figure 6-1

Fission in a protist.

are attached to each other. Plants and animals are *multicellular*. A multicellular plant or animal is made up of many different types of cells. Your body, for example, contains skin cells, blood cells, bone cells, and many other types of cells. Protists and monerans may form colonies, but these colonies are not multicellular organisms.

Most protists live in water. They can be found in both the fresh water of rivers and streams and the salt water of the oceans. A few protists can be found in moist places on land, such as damp soil. Scientists have found many thousands of species of protists in all regions of the earth.

Species of protists differ from each other in several ways. One important difference is the way in which they get food. Some protists are like animals in that they both eat other living things. An animallike protist is called a **protozoan** (proh tuh ZOH uhn). Some protists have chloroplasts and can make their own food. These protists are like plants because they both use the energy in sunlight to make sugars. Recall that this food-making process is called photosynthesis. Protists that make their own food in this way are sometimes called plantlike protists. Some protists are neither plantlike nor animallike and get their food in yet other ways.

Most protists reproduce by fission. Fission is the splitting of a cell to produce two new cells. You learned that monerans reproduce by fission. Fission is a form of asexual reproduction, since only one parent is needed to make new organisms. In this type of reproduction, the new cells that are formed are identical to the parent cell. Figure 6-1 shows a protist dividing by fission. Some protists also can reproduce by sexual means. In sexual reproduction, two parent cells come together and new cells are formed. The new cells that are formed are not identical to either parent cell.

REVIEW

1. How are protists similar to monerans? How do protists differ from monerans?
2. How do most protists reproduce?
3. Identify an animallike trait found in some protists. Identify a plantlike trait.

CHALLENGE Suppose that you find a single-celled organism living in pond water. Using a microscope, you observe that this organism has chlorophyll. The chlorophyll is contained in a chloroplast. Could it be a blue-green bacterium or a protist? Explain your answer.

6-2 PLANTLIKE PROTISTS

EUGLENAS

A protist called euglena (yoo GLEE nuh) is shown in Figure 6-2. A **euglena** is a plantlike protist that is common in fresh water and in damp soils. How can you tell from the drawing that this organism is not a moneran? Notice the chloroplasts and the structures called *starch granules*. Photosynthesis takes place in the chloroplasts. Sugar formed during photosynthesis is stored as starch in the granules.

A euglena is thought to be a plantlike protist, mainly because it can make its own food. But a euglena also has some animallike traits. Like an animal, a euglena lacks a cell wall. It also can move through the water by a rapid beating of its flagellum. Recall that a flagellum is a whiplike structure that allows movement. A euglena has another animallike trait. It is able to take in food from the surrounding water. It takes in food when there is not enough light for photosynthesis to occur. Movement and getting food from the surroundings are animallike traits.

After completing this section, you will be able to

- **identify** the plantlike and animallike traits of a euglena.
- **describe** the traits of diatoms.
- **identify** one use of diatoms.
- **list** the traits of dinoflagellates.

The key terms in this section are
diatom   euglena
dinoflagellate

Figure 6-2

Structure of a euglena.

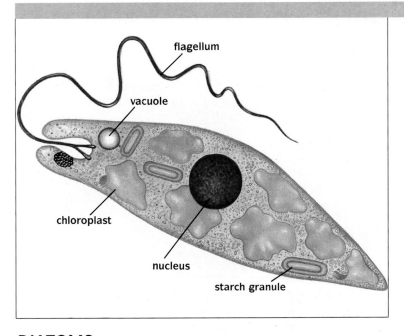

flagellum

vacuole

chloroplast

nucleus

starch granule

DIATOMS

A second group of plantlike protists can be found in both fresh water and salt water. A **diatom** (DĪ uh tahm) is a plantlike protist that is surrounded by a cell wall. The cell wall is made of a glassy substance. This glassy cell wall forms a two-part shell. The two parts of the shell fit together like the two halves of a gift box, as shown in

diatomos (cut in half)

121

Figure 6-3A. There are many species of diatoms. In Figure 6-3B you can see that each species has a shell with a different shape. Look for the two parts of the shell. You can also see that a diatom, unlike a euglena, does not have a flagellum.

Diatoms exist in great numbers in the ocean and are food for many organisms. All diatoms carry on photosynthesis and, as a result, release much oxygen into the water. The oxygen is thus available for use by other organisms. As diatoms die, their shells fall to the bottom of the ocean. Large numbers of diatom shells may collect, forming a powdery substance called *diatomaceous* (dī uh tuh MAY-shuhs) *earth*. Because of its gritty nature, this substance is used in making toothpaste and scouring powders. It is also used in making filters. One use of diatomaceous earth is shown in Figure 6-3C.

Figure 6-3

Types of diatoms (A). Notice the boxlike structure of this diatom (B). One use of diatomaceous earth (C).

DINOFLAGELLATES

A third group of plantlike protists includes the dinoflagellates (dī nuh FLAJ uh layts). A **dinoflagellate** is a plantlike protist that lives mainly in salt water and has two flagella used in movement. Note the positions of the flagella in the protist shown in Figure 6-4. The flagellum that trails behind is used in moving the protist forward. The flagellum that circles around the middle part of the protist is used in steering.

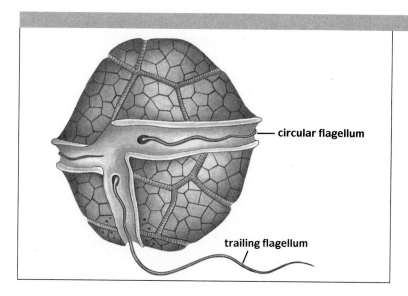

Figure 6-4

Structure of a dinoflagellate.

— circular flagellum

trailing flagellum

Like all plantlike protists, dinoflagellates contain the pigment chlorophyll. These protists also contain other pigments, especially red ones. The red pigments may mask the chlorophyll and cause the organism to look red. Some red dinoflagellates release poisons into the water. A large number of these dinoflagellates can make the water appear red, causing a "red tide." The poisons released by these protists during a red tide may cause many fish to die. Shellfish do not die but store the poisons in their body. People who eat the affected shellfish may become ill.

REVIEW

1. Name two ways that diatoms and euglenas differ.
2. What animallike feature is shared by euglenas and dinoflagellates? What plantlike feature do they both have?
3. What is a red tide? What protist is the cause of this event?

CHALLENGE Some protists move toward light, and some protists move away from light. Which way do you think a euglena moves? Give reasons for your answer.

6-3 ANIMALLIKE PROTISTS

Recall that animallike protists are called protozoans. Protozoans have no chloroplasts and get their food from other organisms. Many varieties of protozoans exist. Scientists have classified them into four groups based on the ways in which the protists move about.

FLAGELLATES

Flagellates (FLAJ uh layts) are protozoans that use flagella for movement. Most flagellates live inside other organisms and use the food produced by these organisms. Some flagellates are useful to the animals they live inside. Those in the intestines of termites help the termites digest wood. Other flagellates cause harm to the animals in which they live. A flagellate known as a *trypanosome* (trih PAN-uh sohm) is a parasite. Recall that a parasite is an organism that lives in or on another organism and harms it. Trypanosomes live in the blood of insects and other animals, including humans. These protists, shown in Figure 6-5, cause the disease called African sleeping sickness.

Figure 6-5

Protists that cause African sleeping sickness.

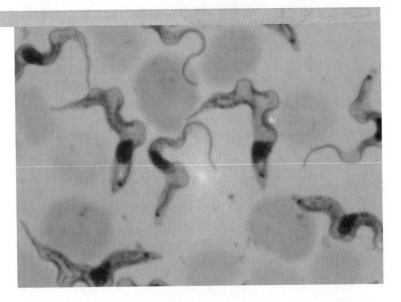

AMOEBAS

pseudo (false)
podium (foot)

A second group of protozoans includes those that move by pseudopods (SOO duh pahdz). A **pseudopod** is a fingerlike extension of the cytoplasm and is used in moving and feeding. The pseudopod stretches out ahead of the rest of the cell. Then the remaining cytoplasm flows toward the pseudopod, moving the cell forward.

An **amoeba** (uh MEE buh) is a freshwater protozoan that moves by forming pseudopods. This protozoan has no definite shape. Its shape changes as it forms new pseudopods. Notice the pseudopods formed by the amoeba shown in Figure 6-6. In feeding, pseudopods move toward a piece of food and then surround it. The food particle and some water are then taken into the cell. Inside the cell the food and water are held within a food vacuole (VAK yoo uhl). A **food vacuole** is an organelle in which food is digested. Any wastes that remain after the food is digested are released from the cell.

Many amoebas live in ponds that dry up when there is no rain. During a drought an amoeba forms into a ball and develops a thick, protective coating. A protozoan with a protective coating is called a **cyst** (sihst). Amoebas that have formed cysts can survive during times of dryness or extreme temperatures. When favorable conditions return, the amoeba becomes active again.

Although most amoebas are harmless organisms, a few types can cause disease. One disease caused by amoebas is *amoebic dysentery* (DIHS uhn tehr ee). These amoebas are parasites that live in human intestines. The disease is spread when humans drink water that is polluted with human wastes containing the amoebas.

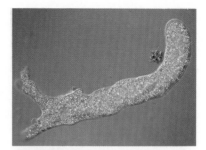

Figure 6-6

An amoeba forming pseudopods as it surrounds food.

CILIATES

A third group of protozoans, the *ciliates* (SIHL ee ayts), have cilia. **Cilia** are short hairlike structures that extend from a cell and are used in movement. Cilia are much shorter and more numerous than flagella. A **paramecium** (par uh MEE shee uhm) (pl., *paramecia*) is a slipper-shaped protozoan that has cilia. Notice the many cilia on the paramecium in Figure 6-7. The cilia beat together in a

cilium (eyelash)

Figure 6-7

Structure of a paramecium.

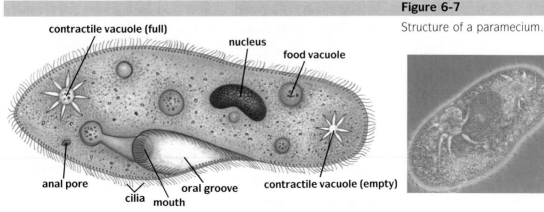

contractile vacuole (full)

nucleus

food vacuole

anal pore

cilia mouth

oral groove

contractile vacuole (empty)

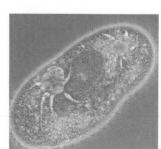

OBJECTIVE

Observe the structures, movement, and feeding of a paramecium.

MATERIALS

lab apron, 2 toothpicks, petroleum jelly, depression slide, 3 droppers, culture of paramecia, coverslip, methyl cellulose, microscope, yeast cells stained with crystal violet

PROCEDURE

A. Wear a lab apron during this activity.

B. Using a toothpick, make a ring of petroleum jelly in the center of a depression slide.

C. Use a dropper to place a drop of a culture of paramecia on a coverslip. Use a clean dropper to add a drop of methyl cellulose. This substance will slow the movements of the paramecia for easier observation.

D. Quickly turn the coverslip over and lower it onto the ring of petroleum jelly. Observe the slide with a microscope. Locate and study some paramecia.

E. Use the point of a clean toothpick to carefully lift the coverslip without moving it from side to side. Use a clean dropper to add a drop of stained yeast to the slide, and then replace the coverslip.

F. Place the slide on a microscope and locate some paramecia. Observe the paramecia feeding on the yeast. Record your observations of how the paramecia feed.

G. Look for a paramecium that is getting rid of wastes. Note the location of the structure that rids the cell of wastes.

H. Make a drawing of a paramecium as you observe it through the microscope. Label as many structures as you can find.

RESULTS AND CONCLUSIONS

1. Describe how a paramecium moves.

2. Explain how a paramecium gets its food. What do you think a paramecium might eat besides yeast?

3. In what structure or structures were the yeast cells digested?

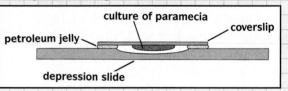

rhythmic manner. This beating causes the organism to move through the water.

Beating cilia also move bits of food into the *oral groove*. An oral groove is a cilia-lined channel through which food passes to the mouth. The oral groove carries food from the surroundings to the inside of the paramecium. Once inside the cell, the food is enclosed in food vacuoles. The food vacuoles move around the cytoplasm while the food within them is digested. Undigested food passes out through a structure called the *anal pore*.

A paramecium forms wastes other than those left in the food vacuoles. Extra water may also collect in these protozoans. The **contractile vacuole** (kuhn TRAK tuhl VAK yoo uhl) is a structure from which extra water and liquid wastes are released from the cell. Notice in Figure 6-7 that the contractile vacuole looks like a star.

A paramecium can reproduce by fission. It can also com- (together) reproduce sexually, through conjugation. **Conjugation** (kahn juh GAY shuhn) is a type of sexual reproduction in which two organisms join and exchange nuclear material. Two paramecia join together at their oral grooves during conjugation, as shown in Figure 6-8. The two protists exchange part of their nuclear material and then separate. The new cells formed have traits from both parents.

SPOROZOANS

A fourth group of protozoans includes the sporozoans (spawr uh ZOH uhnz). A **sporozoan** is a protozoan that has no means of movement and sometimes forms *spores*. A spore is an asexual reproductive cell with a thick, protective coating. Most sporozoans live inside other organisms. Many of these sporozoans are disease-causing parasites. One type causes malaria (muh LAIR ee uh). Malaria is a disease that affects humans. This sporozoan is carried from person to person by mosquitoes. Malaria is one of the most widespread diseases in the world. The life cycle of the sporozoan that causes malaria is shown in Figure 6-9. Notice that this protist spends part of its life cycle in an insect and part inside the human body.

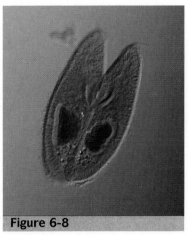

Figure 6-8

Conjugation.

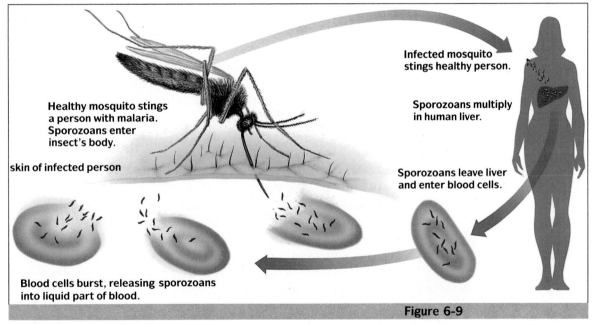

Infected mosquito stings healthy person.

Sporozoans multiply in human liver.

Sporozoans leave liver and enter blood cells.

Healthy mosquito stings a person with malaria. Sporozoans enter insect's body.

skin of infected person

Blood cells burst, releasing sporozoans into liquid part of blood.

Figure 6-9

Life cycle of a parasite that causes malaria.

REVIEW

1. What feature is used to classify protozoans into four groups? What are the four groups, and how do they differ?
2. Compare the functions of contractile and food vacuoles.
3. Name three diseases that are caused by protists. Identify the kinds of protists that cause them.
4. What are two ways in which a paramecium can reproduce?

CHALLENGE   Distinguish between protists and protozoans.

6-4 FUNGI

TRAITS OF FUNGI

Yeasts, mushrooms, and molds are examples of fungi (FUHN jī). A **fungus** (FUHN guhs) (pl., *fungi*) is an organism that lacks chlorophyll, produces spores, and absorbs food from living or once-living things. Fungi were once classified as plants. They have certain plantlike traits: they do not move, and their cells have cell walls. However, fungi differ from plants in a number of ways. Because fungi lack chlorophyll, they cannot make their own food. The cell walls of fungi are made of different materials than those of plants. Fungi, like animals, must get their food from other living things. But fungi are not animals. Fungi have traits different from both plants and animals. They are placed in a separate kingdom—kingdom Fungi.

Fungi digest their food differently than do animals. Fungi release chemicals called *enzymes* into their food source. The enzymes break down large molecules of food into smaller molecules. The fungi then absorb this digested food. This method of getting food is different from that used by animals. An animal's food is digested by enzymes inside the animal's body. The food of a fungus is digested by enzymes outside the body of the fungus. Fungi absorb their food either from living things or from the remains of once-living things.

Fungi grow best where there is warmth and moisture, such as in damp soil. They can also be found inside the tissues of animals and plants. Fungi that live within other organisms, taking food from them and harming them, are parasites.

Recall that an organism that uses the remains of dead organisms for food is called a saprobe. Saprobes may use such things as dead leaves and rotting wood as food. Most fungi are saprobes. Their actions help to keep dead materials from building up in the environment.

Fungi are divided into three main groups. The three main groups of fungi are the *threadlike fungi*, the *sac fungi*, and the *club fungi*.

THREADLIKE FUNGI

A **threadlike fungus** is a fungus that grows in the form of fine threads that collect to form fluffy, cottony masses. The black mold that is seen on bread is an example of this type of fungus. Look at the drawing of a bread mold in Figure 6-10. The cells grow end-to-end to form threadlike structures. The threadlike structures of mold

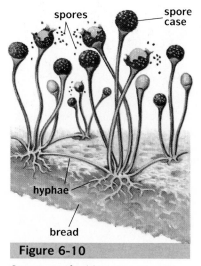

Figure 6-10

Structure of a black bread mold.

are called **hyphae** (HĪ fee). The body of a threadlike fungus consists almost entirely of fluffy, tangled masses of hyphae. In Figure 6-10 you can see that most of the hyphae grow along the surface of the bread. But some of the hyphae are rootlike and grow downward into the bread. These hyphae anchor the mold and transport food to other parts of the fungus.

Some hyphae grow upward from the surface of the bread. On the tips of these hyphae are *spore cases* filled with spores. Recall that a spore is an asexual reproductive cell with a thick, protective coating. Each spore case contains a large number of spores.

In their early stages of growth, black bread molds are a whitish color. As the fungus matures, the spore cases turn black. The ripening of the spore cases causes the mold to look black. The ripe spore cases break open, releasing many spores into the air. Each spore can grow into a new mold if it lands in a suitable place.

Most threadlike fungi grow in soil as saprobes. They feed on bits of dead leaves and remains of other living things. Some threadlike fungi are disease-causing parasites. They harm insects and plants. One type of fungus called the *downy mildews* damages fruit trees. Common downy mildews are shown in Figure 6-11. Some saprobic threadlike fungi also feed on and damage natural products such as leather or wood. Where would you store leather shoes to prevent damage by these fungi?

SCIENCE PUZZLER

Two loaves of the same kind of bread were purchased for a family. One loaf was set out in a basket for dinner. The other loaf was refrigerated at once. Some of the bread in the basket was not eaten and was later refrigerated. The family went away on vacation for two weeks. When they returned, one of the loaves was covered with mold. The other was mold-free. Which loaf do you think was moldy? Account for the differences in the two loaves.

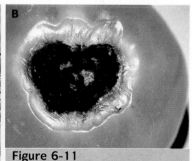

Figure 6-11

Downy mildew on oak leaves (*A*), tomato (*B*), and grape (*C*). Enlargement of downy mildew on grape (*D*).

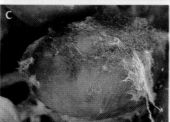

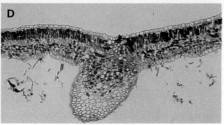

SAC FUNGI

A **sac fungus** is a fungus that forms reproductive cells, or spores, within sacs. Yeasts are the best-known examples of sac fungi. Sac fungi exist in many shapes and sizes. They vary from single-celled microscopic yeasts to the large morels (muh REHLZ), which resemble mushrooms. Morels, like certain mushrooms, can be eaten. The many kinds of sac fungi look very different from each other, but they all produce spores in sacs. Yeasts and morels are both saprobes, but many sac fungi are parasites.

Sac fungi cause diseases in many plants and animals. Ringworm and athlete's foot are skin diseases that are caused by sac fungi. Dutch elm disease has killed most of the elm trees in North America in the past 50 years. This disease is caused by a parasitic sac fungus. *Powdery mildews* are a group of sac fungi that are saprobes. These mildews may damage damp clothing, paper, or wood.

Figure 6-12 shows a sac fungus growing on the skin of an orange. Although this fungus damages the orange, it also makes a product useful to people. This type of sac fungus produces the antibiotic penicillin. Recall that this drug is often used to treat diseases caused by bacteria. Other similar sac fungi are used in making cheeses.

Yeasts are among the most useful of all fungi. Yeasts use sugar as a source of energy to carry on life processes.

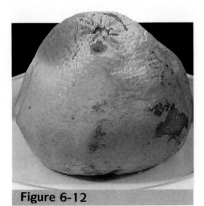

Figure 6-12

A sac fungus used to produce penicillin is growing on the skin of this orange.

SCIENCE & TECHNOLOGY

The ancient Egyptians were among the first people to discover the special qualities of yeasts. They were delighted to find that yeasts could turn fruit juice into wine. Some 5000 years later, scientists are discovering new uses for yeasts. Today, yeasts are used to produce new vaccines.

About 200 million people are affected by hepatitis B, a disease that damages the liver. The disease is caused by a virus. One out of every four people with hepatitis B dies. A vaccine against hepatitis B is now available, but it is expensive and difficult to produce. It is made from a virus found in the blood of hepatitis B carriers. Through genetic engineering, shown in the photograph, scientists have used yeasts to produce copies of the hepatitis B virus. Using copies of the virus, scientists have made a new vaccine against the disease. This vaccine is not yet widely used.

In tests of both vaccines, the yeast-produced vaccine was as effective as the vaccine now used. Since the yeast-produced vaccine is much less costly to produce, it may soon replace the currently used vaccine. Yeasts are thus being used today to prevent hepatitis B and to save lives.

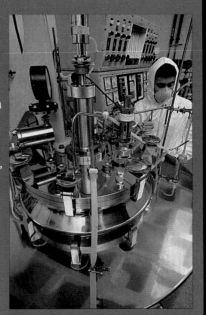

ACTIVITY   What Substances Do Yeasts Need for Growth?

When yeasts use sugar in this way, alcohol and carbon dioxide gas are given off. The process in which energy is released from sugar and in which alcohol and carbon dioxide are produced is called **fermentation** (fer mehn TAY-shuhn).

Yeast is mixed into bread dough. The carbon dioxide bubbles produced during fermentation cause the dough to rise. During baking the carbon dioxide is forced out, leaving small holes in the bread.

Wine is produced by the action of yeasts on grape juice. How is this done? Grape juice contains much sugar. When yeasts are allowed to ferment grape juice, they use the sugar for energy. Alcohol is produced as a by-product of this fermentation. As alcohol collects, the grape juice becomes wine.

All sac fungi form spores as a means of reproduction. **Budding** is a means of asexual reproduction in which a new organism develops from an outgrowth of the parent. As you can see in Figure 6-13, during budding a yeast cell grows a small bud on one side of the cell. The bud later grows to the size of a mature yeast cell. Under good growing conditions, yeasts reproduce mostly by budding. If growing conditions become poor, the yeasts may produce spores instead of buds. How are spores useful to yeasts?

Figure 6-13
Budding yeast cells.

Figure 6-14

Bracket fungi.

CLUB FUNGI

A **club fungus** is a fungus that forms spores on microscopic club-shaped stalks. Some club fungi reach 20 or 30 cm in height. Mushrooms, bracket fungi, and puffballs are all examples of club fungi. An example of these fungi is shown in Figure 6-14. Bracket fungi, also called shelf fungi, grow on the bark of dead trees in damp forests. Puffballs burst open when touched and give off clouds of trillions of spores.

The part of a mushroom seen aboveground is just a small part of a much larger organism. Most of a mushroom is made of hyphae that spread over a large area underground. The part aboveground is the reproductive structure of this fungus. Look at the mushroom in Figure 6-15A. The **stalk** is the upright part of a mushroom. The **cap** is the umbrella-shaped part of a mushroom. Both the stalk and cap are made of hyphae that are tightly packed together. These hyphae are attached to the underground hyphae, which absorb food from bits of dead matter in the soil.

The many thin sheets on the underside of a mushroom cap are called **gills**. The enlarged view of gills in Figure 6-15C shows the club-shaped structures that carry the spores. A single mushroom may produce many hundreds of millions of spores.

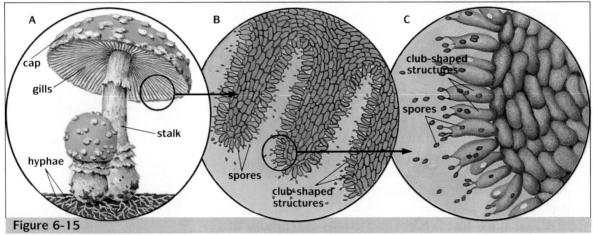

Figure 6-15

Structure of a mushroom (A), enlargement of gills (B), and enlargement of club-shaped structures that carry the spores (C).

People in many parts of the world eat mushrooms, both raw and cooked. Mushroom farming is a large industry. Some people also look for and eat wild mushrooms. Many types of wild mushrooms contain deadly poisons. Only an expert can safely tell the difference between an edible wild mushroom and a poisonous one. *Never* eat a mushroom you find growing in the wild.

ACTIVITY   What Is the Structure of a Fungus?

OBJECTIVES
Observe the structure of a black bread mold.
Identify changes in a black bread mold during several days of growth.

MATERIALS
slice of bread, scissors, metric ruler, petri dish, dropper, masking tape, glass-marking pencil, hand lens, forceps, microscope slide, coverslips, microscope, prepared slide of mature black bread mold, wrappers from packaged bread

PROCEDURE
A. Obtain a slice of fresh bread. Use scissors to cut a square piece of bread about 4 or 5 cm on each side. Let other class members cut a square from the slice. Discard any remaining bread. Lightly rub the square of bread along a dusty windowsill or counter.
B. Place the bread in a petri dish. Use a dropper to place 2 to 3 drops of water on the bread.
C. Cover the petri dish and tape it shut with masking tape. With a glass-marking pencil, label the dish with your name and date. Place the petri dish in a dark place, such as in a drawer or a closet.
D. Check the petri dish every day to see if any mold has grown on the bread.
E. When mold has begun to grow, open the petri dish. **Caution:** Some students may be allergic to mold spores. Students with known allergies should not open the petri dish. They should look at a slide prepared by a classmate. Observe the mold with a hand lens. Note the color of the mold.
F. Use forceps to remove a small bit of mold. Place the mold on a microscope slide. Add a drop of water, and cover it with a coverslip. Examine the slide with a microscope, under both low and high power. Look at a prepared slide of mature black bread mold. Compare the prepared slide with the one you made with fresh mold.
G. Make a drawing of what you saw through the microscope. Label the spore cases and hyphae. Compare your drawing with Figure 6-10.
H. Obtain several wrappers from loaves of bread. Read the list of ingredients on the wrappers. Look for ingredients that might keep bread mold from growing.

RESULTS AND CONCLUSIONS
1. Describe the color of the black bread mold as seen with a hand lens and under the microscope. What gives the mold its color? What part of the mold is white?
2. What structures did you see that are used in reproduction? What is inside these structures?
3. How did the mold get onto the bread?
4. If the mold were allowed to grow for many weeks, what do you think would happen to the bread? Explain your answer.
5. Did any of the bread wrappers list ingredients that might keep mold from growing? Suppose you had used home-baked bread in this activity. How would the kind of bread affect the time needed for mold to grow?

REVIEW

1. Describe four major traits of fungi.
2. Compare digestion of food in fungi and in animals.
3. What are the three main groups of fungi? Write a brief description of each group, and give the name of an organism from each group.
4. Name four kinds of fungi that are useful to people. Briefly describe the use of each fungus.

CHALLENGE   Morels and mushrooms look very much alike. Why are these organisms placed in separate groups? You may use a reference book, if needed.

6-5 RELATIVES OF FUNGI

There are two groups of organisms that are related to fungi. One of these is a group of funguslike protists that reproduce by spores. The spore cases produced by these protists are similar to those of threadlike fungi. The second group of organisms contains both fungi and plant cells within their bodies.

SLIME MOLDS

A **slime mold** is a protist that has stages in its life cycle that are similar to those of both protozoans and fungi. Slime molds get their name from the fact that they often appear as slimy masses on the floor of damp, shady forests. These masses are large enough to be seen with the unaided eye. Protists are not usually so large. The slimy mass of cytoplasm that is one stage in the life cycle of a slime mold is called a **plasmodium** (plaz MOH dee uhm). A plasmodium can grow to be as large as 1 m in diameter. This stage looks like a giant amoeba that contains many nuclei. These nuclei are not separated by cell membranes.

Figure 6-16 shows the life cycle of a slime mold. The plasmodium spreads along the forest floor. It feeds by forming pseudopods that surround bits of food. When

plasma (mold)

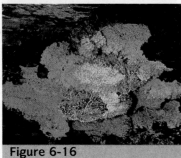

Figure 6-16

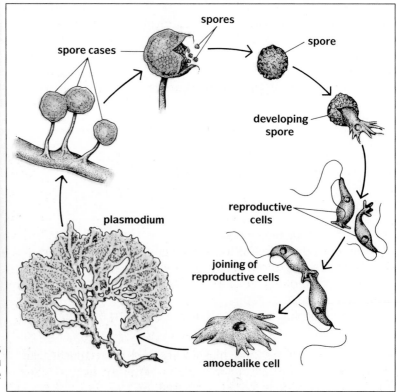

Slime mold developing spore cases (*top left*). Slime mold plasmodium (*bottom left*). Life cycle of a slime mold (*right*).

conditions for growth are poor, the plasmodium grows many stalks, each with a round spore case on top. This stage in the life cycle is funguslike. Within the spore cases are the reproductive cells, or spores, of the slime mold. When ripe, the case splits open and the spores may be carried by the wind. Spores that land on damp, shaded soil may grow into reproductive cells that move by flagella. Pairs of these cells join and grow into amoebalike cells. Many of these cells join together to form a plasmodium. The cycle continues.

Spores of slime molds and cysts of amoebas are similar in some ways. Both allow organisms to survive during times when food or water are scarce. However, spores and cysts are formed in different ways. Spores are formed in large numbers and are often found inside a case. Cysts are formed singly and are not enclosed in a case. Spores and cysts do have major differences. Recall that a spore is a reproductive cell. In contrast, a cyst is a mature amoeba with a protective coating that forms around the organism. Protozoans besides amoebas also form cysts.

LICHENS

There are many examples in nature of two different kinds of organisms living together. **Symbiosis** (sihm bī-OH sihs) is a close relationship between two organisms. One of the most widespread examples of symbiosis involves fungi. A **lichen** (LĪ kuhn) is made up of a fungus and an alga (AL guh) (pl., *algae*) living together. The living together of the fungus and the alga is a type of symbiosis. An *alga* is a simple plant with no roots, stems, or leaves. Several types of lichens are shown in Figure 6-17. Note the variety of shapes and colors of these lichens.

syn (together)
bios (life)

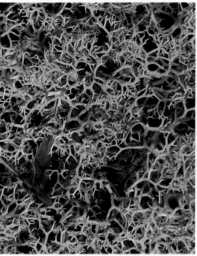

Figure 6-17

Types of lichens.

There are several types of symbiosis. The symbiosis between an alga and a fungus is a type that aids both living things. An alga is a plant, even though it is very simple. It can make its own food, using energy from the sun. A fungus cannot make its own food. The alga in a lichen produces food that it uses for itself and that is also used by the fungus.

Algae usually live in water and can live on land only in wet places. Although a fungus cannot make its own food, it can store a good deal of water. The inside of a fungus can make a good home for an alga. Notice in Figure 6-18 that the cells of the alga are inside the fungus. The fungus forms the outer part of the lichen. The algae of a lichen are found mostly on the side of the lichen that faces the light. How is this position helpful?

Figure 6-18

Cross section of a lichen.

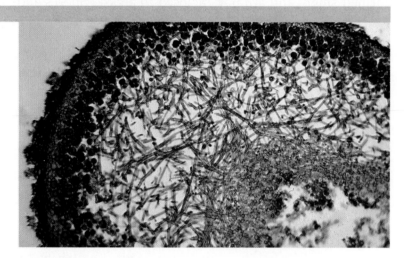

Because of the partnership between the alga and the fungus, a lichen can live almost anywhere. The alga makes food and the fungus stores water. Thus, a lichen can live where there is no food and very little water. Lichens are often found growing on the surface of bare rocks, where almost nothing else can grow. The fungus in a lichen makes acids that can break down rock into particles of soil. When soil has formed, small plants can grow where there was once only rock.

Lichens are an important food for animals that live in harsh climates. A type of lichen called *reindeer moss* grows in arctic regions. You can easily guess what animal eats these lichens. Lichens are also eaten by some desert animals. Lichens are very easily damaged by air pollution. For this reason they are sometimes used by scientists to determine the level of air pollution.

REVIEW

1. How is a slime mold like a fungus? How is it like a protist?
2. List the major stages in the life cycle of a slime mold.
3. Explain the relationship that occurs in a lichen. What is the name of this relationship?
4. In what ways are lichens useful?

CHALLENGE Lichens are often called pioneer organisms. Suggest reasons for this name.

CHAPTER SUMMARY

The main ideas in this chapter are listed below. Read these statements before you answer the Chapter Review questions.

- Protists are single-celled or colonial organisms with complex cells. Protists include both animallike and plantlike forms. (6-1)

- Plantlike protists produce their own food by photosynthesis. Plantlike protists provide food and oxygen for other organisms that live in water. (6-2)

- Protozoans are animallike protists. Protozoans are divided into four groups based on their method of movement. One group (the flagellates) moves by means of flagella. A second group (the ciliates) moves by cilia. A third group uses pseudopods for movement. A fourth group (the sporozoans) has no means of movement. Several protists cause disease in humans. (6-3)

- A fungus is an organism that does not contain chlorophyll and produces spores. It absorbs food from living or once-living things. Fungi are divided into three groups based on their growth habits and methods of reproduction. (6-4)

- Threadlike fungi, such as black bread mold, grow in the form of threads that collect to form cottony masses. Sac fungi, which include yeasts and morels, form spores inside sacs. Club fungi such as mushrooms, bracket fungi, and puffballs, form spores on club-shaped stalks. (6-4)

- Slime molds are protists that reproduce by spores like those of fungi. Part of its life cycle is like that of a protozoan; part is like that of a fungus. Lichens are organisms that are made up of an alga and a fungus living together in a symbiotic relationship. A lichen has features that are not found in either the alga or the fungus that form it. (6-5)

The key terms in this chapter are listed below. Use each term in a sentence that shows the meaning of the term.

amoeba	cyst	gills	pseudopod
budding	diatom	hyphae	sac fungus
cap	dinoflagellate	lichen	slime mold
cilia	euglena	paramecium	sporozoan
club fungus	fermentation	plasmodium	stalk
conjugation	food vacuole	protists	symbiosis
contractile vacuole	fungus	protozoan	threadlike fungus

Chapter Review

Write the letter of the term that best matches the definition. Not all the terms will be used.

1. A fingerlike extension of cytoplasm that is used for movement
2. A fungus and an alga living together in symbiosis
3. Animallike protists
4. A spore-forming organism that lacks chlorophyll and absorbs food substances made by other organisms
5. A protozoan that uses pseudopods in movement
6. The process in which alcohol and carbon dioxide are formed and energy is released from sugar
7. A plantlike protist with a glasslike cell wall
8. Threadlike structures that form the body of a fungus
9. The umbrella-shaped part of a mushroom
10. Short, hairlike structures that extend from a cell and are used in movement

a. amoeba
b. cap
c. cilia
d. conjugation
e. diatom
f. euglena
g. fermentation
h. fungus
i. hyphae
j. lichen
k. protozoans
l. pseudopod
m. symbiosis

CONCEPTS

1. What traits do monerans and protists have in common? (6-1)
2. Explain why protists that live in colonies are not considered multicellular organisms. (6-1)
3. Identify three kinds of plantlike protists. Briefly explain how they can be distinguished from each other. (6-2)
4. What useful substance forms from the shells of diatoms? What is this substance used for? (6-2)
5. How are diatoms useful to other organisms that live in water? (6-2)
6. Explain how an amoeba gets food. (6-3)
7. Where do most flagellate protozoans live, and how do they get food? (6-3)
8. Name and describe three structures that protozoans use in movement. (6-3)
9. How do amoebas survive during unfavorable conditions? (6-3)
10. Explain how a paramecium gets food. (6-3)

11. How do paramecia that result from conjugation differ from paramecia produced by fission? (6-3)

12. How do fungi digest food? (6-4)

13. Distinguish between fungi that are parasites and fungi that are saprobes. (6-4)

14. In what ways are threadlike fungi useful? (6-4)

15. What do all sac fungi have in common? (6-4)

16. In what ways are some sac fungi useful? (6-4)

17. What do all club fungi have in common? (6-4)

18. Describe the parts of a mushroom. What part of this fungus grows underground? (6-4)

19. Describe the life cycle of a slime mold. (6-5)

20. What organisms make up a lichen? What does each organism contribute to the other? (6-5)

APPLICATION/ CRITICAL THINKING

1. Suppose you find a protist in pond water. The protist has no cilia and no flagella but is able to move around. What type of protist might it be?

2. Since dinoflagellates have flagella, they might be grouped with the flagellate protozoans. Why would this grouping be incorrect?

3. The body of a slime mold plasmodium is made of many cells. But the plasmodium is not considered to be a multicellular organism. Explain why.

4. Fungi were once thought to be plants. Why do you think scientists thought this? Why is this idea incorrect?

EXTENSION

1. Use a reference book to find out how to grow a hay infusion. Make drawings of the organisms you observe. Take notes on the ways these organisms move and take in food. Ask your parents' permission before you try this activity.

2. Make a spore print using the cap of a mushroom. Place a sheet of black paper and a sheet of white paper side by side. Tape them together. Remove the cap of a mushroom. Place the cap, gill side down, half on the black sheet and half on the white sheet. Wash your hands thoroughly after handling the mushroom. Wait a few days. Carefully lift off the cap. You will see the pattern of spores on the sheets of paper.

READINGS

Jahn, Theodore. *How to Know the Protozoa*. Dubuque, Iowa: W.C. Brown & Co., 1979.

Lee, D. ''Slime Mold—The Fungus That Walks.'' *National Geographic*, July 1981, p. 130.

Sharnoff, S. ''Lowly Lichens Offer Beauty—Food, Drugs, and Perfume.'' *Smithsonian*, April 1984, p. 135.

139

Have you ever closely examined groceries after you bought them? You may have noticed that meats contain certain amounts of fat. Canned fruits may contain added juice. It is the job of food laboratory technicians to make sure that food quality is high. They conduct different tests to determine food quality.

Food lab technicians also run tests to make certain that foods are free of bacteria and are safe to eat. Tuna fish and other seafoods might contain mercury that was in ocean water. A food lab technician tests these foods to check for mercury.

Some food lab technicians work for the government. Others work for food companies. Food lab technicians must have a four-year college degree in science. If you are interested in this career, you should take courses in biology and chemistry in high school.■

Food Technician

Did you know that yeasts are important fungi to bakers? Of course, bakers must know about cooking and baking. But they must also understand the biology and chemistry of some of the materials they use.

When yeasts carry on fermentation, they break down sugar and give off carbon dioxide gas. The carbon dioxide gas that is released makes bread rise. A baker must know how much sugar to add and how warm to keep yeast to make sure that bread rises properly.

Bakers make pastries and breads for bakeries, groceries, and restaurants. Bakers receive on-the-job training and often learn skills from more experienced bakers. Cooking schools also offer courses in baking. If you are interested in this career, you will benefit from courses in biology and home economics in high school.■

Baker

Dr. Hattie E. Alexander, Medical Doctor

Dr. Hattie E. Alexander was a medical doctor and microbiologist. A microbiologist is a scientist who studies bacteria and other types of microscopic organisms.

Dr. Alexander was interested in influenzal meningitis, a disease caused by a bacterium. This kind of bacterium was found to affect tissues around the nervous system. The disease usually is fatal in infants. Dr. Alexander developed a medicine that was given to infants who were critically ill with the disease. The complete cure of these infants resulted. This work, and work that she did with antibiotics, has greatly reduced the number of cases of influenzal meningitis.

Dr. Alexander managed her time well. She was a pediatrician in a hospital, a researcher, and a teacher, all at the same time. Dr. Alexander wrote organized and detailed research reports about the meningitis bacterium. She also studied other disease-causing bacteria and viruses.■

People go to a hospital to get well. But for about 5 percent of the people who go to American hospitals each year, the trip means becoming ill with something they did not have when they arrived. Each year two million people get infections that originate in hospitals.

Nosocomial (nahs uh KOH mee-uhl) infections are infections that patients develop while they are in the hospital. Usually a nosocomial infection is more of a nuisance than a danger. However, for about 3 percent of the patients who get nosocomial infections, the result is death.

In 1970 the National Nosocomial Infection Study (NNIS) was started. Hospitals that take part in the study collect information about these infections. This information includes the number of infections as well as the kind and source of each infection. The purpose of the NNIS is to find out why nosocomial infections occur.

One reason that these infections are so common in hospitals is that people who are ill tend to be more susceptible to infection. Bacteria that can cause infection are everywhere. Healthy people can resist many infections, but sick people are weakened and less able to resist infection.

Nosocomial infections are spread in hospitals in many ways. Some infections are transmitted through air, food, or water. Others are transmitted through objects, such as sheets and towels, or through contact with other people.

Infections also can be spread through medical procedures. For example, some patients need transfusions of blood or injections of medications. In surgery and in some kinds of tests, openings are made in the skin. This breaks the body's first barrier to infection.

Some scientists say that part of the problem is in the way hospi-

tals are designed. In hospital nurseries and intensive care units, patients are often cared for in large open areas. It is easy for bacteria to be spread from one person to another under these conditions. Figure 1 shows some of the data from the NNIS.

APPLYING CRITICAL THINKING SKILLS

1. How did the rate of nosocomial infection change over the 5-year study?
2. In what year did the lowest rate of infection occur? What was this rate?
3. How does the rate of infection in the study compare with the national average of 5 percent? What does this difference suggest about the hospitals that took part in the NNIS?
4. Of the factors involved in nosocomial infections, which do you think would be the easiest to control? How would you control this factor?

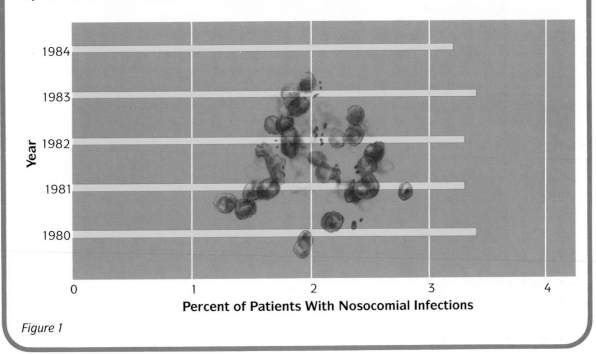

Figure 1

5. Of the factors given, which do you think would be the most difficult to control? Why?

There are several ways to control bacterial infections. Patients are treated with antibiotics. Hospitals also use antiseptics and disinfectants to keep things clean.

These practices kill most ordinary kinds of bacteria. But they do not kill all bacteria. The bacteria that survive are those that are especially strong and resistant. They live and multiply in hospitals. In fact, hospitals may be helping the resistant bacteria by killing competing bacteria. As a result, new resistant strains of bacteria are developing all the time.

Another part of the problem may be caused by doctors. Some doctors prescribe antibiotics very often. They prescribe antibiotics for viral infections, such as colds, even though antibiotics do not kill viruses. The resistant strains of bacteria that develop can live in the patient and be spread to other patients, as well.

There are about 80 different antibiotics in use today. They are used to treat infections such as pneumonia, dysentery, typhoid, cholera, and tuberculosis. These drugs are valuable and save many lives. However, many scientists believe that antibiotics should not be prescribed too freely. Controlling the use of antibiotics could help to reduce the number of resistant strains of bacteria.

The infections that people get from the resistant bacteria often are difficult to treat. The usual antibiotics are not effective. It takes strong and sometimes dangerous drugs to stop these infections.

Staphylococcus aureus (S. aureus) is a type of bacteria that is often involved in nosocomial infections. This species of bacteria has many resistant strains. Figure 2 shows the cases of nosocomial infection caused by resistant strains of *S. aureus.*

APPLYING CRITICAL THINKING SKILLS

1. What percent of infections were resistant in 1980? In 1984?
2. What year showed a decrease in resistant infections? Suggest a reason for this decrease.
3. Taking antibiotics for viral infections does not affect the virus. What might be a benefit of using an antibiotic in such a case?
4. Some people say that doctors prescribe antibiotics in cases when the patient's own defenses could fight the infection. What is the advantage of using antibiotics in such a case? What might be a disadvantage?

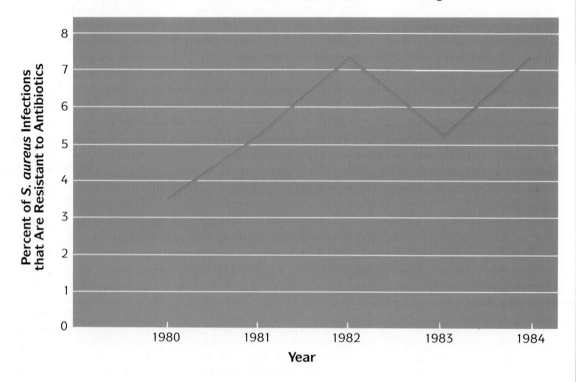

Figure 2

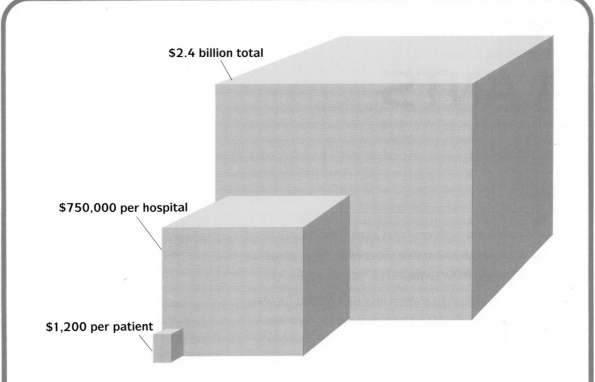

$2.4 billion total

$750,000 per hospital

$1,200 per patient

Figure 3

In addition to being a health problem, nosocomial infections can be an economic problem. Often, patients have medical insurance plans. Under many plans the insurance company will pay a preset fee for the treatment of a certain illness. This fee is based, in part, on the number of days the patient is expected to stay in the hospital. If the patient stays longer because of a nosocomial infection, the insurance will not pay the extra cost. The patient or the hospital has to pay the extra amount. Figure 3 shows the cost of nosocomial infections.

Many hospitals have infection control programs. In some cases, medical personnel—mostly nurses—take courses on infection control. They learn how to observe patients and to study records to look for evidence of nosocomial infections. They also learn ways to combat these infections.

Not all hospitals have infection control programs. Some doctors are worried about close monitoring of patients for nosocomial infections. These doctors fear that the collection of data about infections will give patients information to use in lawsuits against doctors or hospitals.

Other doctors think that an infection control program is a good idea. They say that the improved health care is an important benefit. Also, the extra concern about infection makes patients more secure.

It will cost money to continue to study nosocomial infections. It will also cost money to make changes in hospital procedures. Some people think that these expenses are too great for a problem that affects only 5 percent of all hospital patients. Other people say that the expense is worth it. They believe that any expense is justified if it saves a life.

APPLYING CRITICAL THINKING SKILLS

1. What is the cost per patient of a nosocomial infection? What expenses does this money pay for?
2. Suppose a patient develops a nosocomial infection and the insurance company will not pay the extra expense. Should the patient pay? Should the hospital pay? Should patients take out extra insurance to cover such a problem? Explain your answer.
3. Do you think infection control programs are a good idea? Who should pay for these programs?
4. Studies like the NNIS cost money. Many such studies are funded by the government. If the government were to stop paying for the NNIS, should the study continue? If so, who should pay for the study?

PLANTS

S cientists have evidence that plants first appeared on the earth about 230 million years ago. Today, plant life covers much of the surface of our planet. Plants are important because they provide food and oxygen for the earth's creatures. Plants also provide shelter for some organisms. Humans depend on plants for many products, such as paper and lumber. In this unit you will learn about the structure, function, and many uses of plants. ■

▲ This drawing of a bramble bush is in a Byzantine-Greek medical book from the tenth century.

◄ This colorful poster from the 1880s advertises seeds from a particular company.

▼ Milkweed seeds being blown by the wind.

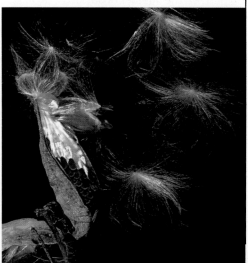

▶ This Venus's-flytrap will soon close, trapping the fly inside. The plant uses substances in the fly's body.

◀ This view of a tulip flower shows the arrangement of some of the plants' reproductive structures.

▼ This colorful pattern results from growing different crops in the same field.

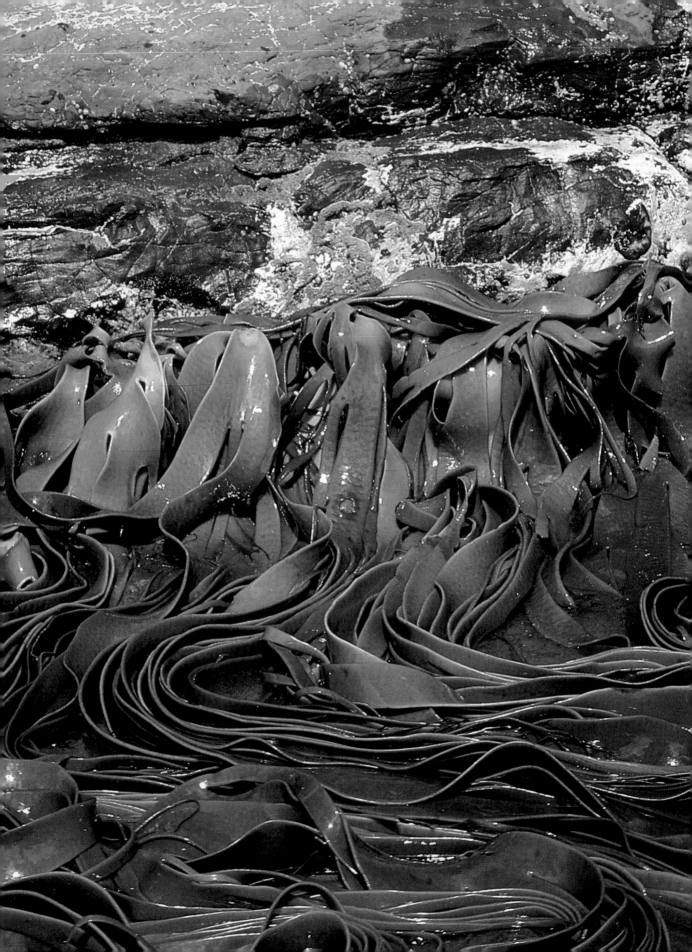

NONSEED PLANTS

What floats on the surface of the water and looks like giant strands of green noodles? It is a type of seaweed, or kelp. You can see this strange-looking plant in the photograph. Kelps grow in warm ocean water in many parts of the world. The plants can grow to an enormous size. Off the coast of California, kelps form large floating mats. The floating mats can be up to 15 m across. Kelps are not like the plants with which you are likely to be familiar. They do not produce flowers or seeds. Kelps are nonseed plants.

- *Besides kelps, what are other nonseed plants?*
- *What are the traits of nonseed plants?*
- *How can plants without seeds reproduce?*
- *In what ways are nonseed plants of value to humans?*

7-1 TRAITS OF NONSEED PLANTS

Look at the plants in Figure 7-1 on the next page. What do all these plants have in common? Although they look very different from one another, these plants share one trait. They all reproduce sexually without forming seeds. Because of the way they reproduce, all of these plants are placed in a group called nonseed plants.

There are three main groups of nonseed plants. The first group includes kinds of algae (AL jee). An **alga** (AL-guh) (pl., *algae*) is a plant that lacks roots, stems, and leaves. Green algae, red algae, and brown algae are all nonseed plants. A second group includes mosses and liverworts. Club mosses, horsetails, and ferns make up the third group.

In addition to reproducing without seeds, nonseed plants have other important features in common. Most of them have specialized parts that perform certain functions. Nonseed plants share another trait—they can carry out photosynthesis (foh tuh SIHN thuh sihs). **Photosynthesis** is a process by which green plants use light energy from the sun to make their own food. **Chlorophyll** (KLAWR uh-fihl), a green pigment inside some of the cells of nonseed plants, aids in trapping light energy. During photosyn-

After completing this section, you will be able to

- **name** the three main groups of nonseed plants.
- **distinguish** between vascular and nonvascular plants.
- **explain** the function of vascular tissue.

The key terms in this section are
alga
chlorophyll
nonvascular plants
photosynthesis
vascular plants
vascular tissue

photo- (light)
syn- (together)

chloros (green)
phyllon (leaf)

thesis the light energy is changed to chemical energy, which is then stored in the form of a sugar called glucose.

The classification of nonseed plants is based on the presence or absence of vascular tissue. A *tissue* is a group of similar cells that perform a certain function. **Vascular tissue** is a group of tubelike cells that carries food, water, and minerals from one part of a plant to another. Vascular tissue also provides support for the plant. Some plants with vascular tissue can grow to be over one hundred meters tall. Plants with tissue of tubelike cells that carries food, water, and minerals are called **vascular plants**. Nonseed plants such as club mosses, horsetails, and ferns, are vascular plants. These three groups of plants are also known as *tracheophytes* (TRAY kee uh fits), which means "tube plants."

vasculum (vessel)
non- (not)

Plants that lack vascular tissue are called **nonvascular plants**. Algae, mosses, and liverworts are nonvascular plants. Most nonvascular plants live in water. The water provides support for the plant. Nonvascular plants are either very small or very thin. For example, some green algae consist

Figure 7-1

Types of nonseed plants: green algae (*A*), brown algae (*B*), red algae (*C*), fern (*D*), and moss (*E*).

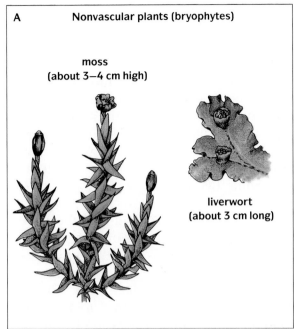

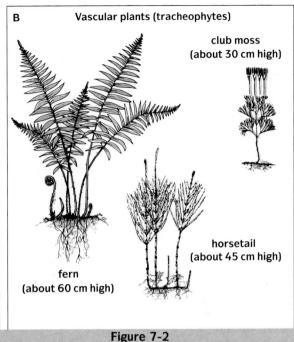

Figure 7-2

Nonvascular plants (*A*) and vascular plants (*B*).

of only a single cell. Some brown algae grow to be several meters long but are only a few cells thick. Plants such as brown algae can grow to be large because the plant floats in or on water. The water surrounds the plant and supports its mass. In plants that live in water, materials can be easily carried from one part of the plant to another by diffusion. Almost all cells of algae are in contact with water. Thus, it is easy for needed materials to be taken in and for wastes to be given off into the water.

Only a small group of nonvascular plants live on land. Mosses and liverworts are examples of such nonvascular land plants. These plants are also known as *bryophytes* (BRĪ uh fīts), which means "moss plants." You can see examples of vascular and nonvascular plants in Figure 7-2. How do the sizes of the plants in the two groups compare?

REVIEW

1. What features do all nonseed plants have in common?
2. What are the three main groups of nonseed plants?
3. Describe the functions of vascular tissue.

CHALLENGE You have learned that some vascular plants can grow to be over one hundred meters tall. How tall would you expect nonvascular plants to grow? Give a reason for your answer.

7-2 GREEN ALGAE

alga (seaweed)

The most common of the algae are the green algae. **Green algae** are simple organisms with cells that contain chloroplasts and a rigid cell wall. A **chloroplast** is an organelle in which the food-making processes of the cell take place. It is a structure that contains the green pigment chlorophyll. Green algae can make their own food by photosynthesis. Most green algae live in water—either fresh water or salt water. A few species live in salt lakes and hot springs. Some live in soil, on rocks, or on tree bark.

Green algae can be grouped according to their structure. One group of green algae consists of plants made up of only one cell. A second group is made up of colonies. A *colony* is a group of similar cells attached to each other. A third group consists of multicellular plants. The cells of some green algae are joined together to form long threadlike structures called *filaments* (FIHL uh muhnts). One alga plant may consist of a single branching filament or several branching filaments. Other green algae are tube-shaped. Still others have a flat bladelike body that floats on the water. Although some algae have leaflike parts, none have true roots, stems, or leaves.

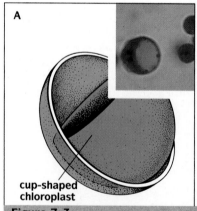
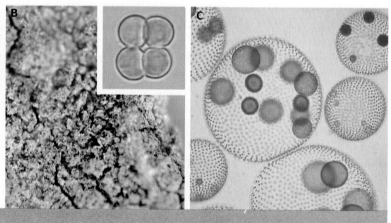

Figure 7-3

Kinds of green algae: cell of *Chlorella* and inset of cells (*A*); *Protococcus* on tree bark and inset of cells (*B*); and *Volvox* (*C*).

Chlorella (kluh REHL uh) is a single-celled green alga. Each cell of *Chlorella* has a distinct nucleus and a cup-shaped chloroplast. Look for this oddly shaped chloroplast in Figure 7-3A. *Chlorella* is very easy to grow in the laboratory. Biologists have used *Chlorella* for many years to study the process of photosynthesis. Figure 7-3B shows another green alga, called *Protococcus* (proh tuh KAHK uhs). This plant is often found on tree bark.

Figure 7-4

Conjugation in *Spirogyra*. In *D*, what will each cell become?

SCIENCE PUZZLER

The photograph shows chloroplasts that were removed from a living plant cell. They were put into a test tube of water and placed in bright light. A few hours after the chloroplasts were removed from the cell, the cell died. The free chloroplasts, however, continued to live for several days. What does this show about the relationship between the cell and the chloroplasts? How might it be possible to keep the cell alive without chloroplasts?

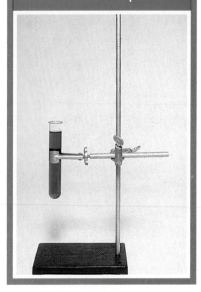

Volvox is an example of a green alga that forms colonies. A *Volvox* colony, shown in Figure 7-3C, is a hollow sphere made up of hundreds of nearly identical cells. The cells of the colony are held together by a clear mucuslike substance. Each cell of *Volvox* has two flagella. The flagella move the colony through the water.

Spirogyra (spī ruh jī ruh) is a green alga in which the cells are joined end to end to form filaments. In *A* of Figure 7-4 you can see a single filament of this alga. Note the coils of chloroplasts inside each cell.

Spirogyra reproduces both by asexual and by sexual means. Asexual reproduction occurs when one cell divides by mitosis, forming two cells. In *Spirogyra,* asexual reproduction takes place when the cells in the filament divide crosswise by fission. The crosswise divisions increase the number of cells in the filament, making it longer.

Sexual reproduction occurs when the nuclear material from one cell joins with the nuclear material of another cell. *Spirogyra* reproduces sexually by conjugation. In *Spirogyra,* conjugation involves the transfer of nuclear material from one cell to another. Figure 7-4 shows the process of conjugation in these green algae. Two filaments line up side by side, as shown in *B*. You can see that a tube has formed between many of the cells that are opposite each other. The contents of one cell flow into the opposite cell, as shown in *C*. You can see in *D* that the nuclear material of the two cells unites. Each cell that forms will develop into a new filament.

ACTIVITY · What Is the Structure of Green Algae?

OBJECTIVE
Compare the structure of unicellular, colonial, and multicellular green algae.

MATERIALS
hand lens, *Protococcus* on bark, forceps, 3 microscope slides, 3 droppers, 3 coverslips, microscope, *Volvox* culture, *Ulva* culture

PROCEDURE
A. Use a hand lens to examine a few cells of *Protococcus* on bark.
B. Use forceps to remove a small sample of *Protococcus*. Place this material on a microscope slide. With a dropper, add a drop of water to the *Protococcus*. Cover the drop with a coverslip. Look at the cells under low and high power of a microscope.
C. Make a drawing of several *Protococcus* cells. Label the nucleus and chloroplasts.
D. Use a hand lens to locate several colonies of *Volvox* in a beaker. Use a dropper to remove several colonies. To make a wet mount, place a drop of water containing colonies of *Volvox* on a slide. Cover the drop with a coverslip, and observe the *Volvox* under low power of the microscope.
E. Draw several cells in the *Volvox* colony. Show how the cells appear in relation to one another. Label a chloroplast of one cell.
F. Use forceps to place a small piece of *Ulva* on a microscope slide. Make a wet mount of the material. Add a coverslip. Observe *Ulva* under low and high power of the microscope. Make a drawing of several cells. Label a chloroplast and the nucleus of one cell.

RESULTS AND CONCLUSIONS
1. How does the appearance of *Protococcus* on bark differ from the appearance of a culture of *Ulva* in water?
2. Compare the appearance of *Protococcus, Volvox,* and *Ulva* as seen under the microscope.
3. Write a description of a *Volvox* colony.

Ulva, also called sea lettuce, is a multicellular green alga. The body of this alga is made up of flat, wide structures that look like leaves. These structures are not true leaves, because they lack vascular tissue. The leaflike structures are only a few cells thick.

Green algae perform several important functions in the environment. Like green plants, green algae are a major source of food for organisms that cannot make their own food. Green algae make up an important part of plankton. **Plankton** consists of small organisms, some microscopic, that float or swim near the surface of ocean water. Larger organisms, such as fish, feed on plankton. Green algae also release a large amount of oxygen during photosynthesis. Some scientists estimate that one half of the oxygen in the atmosphere is produced by green algae.

plankto- (drifting)

Figure 7-5

Ulva, or sea lettuce.

REVIEW
1. Where are green algae likely to be found growing?
2. Describe and give examples of three types of green algae.
3. What is a colony?
4. Describe the process of sexual reproduction in *Spirogyra*.

CHALLENGE Suppose all the green algae growing in a pond were destroyed. How would this affect the pond?

7-3 BROWN ALGAE AND RED ALGAE

BROWN ALGAE

Many of the plants called seaweed are brown algae. **Brown algae** are water-dwelling multicellular organisms that contain both a green pigment and a brown pigment. These pigments give the algae a brown or olive-green color. Most brown algae live in salt water. They are common along the rocky coasts of the Pacific Ocean and in the cool waters of the North Atlantic Ocean.

Fucus (FYOO kuhs), also known as rockweed, is a common brown alga that grows in shallow ocean water. It often washes up on the beach. At the base of the plant is a holdfast. A **holdfast** is a structure that anchors algae to rocks or other objects in water. A stemlike structure called the *stipe* grows up from the holdfast. At the top of the plant are wide, flat structures called *blades*. Photosynthesis takes place in the blades. Because they lack vascular tissue, these parts of the algae are not true roots, stems, and leaves. In Figure 7-6 look for the *air bladders,* which are filled with gas. What do you think is the function of the air bladders?

> After completing this section, you will be able to
>
> - **describe** where brown algae and red algae usually grow.
> - **give examples** of brown algae and red algae.
> - **list** some commercial uses of brown algae and red algae.
>
> *The key terms in this section are*
> brown algae   red algae
> holdfast

Figure 7-6

Fucus, showing holdfast, stipe, and air bladders.

Figure 7-7

A kelp of the North Pacific.

Brown algae called *kelps* are among the largest plants known. Kelps may grow to a length of 58 m. Figure 7-7 shows a large mat of seaweed, or kelp, that has been washed up on the shore. Some kelps contain large amounts of minerals, such as iodine and iron. These plants are harvested and used to fertilize soil and to feed livestock.

153

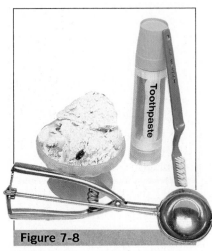

Figure 7-8

Products in which algin is used.

Kelps also produce a gummy substance called *algin* (AL-juhn). Algin is removed from kelps and used in a variety of ways. Algin is added to some kinds of ice cream to produce the smooth texture. Look at Figure 7-8 to see two products in which algin is used.

RED ALGAE

Red algae are many-celled algae that live in water and contain green, blue, and red pigments. They are usually red, purple, or green in color. Most red algae live in salt water. They are most common in warm tropical oceans. Red algae can live at greater depths than most brown and green algae. Scientists have found red algae growing as far as 268 m below the surface of the water. This distance is as great as the height of a 50-story building. Few plants can live at depths greater than 160 m. Below this depth, most plants do not receive enough light to carry on photosynthesis.

Chondrus, also called Irish moss, is a red alga that grows along the Atlantic coast from Maine to South Carolina. It is called Irish moss because it is also commonly found along the coast of Ireland. A close-up of Irish moss is shown in Figure 7-9. It grows among the rocks at the edge of the shore. A jellylike substance removed from this alga is used to thicken some salad dressings and puddings. This same substance is also used in some toothpastes, skin lotions, and shoe polishes. Other species of red algae also

Figure 7-9

Red algae.

Researchers have found red algae growing at a greater depth than anyone believed possible. They found the algae near the Bahama Islands, in water 268 m deep. Before this discovery, scientists thought that no marine plants could live in water deeper than 160 m, because there would not be enough light for photosynthesis to occur. The discovery was made possible through the use of a new submarine. This submarine, called the *Johnson Sea Link I,* is shown in the photograph.

These deep-sea red algae can carry on the food-making process for two reasons. First, unlike algae growing at lesser depths, these red algae contain certain pigments that can capture the tiny amounts of light energy that reach great depths. These pigments then pass the energy on to chlorophyll *a*—the pigment that most plants contain. Second, the cell walls of the red algae are very thin. The thin walls allow light to pass through the cells and reach the pigments easily.

The discovery of this deep-sea red algae has raised new questions for scientists. Scientists now wonder what the lowest level of light is that would keep plants alive.

have important uses. Some red algae produce a substance used to make agar (AH guhr). *Agar* is a jellylike substance used to grow bacteria and fungi in the laboratory. A food source, such as sugar, is added to the agar. In Figure 7-10 you can see yeast, a type of fungus, growing in an agar-filled petri dish.

Some kinds of red algae are used as food in many parts of the world. In Japan, one kind of red algae is grown as a crop. Small pieces of algae are attached to nets on bamboo racks and are placed in shallow water. When the algae have grown to a certain size, they are harvested and dried. Red algae are valuable as food because they contain protein, vitamins, and minerals.

Figure 7-10

One use of agar. Where do the fungi grow?

REVIEW

1. Where are brown algae and red algae likely to be found growing?
2. Name and describe one brown alga and one red alga.
3. Describe some commercial uses of brown algae.
4. How are red algae useful in the study of bacteria and fungi?

CHALLENGE Compare the harvesting of red algae with the harvesting of a common crop, such as corn or wheat.

7-4 BRYOPHYTES

bryon (tree moss)
phyton (plant)

rhiza- (root)
-oides (in the form of)

TRAITS OF BRYOPHYTES

Bryophytes are found in all parts of the world—from the polar regions to the tropics. Most bryophytes live on land in moist places. A few live on land in dry, hot places and on rocks exposed to the sun.

A **bryophyte** is a small green nonvascular plant that lives on land. The green leaflike parts of a bryophyte are made up of cells that contain chloroplasts. Photosynthesis occurs in those cells that have chloroplasts.

The lack of vascular tissue in bryophytes limits their size. Why are nonvascular land plants often small? In plants without vascular tissue, water, food, and minerals can move from one part of the plant to another only by diffusion. Diffusion takes place slowly. Substances moving by diffusion cannot move quickly enough to supply all the parts of a large plant.

Vascular tissue provides support for a plant. Nonvascular plants lack this supporting tissue. Thus, nonvascular plants that live on land cannot grow very tall. They usually are not more than a few centimeters in height.

Bryophytes have several traits that allow them to survive on land. They have structures called rhizoids (RĪ zoids). A **rhizoid** is a rootlike structure that anchors a bryophyte to the soil and absorbs water and minerals. Water moves from the rhizoids to the rest of the plant. The cells in the other parts of the plant do not have to be directly in contact with water to receive water.

The structure of bryophytes allows them to conserve water. Although these plants have many cells, only a few are exposed to the air. Thus, very little water is lost to the air. In some bryophytes a waxy substance called *cutin* (KYOO tihn) covers the surface of the plant. Cutin cuts down on the amount of water lost by evaporation. Also, bryophytes often grow in clusters. This growth pattern helps to reduce water loss.

MOSSES AND LIVERWORTS

There are two main groups of bryophytes—mosses and liverworts (LIVH uhr werts). A **moss** is a small nonvascular plant that often grows in moist areas in woods or near stream banks. Mosses have stemlike parts that grow upright. These stemlike parts have small leaflike parts. Compared to a familiar plant, such as a rosebush, the structure of a moss plant is simple. The part of the plant that is aboveground is only a few centimeters tall.

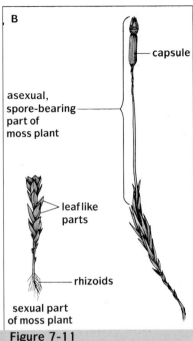

asexual, spore-bearing part of moss plant

capsule

leaflike parts

rhizoids

sexual part of moss plant

Figure 7-11

Cluster of moss plants (A) and close-up of a moss plant (B). In what structure are the spores found?

At the base of the plant are the rootlike rhizoids. These rhizoids anchor the moss and take in water and minerals. During part of its life cycle, the moss plant bears *spores*. The spores are in a structure called a *capsule* at the tip of a long stalk as shown in Figure 7-11. You will read more about the life cycle of a moss later in this section.

A number of plants are incorrectly called "mosses." For example, you read earlier in this chapter that Irish moss is really a red alga. Other "mosses" you may hear about are *Spanish moss* and *reindeer moss*. Neither is a true moss. Spanish moss, which grows on trees in the southeastern United States, is a flowering vascular plant. Reindeer moss is a lichen that grows in cold climates.

A **liverwort** is a small nonvascular plant that grows flat along a surface. It has flat, lobed, leaflike parts. These plants are closely related to mosses. Liverworts, like mosses, are bryophytes. Liverworts grow in wet places, such as along streams or on rocky ledges near water. The leaflike parts of a liverwort are shaped like the human liver. You can see the unusual shape of a liverwort in Figure 7-12. At one time, people thought that a plant shaped like a body organ could be used to treat diseases of that organ. Plants were often given names related to their use as medicines. Thus, this small flat plant was named *liverwort*, meaning "liver herb." Today it is known that liverworts are not useful in treating liver diseases.

Figure 7-12

Liverworts.

REPRODUCTION OF BRYOPHYTES

The way bryophytes reproduce also allows them to live on land. Bryophytes have two main stages in their life cycle. Male reproductive cells and female reproductive cells are produced in one stage. A male reproductive cell is called a **sperm cell**. A female reproductive cell is called an **egg cell**. Spores (spawrz) are produced during the other stage in the life cycle. A **spore** is an asexual reproductive cell with a hard covering. A spore can survive harsh conditions, such as cold or dryness.

sperma- (seed)

The stages in the moss life cycle are shown in Figure 7-13. Refer to the drawing as you read about these stages.

1. The mature moss plant is the sexual stage of the life cycle. Sperm cells and egg cells are produced at the tips of the plant.
2. Sperm cells swim in water to an egg cell. The source of water is rain or dew that collects on the moss. A sperm cell and an egg cell join in a process called **fertilization** (fer tuh luh ZAY shuhn). The fertilized egg is called a **zygote** (ZĪ goht).

ferre- (to bear)
-tion (the act or process of)

3. The zygote develops into a stalk that grows up from the top of a shoot with leaflike parts. Hundreds of spores develop at the tip of the stalk in the capsule. The asexual stage consists of the stalk and the capsule with spores.
4. The mature spores are released when the capsule breaks open. They may be carried long distances by wind.
5. If a spore lands in a suitable environment, a new moss plant will develop. The young moss plant grows from a bud on a branching structure.

Figure 7-13

Life cycle of a moss. Where are the eggs and sperm found in the moss?

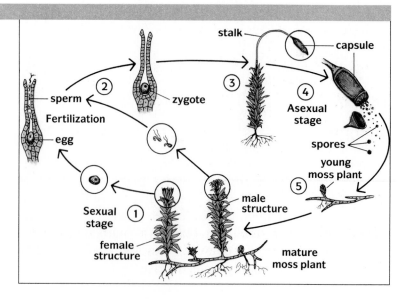

OBJECTIVE
Observe the structure of a moss.

MATERIALS
moss plants with and without spore capsules, toothpick, hand lens, microscope, 2 microscope slides, 2 coverslips, dropper

PROCEDURE
A. Use a toothpick to separate from a clump of other moss plants a single moss plant that lacks a stalk and capsule.
B. Examine the plant with a hand lens. Make a drawing of the moss. Label rhizoids and leaflike structures. Draw a circle around the part of the plant where the zygote would be formed.
C. Use the same toothpick to separate a moss plant that has a stalk and a capsule. Examine the parts of the plant with a hand lens. Make a drawing of the moss with the stalk and capsule. Label the rhizoids, leaflike structures, stalk, and capsule. Draw an arrow to the part of the plant where the spores are located.
D. Place a capsule on a sheet of paper and examine it with a hand lens. Look for a small lidlike structure at the top of the capsule.
E. Place the capsule on a microscope slide. Use a pencil eraser to press down on the capsule until it splits open and spores fall onto the slide. Discard the capsule.
F. Use a dropper to add a drop of water to the spores on the microscope slide. Cover with a coverslip. Look at the spores under low and high power of a microscope. Make a drawing of several spores.

RESULTS AND CONCLUSIONS
1. What parts of the plant make up the sexual stage in the moss life cycle? What parts of the plant make up the asexual stage?
2. Which parts of the moss plant can carry on photosynthesis? Which parts are unable to photosynthesize? How can you distinguish between the parts that can photosynthesize and those that cannot?
3. What might be the function of the lidlike structure on the capsule?

USES OF BRYOPHYTES

Bryophytes, especially mosses, play an important role in the environment. These plants can live on the surface of bare rock. They take part in soil formation and help to provide a proper environment for other plants. The rhizoids of mosses produce chemicals that break down rock. Over many years, rock particles and the remains of dead mosses form soil.

Sphagnum (SFAG nuhm) moss has many practical uses. Florists pack wet sphagnum moss around flowers and seedlings for shipping. In some countries, partly decayed, compressed sphagnum, called *peat,* is used as a fuel.

REVIEW

1. How can a moss be distinguished from a liverwort?
2. Briefly describe the life cycle of a moss.
3. What traits of bryophytes allow them to live on land?
4. How are bryophytes important in the environment?

CHALLENGE In a moss the capsule is usually at the end of a long stalk. What advantage does this tall stalk provide for mosses?

Figure 7-14

Worker cutting up peat.

7-5 TRACHEOPHYTES

trachia (vessels)
phyton (plant)

TRAITS OF TRACHEOPHYTES

Club mosses, horsetails, and ferns are tracheophytes. A **tracheophyte** is a plant that has vascular tissue. The vascular tissue provides support for these plants. It allows them to grow taller than nonvascular plants. This tissue also quickly transports dissolved materials throughout the plants.

Many scientists believe that about 300 million years ago, club mosses, horsetails, and ferns were much more common than they are today. The earth was much warmer at that time. Large forests of these plants covered many parts of the earth's surface. Figure 7-15 shows how a forest of these early tracheophytes might have looked. As the climate of the earth changed, these plants died and were buried beneath layers of soil and rock. Over time the remains of these plants were changed to coal, oil, and natural gas, which are burned as fuel today.

Figure 7-15

An ancient forest of tracheophytes, and inset of a fossil fern. How do modern tracheophytes differ from these plants?

Scientists have found traces of these early plants in rock. By comparing these traces with plants now alive, scientists have drawn some conclusions. They have found that the structure of the club mosses, horsetails, and ferns living today is much like that of the early plants. The greatest difference is in the size of the plants. Many of the early plants were the size of trees and grew to a height of 30 m. Most of the club mosses, horsetails, and ferns of today are less than 1 m tall.

CLUB MOSSES AND HORSETAILS

A **club moss** is a small evergreen vascular nonseed plant with tiny, pointed leaves. The leaves grow in a circle around the stem, or they grow in overlapping rows along the stem. Because club mosses contain vascular tissue, they are not true mosses. Recall that mosses are nonvascular plants. Most club mosses grow in shady, damp woods and along rocky mountain slopes. A few species of club mosses grow in deserts. Club mosses have a life cycle similar to that of ferns.

The leaves of some species of club mosses look like small scales that grow close to the stem. These club mosses look like small evergreen trees, as you can see in Figure 7-16. In some parts of the country, certain kinds of club mosses are called ground pine. They are not, however, related to pine trees. You will learn later that the pine is a more complex type of plant.

Figure 7-16

Club mosses.

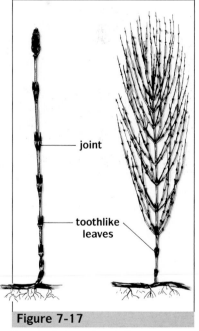

Figure 7-17

Horsetails in spring (*left*) and in summer (*right*).

A **horsetail**, like a club moss, is a vascular nonseed plant. Most horsetails grow in wet, swampy areas or at the edge of lakes or ponds. Some grow in well-drained soil. Like the club moss, the life cycle of a horsetail is similar to that of a fern. Horsetails have hollow stems that are jointed. At each joint is a ring of small toothlike leaves. Some stems have many branches that grow from between the leaves. Look for these leaves and branches in Figure 7-17. These horsetails have a bushy appearance, much like a horse's tail.

The outer covering of a horsetail stem has many tiny ridges that extend up and down the stem. The cells that cover the stem contain silica. Silica is a hard mineral used in making glass. The silica gives the cells a rough texture. Because of their rough texture, horsetail stems were used by pioneers in America to clean pots and pans. The use of horsetails for cleaning pots and pans led to another common name for these plants. A horsetail is sometimes called a scouring rush.

In addition to their aboveground stems, horsetails have underground stems. The underground stem is called a **rhizome** (RĪ zohm). The parts of the plant above the ground may shrivel up during periods of cold or drought. When conditions are again favorable, new stems and leaves develop from the rhizome.

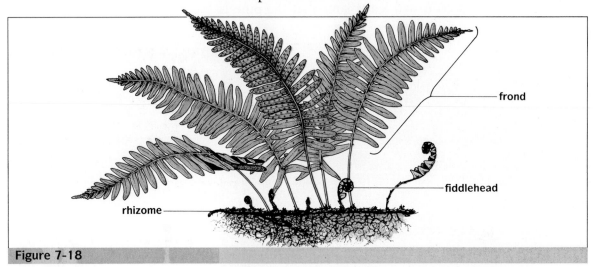

frond

fiddlehead

rhizome

Figure 7-18

Structure of a fern. What does a fiddlehead develop into?

FERNS

A **fern** is a seedless vascular plant with roots, stems, and leaves. Ferns are the most common nonseed vascular plants. They grow in moist, shady areas, such as in swamps, forests, and along stream banks. The roots take up water and minerals, and they anchor the fern in the soil. As in horsetails, the underground stem of a fern is called a rhizome. It grows horizontally, just beneath the surface of the soil. Locate the fern rhizome in Figure 7-18. The mature leaf of a fern is called a **frond**. Fronds develop from a rhizome. As you can see from Figure 7-18, the developing fronds of a fern are tightly coiled. They look much like the curved scroll at the head of a violin. Because of the way they look, these coiled fern leaves are called *fiddleheads*. Each fiddlehead slowly uncoils and develops into a mature frond.

ACTIVITY   What Is the Structure of a Fern?

OBJECTIVE
Observe the major structures of a fern.

MATERIALS
mature fern plants with sori, hand lens, metric ruler, 2 microscope slides, dropper, water, 2 coverslips, microscope, paper towel, prepared slide of sexual stage of fern

PROCEDURE
A. Examine a fern plant. Locate a rhizome. Look for evidence of developing leaves.
    1. What is the shape of these leaves?
B. Locate the fronds. Examine both surfaces. Use a hand lens to examine the sori, or yellowish-brown dots on the backs of the leaves.
C. Draw a picture of the fern plant. Label a rhizome, frond, and sorus. Use a metric ruler to measure the length of the frond. Indicate this length on your drawing.
D. Examine the sori with a hand lens. With your fingernail, scrape a number of spore cases off the frond and onto a microscope slide. Use a dropper to place a drop of water on the spore cases. Cover the drop with a coverslip. Observe under low power of a microscope. Make a drawing of one of the spore cases.

E. Remove the slide from the microscope stage, and carefully remove the coverslip. Without disturbing the spore cases, blot the water from the slide with a small piece of paper towel. Observe the slide under low power of the microscope.
F. Wait 10 minutes and again observe the spore cases. Note any changes that took place in the spore cases.
    2. How do the dried spore cases look, compared to the wet spore cases?
G. Make another drawing of the spore case and any spores that you see.
H. Using a hand lens, observe a prepared slide of the heart-shaped sexual stage of a fern. Draw what you see.

RESULTS AND CONCLUSIONS
1. What is the shape of the sori on the fern frond? Describe the location of the sori on the frond.
2. Describe any changes you observed in the spore cases in steps **E** and **F**.
3. What is the function of the spore case? In what kind of weather are spores most likely to be released?
4. Compare the shape and size of the heart-shaped plant with that of the mature fern.

For hundreds of years no one knew how ferns reproduced. No one had ever seen the seeds of a fern. Some people believed that if they could find fern seeds, the seeds would give them magic powers. By closely studying the fern life cycle, scientists finally solved the mystery. Ferns do not form seeds at all. Ferns reproduce by spores, not seeds.

The life cycle of a fern is similar to that of a moss. A sexual stage that produces sperm and eggs alternates with an asexual stage that produces spores. The roots, rhizome, and fronds make up the asexual stage. Spores are produced inside spore cases that, in many ferns, develop on the underside of a fern frond. Clusters of these spore cases are called **sori** (SAWR ee) (sing., *sorus*). The sori may look like dark brown dots or like short lines on the underside of the leaf. These sori are sometimes mistaken for brown bugs or disease spots on the leaves of ferns. In some types of ferns, the spore cases are on a separate stalk rather than on the back of a frond. When

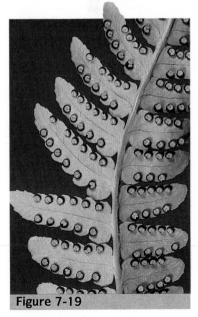

Figure 7-19

Fern frond and spore cases.

163

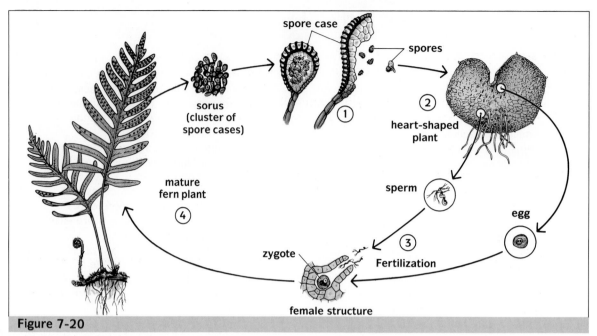

Figure 7-20

Life cycle of a fern.

the spores are mature, the spore cases split open. The spores are released and carried by the wind. Fern spores are quite light and can be carried great distances.

Refer to Figure 7-20 as you read about the stages in the life cycle of a fern.

1. Spores are released from a spore case. Notice that in this type of fern, the spore cases are on the underside of the frond.
2. A spore develops into a flat, green heart-shaped plant that is smaller than a dime. The heart-shaped plant grows close to the surface of the soil. Sperm and eggs are produced inside structures that develop on the underside of the small plant. This heart-shaped plant is the sexual stage of the fern.
3. Sperm swim to the egg in rain water or dew that collects on the plant. The sperm and egg join. The fertilized egg, or zygote, forms. When the zygote forms, the asexual stage in the life cycle begins.
4. The zygote develops into the familiar spore-producing fern plant, with roots, rhizome, and fronds.

Ferns are often used as house plants. The tender young fiddleheads are collected and cooked as a vegetable by some people. Some ferns are grown as a crop and harvested as food for animals. Ferns, along with club mosses and horsetails, lived millions of years ago. The coal, oil, and natural gas formed from those decayed plants are important sources of fuel today.

REVIEW

1. How are club mosses different from true mosses?
2. Why is vascular tissue an important structure in club mosses, horsetails, and ferns?
3. How would you distinguish a horsetail from a club moss?
4. Describe the sexual and asexual stages in the life cycle of a fern.
5. Distinguish among a spore, a spore case, and a sorus.

CHALLENGE Club mosses, horsetails, and ferns need water for sperm to reach the egg. Why? How is this dependence on water a disadvantage to these plants?

CHAPTER SUMMARY

The main ideas in this chapter are listed below. Read these statements before you answer the Chapter Review questions.

- Nonseed plants are plants that reproduce without forming seeds. Algae, mosses, liverworts, club mosses, horsetails, and ferns are all nonseed plants. Vascular plants are plants with tissue of tubelike cells that carries food, water, and minerals. Nonvascular plants are plants that lack vascular tissue. (7-1)

- Green algae are simple organisms with cells that have chloroplasts and a rigid cell wall. They may be single-celled, colonial, or multicellular. Most green algae live in water. They reproduce asexually by fission. Some reproduce sexually by conjugation. (7-2)

- Brown algae are multicellular organisms that live in water and contain both chlorophyll and a brown pigment. Some brown algae may be harvested as food for livestock. Red algae are multicellular organisms that live in water and contain chlorophyll and red and blue pigments. Some red algae are a food source for humans. (7-3).

- Bryophytes are small green nonvascular plants that live on land. Mosses and liverworts are examples of bryophytes. Bryophytes have a life cycle in which an asexual spore-producing stage alternates with a sexual sperm- and egg-producing stage. (7-4)

- Tracheophytes are plants with vascular tissue. Club mosses, horsetails, and ferns have a life cycle in which a spore-producing stage alternates with a sperm- and egg-producing stage. The remains of ancient tracheophytes have changed into fuel used today. (7-5)

The key terms in this chapter are listed below. Use each term in a sentence that shows the meaning of the term.

alga	fern	moss	sori
brown algae	fertilization	nonvascular plants	sperm cell
bryophyte	frond	photosynthesis	spore
chlorophyll	green algae	plankton	tracheophyte
chloroplast	holdfast	red algae	vascular plants
club moss	horsetail	rhizoid	vascular tissue
egg cell	liverwort	rhizome	zygote

Chapter Review

VOCABULARY

Use the key terms from this chapter to complete the following sentences correctly.

1. Plants with tissue of tubelike cells that carries food, water, and minerals are _____ .
2. The process by which green plants use light energy from the sun to make their own food is called _____ .
3. The green pigment that captures the energy of the sun in photosynthesis is _____ .
4. A structure found in brown algae that anchors the plant to a rock or to the ocean bottom is a/an _____ .
5. Many-celled plants that are a source of agar are the _____ .
6. A rootlike structure that anchors mosses and liverworts to the soil is called a/an _____ .
7. The male reproductive cell is called a/an _____ .
8. An underground stem of a fern is called a/an _____ .
9. The mature leaf of a fern is called a/an _____ .
10. Clusters of spore cases on the underside of fern fronds are called _____ .

CONCEPTS

1. Explain why algae, mosses, liverworts, club mosses, horsetails, and ferns are all placed in the same major plant group. (7-1)
2. Compare the sizes of vascular and nonvascular land plants. Account for differences in their size. (7-1)
3. What is the main structural difference between bryophytes and tracheophytes? (7-1)
4. Compare the structures of *Volvox* and *Spirogyra*. Describe a single cell as well as an entire plant. (7-2)
5. Describe some of the ways in which green algae are important to the environment. (7-2).
6. Describe brown algae, and give an example of a common brown alga. (7-3).
7. Compare red and brown algae in terms of where they live. (7-3).
8. In what ways are brown algae valuable to humans? (7-3)
9. Why are most plants unable to survive at depths greater than 160 m? (7-3)
10. What traits of bryophytes allow them to survive on land? (7-4)
11. Describe the two main stages in the life cycle of a moss. (7-4)

12. How do bryophytes help to form soil? (7-4)

13. How do club mosses, horsetails, and ferns living today differ from those plants living millions of years ago? (7-5)

14. Compare the external structures of a horsetail and a club moss. (7-5)

15. Explain why a fern can grow much taller than a moss or a liverwort. (7-4, 7-5)

16. Explain how ferns that lived millions of years ago are important today. (7-5)

17. What is the relationship between a fiddlehead and a frond? (7-5)

18. How is a fern better adapted than a moss to life on land? (7-4, 7-5)

19. How do rhizomes help horsetails survive in regions that have cold temperatures during part of the year? (7-5)

20. Describe the main stages in the life cycle of a fern. (7-5)

APPLICATION/ CRITICAL THINKING

1. Algae are much more abundant in water than on land. Why, do you think, are algae not able to grow well on land?

2. There are very few species of club mosses and horsetails living on the earth today. Give one reason why you think they are not more widespread.

3. The spores of which plant—a moss or a fern—are more likely to be carried by the wind? Explain your answer based on the spore-carrying structures of the two plants.

EXTENSION

1. Scientists have sent along green algae, especially *Chlorella,* on space flights. They want to find out if these plants can be successfully cultivated to be used as a food on space flights. Do research on their findings.

2. Certain ferns that are now extinct produced seeds. These ferns were very abundant during a time called the Carboniferous period. Report on the size, structure, and reproduction of these ferns.

3. Find out if algae are available in food stores in your community. If they are available, find out what types they are and how they can be prepared.

READINGS

Berenbaum, M. "Bracken Fern." *Horticulture*, April 1982, p. 20.

Kavaler, L. *Green Magic: Algae Rediscovered*. New York: Thomas Y. Crowell Company, Inc., 1983.

SEED PLANTS

Do you recognize any of the plants in the photograph? When and where have you seen them growing? At what time of the year do they bloom? Some of these plants grow from seeds. Others may be grown from structures other than seeds. Although these plants look very different from each other, they are alike in many ways.

You are probably more familiar with flowering plants than with any other kind of plant. There is great variety in flowering plants. The flowers may be of many different colors, shapes, and sizes. Some plants have small green flowers that are barely noticeable.

- *What are the main structures of plants?*
- *What function does each of these structures serve?*
- *What are the main kinds of flowering plants?*
- *Do any plants produce seeds but not flowers?*

8-1 TRAITS OF SEED PLANTS

KINDS OF SEED PLANTS

Recall that a vascular plant is a plant having vascular tissue that transports water, minerals, and food. A **seed plant** is a vascular plant that reproduces by forming seeds. There are two main groups of seed plants: the gymnosperms (JIHM nuh spermz) and the angiosperms (AN jee uh-spermz). A **gymnosperm** is a vascular plant whose seeds are not enclosed by a special structure such as a fruit. Trees such as pine, spruce, and ginkgo are gymnosperms. Many of the low, bushy plants that are used to decorate the land around buildings are also gymnosperms. Examples include juniper and some varieties of cedar.

The word *gymnosperm* means "naked seed." The seeds are said to be naked because they are not enclosed in a special structure. In many gymnosperms, such as pines, the seeds develop on the woody scales of a *cone*. A gymnosperm has two kinds of cones—male and female. Male

---

After completing this section, you will be able to

- **distinguish** between angiosperms and gymnosperms.
- **distinguish** between evergreen and deciduous plants.
- **describe** several uses of seed plants.

The key terms in this section are
angiosperm   gymnosperm
deciduous   seed plant
  plant
evergreen

gymnos (naked)
sperma (seed)

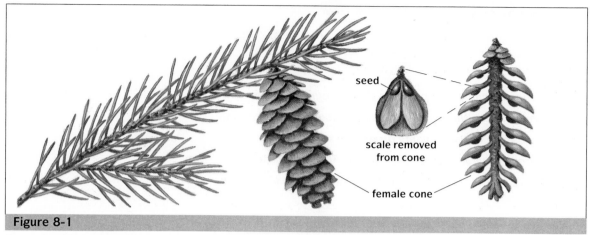

Figure 8-1

Structure of a female cone. Where are the seeds located?

angeion (container)
sperma (seed)

de (off)
cadere (to fall)

cones contain pollen. Female cones hold the seeds. Locate the seeds in the cone on the right in Figure 8-1.

An **angiosperm** is a seed plant that produces flowers. Grasses, apple trees, dandelions, and corn are examples of angiosperms. The word *angiosperm* means "seed in a container." Angiosperm seeds are completely enclosed in a structure called a *fruit*. Tomatoes, cherries, cucumbers, and corn kernels are fruits that people eat.

Most gymnosperms are evergreens. An **evergreen** is a plant that appears green all year because it does not shed all of its leaves at one time. Most evergreens shed only their oldest leaves and keep their newer leaves. Most angiosperms and a few gymnosperms, such as the larch, are deciduous (dih SIHJ yoo uhs). A **deciduous plant** is a plant that sheds all of its leaves at one time. In Figure 8-2, which plants are deciduous? Which plants are evergreen?

Figure 8-2

Blue spruce (A), larch (B), and sugar maple (C).

USES OF SEED PLANTS

Seed plants are the most abundant plants on the earth. People depend on seed plants in many different ways. Seed plants provide cereal, bread, fruits, and vegetables. Lumber for furniture and homes comes from seed plants. What types of cloth are products of seed plants?

The most important use of seed plants is for food. About a dozen kinds of seed plants form the basis of the human diet throughout much of the world. Figure 8-3 shows a graph of the 12 most important crops produced on the earth. Which of these seed plants do you eat?

Even if you do not eat seed plants directly, you depend on them for food. Cows, chickens, and pigs, as well as other animals that are raised for food, feed on seed plants. When you eat beef, chicken, or pork, you are eating seed plants indirectly.

Seed plants provide a number of other products. Many seed plants are used to flavor food. Spices such as pepper, mustard, and nutmeg come from seeds. Fibers from seed plants such as cotton and flax are used to make cloth. Wood and paper products are made from seed plants. Other seed-plant products include medicines, cooking oils, rubber, and dyes.

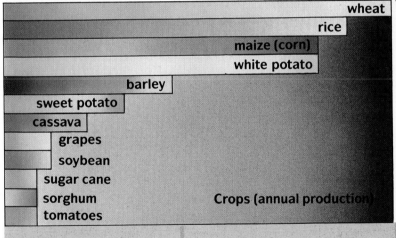

wheat
rice
maize (corn)
white potato
barley
sweet potato
cassava
grapes
soybean
sugar cane
sorghum
tomatoes
Crops (annual production)

Figure 8-3

The 12 most important crops from seed plants (*left*). How does the production of sweet potatoes compare with the production of white potatoes?

REVIEW

1. Compare angiosperms and gymnosperms.
2. What is the difference between an evergreen and a deciduous plant?
3. What is the most important use of seed plants? Explain your answer.

CHALLENGE Which offers better protection to a seed—a cone or a fruit? Explain your answer.

8-2 GYMNOSPERMS

conus (cone)
-fer (bearing)

CONIFERS

Conifers (KAHN ih ferz) make up the most important group of gymnosperms. A **conifer** is a tree or shrub that bears its seeds in cones. A **cone** is a woody reproductive structure on which naked seeds develop. Most conifers are evergreens. Examples of evergreen conifers are pine, fir, hemlock, and spruce. A few conifers, such as the larch, are deciduous—they lose all of their leaves at one time. Examples of several kinds of conifers are shown in Figure 8-4. Conifers are most common in the cooler regions of the United States, Canada, and northern Europe. These trees make up a large portion of the forests in these regions.

Conifers include both the oldest and the largest living organisms. Some bristlecone pine trees are more than 4000 years old. These trees are believed to be the oldest living organisms on the earth. Some giant redwood trees in California and Oregon are about as tall as a 30-story building! Look again at Figure 8-4 to see some of the tallest and oldest conifers on the earth.

Some conifers are fast-growing trees and are grown as a crop in some parts of North America. These trees supply over 75 percent of the lumber and 90 percent of the pulpwood used in making paper. Farmers often plant conifers in rows to act as windbreaks on land used for farming. A windbreak serves as a protection from wind.

Figure 8-4

Types of conifers: Sequoia (*A*), Scotch pine (*B*), and bristlecone pine (*C*).

OTHER GYMNOSPERMS

The other groups of gymnosperms are less well known than the conifers. *Cycads* (sī kadz) are cone-bearing plants with an unbranched stem and a circle of palmlike leaves at the top. These gymnosperms were common during the age of the dinosaurs. Today there are only a few species growing in warm regions. Figure 8-5 shows a cycad that grows in Florida. People often mistake cycads for palm trees, but palm trees are flowering plants.

Ginkgoes (GIHNG kohz) are deciduous trees with fan-shaped leaves. Ginkgoes belong to a group of gymnosperms that was common millions of years ago. Today there is only one living species. There are both male and female ginkgo trees. The male trees produce pollen in conelike structures. As shown in Figure 8-6, the female trees produce pairs of seeds that have a thick outer coat. Ginkgo trees are often planted as shade trees in yards and along city streets. They are hardy plants that are not easily affected by air pollution, insects, and many plant diseases.

Figure 8-5

Zamia, a kind of cycad. Why is this plant considered a gymnosperm?

Figure 8-6

Ginkgo leaves and seeds. Where are ginkgoes often planted?

REVIEW

1. What reproductive structure do conifers have in common?
2. List at least three important uses of conifers.
3. Describe the appearance of a ginkgo leaf. Why are ginkgo trees often planted in cities?

CHALLENGE Suppose you are in Florida and observe a tree with palmlike leaves and coconuts. Is it likely that the tree is a cycad? Explain your answer.

8-3 ANGIOSPERMS

TRAITS OF ANGIOSPERMS

Most species of plants on the earth today are angiosperms. All angiosperms have two traits in common. They form some type of flower, and their seeds are completely enclosed within a fruit. Because they are enclosed, angiosperm seeds are better protected than are gymnosperm seeds.

You are probably familiar with the flowers of angiosperms such as roses and dandelions. Most of the best-known plants—daisies, lilies, marigolds, and sunflowers—are angiosperms. You may not know that grasses and trees such as oak, hickory, and ash also form flowers. The flowers of these plants are small and lack brightly colored petals, as you can see in Figure 8-7.

Figure 8-7

Flowers of mountain ash (*left*) and red oak (*middle*). Indian pipe (*right*).

Angiosperms are found in many kinds of places. Water lilies and water hyacinths are freshwater angiosperms. Eelgrass is a saltwater angiosperm. Cactuses are angiosperms that grow in deserts. Some angiosperms, such as mistletoe, are parasites. Recall that a parasite lives in or on another organism and harms it. Other angiosperms, such as the Indian pipe, also shown in Figure 8-7, are saprobes. You have learned that a saprobe uses the remains of plants and animals as food.

MONOCOTS AND DICOTS

The seed of an angiosperm contains either one or two cotyledons (kaht uh LEE duhnz). A **cotyledon** is a food-storing part of a seed that is used by the developing plant until it can produce its own food. Angiosperms are divided into two groups based on the number of cotyledons in the seed. An angiosperm with one cotyledon is called a **monocot** (MAHN uh kaht). Lilies, irises, tulips, and most grasses are examples of monocots. Almost one third of all angiosperms are monocots. An angiosperm with two cotyledons is called a **dicot** (DĪ kaht). Peanuts, lima beans, daisies, and petunias are examples of dicots. Dicots are the most abundant flowering plants.

mono- (one)

di- (two)

Table 8-1 compares four main traits of monocots and dicots. Refer to Table 8-1 as you read about each trait. Monocots have leaves with parallel veins. The flower parts, such as the petals, are in threes or multiples of three. How many petals are shown on the monocot flower in the table?

Table 8-1 *Comparison of Monocots and Dicots*

	Veins	Flower Parts	Position of Vascular Bundles	Cotyledons
MONOCOTS	parallel	parts in 3's or multiples of 3	scattered bundles	1 cotyledon
DICOTS	netlike	parts in 4's or 5's or multiples of 4 or 5	bundles in rings	2 cotyledons

Inside a monocot stem the vascular tissue occurs in bundles that are scattered throughout the stem. A monocot seed contains only one cotyledon.

Dicot leaves have netlike veins that branch from a large central vein. The flower parts of dicots are in fours or fives or multiples of four or five. In a dicot stem the vascular tissue forms bundles that are in a ring near the outside of the stem. A dicot seed contains two cotyledons.

How Do Monocots and Dicots Differ?

OBJECTIVE

Describe differences in structure between monocots and dicots.

MATERIALS

hand lens, 2 monocot and 2 dicot leaves, 2 monocot and 2 dicot flowers, soaked corn kernels, soaked lima beans, prepared slides of monocot and dicot stem cross sections, microscope

PROCEDURE

A. Use a hand lens to examine two monocot leaves. Observe the pattern of the veins in the leaves. Repeat this procedure for two dicot leaves. Record your observations.

B. Count the parts of two monocot flowers. Record the name of each flower and the number of flower parts you counted. Repeat this procedure for the dicot flowers.

C. Compare the structure of a corn kernel with that of a lima bean seed. Note the location of stored food in each.

D. Examine a cross section of a monocot stem under the low power of a microscope. Make a drawing of the stem, and label some of the vascular bundles. Repeat this procedure for the dicot stem cross section.

RESULTS AND CONCLUSIONS

1. Compare the pattern of the veins in the monocot leaves with that of the dicot leaves.
2. Compare the number of flower parts in the monocot flowers with the number of flower parts in the dicot flowers.
3. Compare the structure of the corn kernel with the structure of the lima bean.
4. Describe the location of the vascular bundles in the cross section of the monocot stem. How does the location of the vascular bundles in the dicot stem compare?

Figure 8-8

Zinnias (*top*) and marigolds (*bottom*) are popular annuals.

LIFE PATTERNS OF ANGIOSPERMS

Angiosperms are often grouped according to their life patterns. *Annuals* (AN yoo uhlz) are plants that live for only one growing season. They develop from a seed, mature, reproduce, and then die in a single growing season. *Biennials* (bī EHN ee uhlz) are plants that live for two growing seasons. During the first year the roots, stems, and leaves develop from the seed. In the second growing season, flowers, fruits, and seeds are produced and then the plant dies. *Perennials* (puh REHN ee uhlz) are plants that continue to grow year after year. Roots, stems, and leaves form during the first growing season. Flowers, fruits, and seeds are produced during the second or following growing seasons.

REVIEW

1. Name two traits shared by all angiosperms.
2. Identify the two main groups of angiosperms. Give two examples of each group.
3. Name three plant parts you would examine to determine whether a plant was a monocot or a dicot.
4. Distinguish annuals from biennials and perennials.

CHALLENGE Suppose that the flowers of a plant have six petals. What type of veins would this plant have?

8-4 ROOTS OF SEED PLANTS

STRUCTURE AND FUNCTION OF ROOTS

The cells of many-celled plants are grouped into tissues and organs. Recall that a *tissue* is a group of cells that are similar in structure and function. An *organ* is a group of two or more different tissues that work together and perform a certain function. Three organs of seed plants—roots, stems, and leaves—will be discussed in this chapter. The reproductive organs, such as cones, flowers, and fruits, will be discussed in the next chapter.

A **root** is an organ that anchors a plant in the ground and absorbs water and minerals from the soil. Vascular tissue in the roots conducts these materials to the stem. Some roots also store food.

Figure 8-9 is a drawing of a cross section of a young root. Locate the main tissue of the root in the diagram. The tissues inside a plant perform different functions. The vascular tissue, made up of both xylem (zī luhm) and phloem (FLOH uhm), is located in the center of the root. The tissue that forms a cross in the center is the xylem. The **xylem** is vascular tissue that conducts water and minerals from the root to the stem and leaves. Locate the bundles of phloem tissue around the xylem. The **phloem** is vascular tissue that conducts food throughout the plant. Outside the xylem and phloem is a tissue that stores food. There is also an outer layer of cells that covers and protects the root.

> *After completing this section, you will be able to*
>
> - **list** three functions of roots.
> - **distinguish** between xylem and phloem.
> - **describe** the structure of a root.
> - **compare** taproot and fibrous root systems.
> - **describe** several adaptations of roots.
>
> *The key terms in this section are*
>
> | | |
> |---|---|
> | adaptation | root cap |
> | phloem | root hairs |
> | root | xylem |

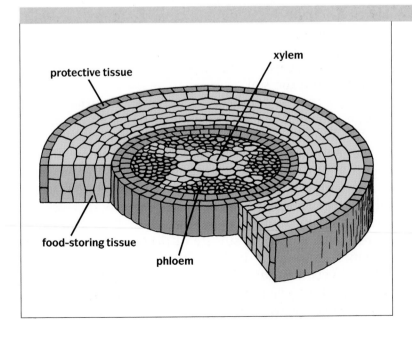

Figure 8-9

Cross section of a root.

protective tissue

xylem

food-storing tissue

phloem

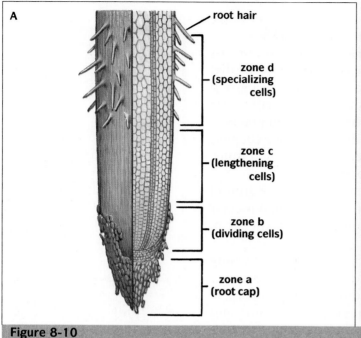

A

root hair

zone d
(specializing
cells)

zone c
(lengthening
cells)

zone b
(dividing cells)

zone a
(root cap)

Figure 8-10

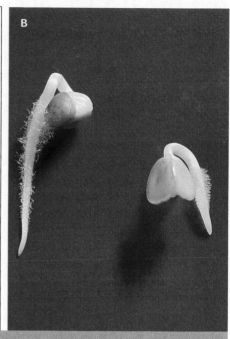

B

Developing root (*A*) and radish seed-lings (*B*). In which zone of the root are the root hairs?

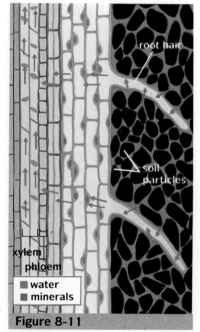

root hair

soil particles

xylem
phloem
■ water
■ minerals

Figure 8-11

Transport of water and minerals into a root.

There are four main zones in a developing root. Each zone performs a certain function. Each of these zones is shown in Figure 8-10*A*. Look at zone **a**, the root cap. The **root cap** is made up of cells that protect the cells of the root tip from being injured as the root grows through the soil. Notice that the cells of the root cap fit like a thimble over the tip of the root. In zone **b** the number of cells increases rapidly by mitosis. In zone **c** the newly formed cells lengthen. The lengthening of cells in this zone pushes the root tip further into the soil. Cells in zone **d** become specialized to perform certain functions, such as taking in water from the soil.

Look carefully at the cells on the outer surface of the root in zone **d**. The long threadlike extensions of cells on the surface of the root are called **root hairs**. Large numbers of root hairs form the fuzzy area of the radish seedling in Figure 8-10*B*. Root hairs grow into the spaces between soil particles. Water and minerals are absorbed through all surfaces of a root hair. Root hairs greatly increase the surface area that can absorb materials. Root hairs may increase the absorbing surface of the root by as much as 20 times. In Figure 8-11 you can see how water and minerals absorbed by the root hairs pass through the cells of the root to the xylem inside the root. These materials are then carried in the xylem to other parts of the plant.

KINDS OF ROOTS

Plants have either a *taproot system* or a *fibrous root system*. A taproot system has a single large root, the taproot, that grows straight down. Smaller roots called *lateral roots* branch outward from the taproot. Taproots anchor the plant firmly in the ground. The dandelion, a common lawn weed, is an example of a plant that has a taproot. If you try to pull up a dandelion, the taproot usually breaks. New leaves and flowers develop from the taproot that remains in the soil. It is thus very hard to get rid of dandelions. Taproots such as carrots, beets, and turnips store food that is eaten by people.

A fibrous root system has several main roots that are all about the same size. These roots spread out in all directions near the surface of the soil. This type of root system also has many small branch roots. Fibrous roots do not anchor the plant as well as do taproots. However, more soil particles cling to fibrous roots than to tap roots. Soil is thus held in place. Plants with fibrous roots, such as grasses, are often planted on steep slopes to prevent erosion of the soil by water.

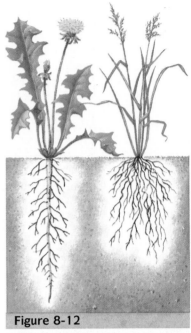

Figure 8-12

Types of root systems: taproot (*left*) and fibrous root (*right*).

SCIENCE & TECHNOLOGY

The famine that has existed in several African countries has been worsened by the growth of witchweed, a parasitic plant. Witchweed attaches to the roots of some plants grown for food. These plants include corn, sorghum, and millet. They are the host plants for the witchweed.

Soon after a witchweed seed sprouts, it releases a chemical that diffuses through the soil. When it reaches a nearby host plant, this chemical digests some of the cells on the surface of the root of that plant. These partly digested root cells produce a special chemical that is like a signal to the witchweed. The chemical causes the witchweed to grow a special organ by

which it attaches to the host plant. The witchweed receives its food through the host's root system.

The witchweed does not kill its host. Rather, the host plant is unable to form fruits and, thus, cannot reproduce. A crop, such as corn, that is attacked by witchweed produces only a few seeds for the next season. These

seeds often cannot grow into strong new plants.

Scientists are working on a new technology that could help to stop the witchweed. They are developing a chemical that would force the witchweed to produce its attaching organ before it finds a host plant. Without food from a host, the witchweed would die.

ADAPTATIONS OF ROOTS

You have just learned about the structure of some common types of roots. The structure of the roots varies in different plants. Root structure varies with the environment of a plant. The roots are adapted to their environment. An **adaptation** (ad ap TAY shuhn) is a trait that makes an organism better able to survive in an environment.

A root that grows above the soil and extends out from the stem is one type of adaptation. Orchids develop thick white roots from the part of the stem that is above the ground. These roots can absorb dew and rain water. Roots that develop along the stems of climbing vines, such as English ivy, anchor the plant to a support. Notice in Figure 8-13 that corn plants may develop aboveground roots called *prop roots*. Prop roots grow down from the stem into the soil, where they branch out. Like other roots, prop roots absorb water and minerals and support the plant. Without the support of its prop roots, what might happen to a tall, heavy corn plant in a strong wind?

The roots of desert plants may be wide-spreading. In desert regions it does not rain very often. When it does rain, the showers are brief and heavy. Most desert plants have shallow root systems that spread out over a wide area. This type of root system allows the plant to take in surface water quickly.

Figure 8-13

Prop roots of a banyan tree (*left*) and of corn plants (*right*).

ACTIVITY   Where Do Root Hairs Develop?

OBJECTIVE

Observe the location and structure of root hairs on radish seedlings.

MATERIALS

10 radish seeds, petri dish, paper towel, scissors, cotton, water, glass-marking pencil, masking tape, forceps, hand lens, microscope slide, dropper, coverslip, microscope, scalpel, metric ruler

PROCEDURE

A. Place ten radish seeds on the bottom of a petri dish. Over the seeds, place a piece of paper towel cut to the size of the dish. On top of the paper towel, place a layer of cotton. Pack the dish with the cotton so that the seeds will be held in place. See the drawing below. Moisten the cotton with water. Cover the dish.

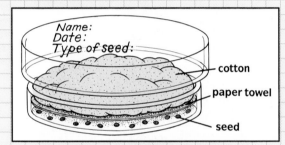

Name:
Date:
Type of seed:
— cotton
— paper towel
— seed

B. Use a glass-marking pencil to label the cover of the dish with your name, the type of seeds, and the date. Use masking tape to seal the dish closed. Place the dish in a warm, light place, such as near a sunny window.

C. Observe the dish each day. Record the day on which you first see roots growing from the seeds. Note any changes you observe in the roots. Watch for the development of root hairs.

D. When several of the radish seedlings have grown root hairs, remove one of the seeds from the dish with a pair of forceps. Place the seedling on a damp paper towel. Observe the root with a hand lens. Try to count the root hairs.
   1. On what part of the root are the root hairs the longest?
   2. Where on the root do the root hairs develop?

E. Use forceps to remove another seedling from the petri dish and place it on a microscope slide. Use a dropper to add a drop of water. Do not put a coverslip on the slide. Observe the root under low power of a microscope. Locate the root tip. After you have found the root tip, look along the root until you locate the root hairs.

F. Use a scalpel to cut a 1-cm piece from the tip of the root. Place the root on a slide. Cover it with a coverslip. Observe the root hairs under both low and high power. Make a drawing of a root hair and a few nearby cells.
   3. Is a root hair made up of one cell or many cells?

RESULTS AND CONCLUSIONS

1. Describe the appearance of the root hairs on the radish seedling.
2. Could you count the root hairs on the surface of the root? Explain why or why not.
3. How did the size of a root hair compare with the size of other nearby cells in the root?

REVIEW

1. What are the three functions of roots?
2. Distinguish between the function of xylem and that of phloem.
3. Describe the two kinds of root systems. Give examples of plants that have these root systems.
4. Name and describe the four zones of a developing root.
5. Give an example of an adaptation of roots. Explain how this adaptation helps the plant survive.

CHALLENGE   Gardeners suggest that plants that are to be moved, be dug out of the ground with a ball of soil left around the roots. Explain why this is a good suggestion.

8-5 STEMS OF SEED PLANTS

herba (plant)

STRUCTURE AND FUNCTION OF STEMS

A **stem** is an organ that supports the leaves and reproductive organs of a plant. It also carries food, water, and minerals to parts of the plant. Vascular tissue inside the stem transports these materials. Many stems are green and can make food by photosynthesis. Some plant stems store food.

There are two main kinds of stems. A stem that is soft and green and that bends easily is called a **herbaceous** (her BAY shuhs) **stem**. Most annuals, such as dandelions, marigolds, and petunias, have herbaceous stems. A **woody stem** is a stem that contains large amounts of xylem cells with thick cell walls. Perennials, such as trees and shrubs, have woody stems. Such plants grow taller and increase in diameter each year.

Figure 8-14

Section of a young woody stem. How do the widths of the xylem and phloem layers compare?

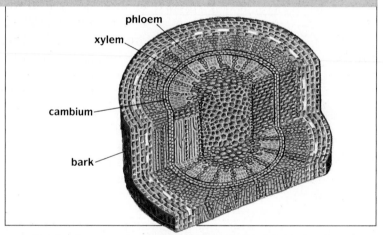

In herbaceous stems, xylem and phloem tissues are grouped together in *vascular bundles*. A vascular bundle is a strand of tissue containing both xylem and phloem. The "strings" in a celery stalk are vascular bundles. The vascular bundles extend up and down the plant—from the roots to the stem to the leaves. In addition to transporting water, minerals, and food, the vascular bundles provide support to the plant.

In most woody stems the xylem and phloem are in a series of rings. Figure 8-14 shows a section of a woody stem. Notice that the outermost layer is the *bark*. The bark is a protective layer of tissue. The inside layer of the bark is made up of phloem, which is the tissue that carries food. The center of the stem consists of rings of xylem, which is the tissue that transports water. Between the xylem and

 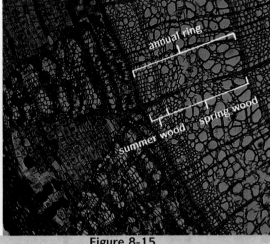

Figure 8-15

the phloem is the cambium (KAM bee uhm). The **cambium** is a layer of dividing cells that produce new xylem and phloem cells. The cells produced toward the outside of the stem develop into phloem cells. The cells produced toward the inside of the stem become xylem cells. The production of new xylem and phloem causes the stem to increase in diameter. All the layers of xylem tissue together form wood. As you can see in Figure 8-14, the woody part of the stem is much thicker than the phloem. The xylem is the main source of support for the plant.

Annual rings, formed of spring wood and summer wood (*left*). Enlargement of rings (*right*). How do cells of spring wood differ from cells of summer wood?

The layers of xylem that are formed each year in turn form *annual rings*. Annual rings are made up of spring wood and summer wood. From Figure 8-15 (*right*) you can see the difference between spring wood and summer wood. Because of their smaller diameter, the cells of the summer wood appear darker than those of the spring wood. The line between the summer wood of one growing season and the spring wood of the following growing season marks the end of an annual ring. By counting the annual rings, you can estimate the age of a woody stem.

ADAPTATIONS OF STEMS

The stems of most plants grow upright. However, some stems have features that show an adaptation to certain environments. For example, some plant stems grow underground. Some of these underground stems store large amounts of starch and are an important source of food for humans and animals. A **rhizome** (RĪ zohm) is an underground stem that grows parallel to the soil surface. It may be thick and may store food. Irises and lilies are plants that have rhizomes. The rhizome of an iris is shown in

rhiza (root)

Figure 8-16

Types of stems: rhizome (*A*), tuber (*B*), and bulb (*C*).

Figure 8-16*A*. Unlike roots, rhizomes have buds. New stems and leaves develop from a bud.

A **tuber** (TOO ber) is an enlarged food-storing part of a rhizome. The white potato, shown in Figure 8-16*B*, is a tuber. The "eyes" of the potato are buds. If a section of a potato containing a bud is planted, the bud can develop into a new potato plant. A **bulb** is a short underground stem surrounded by thick leaf bases that store food. Onions, tulips, and hyacinths all form bulbs.

Some plants, such as the grapes shown in Figure 8-17, have climbing stems called *vines*. Many vines have branches called *tendrils*, which support the plant by curling around objects. Other plants produce runners. A **runner** is a long, slender stem that grows along the surface of the ground. Such aboveground stems allow for reproduction of a plant over a wide area. Strawberry plants and crabgrass can develop new plants from runners.

REVIEW

1. What are two functions of stems?
2. Distinguish between a herbaceous stem and a woody stem.
3. Explain the function of cambium and state where it is located in a plant.
4. What is the difference between a rhizome and a bulb? Give an example of each.

CHALLENGE Two forest rangers are looking at the annual rings of a tree. Some annual rings are narrow and others are wide. Account for the differences in width.

Figure 8-17

The tendrils of this grape plant help support the vine.

8-6 LEAVES OF SEED PLANTS

STRUCTURE OF LEAVES

The third major plant organ is the leaf. A **leaf** is a plant organ in which food is made by photosynthesis. In the next chapter you will learn how food is made in the leaves.

Most leaves consist of two main parts. The wide, flat portion of the leaf is the **blade**. The stalk that joins the leaf to the stem is the **petiole** (PEHT ee ohl). Find these two structures in Figure 8-18. The lines or ridges on the upper and lower surfaces of the leaf are the veins. A **vein** is a structure that contains vascular tissue, which transports materials to and from the leaf. The xylem transports water from the stem to the leaf. The phloem transports food that is made in the leaf to the stem and roots.

On the lower surface of the leaf, and sometimes on the upper surface, are small openings called *stomates* (STOH-mayts). Gases move into and out of the leaf through the stomates. Carbon dioxide passes into the leaf and water vapor and oxygen pass out through these openings.

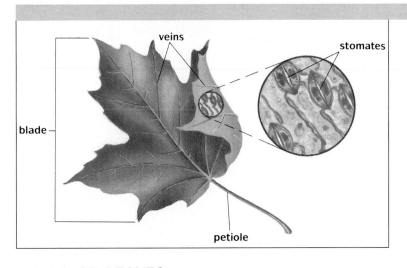

Figure 8-18

Parts of a leaf.

KINDS OF LEAVES

The leaves of angiosperms and many gymnosperms may be grouped as either *broad-leaved* or *needle-leaved.* Angiosperms are broad-leaved plants. Their leaves are wide and flat. The gymnosperms known as conifers are needle-leaved plants. Their leaves are needlelike.

The leaves of broad-leaved plants are of two basic types: simple and compound. A *simple leaf* is a leaf with a single, undivided blade. A *compound leaf* is a leaf with a blade that is divided into several parts called leaflets. In

A

some compound leaves all of the leaflets are attached to the tip of the petiole. In others the leaflets are arranged opposite one another along the side of a central stalk. Compare the simple and compound leaves shown in Figure 8-19A and 8-19B.

The leaves of conifers look like needles or scales. Figure 8-19D shows a cross section of a pine needle. The compact shape of a conifer leaf helps to prevent water loss. Very little surface is exposed to the air. The needlelike leaf also has a tough outer covering. These traits allow conifers to survive in dry climates better than broad-leaved plants can. In needle-leaved plants the number of needles in a cluster and the length of needles vary with the species.

B

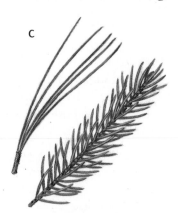

C

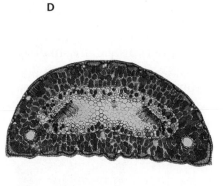

D

Figure 8-19

Simple leaf (*A*), compound leaf (*B*), needlelike leaves (*C*), and cross section of a pine needle (*D*).

Figure 8-20

Living stones, a type of succulent.

ADAPTATIONS OF LEAVES

The leaves of some plants can perform functions other than making food. Leaves of desert plants have adaptations that help prevent water loss. Spines of a cactus are specialized leaves that are hard, slender, and pointed at the tip. Because of their structure, spines, like the needles of conifers, reduce the amount of water given off to the air. This adaptation is very useful to plants living in hot, dry places.

Some plants that grow in dry environments may have thick fleshy leaves that store water. These plants are called succulents (SUHK yuh luhnts). The living stone plant shown in Figure 8-20 is a succulent.

Some leaves and leaf parts are also used as food by humans. For example, the enlarged petioles of rhubarb and celery are eaten. But rhubarb leaves contain poisons that are harmful to people. People do eat the large leaves of cabbage and lettuce. What other plant leaves do you eat?

REVIEW

1. What are the main parts of a leaf?
2. Distinguish between a simple leaf and a compound leaf.
3. Explain how spines on a cactus adapt the plant to a dry place, such as a desert.

CHALLENGE You have a plant growing in a shady spot. As you look down at the plant from above, you can see each leaf. No leaf is completely covered by the leaf above. Of what advantage to the plant is this growth pattern?

CHAPTER SUMMARY

The main ideas in this chapter are listed below. Read these statements before you answer the Chapter Review questions.

- There are two major groups of seed plants: the gymnosperms, which have naked seeds, and the angiosperms, which have seeds enclosed inside a fruit. Deciduous plants shed all of their leaves at one time. Evergreen plants lose only their oldest leaves and retain their younger leaves. (8-1)

- The most important gymnosperms are the conifers, which are trees or shrubs with needlelike leaves that bear seeds in cones. (8-2)

- Cycads and ginkgoes are unusual plants that are classified as gymnosperms. (8-2)

- The most abundant plants are the angiosperms, which are plants that form flowers and have seeds enclosed in fruits. The two major groups of angiosperms are the monocots, which have seeds with one cotyledon, and the dicots, which have seeds with two cotyledons. (8-3)

- Roots are structures that anchor and support the plant, absorb water and minerals, conduct these materials to the stem, and store food. Various types of adaptations of roots help some plants survive in their environment. (8-4)

- A stem supports the leaves and reproductive organs and conducts food, water, and minerals to all parts of the plant. Some stems also store food. There are two major types of stems: herbaceous stems and woody stems. Stem adaptations include runners, rhizomes, and tubers. (8-5)

- A leaf is the plant organ that manufactures food. A leaf consists of two main parts: a petiole and a blade. Angiosperms are broad-leaved plants. Conifers are needle-leaved plants. Leaves may show adaptations for water storage or food storage. (8-6)

The key terms in this chapter are listed below. Use each term in a sentence that shows the meaning of the term.

adaptation	cotyledon	monocot	runner
angiosperm	deciduous plant	petiole	seed plant
blade	dicot	phloem	stem
bulb	evergreen	rhizome	tuber
cambium	gymnosperm	root	vein
cone	herbaceous stem	root cap	woody stem
conifer	leaf	root hairs	xylem

Chapter Review

Write the letter of the term that best matches the definition. Not all the terms will be used.

1. Angiosperm with two cotyledons
2. Angiosperm with one cotyledon
3. Plant that bears its seeds in cones
4. Plant that loses all of its leaves at one time
5. Seed plant that produces flowers
6. Thick underground stem
7. Vascular tissue that conducts water and minerals
8. Layer of cells that produces xylem and phloem in a stem
9. Wide, flat portion of a leaf
10. Layer of cells that protects the tip of a growing root

a. angiosperm
b. blade
c. cambium
d. conifer
e. cotyledon
f. deciduous plant
g. dicot
h. gymnosperm
i. monocot
j. petiole
k. phloem
l. rhizome
m. root cap
n. root hairs
o. xylem

CONCEPTS

1. What is the major difference between angiosperms and gymnosperms? (8-1)
2. How do evergreen and deciduous plants differ in the way they shed their leaves? (8-1)
3. Discuss four ways in which seed plants are useful to people. (8-1)
4. Describe the reproductive structure of conifers. (8-2)
5. Distinguish between a cycad and a ginkgo. (8-2)
6. List three important uses of conifers. (8-2)
7. What trait of angiosperms makes them better able to survive than gymnosperms? (8-3)
8. What is a cotyledon? How is this structure used to distinguish monocots from dicots? (8-3)
9. What traits of monocot flowers distinguish them from dicot flowers? (8-3)
10. Suppose a plant in your yard develops roots, stems, and leaves one year. It forms flowers, fruits, and seeds the next year and each year from then on. Is the plant an annual, a biennial, or a perennial? Explain your answer. (8-3)
11. Suppose you found a plant with 20 petals, 10 stamens, and leaves with netted veins. Is the plant a monocot or a dicot? Give a reason for your answer. (8-3)

12. Distinguish between the functions of xylem and phloem in a root. (8-4)

13. Describe the four main zones of a developing root and give the function of each. (8-4)

14. Explain the difference between a taproot system and a fibrous root system. Give examples of plants that have each type of root. (8-4)

15. Distinguish between woody and herbaceous stems. (8-5)

16. What is a vascular bundle? Describe two major functions of vascular bundles. (8-5)

17. What is cambium? Where is it located in a woody stem? (8-5)

18. Describe how an annual ring is formed. (8-5)

19. Describe two examples of adaptations of stems. (8-5)

20. What is the difference between a simple leaf and a compound leaf? (8-6)

1. Explain how the cambium is related to an increase in the diameter of a woody stem.

2. To survive, plants must be adapted to their environment. Describe some adaptations of a plant living on a hot, dry, windy hill.

3. Which of the four zones in a growing root tip is most important to root development? Give a reason for your answer.

1. Look for foods and seasonings in your house that come from seed plants. Name the part of the plant from which the foods or seasonings come.

2. Find a stump that is at least 15 years old. Examine the annual rings. Hypothesize the conditions that existed during each growing season. Try to find in what year the tree was cut down. Check your hypotheses with the weather bureau's records of weather conditions during the years of growth.

3. Germinate a corn seedling and allow the root to grow about 2.5 cm. Make a mark with ink about every 0.5 cm on the growing root. Measure the distance between the marks each day for a week. Which region of the root grows most quickly?

Brown, A. *Monarchs of the Forest: The Story of the Redwoods*. New York: Dodd, Mead, and Company, 1984.

Del Tredici, Peter. "Resurrecting Gardener Green's Ginkgo." *Horticulture*, November 1983, p. 12.

LIFE PROCESSES OF PLANTS

The life of a flower may be very short. Some flowers bloom for only a single day. Others remain open for several days. As the petals fade, other activities are occurring in other parts of the flower. Parts of the flower develop into a fruit with seeds inside. In the photograph you can see some of the structures from which the fruit and seeds develop. The photograph shows a flower that has been cut to reveal the structures inside.

- *What part of a flower becomes the fruit?*
- *What parts of a plant manufacture food?*
- *How can a plant reproduce without seeds?*

9-1 FOOD MAKING AND ENERGY RELEASE

FOOD FROM PLANTS

All organisms need both energy and materials for growth and for other life processes. Animals get the needed energy and materials by eating food in the form of plants and other animals. Plants manufacture their own food. The process by which plants use light energy from the sun to make their own food is called **photosynthesis** (foh-tuh SIHN thuh sihs). Photosynthesis is one of the most important of all chemical processes that occur in living things. The energy required for the life processes of living things comes from the sun. But organisms cannot use the energy from sunlight directly. The light energy must first be changed to chemical energy.

Of the many kinds of living things, only plants, certain plantlike protists, and some kinds of bacteria can make their own food. By making their own food, these organisms make the energy from the sun available to other living things. During photosynthesis these organisms capture the energy from sunlight. They change this energy into the chemical energy that is stored in glucose. Animal life is dependent, either directly or indirectly, on the food made by these organisms.

After completing this section, you will be able to

- **explain** how plants are important to other organisms.
- **describe** the internal structure of a leaf.
- **summarize** the process of photosynthesis.
- **distinguish** between photosynthesis and respiration.

The key terms in this section are
epidermis
guard cells
palisade layer
photosynthesis
respiration
spongy layer
stomate

STRUCTURE OF A LEAF

Most photosynthesis occurs in the leaves of green plants. The internal structure of a leaf is specialized to carry out photosynthesis. The drawing in Figure 9-1 shows a cross section of a leaf. As you read about the structure of a leaf, locate the parts that are described.

epi- (on)
-dermis (skin)

The outer layer of a leaf is called the **epidermis** (ehp-uh DERM uhs). It is made up of a single layer of epidermal cells and is found on both the upper and lower surfaces of the leaf. It protects the cells inside the leaf. The epidermis is covered with a waxy layer known as the *cuticle* (KYOO tuh kuhl). The cuticle reduces the amount of water lost from the leaf surface.

Figure 9-1

Cross section of a leaf. In which cell layers of the leaf does most photosynthesis take place?

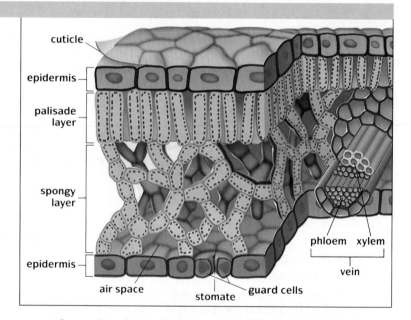

The **palisade** (pal uh SAYD) **layer** is a layer of long, narrow cells below the upper epidermis. Below the palisade layer is a layer of loosely packed cells called the **spongy layer**. The cells of the spongy layer vary in shape. Locate the spongy layer in the drawing. Note that the cells of both the palisade and spongy layers contain many chloroplasts. Most photosynthesis takes place in these two cell layers. Observe the great number of spaces between the cells of the spongy layer. Air, which contains gases used in photosynthesis, is found in these spaces.

Look at the vein shown in the cross section. You can see that the vein contains both xylem tissue and phloem tissue. The xylem transports water to the cells of the leaf. The phloem carries the glucose made during photosynthesis to other parts of the plant.

Gases pass into and out of the leaf through small openings in the epidermis. An opening in the leaf epidermis through which gases are exchanged with the air is called a **stomate** (STOH mayt).

The two kidney-bean-shaped cells that control the opening and closing of the stomate are called **guard cells**. The guard cells surround the stomate. When the guard cells are full of water, they swell and bend outward, as shown in Figure 9-2A. The space that is formed between the guard cells is the open stomate. When the guard cells lose water, they shrink and move toward each other. As you can see in Figure 9-2B, there is no longer a space between them. The stomate is thus closed. How does the closing of the stomate benefit the plant?

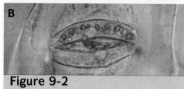

Figure 9-2

Guard cells full of water form an open stomate (A). Guard cells that have little water form a closed stomate (B).

ACTIVITY How Do Stomates Function?

OBJECTIVE
Observe the structure and function of stomates in a lettuce leaf.

MATERIALS
hand lens, lettuce leaf soaking in distilled water, metric ruler, forceps, dropper, microscope slide, coverslip, microscope, salt water, paper towel, clock or watch

PROCEDURE
A. Use a hand lens to observe both the upper and lower surfaces of a lettuce leaf. Look for small openings on the leaf surfaces.
B. Tear a 5-cm-square piece off the lettuce leaf. Bend the square of lettuce in half. Use forceps to remove a thin layer of epidermis.

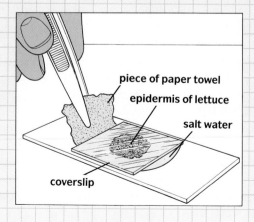

piece of paper towel
epidermis of lettuce
salt water
coverslip

C. Use a dropper to place a drop of distilled water on a microscope slide. Place the thin layer of epidermis in the drop. Cover with a coverslip. Observe the epidermis under low power of a microscope. Locate the pairs of bean-shaped guard cells. Make a drawing of the epidermis, showing at least two pairs of guard cells. In your drawing include several epidermal cells. Label a guard cell, a chloroplast, a stomate, and an epidermal cell.
D. Use the dropper to place a drop of salt water next to the edge of the coverslip, as shown in the drawing. Touch a piece of paper towel to the edge of the coverslip on the side opposite the drop of salt water, as shown. The salt water should flow under the coverslip. Wait 5 minutes, and then observe the epidermis under the low power of the microscope. Make a drawing of the epidermis. Label the same structures labeled in step **C**.

RESULTS AND CONCLUSIONS
1. How are guard cells different from other epidermal cells?
2. Describe how the guard cells and stomates looked as you observed them in step **C**.
3. Compare the appearance of the guard cells and stomates in step **C** with their appearance in step **D**. How does the salt water affect the guard cells and stomates?

PHOTOSYNTHESIS

Photosynthesis is a very complex process. This process is summarized in the following equation.

$$6CO_2 + 6H_2O + \text{light energy} \xrightarrow{\text{chlorophyll}} C_6H_{12}O_6 + 6O_2$$

(carbon (water)   (glucose)   (oxygen)
dioxide)

Carbon dioxide and water are the raw materials needed for photosynthesis. Sunlight is the source of energy. *Chlorophyll*, a green pigment found in the chloroplasts of plant cells, captures light energy. In a series of chemical reactions, or chemical changes, the sugar glucose is formed. Oxygen is also produced during this process.

Research has shown that photosynthesis occurs in two distinct stages. Refer to Figure 9-3 as you read about these stages. The first stage requires light. This stage is a set of chemical reactions called the *light reactions*. In the light reactions the chlorophyll molecules inside the chloroplasts capture light energy from the sun. Some of this energy is used to split water molecules into hydrogen atoms and oxygen atoms. The rest of the energy made available by the chlorophyll is used to form an energy-rich compound called ATP. During the light reactions, oxygen gas is released into the atmosphere.

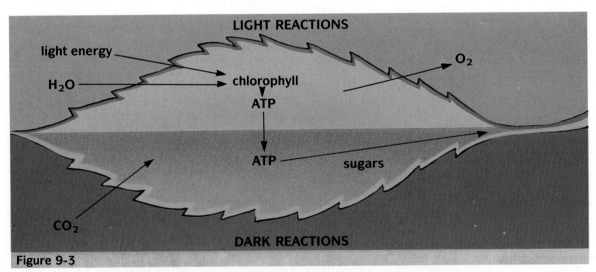

Figure 9-3

Photosynthesis: light and dark reactions.

The second stage of photosynthesis involves a set of reactions called the *dark reactions*. The dark reactions do not require light. These reactions use the energy stored in the ATP that was formed during the light reactions.

This energy is used to combine carbon dioxide with carbon compounds in the cell to form simple sugars.

Most living things that carry on photosynthesis make more glucose than they use for their life processes. The extra glucose can be stored as starch. A white potato, shown in Figure 9-4, contains stored starch. This starch can be used by the potato plant at a later time. It may also be used by animals that eat the plant. Plants other than potatoes also store starch.

RESPIRATION

Plants do use some of the glucose formed during photosynthesis to supply energy for their life processes. The process by which foods are broken down and energy is released is called **respiration** (rehs puh RAY shuhn). You have learned that all living things carry out respiration. The equation that follows is a summary of the process of respiration.

$$C_6H_{12}O_6 + 6O_2 \longrightarrow 6CO_2 + 6H_2O + ATP$$
(glucose) (oxygen) (carbon   (water) (energy)
                              dioxide)

Figure 9-4

Some of the glucose formed during photosynthesis is stored as starch in the potato. What are some other plants that store starch?

Refer to the equation as you read about what happens in this process. During respiration, glucose molecules are broken down by combining with oxygen. Carbon dioxide, water, and energy are released. Much of the energy that is stored in the glucose molecule is released during respiration. Some of this energy is given off to the environment in the form of heat. But most of the energy is stored in ATP. The energy in ATP is used by the plant for growth, reproduction, and other life processes.

REVIEW

1. Explain why living things are dependent on organisms that carry on photosynthesis.
2. Name and give the function of each of the cell layers inside a leaf.
3. Describe how guard cells control the opening and closing of the stomates.
4. Compare the processes of photosynthesis and respiration in terms of materials used, products formed, and energy taken in or released.

CHALLENGE You have been given leaves from two different kinds of plants. One plant is from a very hot, dry region. The other plant is from a warm, moist region. Describe how the structure of the leaves might differ.

9-2 TRANSPORT OF MATERIALS

After completing this section, you will be able to

- **compare** transport in nonvascular and vascular plants.
- **describe** transpiration and **identify** the cause of wilting.

The key term in this section is transpiration

Plants are made up of cells that are organized into tissues and organs. All parts of a plant need water, minerals, and food. A transport system moves these materials throughout the plant.

Nonvascular plants, such as mosses, do not have vascular tissue to transport water, minerals, and food. These materials are transported throughout the plant by diffusion. Diffusion takes place very slowly. So it takes a long time for substances to move from one part of the plant to another.

Vascular plants, such as ferns, gymnosperms, and angiosperms, have a transport system called a vascular system. The vascular system is composed of xylem and phloem. The *xylem* transports water and minerals upward from the roots. The *phloem* transports glucose made in the leaves to other parts of the plant. Figure 9-5 (*right*) shows the location of the vascular tissue in a typical plant. In Figure 9-5 (*left*) notice that the cells of xylem are joined end to end, forming long tubes. Phloem cells also form long tubes. The vascular tissue extends from the tip of the roots to the tip of the leaves. Every plant cell is close to a source of water, minerals, and food.

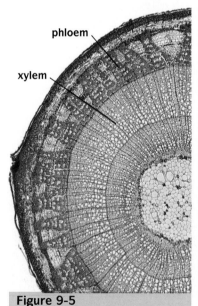

phloem

xylem

Figure 9-5

Enlargement of vascular tissue showing xylem and phloem (*left*). Xylem and phloem in a tree (*right*). In which direction are water and minerals carried in the xylem?

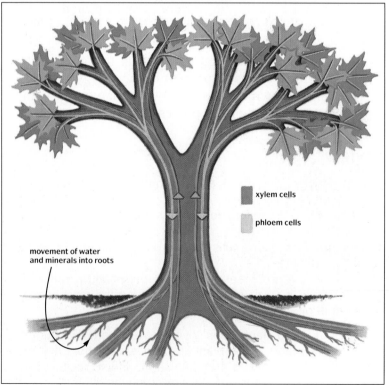

xylem cells

phloem cells

movement of water and minerals into roots

Water enters the plant through the root hairs by *osmosis*. Recall that osmosis is the diffusion of water through a semipermeable membrane. Water moves by osmosis from an area where water molecules are more crowded to an area where they are less crowded. Normally, water molecules are more crowded outside the root than inside. Inside the root there are many minerals and salts crowded together. Thus, water diffuses from the soil through the cell membrane of the root hair. Water moves by osmosis from the root hair through the root tissues to the xylem in the root. As you know, xylem tissue extends from the roots to the leaves. The water moves through the xylem up the stem to the leaves.

Some of the water absorbed by the roots is used by the plant. The water that is not used by the plant is given off to the air as water vapor. Most of the water is given off through the stomates in the epidermis of the leaves. The loss of water through the stomates of the leaves is called **transpiration** (trans puh RAY shuhn). Have you ever visited a greenhouse? You may have noticed that the air inside was very humid. This humid air was due to the large amounts of water given off by the plants through transpiration. In Figure 9-6 you can see droplets of water lost through the process of transpiration.

Suppose water is lost through transpiration more quickly than it is absorbed by the root hairs. The plant cells will lose water. The leaves, stems, and flowers will droop in a condition called *wilting*. Figure 9-7 shows the effects of wilting in a house plant. How does the plant look after watering?

Figure 9-6

A plant inside a sealed jar. What caused the water droplets to collect on the inside surface of the jar?

Figure 9-7

Plant that has not been watered for 10 days (*A*); 1¼ hours after watering (*B*); 2¾ hours after watering (*C*).

Most of the minerals needed by plants are dissolved in the water that is in soil. Molecules of minerals are often more crowded inside the root hairs than they are in the soil, as shown in Figure 9-8A. Root hairs can still absorb minerals from the soil, even under this conditon. The movement of molecules from an area where they are less crowded to an area where they are more crowded is called *active transport*. Recall that active transport requires the use of energy by cells. Minerals enter the plant by way of active transport through the root hairs, as shown in Figure 9-8B. The minerals are then transported through the xylem to all parts of the plant.

All of the living cells in the plant, including those in the roots and stem, need energy. This energy is supplied by sugar molecules made in the leaves during photosynthesis. These molecules are transported throughout the plant by phloem. Look back at Figure 9-5, which shows the location of the phloem. Like the xylem, the phloem is found throughout the plant. Thus, all of the cells of the plant can be supplied with food.

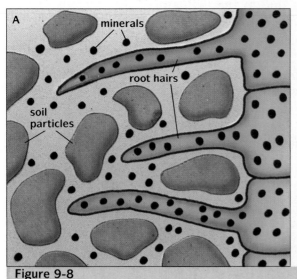

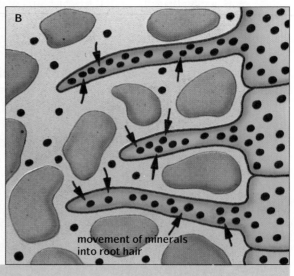

Figure 9-8

Active transport of minerals into root hairs. How does this process differ from osmosis?

REVIEW

1. Compare the transport of materials in nonvascular plants with transport in vascular plants.
2. Describe what occurs in the leaf during transpiration.
3. What is wilting?

CHALLENGE You have learned that some of the water that is absorbed by the roots is lost through the leaves. Design an experiment to find out how much water is lost through a plant's leaves in a certain period.

9-3 REPRODUCTION IN GYMNOSPERMS

In both gymnosperms and angiosperms, sexual reproduction results in the formation of a seed. Recall that conifers are gymnosperms that produce seeds inside structures called cones. A *cone* is a reproductive structure made up of scales that overlap one another. Reproduction in pines is similar to that in other conifers. Like most conifers, pine trees form two kinds of cones—male cones and female cones. About two years are needed for a pine seed to develop. Refer to Figure 9-9 as you read about seed formation in the pine tree.

After completing this section, you will be able to

- **distinguish** between male and female cones in conifers.
- **describe** seed formation in a pine.

The key terms in this section are
embryo   seed
pollen grain   seed coat
pollination

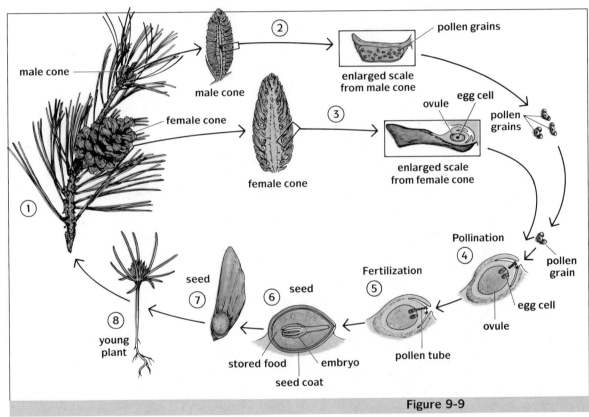

Figure 9-9

Life cycle of a pine tree.

1. The mature tree contains both male cones and female cones.
2. Male cones produce and release large amounts of pollen in the spring. The pollen is formed in sacs on the lower surface of the scales of the male cone. A **pollen grain** is a structure that will form the sperm cell in seed plants.
3. Female cones have egg cells near the base of the scales. The egg cells form inside an *ovule*.

pollen (fine flour)

Figure 9-10

Pollen grains of a pine tree. Note the winglike parts. How are these parts helpful in the movement of pollen grains over an area?

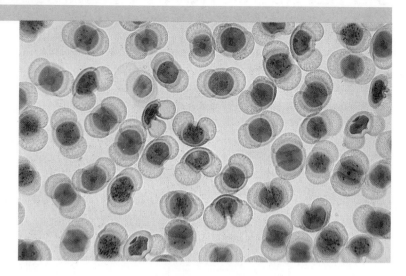

4. **Pollination** (pahl uh NAY shuhn) is the transfer of pollen from the male reproductive structure to the female reproductive structure. In conifers, it is the transfer of pollen from the male cone to the female cone. As shown in Figure 9-10, the pollen grains have winglike parts. The pollen grains are carried by the wind.

5. One of the cells in the pollen grain produces a pollen tube. The tube grows through an opening in the ovule, toward an egg cell. A sperm cell travels through the pollen tube to the egg cell. The sperm cell and egg cell join in a process called *fertilization*.

6. The fertilized egg develops into an embryo (EHM bree-yoh). An **embryo** is a developing, many-celled young organism. In plants the embryo is inside a seed. A **seed** is a structure made up of a plant embryo, stored food, and a seed coat. A **seed coat** is a tough outer covering that protects the seed.

7. When the seeds are fully developed, the cones open and the seeds are released.

8. Under the right conditions, a seed will sprout and develop into a new plant.

REVIEW

1. Describe the two kinds of cones produced by conifers.
2. What is pollination, and how does it occur in pines?
3. Describe how seeds form in pines.

CHALLENGE Suppose you shake a small pine tree in the spring. You find that something resembling smoke comes from the tree. Explain what might cause this "smoke."

9-4 REPRODUCTION IN ANGIOSPERMS

FLOWER STRUCTURE

Figure 9-11 is a drawing of a typical flower. A **flower** is the reproductive structure of an angiosperm. The function of the flower is to form seeds that can develop into new plants. Locate each flower part as you read about it. A **sepal** (SEE puhl) is a leaflike structure found at the base of a flower. A **petal** (PEHT uhl) is a brightly colored structure above the sepals. The petals surround and protect the inner reproductive parts.

A **stamen** (STAY muhn) is a male reproductive structure of a flower. A stamen consists of a stalk with a sac at the top. A *filament* (FIHL uh muhnt) is the stalk of a stamen. An *anther* (AN thuhr) is the sac at the end of the stamen that produces and holds pollen grains. How many stamens are shown in Figure 9-11?

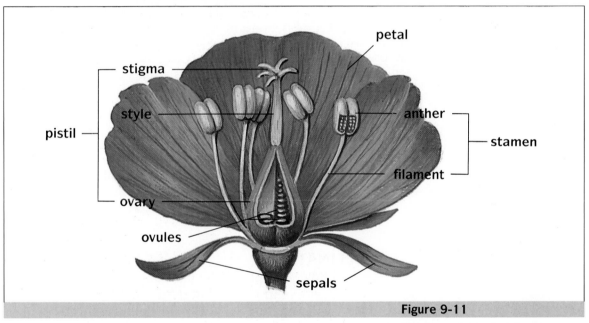

Figure 9-11

Structure of a typical flower.

A **pistil** (PIHS tuhl) is a female reproductive structure of a flower. There may be one or several pistils, depending on the plant species. The pistil is found in the center of a flower. A pistil is formed of three main parts. The upper part of a pistil is the *stigma* (STIHG muh). The stigma is a sticky structure on which pollen grains land. The enlarged base of a pistil is the **ovary** (OH vuhr ee). Inside the ovary are the small round structures—the ovules—from which seeds develop. The slender stalk that joins the stigma and the ovary is the *style* (stīl).

ACTIVITY   What Is the Structure of a Flower?

OBJECTIVE
Observe the structure of a flower.

MATERIALS
gladiolus flower, forceps, hand lens, dropper, water, microscope slide, scalpel, coverslip, microscope

PROCEDURE

A. Make a data table such as the one shown. Locate the green sepals. In the data table, record the number of sepals.

Flower Parts	Number
Sepals	
Petals	
Stamens	
Pistil	

B. Observe the petals just inside the sepals. Record the number of petals. Use forceps to remove the petals and sepals. Find the long, slender stamens. Identify an anther and a filament. Record the number of stamens. Use a hand lens to look at the structure of the stamens.

C. Locate the pistil in the center of the stamens. Identify the stigma, style, and ovary of the pistil.

D. Make a drawing of the stamens and pistil.

Label the following parts: stamen, anther, filament, pistil, stigma, style, and ovary.

E. Use a dropper to place a drop of water on a microscope slide. Use the forceps to remove one anther and place it in the water. Use a scalpel to cut open the anther. **Caution:** Always use great care in handling a scalpel. Direct the edge of the blade *away* from your body. Work on a firm surface. Hold the anther with the forceps, and shake the anther so that pollen grains fall into the water on the slide. Remove the anther, and cover the water and pollen grains with a coverslip. Examine the pollen grains under low and high power of a microscope. Make a drawing of several pollen grains.

F. Use the forceps to remove the pistil from the flower. Use the scalpel to cut open the ovary at the base of the pistil. Locate the ovules and examine them with the hand lens.

RESULTS AND CONCLUSIONS

1. How many sepals and petals were there in the flower you examined?
2. Based on the number of sepals and petals, was the plant a monocot or a dicot? Explain your answer.
3. Describe the stamen you examined. What two structures make up a stamen?
4. Describe the shape of the pollen grains you observed.

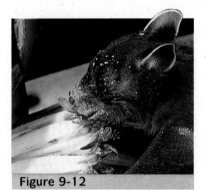

Figure 9-12

Bat pollinating a flower. Notice the pollen clinging to the bat's face.

POLLINATION

In flowering plants the male and female reproductive cells develop within the flower. Sperm cells are produced by the pollen grains. Egg cells are produced in the ovules.

Millions of pollen grains are produced in the anther. The anther breaks open and releases the fully developed pollen grains. For a seed to develop, pollen must be transferred from the male reproductive structure to the female reproductive structure. Recall that this process is called *pollination*. In flowering plants it is the transfer of pollen from an anther to a stigma.

Most flowers are pollinated by insects. But some are pollinated by other animals or by the wind. Most grasses and many trees have flowers that are pollinated by the wind. Wind-pollinated flowers, such as those of the alder

DO YOU KNOW?

Measuring almost 1 m across, *Rafflesia arnoldii* is the largest flower in the world. This giant flower grows on a few islands in Indonesia. *Rafflesia* has no roots and does not carry on photosynthesis. It is a parasite that lives off the roots or stems of grapevines.

Rafflesia blooms for just four days. Its flower is pollinated by flies that are attracted by the flower's odor. This odor is similar to that of rotting meat.

After four days, the flower becomes a slimy mass. The fruit that develops contains thousands of tiny seeds. Scientists think the seeds are carried to the grapevines by squirrels that feed on the fruit.

After 18 months, a bud about 5 cm in diameter appears among the grapevines. During the next 9 months, the bud grows into a giant flower.

Rafflesia is in danger of dying off. The forests where it grows are being cut down. Scientists are trying to save the world's largest flower.

shown in Figure 9-13*B*, are usually small and lack brightly colored petals. They also lack a strong, sweet scent. The large amounts of pollen produced cause some people to sneeze and to have itchy, watery eyes.

Flowers that are pollinated by insects or birds usually have brightly colored petals. These flowers produce a sweet substance called *nectar*. Animals such as bees, ants, and birds are attracted by the petals or the nectar of flowers. While they enter the flower, these animals may brush against the anthers. Pollen grains may stick to their body. As they enter another flower, they may transfer pollen to that flower.

Figure 9-13

Pollen grains of the alder (*A*), and flowers of the alder, a wind-pollinated tree (*B*).

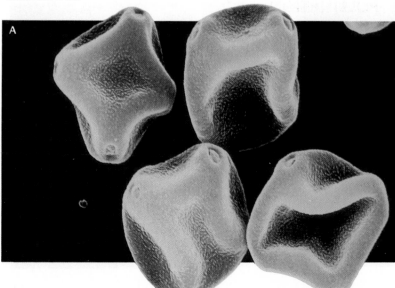

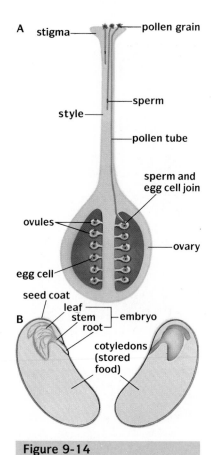

A stigma — pollen grain

style

sperm

pollen tube

sperm and egg cell join

ovules

ovary

egg cell

seed coat

B leaf
stem — embryo
root

cotyledons (stored food)

Figure 9-14

Growth of pollen tubes (A), and parts of a seed (B). What is contained in the cotyledon?

SEED AND FRUIT FORMATION

Once a pollen grain reaches the stigma, it begins to grow a pollen tube. The pollen tube grows down through the style to the ovary. Look for the pollen tubes in Figure 9-14A. A sperm cell travels down each pollen tube and joins with the egg cell inside an ovule. The joining of an egg cell and a sperm cell is called *fertilization*.

After fertilization, the ovules develop into seeds. Look for the main parts of a seed in Figure 9-14B. Notice that the embryo has two small leaves and a root. Some seeds contain stored food in the form of a cotyledon. Others contain a cotyledon and *endosperm* (EHN doh sperm), a food-storing tissue. The embryo uses this food until it makes its own food by photosynthesis.

Once the seed is fully developed, it may stop growing for a while. During this time, the embryo does not develop further. When conditions are suitable, the embryo will develop into a mature plant.

While the ovules develop into mature seeds, the ovary develops into a fruit. A **fruit** is a ripened ovary that contains one or more mature seeds. The fruit protects the seeds from disease and insects. You have probably eaten many kinds of fruits, such as peaches and apples. Many foods that are commonly called vegetables, such as cucumbers and tomatoes, are also fruits. Figure 9-15 shows some of the stages in the development of a tomato.

The fruit is also important in *seed dispersal* (dihs-PUHR suhl). Seed dispersal is the scattering of seeds away from the parent plant. Animals, wind, and water can transport fruits and their seeds over long distances. What are some ways that animals disperse seeds?

Figure 9-15

Development of a tomato: flower (*left*), unripened fruit (*middle*), and ripened fruit (*right*).

GERMINATION

When conditions are proper for growth, seeds undergo germination (jer muh NAY shuhn). **Germination** is the development of a plant embryo into a young plant. The conditions needed for seeds to germinate include water, oxygen, and the proper temperature. Some seeds also need a resting period before they germinate. Other seeds may need periods of cold. Refer to Figure 9-16 as you read about the stages in the germination of a bean seed.

germen (sprout)

1. Water enters the seed, the seed swells, and the seed coat begins to split. A young root pushes out through the seed coat.
2. Root hairs and side roots develop. A short stem pushes the cotyledons aboveground. Photosynthesis begins.
3. The roots and stem lengthen, and the leaves grow larger and open up. The seed coat falls off. The cotyledons begin to shrivel as the stored food is used up.
4. New leaves grow. The cotyledons fall off. The seedling will soon become a mature plant.

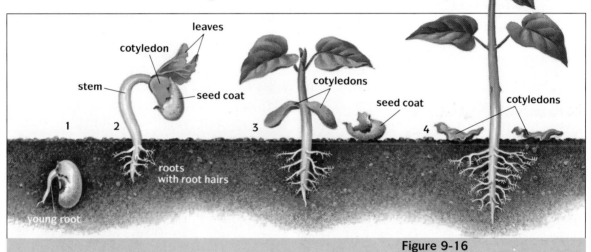

Figure 9-16

Stages in the germination of a bean seed. When can cotyledons drop off without harming the plant?

REVIEW

1. What are the main structures of a flower?
2. How are wind-pollinated flowers different from insect-pollinated flowers?
3. Describe the events that lead to the formation of seeds in a flower.
4. Define the term *fruit*. Explain the function of a fruit.
5. Describe the germination of a bean seed and its development into a mature bean plant.

CHALLENGE An imperfect flower is one that has either stamens or pistils—but not both—in the same flower. Can such a flower pollinate itself? Explain your answer.

9-5 REPRODUCTION FROM PLANT PARTS

After completing this section, you will be able to

- **distinguish** between vegetative propagation and sexual reproduction in plants.
- **describe** methods used to grow new plants from stems, roots, and leaves.

The key terms in this section are
cutting
vegetative propagation

Many plants that produce seeds can also reproduce by asexual means. Recall that asexual reproduction involves only one parent. Asexual reproduction in seed plants is called vegetative propagation (VEHJ uh tay tihv prahp-uh GAY shuhn). **Vegetative propagation** is the development of a new plant from a stem, root, or leaf of the parent plant. In this process there is no union of an egg cell and a sperm cell, and no seed forms.

New plants may be propagated, or grown, from above-ground stems in several ways. One method makes use of cuttings. A **cutting** is a plant part that has been removed from the parent plant and used to grow a new plant. The plant part used as a cutting is often a stem with a leaf attached. The cutting may be placed in water, in wet sand, or in some other wet substance. As shown in Figure 9-17, roots develop at the lower end of the stem. Once the cutting is planted in soil, it will grow new stems and leaves. Some important food plants, such as sugar cane and pineapple, are grown from stem cuttings.

Figure 9-17

Cutting of an African violet (*A*), and a rooted cutting that has developed new leaves (*B*).

Grafting is a method in which a stem cutting from one plant is attached to the rooted stem of another plant. As it grows, the cutting becomes a part of the rooted plant but retains its own traits. You can see how grafting is done in Figure 9-18. Grafting is usually done on trees. It can be used to increase the amount of fruit a tree produces. Grafting can also be used to grow fruits on trees that resist disease and drought.

206

New plants can also be grown from corms. A *corm* is a thickened underground stem. Gladiolus is a plant that forms corms. *Tubers* are enlarged food-storing underground stems. Recall that tubers, such as white potatoes, have many small buds called "eyes." A new plant can be grown from each eye. Some plants, such as sweet potatoes, are grown from roots. Stems and roots develop when a sweet potato is placed in water. Once new shoots and roots develop, the new plant can be planted in soil.

New plants can also be grown from whole leaves or pieces of leaves. Usually only plants with fleshy leaves, such as African violets, can be grown from their leaves. Fleshy leaves supply enough food and water reserves to keep the leaf alive as the new plant develops. The leaves of the kalanchöe (kal uhn KOH ee) plant, shown in Figure 9-19, produce buds from which tiny new plants grow.

Vegetative propagation is useful for many reasons. Some plants, such as bananas, are not grown from seeds. Other plants, such as grapes, can be grown by vegetative propagation so that the fruits do not contain seeds. Seedless fruits are easier to eat. This method is also often a faster method of growing plants than growing them from seeds.

Figure 9-18

Grafting, one form of vegetative propagation.

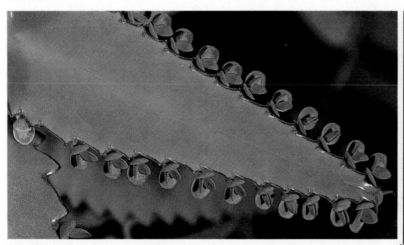

Figure 9-19

Tiny new plants develop along the edge of the kalanchöe leaf (*left*). The tiny plants fall to the ground and can develop into mature plants (*right*).

REVIEW

1. Why is vegetative propagation considered a form of asexual reproduction?
2. Describe how a new plant can be grown from a stem, a root, and a leaf.
3. Give two reasons why vegetative propagation is used.

CHALLENGE Imagine finding a tree on which several different varieties of apples are growing. Explain how this plant could have been developed.

9-6 PLANT GROWTH AND BEHAVIOR

auxein (to increase)

PLANT HORMONES

Growth in plants is different from growth in animals. Most animals grow only when they are young. In contrast, many kinds of plants continue to grow throughout their life cycle. They grow taller, and they become larger in diameter. Growth occurs in the tips of roots and stems, in young leaves, and in developing fruits. Growth also occurs in the *cambium*, which is a layer of dividing cells that produces xylem and phloem cells.

Plant growth and many other plant activities, such as flower and fruit production, are controlled by chemicals called hormones (HAWR mohnz). A **hormone** is a chemical that is produced in one part of an organism and controls an activity in another part of that organism. Hormones are produced in very small amounts in rapidly growing tissue, such as in root tips and stem tips. The hormones are then transported to other parts of the plant.

The most important plant hormones are the auxins (AWK sihnz). An **auxin** is a hormone that regulates plant growth and development. Auxins cause plant cells to lengthen. Some auxins help to begin root development. Auxins may prevent growth in some parts of a plant. Besides auxins, other hormones affect plant growth.

Figure 9-20

Control plant (*left*). Plant treated with a hormone (*right*). How do the plants differ?

Plant hormones have many practical uses. They are put on the ends of cuttings to cause root growth to occur. They also cause fruit production in plants such as tomatoes and apples. Auxins sprayed on potatoes and onions prevent sprouting. Some plant hormones are used as weed killers. When sprayed with these chemicals, weeds grow too quickly for proper development.

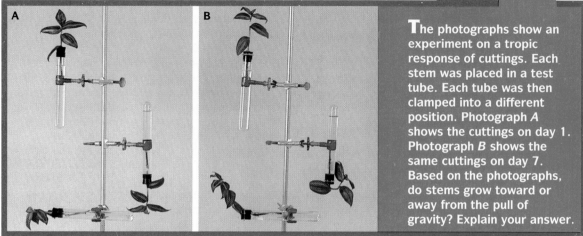

A

B

The photographs show an experiment on a tropic response of cuttings. Each stem was placed in a test tube. Each tube was then clamped into a different position. Photograph *A* shows the cuttings on day 1. Photograph *B* shows the same cuttings on day 7. Based on the photographs, do stems grow toward or away from the pull of gravity? Explain your answer.

TROPISMS

Hormones also help a plant respond to its environment. They cause growth in certain areas of the plant in response to light, water, and other factors. The growth of a plant toward or away from an outside stimulus is called a **tropism** (TROH pihz uhm). The stimulus causes hormones to collect in one part of the plant. Often the plant cells grow longer in the presence of the hormones. This increased growth can cause part of the plant to grow toward or away from a stimulus.

trope (a turning)

The growth of a plant in response to light is called *phototropism* (foh toh TROH pihz uhm). Most plant stems and leaves grow toward light. In Figure 9-21*A* you can

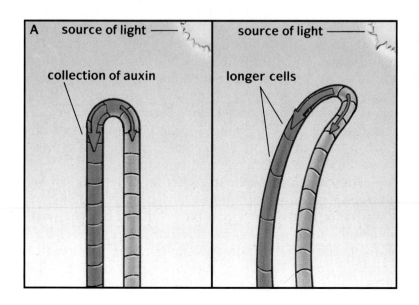

A   source of light ———

collection of auxin

source of light ———

longer cells

B

Figure 9-21

The effect of auxin on growth (*A*). On which side of the plant do the cells lengthen? A plant showing a phototropic response (*B*).

209

ACTIVITY What Is the Effect of Water on Bean Growth?

OBJECTIVE
Observe the effect of water on the growth of bean seedlings.

MATERIALS
potting soil, metric ruler, clear plastic storage box, modeling clay, small clay flowerpot, glass-marking pencil, 10 bean seedlings, 250-mL beaker, water

PROCEDURE
A. Pour potting soil into a clear plastic storage box to a depth of about 4 cm.
B. Use modeling clay to plug the drainage hole in the bottom of a clay flowerpot. Place the pot in the center of the box.
C. Use the blunt end of a glass-marking pencil to make ten evenly spaced holes in the soil near the side of the box: five holes to the left of the pot and five holes to the right.

D. Carefully insert a bean seedling in each hole. Place the seedlings next to the side of the box so that they can be seen through the side of the box.
E. Use a glass-marking pencil to number each seedling on the outside of the box, as shown in the drawing. Make a drawing of the box and seedlings. Date the drawing.
F. Use a 250-mL beaker to pour water into the flowerpot so that it is half full. The water will pass slowly through the walls of the pot and into the soil. Do not water the soil directly.
G. Observe the seedlings each day for 1 week. Note any changes in stems, leaves, and roots. Add water to the flowerpot as needed, so that the soil is always moist.
H. After 1 week, make another drawing of the seedlings in the box. Compare this drawing with the one you made in step **E**.

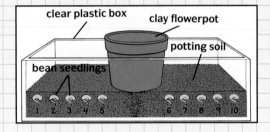

clear plastic box   clay flowerpot
potting soil
bean seedlings
1 2 3 4 5   6 7 8 9 10

RESULTS AND CONCLUSIONS
1. Describe how the bean seedlings looked on the first day of the activity.
2. How did the bean seedlings look after 1 week? Describe any changes you observed. Were there any differences from seedling to seedling? Refer to the seedlings by number.
3. Compare seedlings 1 and 10 with seedlings 5 and 6. Give a reason for any differences you observe in these seedlings.

Figure 9-22

Notice how part of the cucumber plant curls around the stake. What is this kind of response called?

see what happens inside a plant stem to cause it to grow toward light. When light strikes the plant stem, auxins collect in the cells on the side of the stem away from the light source. The cells on this shady side grow longer than the cells on the side facing the light. As the cells on the shady side grow longer, the stem bends toward the light.

Plants show many other kinds of tropisms. The growth response of a plant to gravity is called *geotropism* (jee oh-TROH pihz uhm). Roots grow toward the pull of gravity. Stems grow away from the pull of gravity.

The growth response of plants to water is called *hydrotropism* (hī droh TROH pihz uhm). The growth of roots toward moisture ensures that the roots will be near available water in the soil. A growth response to touch is called *thigmotropism* (thihg moh TROH pihz uhm). Climbing or twining plants, such as grapevines, grow around solid objects, such as tree trunks.

REVIEW

1. In what parts of plants does growth occur?
2. Define the term *hormone*.
3. Give two examples of practical uses of auxins.
4. Explain how hormones cause stems to grow toward light.

CHALLENGE Design an experiment to find out whether a plant root responds to light.

CHAPTER SUMMARY

The main ideas in this chapter are listed below. Read these statements before you answer the Chapter Review questions.

- The energy needed by animals is supplied either directly or indirectly by organisms that carry on photosynthesis. The exchange of gases and water and the production of glucose occur inside a leaf. (9-1)

- During photosynthesis, carbon dioxide and water join in the presence of light; glucose and oxygen are produced. During respiration, glucose and oxygen join; carbon dioxide and water are produced, and energy is released. (9-1)

- In nonvascular plants, transport occurs by diffusion. In vascular plants, transport occurs in the xylem and phloem. (9-2)

- Wilting occurs when more water is lost by transpiration from the leaves than is absorbed through the roots. (9-2)

- During the life cycle of a pine, the female cone is pollinated by pollen from the male cone. After the egg cells of the female cone are fertilized by sperm cells, seeds develop on the female cone. Seeds are carried by the wind and germinate under the proper conditions. (9-3)

- The flower is the reproductive structure of an angiosperm. Pollination is the transfer of pollen from anther to stigma. (9-4)

- A seed consists of an embryo, stored food, and a seed coat. Seeds form inside the ovary. Seeds can be dispersed by animals, wind, and water. Germination is the development of a plant embryo into a young plant. (9-4)

- Vegetative propagation is one form of asexual reproduction in plants. New plants can be grown asexually from leaves, stems, and roots. (9-5)

- Growth in plants occurs only in certain regions—stem tips, root tips, young leaves, developing fruits, and cambium. A hormone is a chemical that is produced in one part of an organism and controls a response in another part of the organism. A tropism is the growth of a plant toward or away from an outside stimulus. (9-6)

The key terms in this chapter are listed below. Use each term in a sentence that shows the meaning of the term.

auxin	guard cells	pollen grain	stamen
cutting	hormone	pollination	stomate
embryo	ovary	respiration	transpiration
epidermis	palisade layer	seed	tropism
flower	petal	seed coat	vegetative
fruit	photosynthesis	sepal	propagation
germination	pistil	spongy layer	

Chapter Review

VOCABULARY

Write the letter of the term that best matches the definition. Not all the terms will be used.

1. The process by which plants make their own food by using light energy from the sun
2. The process by which foods are broken down and energy is released
3. A layer of loosely packed cells in a leaf
4. The transfer of pollen from the male reproductive structure to the female reproductive structure
5. Loss of water through the stomates of leaves
6. The flower structure that bears the pollen grains
7. The reproductive structure of a flowering plant
8. A leaflike structure at the base of a flower
9. A plant growth response to an external stimulus
10. The development of a plant embryo into a young plant

a. auxin
b. flower
c. fruit
d. germination
e. hormone
f. ovary
g. palisade layer
h. photosynthesis
i. pollination
j. respiration
k. sepal
l. spongy layer
m. stamen
n. transpiration
o. tropism

CONCEPTS

1. Explain how a meat-eating animal depends on plants. (9-1)
2. Name the types of cells found in a leaf and the function of these cells. (9-1)
3. Explain how the guard cells control the opening and closing of the stomates. (9-1)
4. Describe the major events that occur during the dark reaction of photosynthesis. (9-1)
5. Compare the raw materials and products of photosynthesis with the raw materials and products of respiration. (9-1)
6. What is the main difference between transport of materials in nonvascular and in vascular plants? (9-2)
7. Compare the function of xylem with that of phloem. (9-2)
8. Describe wilting and transpiration. (9-2)
9. What is the main difference in function between a male cone and a female cone? (9-3)
10. Describe how a sperm cell reaches an egg cell inside the ovule of a pine cone. (9-3)

11. Where on a pine tree do seeds develop? How are these seeds scattered? (9-3)

12. Name the three parts of a seed, and give the function of each part. (9-3)

13. Describe the functions of a stamen, a pistil, and an ovary. (9-4)

14. What is the main difference between pollination and fertilization? (9-4)

15. Describe the main events leading to the formation of a seed in an angiosperm. (9-4)

16. Name three ways in which seeds are dispersed. Give an example of each of these ways. (9-4)

17. What three requirements must be met before a seed can germinate? (9-4)

18. Explain why the cotyledons of a bean plant drop off when the seedling matures. (9-4)

19. Explain why plant growers use the process of vegetative propagation. Give two examples of plants grown by this method. (9-5)

20. Explain the relationship between auxins and phototropism in a plant. (9-6)

APPLICATION/ CRITICAL THINKING

1. Give an example of phototropism and geotropism in a plant. Explain how each response helps the plant survive.

2. Why is it not necessary that a pine cone be brightly colored or have a lovely fragrance?

3. Suggest one reason why it might be an advantage to a species to have seeds scattered far away from the parent plant.

4. Describe one method by which a pear tree with many varieties of pears on it could be developed.

EXTENSION

1. Determine what food crops are grown in your area. Find out how plant hormones are used to improve these crops.

2. Visit a local nursery. Find out how the dealers use vegetative propagation to grow new plants.

3. Take photographs of wild flowers common in your area. Learn something about each of the flowers. Give a slide presentation to your class, and give information about each of the flowers shown.

READINGS

Cook, R. "Plant Cloning." *Natural History*, March 1980, p. 88.

Overbeck, S. *How Seeds Travel*. Minneapolis, Minn.: Lerner Publications, Inc., 1982.

Squire, S. "Frozen Assets." *Natural Wildlife*, August-September 1984, p. 6.

How much water do the plants in your home and school need? How much sunlight do they need? What soils are best for which plants? A florist can answer these questions.

Florists sell plants and cut flowers. They must know how to care for the plants they keep. They must know under what conditions the flowering plants will bloom. Florists often make attractive arrangements of flowers. Florists also must be able to help customers with plants that are diseased or that have other problems. Florists should know how to recognize certain common plant diseases. A knowledge of how to cure plant diseases is also helpful.

Florists usually work in shops. Some work for hotels and restaurants. Florists may run their own businesses or work for others. Most receive on-the-job training. If you are interested in this career, you will benefit from biology and art courses in high school.■

Florist

How is information about photosynthesis and other plant processes learned? Who gathers data about plant functions? Botanists are scientists who study plants. They work in laboratories and in the field.

Some botanists study which plants are resistant to disease and how to yield more food from crop plants. Others study the chemical reactions, such as photosynthesis, that occur within plant cells.

Botanists who do research at universities may teach courses there as well. Other botanists work for the government or in private industry. Certain botany careers may require a four-year college degree. Some require an advanced degree. If you have a special interest in plants, you may want to become a botanist. You should take courses in biology and chemistry in high school.■

Botanist

People in Science

Dr. Nam-Hai Chua, Cell Biologist

Scientists know that light affects plants in special ways. Without light, plants cannot make food. Dr. Nam-Hai Chua has a special interest in understanding photosynthesis and the functioning of the chloroplast. Dr. Chua and members of his research team want to learn what occurs in plant cells when the cells are exposed to light.

In his work, Dr. Chua removed parts of chromosomes from cells of pea plants. He moved them to cells of petunia plants. He found that the petunias reacted to light much as the pea plants did. In this way, he was able to tell the function of the parts of chromosomes that he moved.

Today, Dr. Chua's work is helping farming. His work with other scientists is improving crop plants. One possible outcome of Dr. Chua's research might be the development of crop plants that can resist heat. Dr. Chua works at Rockefeller University in New York City.■

Issues and Technology

The Green Revolution started in North America and Europe in the late 1940s. It was a great change in agriculture, allowing farmers to grow more food than ever before. The new farming methods made possible an increased food supply.

What are these changes in farming? One change involves seeds. New varieties of seeds are created in the laboratory by crossbreeding natural plant varieties. With the help of chemical fertilizers and pesticides, the new varieties of plants grow bigger and faster than some natural varieties.

The Green Revolution has spread to countries outside North America and Europe. Figure 1 shows the parts of the world where the Green Revolution has had the greatest effect. In 1981 the world average grain

production was 2,250 kilograms per hectare. This is nearly twice the amount that was produced in 1965.

Much good has come from the Green Revolution. But there also have been some problems. For some scientists the biggest problem is the kinds of food crops being grown. These laboratory-produced food varieties don't grow well naturally. They need chemical pesticides and fertilizers. They often need large amounts of water. And they need to be tended with expensive machinery.

APPLYING CRITICAL THINKING SKILLS

1. The United States shows a crop yield above the 1981 world average. Name three other countries with a similar yield.

2. Which areas of the world have the highest yields? How do these yields compare with the world average?

3. Some countries do not have yields above the 1981 average. Buy they *have* increased their yields between 1965 and 1981. Name three such countries.

4. Which country has increased its yields more since 1965, the Philippines or the United States? Does this mean the Philippines has a higher crop yield than the United States? How do you know?

5. The Green Revolution depends on the use of fertilizers and other chemicals. Many of these substances are produced from oil. What problems could result from this dependence on oil-based chemicals?

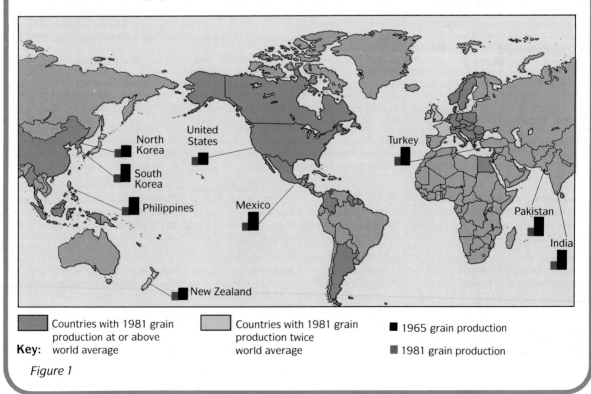

Key:
- Countries with 1981 grain production at or above world average
- Countries with 1981 grain production twice world average
- ■ 1965 grain production
- ■ 1981 grain production

Figure 1

215

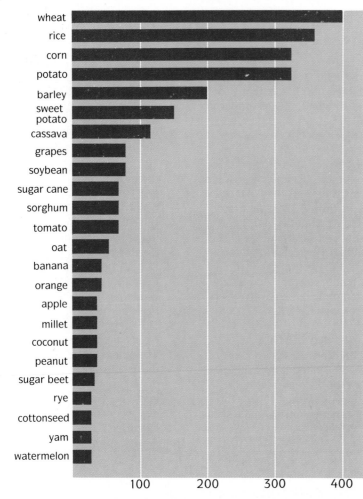

Crop Size (millions of metric tons)

Figure 2

Scientists estimate that there are 80,000 kinds of edible plants on the earth. Today, only about 150 are widely raised by people. Of these, only 20 provide about 90 percent of our food.

Figure 2 shows the most common food crops and the amounts that are grown. As you can see, farmers all over the world are growing the same crops. Is this concentration on a few crops a problem? Some scientists believe that the crops are so similar that they could be easily wiped out by a single disease.

Each living thing has its own set of characteristics. The characteristics of an organism are de- termined by its *genes*. Genes are made up of DNA, the substance that controls the activities of cells. In a plant, some genes con- trol the plant's color. Other genes control how it grows. Still others control how well the plant can fight certain diseases.

Each of the 80,000 kinds of edible plants has its own set of genes and its own special charac- teristics. Thus, there is a great variety of possible plant charac- teristics. However, the farm crops that are grown show only a small part of this variety. For ex- ample, there are dozens of vari- eties of wheat. But only nine kinds of wheat are commonly grown in the United States. There are also many kinds of potatoes. But nearly three fourths of Amer- ican potatoes are produced from just four varieties.

Suppose farmers planted many different kinds of potatoes. Each type would have a different set of genes. If a disease killed one kind of potato, a different va- riety of potato might have a gene that makes it resistant to the dis- ease. But if all the potatoes are the same, a disease that can kill one plant can probably kill the others, too.

Over 100 years ago, Irish farm- ers grew only one kind of potato, the lumper. In the 1840s a fungus attacked the potato crop. The lumper had no resistance to the fungus, and almost all the potato plants died. One million people died of starvation. One and one- half million others left Ireland for other countries.

APPLYING CRITICAL THINKING SKILLS

1. The top four crops planted worldwide account for more than all of the rest together. What are the top four crops? Do these foods make up a large part of your diet?
2. Amaranth is one of the 80,000 edible plants not commonly grown for food. Amaranth seeds are a good source of protein and vitamin C. If you were a farmer, what would you need to know about amaranth before you could grow it?
3. If amaranth were available in stores, would you be willing to try it? Why or why not? What information would you want to help you make up your mind?
4. If research is required to pro- vide the information needed in questions 3 and 4, who should do this research? Who should pay for this research?

Scientists can now crossbreed plants and transfer genes from one plant to another. Wild plants often are resistant to plant diseases. The genes from these plants may be useful in producing new resistant varieties of crop plants.

Scientists look for these wild plants in special areas of the world called Vavilov centers. These areas are named for N.I. Vavilov, a scientist who traced the origins of many food plants. Figure 3 shows the location of several Vavilov centers and lists some of the important plants that originated in each one. From these centers the plants spread around the world. Many of the original kinds of wild plants still grow in these centers of origin.

Unfortunately, the centers are not being preserved. The wild plants are being cleared for new roads, villages, and farms. Often the natural plant varieties are replaced by laboratory-bred plants. Vavilov centers contain a great variety of plant types. Once the source of this great variety of wild plants is lost, it cannot be replaced.

One idea is to create national parks to protect the plants that grow in the Vavilov centers. This idea may be necessary because some plants cannot be grown outside their native areas. Others can't be preserved as seeds because storage destroys their DNA.

APPLYING CRITICAL THINKING SKILLS

1. Where did the potato originate? Name two other places where potatoes are grown in the world today.
2. Today the central United States grows a large amount of wheat and corn. These grains did not originate in this region. How might each of these crops have come to this region?
3. Look back at Figure 1. Are any of the Green Revolution grains being grown in Vavilov centers? What would you expect to happen to the natural food plants in these areas?
4. Many scientists believe that preserving the Vavilov centers is important. Why?
5. Vavilov centers exist all over the world. Some areas span several countries. Who should be in control of these centers? Should all the centers be under one control, or should each center be independent of the others? Defend your answer.
6. Vavilov centers provide plants and seeds for breeders who are trying to develop new crop plants. These breeders then sell the new seeds. Farmers in the Vavilov centers complain that they should not have to pay for seeds that were developed from their own plants. Breeders say that someone has to pay for the experiments. How would you settle this dispute?

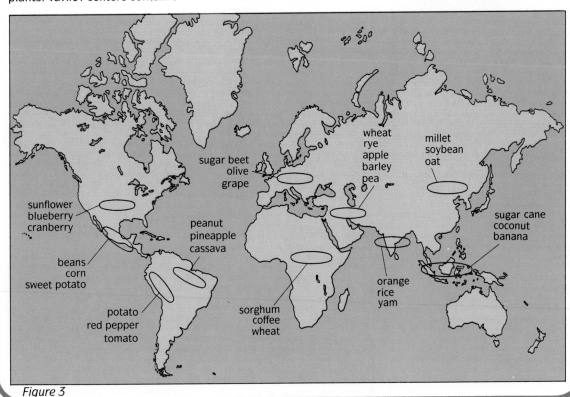

Figure 3

ANIMALS

*T*he great variety of animal life has long been a source of wonder and delight for many people. There are over a million different kinds of animals on the earth. Some are quite familiar to you. Others are rare and unusual. The Loch Ness monster and the abominable snowman are animals whose existence has not yet been proven. In this unit you will study major groups of animals and see how they are alike and how they differ. ■

▲ *Lions have come to symbolize strength and courage. This statue of a lion guards the New York Public Library.*

▼ *Animals have always been important to humans. These prehistoric cave paintings were found in a cave at Lascaux in Montignac, France.*

▲ *A coral skeleton from the West Indies. Corals are animals that remove lime from seawater and use it to produce a hard outer covering.*

▶ *This colored woodcut from 1550 depicts sea monsters that were thought to exist in the North Atlantic Ocean.*

◀ *A louse viewed through a microscope using polarized light.*

▲ *A beard-lichen grasshopper on a lichen. Notice how well the grasshopper blends in with its surroundings.*

SIMPLE INVERTEBRATES

Can you guess what kind of organism is shown in the photograph? It looks like a brightly colored, undersea flower. But it is really an animal! This "flower-animal" is called a sea anemone. Species of anemones vary in color. The body may be blue, pink, red, green, or many colors. Some anemones are as small as 5 mm in diameter. Other species can grow to be as large as 1 m in diameter. Anemones are found in salt water along coasts all over the world. The body parts that look like flower petals are used in food getting. Where do you think the anemone's mouth is?

- *What other animals are similar to anemones?*
- *How is the body of a simple invertebrate supported?*
- *How do simple invertebrates eat? How do they reproduce?*

10-1 TRAITS OF INVERTEBRATES

About one and one-half million species of animals living today have been named by scientists. It is likely that many animal species have not yet been identified. Animals live all over the world and in every kind of climate. They differ widely from one another in size and appearance. All animals are alike in that they are many-celled organisms that cannot make their own food.

Animals can be divided into two major groups. These groups are invertebrates and vertebrates. An **invertebrate** (ihn VER tuh briht) is an animal that does not have a backbone. Invertebrates include the starfish, sponge, jellyfish, earthworm, and butterfly shown in Figure 10-1 on the next page. A *vertebrate* is an animal that has a backbone. Sharks, frogs, snakes, robins, cats, and humans are vertebrates. Each of these animals has a skeleton with a backbone inside its body. You will learn more about vertebrates in Chapter 12 and Chapter 13.

The animal kingdom is divided into about 30 major groups called phyla. Of these phyla, only one includes animals that are vertebrates. All the other phyla are made

After completing this section, you will be able to

- **define** the term *invertebrate.*
- **identify** three cell layers from which some invertebrates form.
- **list** the eight largest phyla of invertebrates.

The key terms in this section are

ectoderm	invertebrate
endoderm	mesoderm

in- (not)
-vertebratus (jointed)

Figure 10-1

The starfish (*A*), sponge (*B*), jellyfish (*C*), earthworm (*D*), and butterfly (*E*) are all invertebrates.

Figure 10-2

A lobster (*top*) and a spider (*bottom*) are in the same phylum.

up of animals that are invertebrates. Animals are grouped in the same phylum if they have basic traits in common. Sometimes animals within a phylum look quite different, but their internal structure is similar. For example, many kinds of sponges belong to one invertebrate phylum. Sponges vary in their color, size, and shape, but they have certain traits in common. Sponges are similar in body structure, in the way they get food, and in the ways in which they reproduce. Look at Figure 10-2. Spiders and lobsters are in the same phylum. How do these animals differ? How might they be alike?

Many invertebrates can reproduce by both asexual and sexual means. *Asexual reproduction* involves only one parent. In *sexual reproduction* a sperm and an egg, usually from two parents, join to produce a new individual.

The animals that make up the invertebrate phyla can be grouped according to their body structure. Some invertebrates have a simpler body than others have. Some of these simple animals, such as the sponges, have a body that is only two cells thick. Others, such as flatworms, have several cell layers that form *tissues*. A tissue is a group of similar cells that work together and perform a common function. Look at Figure 10-3, which shows tissue layers in developing animals. Some simple animals form from two tissue layers, as shown in part *A*. Other, more complex animals form from three tissue layers, shown in part *B*.

Scientists are turning to marine invertebrates for the development of new drugs and other useful chemicals. Sponges, coelenterates, and mollusks are among the animals that are being studied.

Mussels are mollusks that produce a sticky protein that enables them to cling tightly to rocks. Even the battering force of ocean waves does not loosen them. The sticky protein that mussels produce is a glue, or adhesive. Scientists are trying to make this adhesive through genetic engineering in their laboratories. It is thought that the adhesive will be useful in situations where cemented materials are constantly exposed to water or water-containing liquids. For example, scientists hope that the adhesive could be used to cement materials together underwater. The substance might be used to repair torn human skin or to patch broken bones together. It might also be used as a dental cement.

Another marine adhesive being developed is a molasseslike protein given off by bacteria that live in oysters. Researchers are discovering a wide range of applications for this protein. It may be used as a paint thickener, a waterproofing material, and a material for sewing cuts in surgery.

Sponges and coelenterates contain substances that are being tested for use as medicines. One promising substance, found in sea anemones (uh NEHM uh neez), is being studied as a possible drug to help diseased human hearts function better.

The outer tissue layer is called the **ectoderm**. The **mesoderm** is the middle tissue layer. The inner tissue layer is called the **endoderm**. These tissue layers in developing young form the tissues and organs of some adult animals.

Many of the invertebrate phyla contain only a few species. These species are not well known by most people. You will learn about the eight largest phyla of invertebrates. Six phyla of simple invertebrates—sponges, coelenterates (sih LEHN tuh rayts), flatworms, roundworms, segmented worms, and mollusks—will be discussed in this chapter. In the next chapter you will learn about more complex invertebrates—the echinoderms (ih KĪ nuh dermz) and arthropods (AHR thruh pahdz).

REVIEW

1. What is an invertebrate?
2. Name the three body layers of some invertebrates, and describe the location of each layer.
3. What eight phyla of invertebrates contain the greatest number of species?

CHALLENGE A snail and a clam are classified in the same invertebrate phylum. What traits common to both animals might be the basis for this classification?

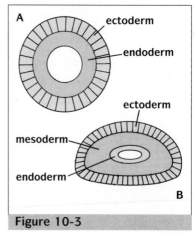

Figure 10-3

Tissue layers in developing animals: animal with two tissue layers (A); animal with three tissue layers (B).

10-2 SPONGES

Sponges make up one phylum of invertebrates. A **sponge** is the simplest invertebrate. Sponges live in fresh water and in salt water. Until the late eighteenth century, people thought that sponges were plants. That was because adult sponges do not move from one place to another, as most other animals do. Instead, like some sea plants, sponges grow attached to rocks, shells, or other objects at the bottom of a body of water. But a sponge is not a plant. Unlike a plant, a sponge cannot make its own food. It must take in food to survive. Sponges vary greatly in color, size, and shape. You can see some of the great variety among sponges in Figure 10-4.

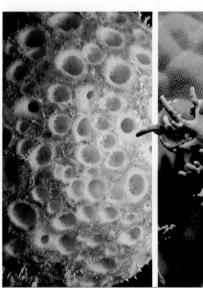  

Figure 10-4

Three types of sponges.

spiculum (sharp point)

Sponges lack an internal skeleton. Support for the body of a sponge comes from other structures. Some kinds of sponges contain spicules (SPIHK yoolz). A **spicule** is a hard, pointed structure that is found in some sponges and that supports the animal's body. Other kinds of sponges contain spongin. **Spongin** is a flexible substance that forms a network between cells of some sponges and that helps to support the animal's body. Some kinds of sponges contain both spicules and spongin.

Most sponges have a large opening at the top. Sponges also have many small openings called *pores*. Water enters a sponge through its pores. Sponges remove food from the water around them. Because they filter food from the water, sponges are called *filter feeders*.

Figure 10-5 shows a lengthwise section of a sponge. The body of a sponge is two cells thick. A jellylike material between the two cell layers contains spicules. Water containing food and oxygen enters the sponge through its many pores. Locate the pores. Find the central cavity of the sponge. Look at the *collar cells* that line the central cavity. Notice that each collar cell has a flagellum (fluh-JEHL luhm) (pl., *flagella*). A **flagellum** is a whiplike structure on a cell. Each flagellum beats back and forth rapidly. A current is produced by this beating action. The current helps to draw water into the pores. The water moves to the central cavity through a system of canals. The current produced by the flagella of the collar cells keeps the water moving through the sponge.

flagellum (whip)

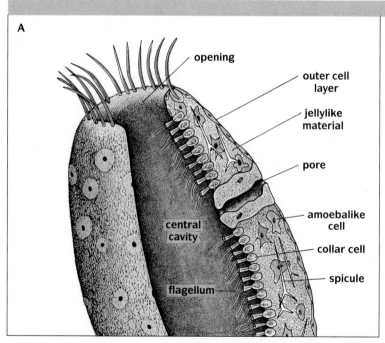

A

- opening
- outer cell layer
- jellylike material
- pore
- central cavity
- amoebalike cell
- collar cell
- spicule
- flagellum

Figure 10-5

Internal structure of a sponge (*A*), and a whole sponge (*B*). Which structures draw water into the sponge?

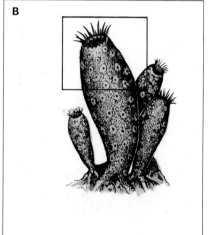

B

As the water passes over the collar cells, tiny bits of food in the water are trapped by these cells. The collar cells digest some of the food. Some of the food passes to the jellylike layer. In this layer are free-moving *amoebalike cells*. These cells also digest food. Some of the digested food is carried by the amoebalike cells to other cells. Water containing wastes and undigested food is constantly moving out of the sponge. The water passes out of the central cavity through the opening at the top of the sponge.

Reproduction in sponges is both sexual and asexual. Sexual reproduction in a sponge occurs by the joining of sperm and eggs within the jellylike layer. There are two

OBJECTIVE
Observe the structure of a sponge.

MATERIALS
preserved sponge, hand lens, microscope, prepared slide of sponge cross section

PROCEDURE
A. Examine a preserved sponge. Use a hand lens to examine the surface and the pores. Make a drawing of the sponge. Label the pores in your drawing.

B. Use a microscope to examine a prepared slide of a sponge cross section. Make a drawing of the cross section. Label each type of cell that is present. Label spicules if they are present. Also label the central cavity and the opening if they are shown in the slide.

RESULTS AND CONCLUSIONS
1. Describe the texture of the sponge.
2. How does your observation of sponge cells support the idea that sponges are not plants?

re- (again)
-generare (to produce)

Figure 10-6

Natural sponges.

types of asexual reproduction. In one type a group of cells forms a bud on the parent sponge. The bud grows as it remains attached to the parent. When it breaks off, it may be carried by the water to another location. It may then attach to a rock, shell, or other object and grow into an adult sponge.

Regeneration (ree jehn uh RAY shuhn) is another asexual method by which new sponges can be produced. **Regeneration** is the regrowth of body parts that have been lost or damaged. It is also the growth of an entire new organism from a part of the body. Sponges can regenerate a whole new organism from a few cells. If a sponge is cut into pieces, each piece can grow into a new sponge.

The body of a sponge is flexible and holds a great deal of water. Because of these traits, sponges have been used for cleaning and bathing. The sponges that are used for bathing contain spongin. Why would a sponge that contains spongin be suited for this use?

Sponge growers use regeneration to increase their crops. Sponges are cut into many small pieces and then returned to the water. Each piece grows into a new sponge that is collected, cleaned, and sold. Figure 10-6 shows natural sponges being displayed for sale.

REVIEW

1. Distinguish between spicules and spongin. What function do they serve?
2. Describe how a sponge obtains food.
3. Describe two ways in which sponges reproduce asexually.

CHALLENGE Suggest a reason why the sponge-growing industry has become much smaller over the last 40 years.

10-3 COELENTERATES

TRAITS OF COELENTERATES

The coelenterates make up another phylum of simple invertebrates, most of which live in the ocean. A **coelenterate** is an invertebrate that has a large central body cavity. The body form is a hollow sac. Coelenterates have two tissue layers. The outer layer of cells forms from the ectoderm. The inner layer of cells forms from the endoderm. There is a jellylike substance between the two tissue layers.

Coelenterates have a single body opening called a mouth. In most coelenterates this opening is surrounded by tentacles. **Tentacles** (TEHN tuh kuhlz) are armlike extensions that are used in catching food and bringing it into the body cavity. Figure 10-7 shows three animals that are in this phylum. Compare the hydra, jellyfish, and sea anemone. How do these animals differ? What features do they have in common?

> After completing this section, you will be able to
>
> - **describe** traits of coelenterates.
> - **describe** reproduction in coelenterates.
>
> *The key terms in this section are*
> budding   stinging cell
> coelenterate   tentacles

coelus (hollow)

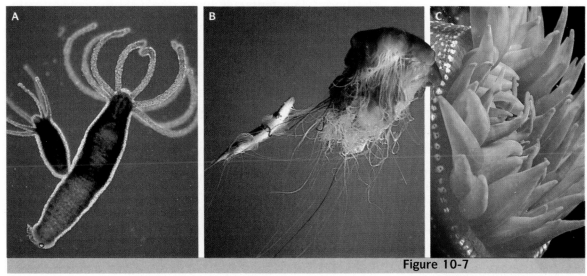

Figure 10-7

A hydra (*A*); a jellyfish, with captured fish, (*B*); and a sea anemone (*C*) are coelenterates. Which of these animals has stinging cells?

The tentacles of a coelenterate have special cells called stinging cells. A **stinging cell** is a cell that has a pointed threadlike part used in food getting. When an animal brushes against the tentacles, the stinging cell reacts. The pointed, threadlike part is released and pierces the animal. A poison in the threadlike part paralyzes or kills the animal. The threadlike part can wrap around the animal and help hold it. The tentacles then carry the animal, which is food, into the mouth of the coelenterate. Stinging cells are also used in defense.

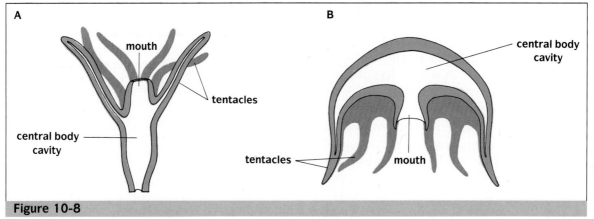

Figure 10-8

Two body forms of coelenterates: tubelike form (A); and umbrella-shaped form (B). Which body type does a sea anemone have?

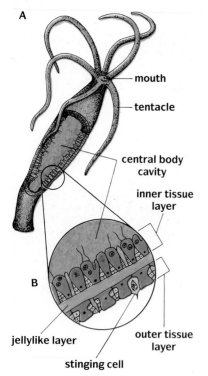

Figure 10-9

Hydra, showing tentacles and tissue layers (A); enlargement of two tissue layers (B).

Most coelenterates have one of two different body forms during their life cycle. Figure 10-8 shows both types. Notice that each has a central body cavity. One body form is a tubelike structure that has a mouth at the top surrounded by tentacles. The other body form is an umbrella-shaped structure that has a mouth on the lower part of the body. The tentacles hang down. Some coelenterates change from one body form to the other during their life cycle.

Although coelenterates are simple animals, they are more complex than sponges. Recall that sponges have two layers of cells. Scientists have found that the cells of a sponge do not form true tissues. Coelenterates are made up of two body layers that are true tissues.

Like sponges, coelenterates reproduce both sexually and asexually. When coelenterates reproduce asexually, it is most often by budding. **Budding** is a process of asexual reproduction in which a new individual develops from an outgrowth of the parent. A *bud* is a group of cells that grows into a new animal while still attached to the parent. Look back at Figure 10-7A, which shows a budding hydra. Compare the bud with the parent. When the bud grows to a certain size, it breaks off the parent and attaches itself to an underwater surface.

TYPES OF COELENTERATES

Coelenterates are divided into three major groups. The hydras make up one group and the jellyfish make up another. The corals and sea anemones are in a third group.

The hydra has a body cavity that is a simple hollow sac. This animal is one of the few freshwater coelenterates. Most hydras are only a few millimeters in length. The body of a hydra can stretch when the animal is getting

OBJECTIVES
Observe the responses of a hydra to stimuli.
Hypothesize about responses of hydra to other stimuli.

MATERIALS
dropper, hydra culture, petri dish, aquarium water, hand lens, toothpick, vinegar

PROCEDURE

A. Use a dropper to remove a single hydra from a hydra culture. Place the hydra in a petri dish. Add enough aquarium water to cover the hydra.
B. Use a hand lens to examine the hydra. Locate the mouth and tentacles. Make a labeled drawing of the hydra.

C. As you observe the hydra with the hand lens, use a toothpick to gently touch the animal in two or three different areas. Record the hydra's response to each touch.
D. Again observe the hydra with the hand lens as you use the dropper to add one drop of vinegar, a weak acid, to the water in the petri dish. Record the hydra's response to the vinegar.

RESULTS AND CONCLUSIONS
1. How did the hydra respond to touch?
2. What effect did vinegar have on the hydra?
3. Form a hypothesis about other stimuli that might produce the same response in hydras as vinegar does. Give reasons for your hypothesis.

---

food. The tubelike body form of the hydra can be seen in Figure 10-9. Notice the two tissue layers separated by a jellylike layer. The single mouth opening, surrounded by tentacles, leads to the central body cavity.

The second group of coelenterates are the jellyfish. The adult has an umbrella-shaped body form. Most of the animal's body is made up of the jellylike substance that is between the two tissue layers.

The third group of coelenterates are animals that have a more complex body structure than the hydras or the jellyfish. Corals and sea anemones belong to this group. Sea anemones have only a tubelike stage in their life cycle. Corals live in colonies and have a tubelike body that produces a hard outer covering made of limestone. When a coral dies, the limestone covering remains. Coral reefs, such as the one in Figure 10-10, are formed by the buildup of countless limestone coverings.

Figure 10-10

Red sponges attached to a coral reef.

REVIEW

1. Describe the body of a coelenterate, and distinguish between the two body forms.
2. What is budding?
3. Briefly describe animals from each of three groups of coelenterates.

CHALLENGE   Like sponges, hydras may remain attached to a rock or other surface as they feed. Why are hydras *not* described as filter feeders?

10-4 FLATWORMS

TRAITS OF FLATWORMS

Animals in the flatworm phylum have a more complex body structure than either sponges or coelenterates. A **flatworm** is an invertebrate with a flattened body. It is the simplest of all the worms. Flatworms form from three tissue layers. Unlike sponges and coelenterates, flatworms have true *organs*. An organ is two or more different tissues that work together and perform a certain function. Flatworms also have *organ systems*, which are groups of organs that work together to perform one or more functions. Flatworms have a distinct head and tail. They are the simplest animals to have these traits.

Flatworms, which include planarians, flukes, and tapeworms, are of two types. They are either parasites or free-living worms. A **parasite** (PAR uh sīt) is an organism that lives in or on another organism and harms it. The organism that is harmed is called the host. A parasite takes its food from the host. Most flatworms are parasites. A free-living worm is one that does not live in or on another organism. It moves about and has different food sources.

PLANARIANS

Planarians are free-living flatworms. Most planarians live in water, although some types are found in moist soil. In Figure 10-11B you can see how flat the animal's body is. Is the mouth on the upper or lower surface? Planarians lack a circulatory system and a respiratory system. Gas exchange occurs through the surface of the animal's body.

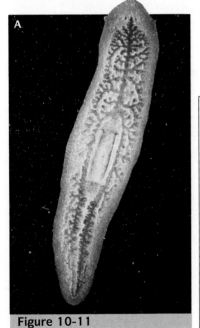

Figure 10-11

A planarian is a flatworm. Note the flattened body, pharynx, and eyespots.

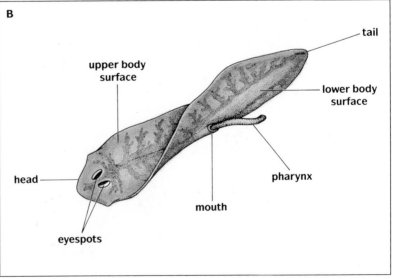

The digestive system of this flatworm consists of a mouth, a pharynx, and an intestine. A **pharynx** (FAR ihngks) is a tube that joins the mouth with the rest of the digestive tract. At times the pharynx can extend out of the mouth on the lower surface, as shown in Figure 10-11. This may occur when food is taken into the body. The digestive tract branches out to different parts of the animal. Planarians eat other small invertebrates and protozoans. They also feed on the bodies of dead animals. Undigested food passes out of the body through the pharynx.

Figure 10-12 shows the nervous system of a planarian. The nervous system consists of two eyespots, two main nerves with smaller, branching nerves, and two large masses of nerve cells that act as a simple brain. The animal's eyespots can detect whether light is strong or dim. But planarians do not see images.

The reproductive system is the most complex system in a planarian. There are both male and female reproductive organs in a single animal. Sexual reproduction occurs when two planarians exchange sperm. The fertilized eggs pass out of the body, and new worms develop from them.

Planarians can also reproduce asexually by means of regeneration. Recall that regeneration is the regrowth of lost body parts or the growth of a new organism from a small part of the body. As shown in Figure 10-13, a planarian that is cut into three parts can grow into three new worms. Experiments show that as little as one tenth of a worm can grow into a whole new planarian.

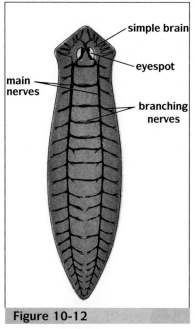

Figure 10-12

Nervous system of a planarian. What can a planarian detect with its eyespots?

Figure 10-13

Regeneration in a planarian. A whole new animal can grow from a small part of the body.

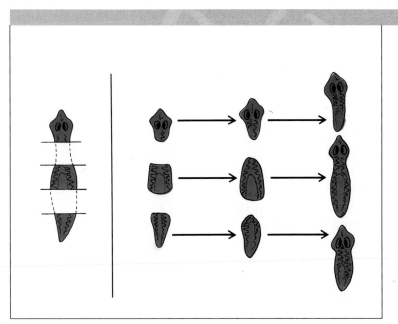

FLUKES AND TAPEWORMS

Flukes are flatworms that live as parasites in the liver or blood of an animal host. One species of liver fluke has caused disease in people living in some Asian countries. There are three hosts in the liver fluke's complex life cycle. They are a snail, a fish, and a human. Humans get liver fluke disease by eating raw or undercooked fish containing this parasite. Proper cooking of fish is one way to safeguard against the disease. Another way is to keep human waste out of water supplies. This prevents the fluke from infecting snail and fish hosts.

Like flukes, tapeworms are also flatworms that are parasites. Tapeworms are found in the intestines of vertebrates, such as fish, pigs, cattle, and humans. A tapeworm has a long ribbonlike body and a rounded head. A closeup of the head is shown in Figure 10-14A. The head has suckers and hooks with which the worm attaches itself to the intestine of the host animal. The tapeworm then feeds on the digested food of its host.

Look at Figure 10-14B. Notice that behind the head are rectangular sections. These sections form most of the body of the worm. Thousands of new tapeworms can be produced from each section. As the tapeworm grows, new sections form behind the head. A human becomes infected with tapeworms by eating undercooked beef, pork, or lamb. Proper cooking and the inspection of meat for the presence of tapeworms can help to control this parasite.

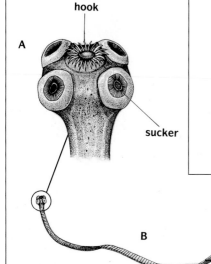

hook

A

sucker

B

Figure 10-14

Close-up of the head of a tapeworm (A); the whole body (B).

REVIEW

1. What are the three body layers of a flatworm?
2. What is the difference between a flatworm that is a parasite and one that is free-living?
3. Describe the nervous system of a planarian.
4. Explain how people can avoid infection by tapeworms.

CHALLENGE How does a mature tapeworm survive despite the fact that it lacks a digestive system?

10-5 ROUNDWORMS

A **roundworm** is a smooth, cylinder-shaped worm that is pointed at both ends and has a tubelike digestive system. The body has an almost clear, tough covering. In Figure 10-15A you can see the tubelike digestive system. Notice that the tube extends the length of the body. There is a mouth at one end and an anus (AY nuhs) at the other end. An **anus** is an opening at one end of the digestive tract, through which undigested food leaves the body. Roundworms are the simplest animals to have a digestive system with two openings.

Roundworms are among the most plentiful of all animals. Hundreds or even thousands of roundworms can be found in a handful of soil. Roundworms live almost everywhere on the earth. Most roundworms are free-living. Many roundworms live in soil, feeding on the remains of dead plants and animals. A roundworm known as the vinegar eel can be seen in Figure 10-15B. This roundworm feeds on bacteria and tiny pieces of fruit in vinegar that has not been pasteurized. Some free-living roundworms live in mud at the bottom of oceans, lakes, and streams.

anus (ring)

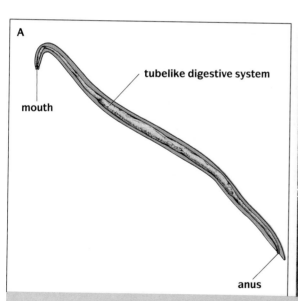

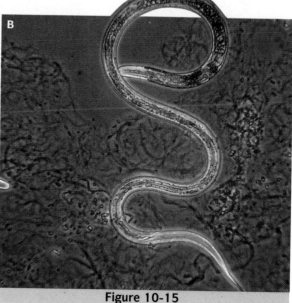

Figure 10-15

The digestive system of a roundworm (*A*); a common roundworm known as a vinegar eel (*B*).

Many roundworms are parasites. Some harm their hosts only slightly; others are very harmful. The hookworm is an example of a roundworm parasite that is very harmful. It lives in soil, often in warm places. The hookworm enters the host's body through the soles of the feet.

Figure 10-16

Hookworm (*A*). Muscle infected with parasitic trichina worms (*B*).

A hookworm, shown in Figure 10-16*A*, has teethlike parts in its mouth that attach to the intestinal wall of its host. It feeds on blood from the damaged wall of the intestine.

The filaria (fih LAIR ee uh) worm is another type of roundworm parasite. This worm passes to humans by the bite of an infected mosquito. Adult filaria worms can cause great swelling in the legs of the host.

Trichina (trih KĪ nuh) worms, shown in Figure 10-16*B*, are parasites usually found in the muscles of pigs. These roundworms cause a disease called trichinosis (trihk-uh NOH suhs). The disease causes great pain in the muscles of the host. Trichinosis can be prevented by inspecting uncooked pork for the presence of the worms. Thorough cooking of pork will also prevent the disease.

Some types of roundworms can damage crops. For example, some roundworm parasites damage plants by feeding on the sap of the roots and stems. But some roundworms are helpful. They live in soil and feed on once-living organic matter and thus help to break it down. The chemicals produced by this breakdown enrich the soil.

REVIEW

1. Describe the body structure of a roundworm.
2. Give an example of a parasitic roundworm and a free-living roundworm.
3. Name three roundworms that cause disease in humans. Describe how each roundworm infects its human host. Explain how each disease can be prevented.

CHALLENGE Someone once said that if the earth were to disappear and only the roundworms were left, the shape of the earth would be outlined by these worms. What does this statement mean?

10-6 SEGMENTED WORMS

TRAITS OF SEGMENTED WORMS

A **segmented worm** is a worm whose body is made up of ringlike sections, or segments. *Annelid* is the scientific name for these worms. The term *annelid* comes from a Latin word meaning "little ring." Segmented worms have three tissue layers. Most organ systems are found in these worms. All annelids have a digestive system with a mouth and an anus.

Scientists have identified more than 9000 species of segmented worms. Most annelids, such as the clamworm in Figure 10-17A, are free-living and are found in salt water. Others live in fresh water. The best-known segmented worm, the earthworm, lives on land.

Some segmented worms are parasites. The leech is an annelid that is a parasite. Figure 10-17B shows a freshwater leech. Some leeches feed on blood. The leech attaches itself to its host by means of two suckers and then draws blood from its host.

Figure 10-17

A clamworm (*A*) and a freshwater leech (*B*) are segmented.

EARTHWORMS

An earthworm has about 100 segments. Each segment except for the first and last has four pairs of setae (SEE-tee). **Setae** are short bristles that help an earthworm move. Look at Figure 10-18A on page 236 and locate the mouth and the anus. Find the swollen band called the *clitellum* (klih TEHL uhm). The clitellum functions in reproduction. An earthworm contains both male and female reproductive organs. Although it has both male and female organs, a single earthworm cannot fertilize its own eggs. Earthworms reproduce sexually by exchanging sperm.

saeta (bristle)

235

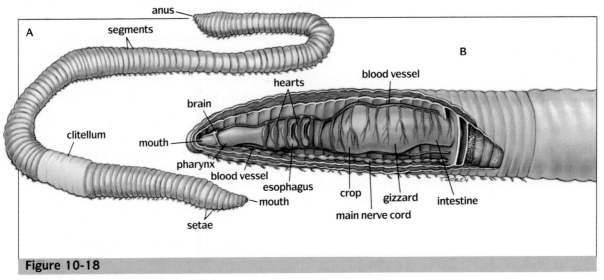

Figure 10-18

Earthworm: external view (*A*); internal view showing digestive, circulatory, and nervous systems (*B*).

Figure 10-19

An earthworm in soil.

Earthworms have a complex digestive system. Look at Figure 10-18*B* to follow the route food takes through the digestive tract. Food enters through the mouth. A muscular pharynx carries food into a tube called the *esophagus* (ee SAHF uh guhs). This tube joins the pharynx and the crop. The **crop** is a chamber that stores food. From the crop, food enters the gizzard (GIHZ uhrd). The **gizzard** is a chamber in which food is broken down into smaller parts by the action of muscles. From the gizzard the food enters the *intestine*, where digestion is completed. Undigested food is passed out through the anus.

Earthworms have a *closed circulatory system*. A closed circulatory system is one in which blood travels through a system of joined tubes. In a closed system, blood moves throughout the body at all times. There are two large blood-carrying tubes called blood vessels. These two blood vessels extend the length of the earthworm's body. These blood vessels are joined by five smaller, muscular tubes that act as hearts. Through the muscle action of these "hearts," blood is pumped throughout the body. Locate the hearts in Figure 10-18*B*.

Earthworms lack a respiratory system. Gas exchange occurs through their skin. The skin is coated with mucus. Oxygen in the air dissolves in the mucus. The gas then passes into the worm's body by diffusion.

The nervous system of an earthworm is made up of a simple brain and a main nerve cord. Find these structures in Figure 10-18*B*. Each segment has smaller nerves that join with the nerve cord. Segments near the brain have nerves that can detect light.

OBJECTIVES

Observe the external features of a live earthworm.

Describe the responses of an earthworm to light, touch, and chemical stimuli.

MATERIALS

covered container of soil with live earthworms, flashlight, paper towel, hand lens, dropper, vinegar, absorbent cotton

PROCEDURE

A. Remove the cover from a container that holds earthworms in soil. Quickly shine a flashlight on the worms. Observe and record their response.

B. Carefully remove one of the earthworms from the container and place it on a moist paper towel. Use a hand lens to observe the structure of the earthworm. Look for its mouth, clitellum, and anus. Estimate the number of segments in the worm's body.

C. Draw the earthworm and label the mouth, clitellum, anus, and setae. Gently rub your finger along the underside of its body to feel the setae. Note and record how the worm responds to being touched. Return the worm to the container.

D. Use a dropper to place a few drops of vinegar on a piece of absorbent cotton. Hold the piece of cotton near the worms in the container. Observe and record their response to the vinegar.

RESULTS AND CONCLUSIONS

1. How did the earthworms react to light? How might this response help an earthworm survive?
2. About how many segments does the earthworm you observed have?
3. How did an earthworm react to touch?
4. Describe how the earthworms responded to vinegar. How might this response help an earthworm survive?

Earthworms are a very important part of the environment. Since they are eaten by many animals, they are an important food source. But they are more important because of their role in changing the soil. The activities of earthworms improve the quality of soil in two ways. As an earthworm moves through the soil, it takes in soil particles through its mouth. It digests bits of food in the soil. Matter that it cannot digest is passed out of the body. These waste products are materials that enrich the soil. Earthworms also improve soil by leaving tubelike holes in the soil as they move through it. These holes provide a passage for air and water that are needed by plants. Plants grow well in soil in which earthworms live.

REVIEW

1. What is a segmented worm? How many body layers does this type of worm have?
2. Trace the path of food through the digestive system of an earthworm.
3. How does blood circulate in an earthworm?
4. Describe the nervous system of an earthworm.
5. Describe two ways that earthworms improve soil.

CHALLENGE Besides its role in respiration, what other function might the mucus coating on an earthworm serve?

10-7 MOLLUSKS

molluscus (soft-bodied)

TRAITS OF MOLLUSKS

Scientists believe that there are over 100,000 species of mollusks (MAHL uhsks). A **mollusk** is an animal that has a soft body, usually covered with a hard shell. The body of most mollusks has three distinct parts: a head, a foot, and a mantle. The head contains the mouth and sense organs. The **foot** is a muscular structure that extends from the body of a mollusk and is used in movement. The **mantle** is a fleshy tissue that covers and protects the organs of a mollusk. In most mollusks the mantle produces a hard shell that protects the soft body. In some mollusks, such as the squid, the shell is inside the body. In others, such as the octopus, there is no shell. Clams, oysters, and snails are mollusks that have an outer shell. Mollusks are important as a source of food for humans. Clams, oysters, mussels, squids, octopuses, and snails are eaten by people all over the world. Jewelry is made using pearls that develop inside oysters.

Mollusks are grouped according to the shape of the muscular foot. One group, which includes clams, is called *hatchet-footed mollusks*. These mollusks have a wedge-shaped foot. A second group, which includes snails, is called *stomach-footed mollusks*. The mollusks in this group have a large flat foot. A third group, which includes squids, is called *head-footed mollusks*. In these mollusks the foot is divided into arms or tentacles. A fourth group has a name not related to the shape of the foot. Mollusks known as *chitons* (KĪ tuhnz) belong to this group. As you can see in Figure 10-20, the shell of a chiton is made up of a number of plates. How many plates does a chiton have?

Figure 10-20

Chitons on a rock.

TYPES OF MOLLUSKS

Clams, oysters, mussels, and scallops are hatchet-footed mollusks. They are also known as bivalves (BĪ valvz). A **bivalve** is a mollusk that has two shells that are hinged together. Figure 10-21 shows several common bivalves. Unlike other groups of mollusks, bivalves do not have a head region. Notice the two hinged shells from which the group gets its name. Look closely at the scallop. Note the tiny dark structures that form a row on each shell. These structures are simple eyes. Most bivalves are filter feeders.

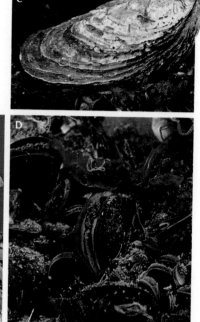

Figure 10-21

Types of common bivalves: scallop (*A*), clams (*B*), oyster (*C*), and mussels (*D*).

Snails, whelks, and slugs are stomach-footed mollusks. These animals are also known as univalves (YOO-nuh valvz). A **univalve** is a mollusk that is usually covered with a single shell. Although it does not have a shell, a slug is grouped with the univalves because it is a snail without a shell. Univalves are found living on land and in water. All univalves have a distinct head and a large flat foot. The head often has small tentacles that are sense organs. Many univalves have simple eyes on the ends of some tentacles. Figure 10-22 shows a snail and a slug. How do these two univalves differ in structure? Land-dwelling slugs and snails are garden pests in some areas.

Squids, octopuses, nautiluses, and cuttlefish are head-footed mollusks. All members of this group live in water. They are the largest and most complex mollusks. The giant squid may reach a length of over 16 m. The foot of a head-footed mollusk forms long arms or tentacles that extend from the animal's head. The tentacles have sucking discs along their length. These discs allow the mollusk to cling to surfaces and to catch and hold other animals that are used as food.

Figure 10-22

A snail (*top*) and a slug (*bottom*) are univalves.

239

The animal in the photograph is a mollusk called a spotted sea hare. It has just released a cloud of thick, purple material into the water. The purple cloud tends to confuse other animals near the sea hare. The substance forming the cloud can clog the gills of fish. It can also irritate the tissues of many other groups of marine animals. Under what conditions might the sea hare emit this material?

In those head-footed mollusks that have a shell, the position of the shell varies. The nautilus, shown in Figure 10-23, has an external shell. Both the squid and cuttlefish have an internal shell that supports the body. The octopus lacks a shell.

Head-footed mollusks can move through the water with great speed. The squid and octopus have a special way of moving quickly. Each animal can force water through a tube that leads out of its body. Jets of water are forced out of the animal's body in one direction. As a result, the body is propelled in the opposite direction.

Figure 10-23

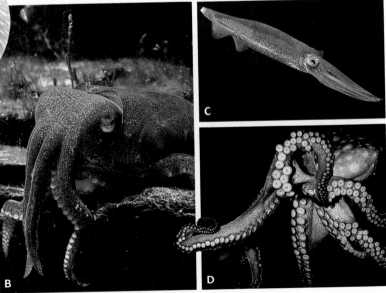

Head-footed mollusks: nautilus (A), cuttlefish (B), squid (C), and octopus (D). Which of these mollusks lack an external shell?

REVIEW

1. Describe the three parts of a typical mollusk body.
2. Name three groups of mollusks and describe the traits of each. Give an example of a mollusk from each group.
3. How do univalves differ from bivalves?

CHALLENGE More fossils of mollusks have been found than fossils of worms. Explain why this is so.

CHAPTER SUMMARY

The main ideas in this chapter are listed below. Read these statements before you answer the Chapter Review questions.

- An invertebrate is an animal that does not have a backbone. Some invertebrates have a body made up of three cell layers that form from tissues—the ectoderm, the mesoderm, and the endoderm. (10-1)

- Sponges, the simplest invertebrates, have a body that is two cells thick. These filter feeders have many pores through which water enters their body. They can reproduce both sexually and asexually. (10-2)

- Coelenterates have a large central body cavity. Tentacles that have stinging cells are used in food getting. (10-3)

- Coelenterates have two body forms—a tubelike form and an umbrella-shaped form. The body contains true tissues. Coelenterates include hydras, jellyfish, corals, and sea anemones. (10-3)

- Flatworms are the simplest worms. They have three cell layers, organs, and organ systems. Flatworms may be parasites or free-living. (10-4)

- Roundworms are smooth, cylinder-shaped worms with a tubelike digestive system. They are the simplest animals to have both a mouth and an anus. (10-5)

- Most roundworms are free-living. Hookworms, filaria, and trichina are parasites that cause disease in humans. (10-5)

- Segmented worms have a body made up of ringlike sections. These worms have three body layers. Earthworms have a complex digestive system and a closed circulatory system. Earthworms enrich soil. (10-6)

- Mollusks have a soft body and a muscular foot used in movement. Most have a hard shell. Hatchet-footed mollusks, stomach-footed mollusks, and head-footed mollusks make up three groups of mollusks. Chitons belong to a fourth group. (10-7)

The key terms in this chapter are listed below. Use each term in a sentence that shows the meaning of the term.

anus	flagellum	mollusk	spicule
bivalve	flatworm	parasite	sponge
budding	foot	pharynx	spongin
coelenterate	gizzard	regeneration	stinging cell
crop	invertebrate	roundworm	tentacles
ectoderm	mantle	segmented worm	univalve
endoderm	mesoderm	setae	

VOCABULARY

Write the letter of the term that best matches the definition. Not all the terms will be used.

1. A chamber in which food is broken down into small parts by muscular action in an earthworm
2. Process of asexual reproduction in which a new individual develops from an outgrowth of the parent
3. Any animal that does not have a backbone
4. A smooth, cylinder-shaped worm that is pointed at both ends and has a tubelike digestive tract
5. A mollusk that is usually covered with a single shell
6. A fleshy tissue that covers and protects the organs of a mollusk
7. A chamber in which food is stored in an earthworm
8. A worm whose body is made up of ringlike sections
9. The outer tissue layer in a developing animal
10. Regrowth of body parts that have been lost or damaged

a. bivalve
b. budding
c. crop
d. ectoderm
e. endoderm
f. flatworm
g. gizzard
h. invertebrate
i. mantle
j. mesoderm
k. regeneration
l. roundworm
m. segmented worm
n. univalve

CONCEPTS

1. How does a vertebrate differ from an invertebrate? (10-1)
2. Name and describe the three tissue layers that form the body of some adult animals. (10-1)
3. Name the eight largest invertebrate phyla. (10-1)
4. Describe the body of a sponge. Identify the function of each type of cell. (10-2)
5. How does a sponge obtain food? (10-2)
6. Describe the process of regeneration in a sponge. (10-2)
7. Describe the body of a typical coelenterate. (10-3)
8. Identify three groups of coelenterates. (10-3)
9. Describe budding in a coelenterate. (10-3)
10. What are some of the traits of a flatworm? (10-4)
11. Distinguish between flatworms that are free-living and those that are parasites. (10-4)

12. Explain how disease caused by liver flukes can be avoided. (10-4)

13. How do tapeworms obtain food? (10-4)

14. What are the traits of a roundworm? (10-5)

15. Where do many free-living roundworms live, and what is their food source? (10-5)

16. Name and describe a roundworm that is a parasite. (10-5)

17. Describe traits of segmented worms. (10-6)

18. Briefly describe circulation in an earthworm. (10-6)

19. How are earthworms important to the environment? (10-6)

20. How does a univalve differ from a bivalve? (10-7)

21. How are mollusks important to humans? (10-7)

22. Name and describe one hatchet-footed mollusk, one stomach-footed mollusk, and one head-footed mollusk. (10-7)

APPLICATION/ CRITICAL THINKING

1. You are asked to classify an animal in the correct phylum. The animal has a soft body and armlike tentacles that have sucking discs. You dissect the animal and find that it has an internal shell. Is the animal a coelenterate or a mollusk? Explain your answer.

2. Someone with a tapeworm disease eats a great deal but feels hungry and tired and loses weight. Explain why.

3. Look back through this chapter to see in what order the six phyla of invertebrates are presented. What pattern is there in this order?

4. Authorities sometimes close beaches to swimmers because of the presence of a large number of jellyfish in the water. Explain why it is wise not to allow people to swim in these waters.

EXTENSION

1. Do research to find out how oysters produce pearls. Write a report on your findings.

2. Ask a veterinarian for information about the kinds of roundworm and flatworm parasites that can affect pets. Find out how infection by these worms can be prevented. Report your findings to your class.

3. Find out how leeches were used in medicine from the Middle Ages to the nineteenth century. Write a brief report on the subject.

READINGS

Boyle, P.R. *Molluscs and Man*. Baltimore, Md.: E. Arnold, 1981.

Taylor, P. ''Sea Shells.'' *Oceans*, May/June 1985, p. 41.

Walls, Jerry G. *Shell Collecting*. Neptune City, N.J.: TFH Publications, Inc., 1981.

COMPLEX INVERTEBRATES

Most spiders live on land. But the type of water spider shown in the photograph spends most of its life underwater in a pond or shallow lake. Like other spiders, it breathes air and cannot use the oxygen dissolved in water. How does the water spider survive underwater? It spins a waterproof, dome-shaped nest. The spider anchors the nest to plants that grow on the bottom of the pond. The nest functions like a diving bell or submarine. The nest is filled with air bubbles that were carried from the water's surface by the spider. Inside its air-filled nest, the water spider eats, mates, and raises its young. The water spider is one member of a large phylum of complex invertebrates.

- *What structures does a spider have in common with other members of its phylum?*
- *What are some other types of complex invertebrates?*

11-1 TRAITS OF ARTHROPODS

What type of animals can be found on the ocean floor, in deserts and swamps, flying through the air, or crawling on a dog's back? Arthropods (AHR thruh pahdz) can be found in all of these places. An **arthropod** is an animal that has a body made up of segments, a hard outer covering, and jointed legs. Lobsters, spiders, mosquitoes, and fleas are all members of the arthropod phylum. There are more species in the arthropod phylum than in all the other animal phyla combined.

Arthropods are considered a very successful animal phylum. The term *successful* has a special meaning to biologists. A group of animals is called successful if its members either are found in many types of environments or exist in great numbers. Since both these conditions describe arthropods, they are a very successful phylum. The *adaptations* of the many species of arthropods are a major factor in the success of these animals. An adaptation is a trait that makes an organism better able to survive in an environment.

After completing this section, you will be able to

- **explain** why the arthropod phylum is such a successful phylum.
- **describe** traits of arthropods.
- **identify** five classes of arthropods.

The key terms in this section are

abdomen	head
arthropod	molting
exoskeleton	thorax

arthron- (joint)
-podus (foot)

245

thorax (chest)

Although arthropods have adaptations that vary, these animals have certain traits in common. The body of most arthropods is divided into three main parts. These parts can be seen in Figure 11-1. The **head** is the first part of the body and contains sense organs. The **thorax** (THAWR-aks) is the middle body part that joins the head and abdomen. Walking legs are attached to the thorax. The **abdomen** (AB duh muhn) is the last part of the body and contains reproductive and digestive organs. In Figure 11-1 notice that the body parts are made up of sections, or segments. In some arthropods these segments are joined, or fused.

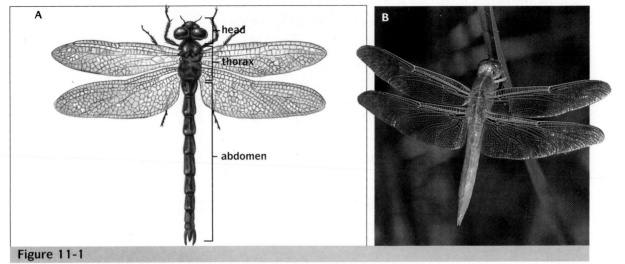

Figure 11-1

The dragonfly shows the three main body parts found in most arthropods.

exo- (outside of)

The hard body covering of an arthropod is called an exoskeleton (ehk soh SKEHL uh tuhn). An **exoskeleton** is a skeleton that covers the outside of an animal's body. This skeleton is like a suit of armor—a nonliving covering that protects the body. The exoskeleton helps to keep the arthropod from being eaten by other animals. This waterproof covering also helps to keep the arthropod from drying out. While some arthropods live in water, many live in dry areas. The protection provided by the exoskeleton is another reason that arthropods are so successful.

The exoskeleton is made up of many parts that are joined. The places where the parts meet are called *joints*. The body parts that meet at joints can bend. Thus, joints allow freedom of movement. The exoskeleton also functions as a rigid structure to which the muscles are attached. To produce movement, muscles must push or pull against something. The attachment of muscles to the hard skeleton allows movement.

Because the exoskeleton is made of a nonliving material, it cannot grow. In order for an arthropod to grow, it must shed this covering. The process of shedding the exoskeleton is called **molting**. In Figure 11-2 you can see an arthropod that has just molted. Molting occurs at regular periods as the arthropod grows. Before an animal molts, a new, soft exoskeleton forms beneath the old one. The new exoskeleton is larger but is somewhat folded, so it fits beneath the old one. Until the new coat hardens, the animal is without protection. Most arthropods hide during this time.

Figure 11-2

An arthropod 1 minute after molting.

All arthropods have pairs of jointed legs. The joints allow the legs to bend and move in many ways. The legs may be used for walking, swimming, hopping, or other kinds of movement. The number of legs varies with the class of arthropod. The number of legs can be used to help to classify an arthropod. Most arthropods belong to one of five major classes—*insects, crustaceans* (kruhs TAY-shuhnz), *arachnids* (uh RAK nihdz), *centipedes* (SEHN tuh-peedz), and *millipedes* (MIHL uh peedz).

REVIEW

1. Why are arthropods considered successful?
2. Describe the three main parts of an arthropod's body.
3. How does an exoskeleton contribute to the success of arthropods?
4. What are five major classes of arthropods?

CHALLENGE After molting but before its new exoskeleton hardens, an arthropod causes its body to swell. It does this by taking in extra air or water. What beneficial result does this behavior produce?

11-2 INSECTS

Flies, ants, grasshoppers, bees, and butterflies are all insects. An **insect** is an arthropod that has three pairs of jointed legs. Insects make up the largest class of arthropods. There are so many insect species that they account for two thirds of all animal species. The large ant shown in Figure 11-3 stands for the large number of insect species. The octopus represents all the other species of invertebrates. The tiny horse stands for the number of vertebrate species. How many species of insects are represented by the ant in Figure 11-3? What is the number of invertebrate species? About how many vertebrate species are there? About how many times larger is the number of insect species than the number of vertebrate species?

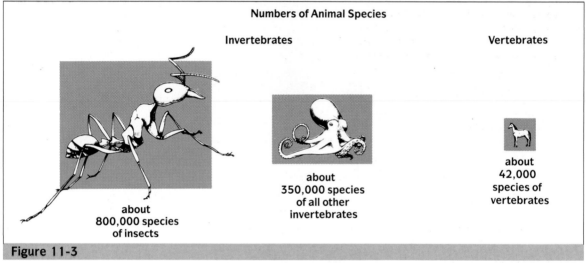

Numbers of Animal Species

Invertebrates

Vertebrates

about 800,000 species of insects

about 350,000 species of all other invertebrates

about 42,000 species of vertebrates

Figure 11-3

There are more species of insects than of all other animals combined.

insectum (divided animal)

mandere (to chew)

TRAITS OF INSECTS

Insects are the most successful class of arthropods. To understand the reasons for their success, it is helpful to learn more about insects. As in other arthropods, the body of an insect has three main parts. In Figure 11-4A, locate the three body parts of the grasshopper—the head, thorax, and abdomen.

Look closely at the head in Figure 11-4B. Notice the mouth parts attached to the head. Locate the mandibles (MAN duh buhlz). The **mandibles** are a pair of jaws that are used for chewing. Grasshoppers cut and chew plants. As the grasshopper bites, these jaws move sideways. Other insects have different mouth structures. The mouth parts are specialized for the kind of food that each type of insect eats.

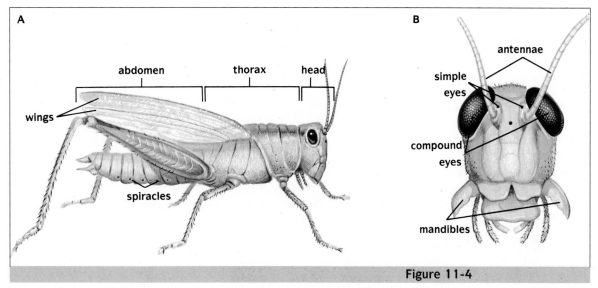

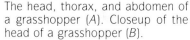

Figure 11-4

The head, thorax, and abdomen of a grasshopper (A). Closeup of the head of a grasshopper (B).

Insects also have feelers, or antennae, on their head. An **antenna** (pl., *antennae*) (an TEHN ee) is a sense organ found in many arthropods. The antennae of most insects function in the senses of touch and smell. Some antennae also function in taste and hearing.

Like most insects, the grasshopper has two types of eyes. In Figure 11-4*B*, locate the small *simple eyes* on the head of the grasshopper. Simple eyes can sense changes in the amount of light but cannot form clear images.

Compound eyes are also located on the head. Unlike a human eye, which has one lens, a compound eye may have several thousand lenses. A *lens* is a structure that focuses light from an object. The focused light forms an image of that object on another part of the eye. A compound eye forms many images. Each image is of a small part of the surroundings. When the images are combined by the brain, they show the complete surroundings. Figure 11-5*A* shows a flower as seen through the compound eye of an insect. Figure 11-5*B* shows the same flower as seen through a human eye. The compound eye senses movement. When an object in the environment moves, its image moves from one lens to the next. Why is sensing movement very important for an insect?

Look again at Figure 11-4*A*. Like all insects, a grasshopper has three pairs of legs. Notice that all three pairs of legs are attached to the thorax. The first two pairs of legs are used for walking. The third pair consists of the large hind legs. Think about how a grasshopper moves. What is the function of these legs?

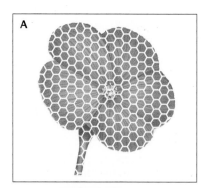

Figure 11-5

A flower as seen by an insect (A). The same flower as seen by a human (B). How do these images compare?

249

By studying dragonflies, engineers hope to learn how to make better and safer airplanes. The common dragonfly can fly as well as any stunt pilot. A dragonfly can move straight up, like a helicopter. A dragonfly can stop in midflight and turn around. It can fly sideways and can even fly backwards.

Engineers who design airplanes are impressed with the dragonfly's skills. To design better planes, engineers are studying how these insects use their wings. Most insects, birds, and airplanes rely on the shape of their wings to lift them in the air. Dragonflies, however, beat their wings in a way that creates tiny whirlwinds around the wings. These whirlwinds are so powerful that they can lift the dragonfly in the air and propel the insect in any direction.

Engineers believe that airplanes could improve their performance by using a technique based on the way the dragonfly flies. The engineers are trying to design airplanes that could create and use the same kind of whirlwinds produced by the dragonfly's wings. Compared with airplanes in use today, such planes would have more powerful lift, fly more safely, use less fuel, and provide a smoother ride.

---

spirare (to breathe)

Also attached to the thorax are two pairs of wings. The long, narrow pair of wings protect a pair of wider, fragile wings that are used for flying. When the insect is not in flight, the flying wings are folded under the narrow pair. Insects are the only invertebrates that can fly.

The movement of the wings and the abdomen pumps air into and out of the spiracles (SPĪ ruh kuhlz). Locate the spiracles on the abdomen of the grasshopper in Figure 11-4A. A **spiracle** is a small opening through which air enters the body of some arthropods. The spiracles function in respiration. These openings lead to a system of air tubes inside the body. Air enters through the spiracles and travels throughout the body in this system of air tubes. Larger tubes branch into smaller tubes. In the smallest tubes, oxygen is released to the body cells. Carbon dioxide from body cells enters the tubes. This waste gas then leaves the body through the spiracles.

REPRODUCTION IN INSECTS

Another reason for the success of insects is the way they reproduce. Reproduction in insects is sexual. The male insect deposits sperm in a special sac within the female insect's body. Only when the female is ready to deposit her eggs do the eggs and sperm come into contact. Then hundreds or, in some species, thousands of fertilized eggs are laid. The female may lay eggs several times within a season. Although many eggs will never become adults, the large number of eggs produced makes possible a large number of offspring. A large number of offspring increases the chances of the species surviving.

Refer to Figure 11-6 as you read about the stages in the life cycle of a grasshopper.

1. A female grasshopper lays eggs in a hole she has dug.
2. The young that hatch from the eggs are called nymphs (nihmfs). A **nymph** is a young insect that looks like a small adult. Notice that the nymph is smaller than the adult and lacks wings. As the nymph grows, it molts several times before becoming an adult.
3. Each time the nymph molts, it looks more like the adult. An **adult** is an animal that has grown and developed enough to reproduce.

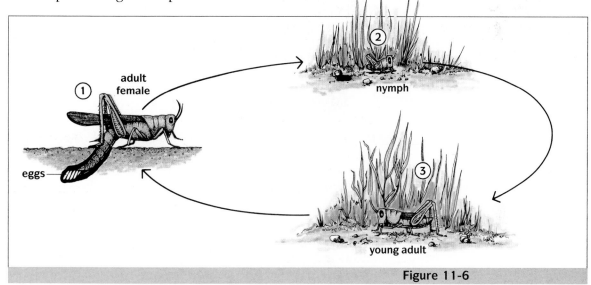

Figure 11-6

The life cycle of a grasshopper. What is the name given to this series of changes?

The changes that occur during the life cycle of a grasshopper are a type of metamorphosis (meht uh MAWR-fuh sihs). **Metamorphosis** is a series of distinct changes in form through which an organism passes as it develops from an egg to an adult. Grasshoppers, crickets, and termites are some of the insects that have *incomplete metamorphosis*. Such insects pass through three stages in their development—*egg, nymph,* and *adult.*

Most insects develop from egg to adult through *complete metamorphosis*. When an insect that has this type of development hatches from an egg, the insect does not look like its parents. An insect that has complete metamorphosis passes through four stages in its development—*egg, larva, pupa,* and *adult.*

meta- (change)
morphe (form)

Refer to Figure 11-7 as you read the stages in the life cycle of a moth, which has complete metamorphosis.

1. The caterpillar hatches from an egg. Notice that it looks more like a worm than like the adult insect.

larva (mask)

2. A caterpillar is the larva (LAHR vuh) (pl., *larvae*) (LAHR-vee) of a moth or butterfly. A **larva** is an insect in the wormlike stage. The larva eats a great deal and grows larger. It molts several times as it grows.

3. The caterpillar produces an outer covering, called a cocoon, around itself. Inside the cocoon, the insect begins the next stage in its life cycle. The **pupa** (PYOO-puh) is the stage of insect development that follows the larva stage. Sometimes the pupa is called a resting stage. But it is not a time of rest. There are many distinct changes in the insect. Within the cocoon the tissues of the larva reorganize to form the adult insect.

4. Finally the cocoon breaks open and the adult insect comes out.

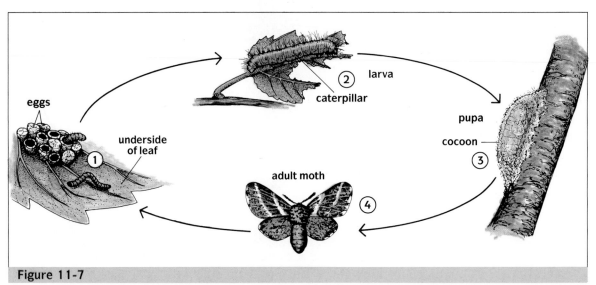

Figure 11-7

The life cycle of a moth. What is the name given to this series of changes?

REVIEW

1. What is the function of the mandibles in a grasshopper?
2. What structures does a grasshopper have for sensing the environment? What are the functions of these structures?
3. How does respiration occur in a grasshopper?
4. Describe the stages of complete metamorphosis. How does incomplete metamorphosis differ from complete metamorphosis?

CHALLENGE A butterfly larva and an adult butterfly have different food sources. How does the difference in food sources help these insects survive?

11-3 SUCCESS OF INSECTS

ADAPTATIONS OF INSECTS

The large size of the grasshopper makes it a good insect to study. But there is no typical insect. Insects vary in their size and form. They also vary in the kinds of structures they have. All of these differences adapt insects to different food sources and to many kinds of environments. Their many adaptations are part of the reason that insects are so successful.

The small size of most insects is a factor in the success of this class. A small insect does not need as much food as a larger animal does. Their small size also means that insects can easily hide from enemies.

How are insects adapted to a variety of food sources? Some insects eat other insects. These meat-eating insects have mouth parts adapted for their food source. Recall that a grasshopper cuts and chews plants with its mandibles. Look at Figure 11-8. Compare the mouth part of the butterfly with the mandibles of the grasshopper. The mouth part of the butterfly is a long tube used in sucking a sweet liquid called nectar from flowers. When the tube is not in use, it curls up. The mouth parts of the housefly are spongy and are used in lapping food. Look at the pointed mouth parts of the mosquito in Figure 11-8C. Mosquitoes feed on blood. The mosquito uses its mouth parts to pierce the skin of an animal and to inject a substance that prevents blood from clotting. How does injecting this substance help a mosquito get food?

After completing this section, you will be able to

- **identify** traits that make insects successful.
- **describe** a honeybee colony in terms of its members.

The key terms in this section are
colony   social insect

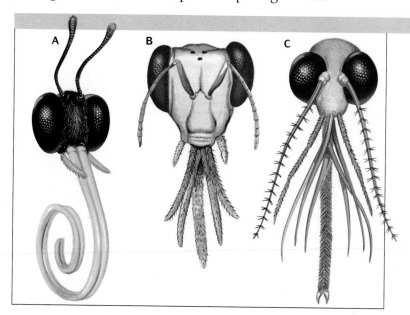

Figure 11-8

The mouth parts of a butterfly (*A*), housefly (*B*), and a mosquito (*C*).

ACTIVITY   What Is the Structure of an Insect?

Flight is an important trait of insects. It allows an insect to travel great distances in search of food, a home, or a mate. Flight also allows an insect to escape danger. Insects vary in the number of wings they have. Flies and mosquitoes have only one pair of wings. Most other insects, including grasshoppers, bees, and butterflies, have two pairs of wings. Some adult insects have no wings and cannot fly. Look back at Figure 11-1. How many pairs of wings does a dragonfly have?

Many insects are adapted to look like their surroundings. Some insects, such as the moth larva in Figure 11-9B, are the color of the plants on which they live. Other insects actually look like parts of a plant. Try to find the thorn mimic in Figure 11-9C. How is the appearance of each insect shown an adaptation for survival?

Figure 11-9

Insects often are adapted to blend in with their surroundings. Look for the walking stick (*A*), moth larva (*B*), and thorn mimic (*C*).

SOCIAL INSECTS

Most insects live independently of other insects. Young insects are usually not cared for by their parents. But some species of insects live together in colonies. A **colony** of animals is a group of animals that live together and share work and food. An insect that lives in a colony is called a **social insect**. Insects that live in a colony depend on each other for survival. Honeybees, ants, wasps, and termites are social insects.

Living in a colony has some benefits over living alone. An insect that lives alone must protect itself from other animals. It must also find its own food and shelter. In a colony these tasks are divided among different members of the colony. Each insect in a colony has one or more special jobs.

A honeybee colony provides a good example of how tasks are divided among members. This colony is made up of a few hundred *drones*, one *queen*, and thousands of *worker bees*. You can see each type of honeybee in Figure 11-10. Drones are the males. The only function of a drone is to mate with the queen. The queen lays eggs for the colony and is the only honeybee that is able to lay eggs. As the queen lays eggs, she is fed and protected by the workers. A worker is a female bee that cannot reproduce.

The worker bees have different jobs, depending on their age. When they are young, workers produce food called royal jelly. The workers feed the royal jelly to the

Figure 11-10

Queen bee marked with a blue dot (*top*); drone (*middle*); worker (*bottom*).

255

Figure 11-11

Workers in a hive, tending the honeybee larvae. What kind of food is fed to a larva that will become the queen?

queen and to very young larvae. Wax is also produced by the workers. They use the wax to build and repair the hive. In time the oldest workers leave the hive to gather pollen and nectar. Young workers feed the pollen and nectar to the larvae, drones, and queen. Figure 11-11 shows young workers in a hive.

When a worker bee finds a good source of nectar, the bee brings some of the nectar back to the hive. She lets the other workers know where the nectar is located. To do this, the returning honeybee releases a drop of nectar and begins a dance. There are two types of dances. If the nectar-filled flower is nearby, the bee dances in circles. If the flower is farther away, the dance is in the form of a figure eight. The direction of the figure eight gives information about the direction of the flower.

REVIEW

1. What are two ways in which the small size of most insects helps make them successful?
2. Using three different insects as examples, explain how the mouth parts of insects adapt them to different food sources.
3. How is living in a colony beneficial to insects?
4. Briefly describe the jobs of each type of bee in a honeybee colony.

CHALLENGE As they feed, flies spit up a drop of their last meal. How might this process result in the spread of disease among humans?

11-4 CRUSTACEANS

Shrimp, lobster, and crabs are crustaceans with which you may be familiar. A **crustacean** is an arthropod that usually has five pairs of jointed legs. Other crustaceans include barnacles and crayfish. Crustaceans are found in water and on land. Most crustaceans live in the oceans. The water flea is a crustacean found in fresh water. Pill bugs are crustaceans that live on land. Crustaceans have a very hard exoskeleton that contains calcium. They also have grinding mouth parts called mandibles.

Look at the crayfish in Figure 11-12. The large size of the crayfish makes it a good crustacean to study. Like all crustaceans, the crayfish has two main body parts. Notice the first body part. The head and the thorax have grown together, or fused. The fused head and thorax form one body part called the **cephalothorax** (sehf uh loh THAWR-aks). A cephalothorax is a trait of both crustaceans and arachnids. What is the second body part?

crusta (shell, rind)

cephalus (head)

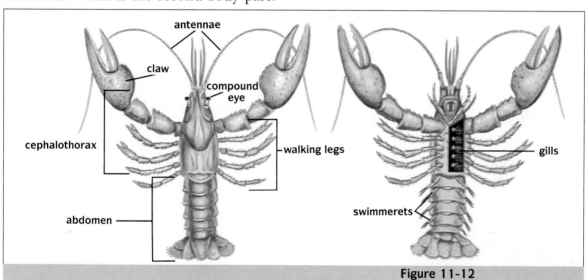

Figure 11-12

A crayfish is an animal that has two main body parts.

Like all crustaceans, the crayfish has two pairs of antennae. The shorter pair are used in touch, taste, and balance. The longer pair function in touch, taste, and smell. The crayfish has compound eyes. Each eye is at the end of a short stalk. The stalks can move, allowing the eyes to see in different directions.

Look again at Figure 11-12. Notice that all five pairs of legs are attached to the cephalothorax. The first pair of legs are adapted as claws. These large claws are used for food getting and for defense. The other four pairs of legs are walking legs.

OBJECTIVES

Observe the external structure of a crayfish.
Describe how the structure of a crayfish adapts it to its environment.

MATERIALS

preserved crayfish, hand lens

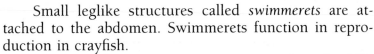

PROCEDURE

A. Examine a preserved crayfish. Note how the exoskeleton feels, and gently tap it with your finger. Count the main body parts. Record your observations.
B. Locate and count the pairs of antennae.
C. Locate the compound eyes near the antennae. Notice that each eye is at the top of a short stalk. Gently try to bend the stalks with your finger.
D. Examine the large claws, which are the first pair of legs. Open and close the claws.

Note that the next four pairs of legs are walking legs.
E. Turn the crayfish over and examine the structures around the mouth. Hypothesize about the function of these structures.
F. Locate the swimmerets on the underside of the abdomen. Observe their structure.
G. Make a drawing of the crayfish. Label the body parts, antennae, eyes, claws, walking legs, and swimmerets.

RESULTS AND CONCLUSIONS

1. Describe the exoskeleton of a crayfish. How does the structure of the exoskeleton aid its function?
2. How might the location of the eyes at the end of stalks aid their function?
3. How does the structure of the claws aid their functions?
4. What traits does a crayfish have in common with other crustaceans?

Small leglike structures called *swimmerets* are attached to the abdomen. Swimmerets function in reproduction in crayfish.

As a crayfish swims, water moves over the *gills*. Gills are structures that function in respiration. As water passes over the gills, oxygen diffuses from the water into the gills. From the gills the oxygen moves to the blood. Carbon dioxide from the blood moves out of the body through the gills. Land-dwelling crustaceans, such as the pill bug, also need moisture for gas exchange to occur. Pill bugs live in damp places, such as under rocks.

Shrimp, lobsters, crabs, and crayfish are a food source for humans. These shellfish, as they are often called, are a large part of the seafood industry. Many tiny crustaceans live in the oceans. These animals are an important source of food for fish and whales.

Figure 11-13

Pill bugs are crustaceans that live on land.

REVIEW

1. Describe three traits of crustaceans.
2. What is the function of the antennae in a crayfish?
3. Describe respiration in a crayfish.

CHALLENGE Many barnacles growing on the hull of a ship can greatly reduce the speed of that ship. How do barnacles cause this loss of speed?

11-5 OTHER ARTHROPODS

ARACHNIDS

Many people think that spiders are insects. But spiders are not in the class of insects. Spiders make up the largest group in the class of arachnids. An **arachnid** is an arthropod that has four pairs of jointed legs. Unlike crustaceans, which live mostly in water, most arachnids live on land. Like crustaceans, arachnids have a fused head and thorax. What is this body part called? The four pairs of walking legs are attached to this body part.

Most arachnids have four pairs of simple eyes that are found on the cephalothorax. Spiders and other arachnids lack compound eyes and antennae. Look at Figure 11-14A, which shows a spider. Locate the spiracle on the abdomen of the spider. Air enters the spider's body through the spiracles. The air passes to the book lungs. **Book lungs** are a series of flat, air-filled plates that function in respiration in most arachnids. In the book lungs, oxygen from the air diffuses into the blood. Carbon dioxide in the blood is released in the book lungs. Notice the structure of the book lung in Figure 11-14B. How does its structure relate to its name?

arachne (spider)

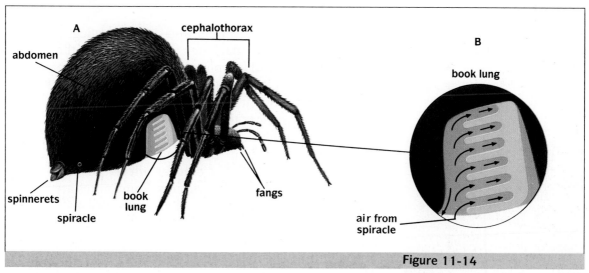

Figure 11-14

Structure of a spider (A). Enlargement of a book lung (B). What takes place in the book lungs?

Some people fear spiders. But most spiders are helpful to humans. Many types of spiders eat insects that are harmful to humans or to crops. Most spiders build webs in which they trap insects. The webs are made of silk thread. Insects become trapped in the sticky threads of a spider's web. A spider has poison fangs near its mouth. The fangs pierce the insect's body and release a poison.

The poison paralyzes or kills the insect. Then the spider sucks out liquid parts of the insect's body.

The silk is a liquid protein produced in special structures in the spider's abdomen. The silk flows out through *spinnerets*. Spinnerets are openings in the spider's abdomen. The liquid silk hardens when it contacts air. The grasshopper in Figure 11-15A has been wrapped in silk.

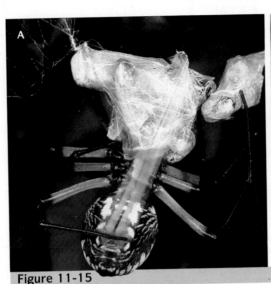 

Figure 11-15

A spider that has wrapped its food in silk (A). A scorpion (B). What is the function of the scorpion's stinger?

Ticks, mites, scorpions, and daddy longlegs are other arachnids. Ticks are parasites. They attach to the skin of their host and feed on blood. Ticks in some areas carry diseases such as Rocky Mountain spotted fever. Ticks pick up this disease by biting an infected host, such as a squirrel. Humans can get the disease when they are bitten by a disease-carrying tick. Pet dogs and cats that spend time outdoors may pick up ticks and mites. Most mites are parasites. A mite called a chigger affects people. Its bite causes severe itching in its victims. Some mites are helpful because they eat insect pests that destroy crops.

Look at the scorpion in Figure 11-15B. How is this arachnid different from a spider? Notice the sharp stinger at the end of the abdomen. The stinger contains poison. The sting of the scorpion is painful, but it usually is not fatal to humans.

Figure 11-16

Daddy longlegs. What does this arachnid eat?

A daddy longlegs, shown in Figure 11-16, has poor vision. It uses its longest pair of legs, the second pair, to explore its environment. A daddy longlegs does not build webs. It is a meat eater that feeds on mites and small insects that it catches. Like most spiders, daddy longlegs are helpful to people, rather than harmful.

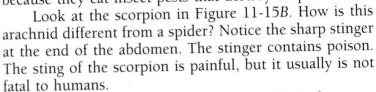

CENTIPEDES AND MILLIPEDES

Centipedes and millipedes make up two classes of arthropods. These animals have a long body with many segments. They look more like segmented worms than like arthropods. But like all arthropods, they have an exoskeleton and jointed legs. They also have antennae and simple eyes.

A **centipede** is an arthropod that has one pair of jointed legs attached to most of its body segments. The most common types of centipedes have about 15 pairs of legs. Centipedes have a flat body and a pair of poison claws attached to the first body segment behind the head. They use their claws to capture and kill insects, worms, and other small animals. They hide in damp places, such as under rocks and logs.

A **millipede** is an arthropod that has two pairs of jointed legs attached to most of its body segments. Most millipedes have between 30 and 40 body segments. Millipedes have no poison claws and eat mostly the remains of dead plants. When disturbed, a millipede may curl up as shown in Figure 11-17.

centi- (hundred)
-podus (foot)

mille- (thousand)

Figure 11-17

Centipede (*left*). Millipede, with inset of millipede curled up in defense (*right*). What are some differences between these arachnids?

REVIEW

1. What is an arachnid?
2. Describe how spiders carry out respiration.
3. How are arachnids both helpful and harmful?
4. How do millipedes differ from centipedes?

CHALLENGE Suppose you find an arthropod that has two main body parts, no antennae, and four pairs of walking legs. To what class does this animal belong? Predict what structures it has for respiration.

11-6 ECHINODERMS

echinos- (spiny)
-derma (skin)

Have you ever seen a sand dollar or a starfish, also called a sea star? If so, you have seen an echinoderm (ih-KĪ nuh derm). An **echinoderm** is a spiny-skinned invertebrate that lives in the ocean. Other echinoderms include sea urchins, sea lilies, sea cucumbers, and brittle stars. Compare the echinoderms shown in Figure 11-18. Which one looks like a pincushion?

Unlike arthropods, echinoderms have an *endoskeleton* (ehn doh SKEHL uh tuhn). An endoskeleton is a skeleton that is inside an animal's body. This hard skeleton is made up of plates, and it functions in support. It also helps to protect an echinoderm from other animals.

The term *echinoderm* means "spiny skin." In most echinoderms, pointy structures called spines cover the animal's body. These spines, which are part of the plates of the skeleton, function in protection.

Figure 11-18

All of these animals are echinoderms: sea cucumber (*A*); sand dollar (*B*); sea urchin (*C*); and brittle star (*D*).

Adult echinoderms have radial symmetry (RAY dee-uhl   SIHM uh tree). **Radial symmetry** is the arrangement of body parts around a central area. Animals with radial symmetry can be divided into mirror-image halves along many lengthwise lines. Look at Figure 11-19. A starfish has five similar parts that extend from the central area of the animal's body. Notice the ways in which the starfish can be divided into mirror-image halves. A starfish body is unlike a human body. Notice that your body has only two mirror-image halves—a left side and a right side.

Echinoderms have an unusual system of movement that involves their tube feet. **Tube feet** are hollow, suction-cuplike structures used in movement by echinoderms. The tube feet are found in rows on the underside of the body. How do tube feet function? Muscles move water through a system of canals inside the body. The canals connect to the tube feet. The movement of water helps to create a suction by which the tube feet attach to surfaces, such as the ocean bottom. When the suction from the attached tube feet is released, the animal moves forward.

The starfish is a common echinoderm that is often studied. Look at Figure 11-20. It shows both the upper surface, or top, and lower surface, or bottom, of a starfish. Notice that the mouth of the starfish is on the lower surface of the body. On which surface is the anus found? The tube feet are in rows on the underside of each arm.

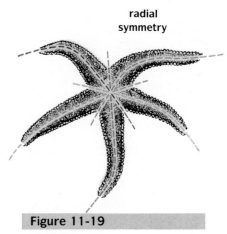

radial symmetry

Figure 11-19

An echinoderm has radial symmetry. How does symmetry in an echinoderm differ from symmetry in a human?

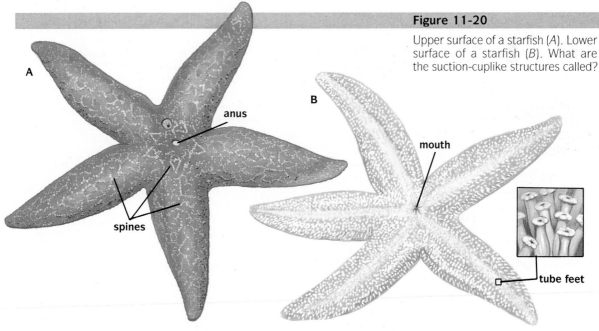

Figure 11-20

Upper surface of a starfish (*A*). Lower surface of a starfish (*B*). What are the suction-cuplike structures called?

A

anus

spines

B

mouth

tube feet

263

Figure 11-21

Starfish using its tube feet to open a clam shell.

Starfish use their tube feet in feeding as well as in moving. Mollusks are an important food source of starfish. The tube feet are used to pull open a mollusk shell, such as that of a clam. Look at Figure 11-21. The starfish wraps its arms over the edge of the clam shell. The tube feet attach to both halves of the shell, and the starfish pulls on each half. The starfish needs to part the shell halves only a tiny amount to feed. Once the halves are parted, the starfish turns its stomach inside out and pushes it out through its mouth. The starfish inserts its stomach into the opening in the clam shell. Then the starfish begins to digest the soft body of the mollusk.

Starfish are either male or female, and they reproduce sexually. They release large numbers of eggs and sperm into the water, where the eggs are fertilized. Starfish can also reproduce asexually by regeneration. Recall that regeneration is the growth of a new organism from a part of the body. In the past this trait of starfish has caused problems for people who gather and sell clams, oysters, and other mollusks. A starfish can eat many mollusks in a single day. In the past, starfish that were caught were cut into pieces and thrown back into the ocean. But rather than killing starfish, this practice increased their numbers. Each piece that was attached to part of the central area grew back into a complete starfish. Today, starfish numbers are controlled by catching these animals and removing them from the ocean.

ACTIVITY   What Is the Structure of a Starfish?

OBJECTIVES
Observe the structure of a starfish.
Describe how the structure of a starfish adapts it to its environment.

MATERIALS
preserved starfish, hand lens

PROCEDURE
A. Examine a preserved starfish. Describe the shape of the starfish. Count the arms. Record your observations.
B. Use a hand lens to examine the spines on the upper surface of the body. Gently touch the spines with your finger. Record how they feel. Make a drawing of the starfish. Label the arms and spines.
C. Gently bend the body of the starfish. Note whether the body bends easily.
D. Locate the mouth on the underside of the body. Examine the mouth with a hand lens.
E. Use a hand lens to examine the tube feet on the underside of the body. Describe their shape. Examine the tips of the tube feet. Draw several tube feet.

RESULTS AND CONCLUSIONS
1. How many arms does a starfish have?
2. What is the function of the spines? How does their structure aid their function?
3. How does the shape of the tube feet aid their function?
4. What traits does a starfish have in common with other echinoderms?

REVIEW

1. Describe the skeleton of an echinoderm.
2. Explain why a starfish is said to have radial symmetry.
3. How do tube feet function in movement in an echinoderm?
4. Describe how a starfish feeds on a mollusk.

CHALLENGE Dried starfish remains are often sold as souvenirs at seaside resorts. What part of a starfish are the dried remains?

CHAPTER SUMMARY

The main ideas in this chapter are listed below. Read these statements before you answer the Chapter Review questions.

- Arthropods are a very successful animal phylum. The body of an arthropod is made up of a head, thorax, and abdomen. Arthropods have jointed legs and are covered by a protective exoskeleton that is molted as the animals grow. (11-1)

- Insects are arthropods that have three pairs of jointed legs. Most insects have both simple and compound eyes. Air enters an insect's body through spiracles. (11-2)

- A developing insect undergoes metamorphosis. Incomplete metamorphosis has three stages—egg, nymph, and adult. Complete metamorphosis has four stages—egg, larva, pupa, and adult. (11-2)

- The many adaptations of insects help make them a very successful class of animals. These adaptations include small size, mouth parts specialized for different food sources, the ability to fly, and the ability to blend in with the environment. (11-3)

- Social insects live in colonies. Members of a colony share work and food. They depend on each other for survival. (11-3)

- Crustaceans are arthropods that usually have five pairs of jointed legs. The head and thorax of crustaceans are fused to form the cephalothorax. (11-4)

- Arachnids, such as spiders, are arthropods that have four pairs of jointed legs. Spiders have book lungs, which function in respiration. (11-5)

- Centipedes are arthropods that have one pair of jointed legs attached to most body segments. Millipedes are arthropods that have two pairs of jointed legs attached to most body segments. (11-5)

- Echinoderms are spiny-skinned invertebrates. These animals live in the ocean. They have radial symmetry and move by means of tube feet. (11-6)

The key terms in this chapter are listed below. Use each term in a sentence that shows the meaning of the term.

abdomen	cephalothorax	larva	pupa
adult	colony	mandibles	radial symmetry
antenna	crustacean	metamorphosis	social insect
arachnid	echinoderm	millipede	spiracle
arthropod	exoskeleton	molting	thorax
book lungs	head	nymph	tube foot
centipede	insect		

Chapter Review

VOCABULARY

Use the key terms from this chapter to complete the following sentences correctly.

1. An arthropod that has one pair of jointed legs attached to most of its body segments is a/an _____ .

2. A spiny-skinned invertebrate that lives in the ocean is a/an _____ .

3. A small opening through which air enters the body of some arthropods is a/an _____ .

4. An arthropod that has three pairs of jointed legs is a/an _____ .

5. A series of distinct changes in form through which an organism passes as it develops from an egg to an adult is called _____ .

6. An arthropod that usually has five pairs of jointed legs is a/an _____ .

7. Hollow, suction-cuplike structures used in movement in echinoderms are called _____ .

8. A series of flat, air-filled plates that function in respiration in most arachnids are called _____ .

9. The fused head and thorax that form one body part in some arthropods is called a/an _____ .

10. A pair of jaws used in chewing in some arthropods are called _____ .

CONCEPTS

1. Name and describe the three main parts of the body of most arthropods. (11-1)

2. What are two advantages and one disadvantage of having an exoskeleton? (11-1)

3. Describe two types of eyes found in insects. (11-2)

4. Describe respiration in a grasshopper. (11-2)

5. How are incomplete and complete metamorphoses different? (11-2)

6. How does their size and ability to fly contribute to the success of insects? (11-3)

7. Give three examples that show how insects are adapted to different food sources. (11-3)

8. What is a colony? What advantages do social insects have that other insects do not? (11-3)

9. Distinguish between a drone, queen, and worker bee in terms of their sex and functions in a hive. (11-3)

10. Describe the first pair of legs of a crayfish and their function. (11-4)
11. What are swimmerets and what is their function? (11-4)
12. Why are land-dwelling crustaceans often found under rocks and logs? (11-4)
13. Describe a way in which crustaceans are helpful to humans. (11-4)
14. What is the function of book lungs in a spider? (11-5)
15. Describe how most spiders get food. (11-5)
16. What types of arachnids are parasites? How are these arachnids harmful to humans? (11-5)
17. Distinguish between centipedes and millipedes in terms of body structures and food sources. (11-5)
18. Describe the skeleton of an echinoderm. (11-6)
19. What structures of echinoderms function in movement? Explain how these structures produce movement. (11-6)
20. What method did people once use to try to destroy starfish? Why did this method fail? (11-6)

APPLICATION/ CRITICAL THINKING

1. How is the appearance of a walking stick an adaptation?
2. Not all the threads of a spider's web are sticky. How might this difference in the stickiness of threads be beneficial to spiders?
3. Compare the skeleton of an echinoderm with that of an arthropod. Describe how the skeletons are alike and different.

EXTENSION

1. Research and present a report to your class on an ant, wasp, or termite colony. Describe the shelter in which the colony lives and the functions of its members.
2. *Locust* is the name for several species of grasshoppers that migrate in large numbers. Write a brief report on the damage these insects can cause to crops.
3. Many types of pesticides have been found to pollute the environment. Find out about the different ways pests can be controlled by natural means. Write a brief report of your findings, and present it to your class.

READINGS

Clark, S.W. "Along Came a Spider." *Sierra*, May/June 1985, p. 86.

Fischer-Nagel, Andreas, and Heidirose Fischer-Nagel. *Life of the Honeybee*. Minneapolis, Minn.: Carolrhoda Books, 1985.

Line, Les, and Louis Milner. *The Audubon Society Book of Insects*. New York: Harry N. Abrams, Inc., 1983.

Whitlock, Ralph. *Insects*. Morristown, N.J.: Silver Burdett Co., 1984.

COLD-BLOODED VERTEBRATES

Can you find the two fish in the photograph? They are sargassum fish. Their body covering and shape are almost identical to the seaweed in which they are hidden. Unlike most fish, the sargassum is not a very good swimmer. But its ability to hide so well makes it almost invisible to its food sources—smaller fish and crustaceans. The ability to conceal itself also helps to keep the sargassum from becoming the meal of larger fish. Like all living things, these fish have many traits that enable them to survive in their environment.

- *What traits of fish enable them to live in water?*
- *How are amphibians able to live in two environments—water and land?*
- *What traits do reptiles have that equip them for life on land?*

12-1 PHYLUM CHORDATA

TRAITS OF CHORDATES

What do a frog, a fish, and a snake have in common? These animals look very different, yet they do have an important trait in common. Figure 12-1 on the next page shows the skeleton of each animal. What similarity do you see among the three? If you examine the skeletons carefully, you will see that each has a backbone. An animal that has a backbone is called a **vertebrate** (VER tuh briht). Frogs, fish, and snakes are vertebrates. So are alligators, deer, eagles, and horses. What other animals have a backbone?

All vertebrates are chordates (KAWR dayts). A **chordate** is an animal that is a member of phylum Chordata. Chordates have three traits in common. A rodlike, flexible structure called a *notochord* (NOH tuh kawrd) is one trait of chordates. The notochord provides support to the animal's body and is present at some time during development. In more complex chordates the notochord is present

chorda (string)

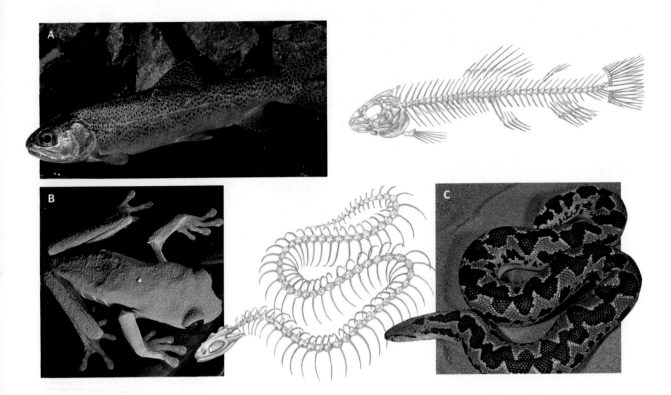

Figure 12-1

The rainbow trout (*A*), the tree frog (*B*), and the sand boa (*C*) are all vertebrates.

only during the early stages of growth, before birth. Another chordate trait is a tubelike *nerve cord* that extends the length of the body, just above the notochord. Chordates also have pairs of *gill slits*. Gill slits are openings that water-dwelling animals use in breathing. Depending on the animal, the gill slits may be present only before birth or throughout an animal's life.

CHORDATE SUBPHYLA

Although chordates have some structures in common, the animals in this phylum differ in many ways. Scientists have divided the phylum into smaller groups called *subphyla*. The chordate phylum is divided into three subphyla. Members of two of these subphyla are less complex chordates. These animals live in ocean waters and may not be familiar to you. The lower chordates do not have a backbone. What are animals that do not have a backbone called? What animals without a backbone have you learned about?

One subphylum of chordates that lack a backbone contains animals called *tunicates* (TOO nuh kihts). Adult tunicates can be found free swimming or attached to rocks as individuals or in colonies. Tunicates have a thick outer covering called a tunic, from which they get their name.

Figure 12-2 shows a tunicate called a sea squirt. The sea squirt gets its name from the method it uses to expel water and wastes from its body. Water is squirted out through the lower opening, which can be seen in the photograph.

Animals called *lancelets* (LANS lihts) make up the other subphylum of lower chordates. A lancelet is a fishlike invertebrate whose notochord remains throughout its life. The kind of lancelet shown in Figure 12-3*A* is an often-studied example of its subphylum. Lancelets are free swimming but are most often found burrowed in the sand. Figure 12-3*B* shows two lancelets with just the upper part of their body in the water. The lower part is buried in broken shells on the ocean bottom. Lancelets feed by filtering their food, tiny living things, from the water.

Most chordates are vertebrates. Subphylum Vertebrata is the third and best-known chordate subphylum. There are seven classes of vertebrates; three of these classes are fish. The other four classes are amphibians (am FIHB-ee uhnz), reptiles (REHP tīlz), birds, and mammals.

Figure 12-2

The sea squirt is a tunicate.

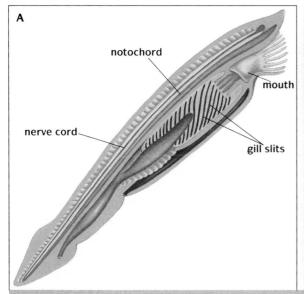

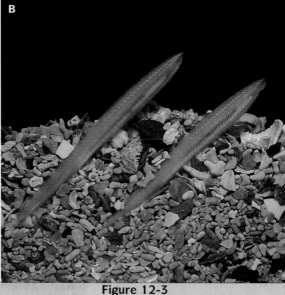

Figure 12-3

Lancelets make up a subphylum of chordates that lack a backbone. Structure of a lancelet (*A*). How are the lancelets (*B*) feeding?

REVIEW

1. What is a vertebrate?
2. What are three traits of animals in phylum Chordata?
3. Name the two kinds of invertebrate chordates.

CHALLENGE   What is one way in which a lancelet is like a sponge?

271

12-2 TRAITS OF VERTEBRATES

After completing this section, you will be able to

- **describe** the skeletal, circulatory, and nervous systems of vertebrates.
- **distinguish** between cold-blooded and warm-blooded animals.

The key terms in this section are

bone
cartilage
cold-blooded animal
endoskeleton
warm-blooded animal

Members of subphylum Vertebrata are animals that have a backbone. You can see another trait shared by vertebrates if you look again at Figure 12-1. Like all vertebrates, the snake, frog, and fish have a type of skeleton called an endoskeleton (ehn doh SKEHL uh tuhn). An **endoskeleton** is a skeleton that is inside an animal's body. This internal skeleton supports as well as protects the organs inside the body.

Unlike the nonliving exoskeleton of arthropods, an endoskeleton contains living cells. Therefore it can grow as the animal grows. In most vertebrates the endoskeleton is made of bone and cartilage (KAHR tuh lihj). **Bone** is the hard tissue that makes up most of the skeleton. **Cartilage** is a tough, flexible tissue. If you feel your ears and the tip of your nose, you will have an idea of how flexible cartilage is. Bone, which contains the minerals calcium and phosphorus, does not bend. In some animals the internal skeleton is made up only of cartilage.

Vertebrates have a *closed circulatory system.* A well-developed heart pumps blood through blood vessels to all parts of the body. The nervous system of vertebrates is more complex than that of invertebrates. All vertebrates have a brain that controls many body functions. The nerve cord, or spinal cord, of vertebrates is protected by the backbone. The notochord is not present in most adult vertebrates. During early development the notochord is replaced by a backbone.

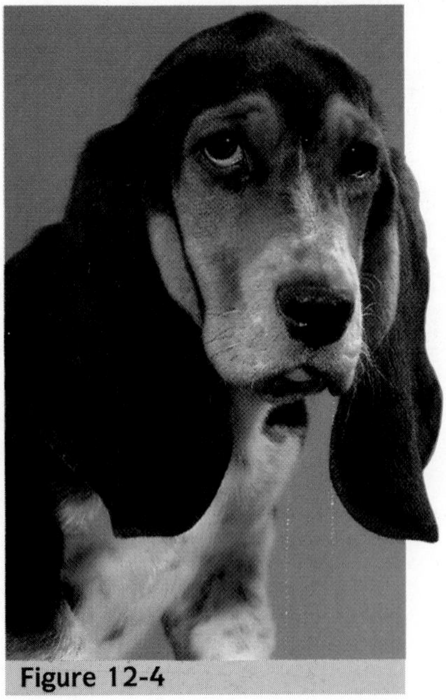

Figure 12-4

The long, floppy ears of the basset hound are made up of flexible cartilage.

Members of five of the seven classes of vertebrates share another trait. The three classes of fish, the amphibians, and the reptiles are all cold-blooded. A **cold-blooded animal** is an animal that has a body temperature that changes with the temperature of the environment. For example, the body temperature of a fish is about the same as the temperature of the water in which it swims.

Air temperature varies a great deal more than does water temperature. So cold-blooded animals that live on land are subject to greater temperature ranges. Through certain behaviors, these animals maintain a body temperature that helps them survive. For example, desert-dwelling lizards live in regions where there are extreme temperature changes between the day and night. During the hot desert day, a lizard seeks shade if the temperature goes too high. Figure 12-5 shows a lizard in sunlight. Was the air temperature likely to have been hot or cold when the picture was taken? At night a lizard burrows in the sand

OBJECTIVE

Test the effect of changes in water temperature on the respiration rate and behavior of a fish.

MATERIALS

goldfish, aquarium water, 250-mL beaker, 1000-mL beaker, thermometer, watch or clock with second hand, crushed ice in cold water

PROCEDURE

A. Place a goldfish in a 250-mL beaker containing water from an aquarium. Place the beaker into an empty 1000-mL beaker.

B. Make a data table with headings like those shown.

Temperature	Beats per Minute	Observations
Start:		

C. Place a thermometer in the water with the goldfish. Read and record the temperature of the water. Locate a gill cover—a flap on the side of the fish's head. Count the number of times the gill cover opens and closes (or beats) in one minute. Record the number of gill cover beats. This is the respiration rate of the fish.

D. Place an ice-water mixture in the large beaker so that the ice water surrounds the outside of the small beaker. Each time the temperature drops 3°C, count and record the number of gill cover beats per minute. Record the temperature also. Continue until the temperature reaches 10°C. Record any changes in the behavior of the fish.

E. Remove the small beaker and pour out the ice water from the large beaker. Put the small beaker back in the larger one. Gradually pour warm water into the large beaker. Each time the temperature increases 3°C, count and record the gill cover beats per minute and record the temperature. Stop adding warm water when the temperature of the water in the small beaker reaches 30°C. Again record your observations of the fish's behavior.

RESULTS AND CONCLUSIONS

1. What is the number of gill cover beats per minute at the starting temperature? What is the number at 10°C? At 30°C?
2. How does a decrease in water temperature affect respiration rate and behavior of a fish?
3. How does an increase in water temperature affect respiration rate and behavior of a fish?

and becomes inactive as its body temperature drops with the cooling air temperature.

Birds and mammals are warm-blooded animals. A **warm-blooded animal** is an animal that has a constant body temperature that is independent of the external temperature. Humans are warm-blooded. Unless you are ill, your body temperature stays about the same, regardless of the external temperature. You will learn more about warm-blooded animals in Chapter 13.

REVIEW

1. What is an endoskeleton, and how does it differ from an exoskeleton?
2. What type of circulatory system do vertebrates have?
3. How do warm-blooded and cold-blooded animals differ?

CHALLENGE Form a hypothesis about whether cold-blooded animals perspire. Explain the reasoning you used in forming this hypothesis.

Figure 12-5

A lizard is a cold-blooded animal.

12-3 TRAITS OF FISH

A **fish** is a cold-blooded vertebrate that lives in water and has gills that are used for breathing. Fish species vary greatly in size, shape, and other traits. Although there are differences among the many kinds of fish, there are some traits that most fish have in common. The bodies of most fish are sleek and streamlined in shape. As the fish swims, water tends to flow around the curves of its body. This helps the fish to move through the water.

Fins are another trait of most fish. **Fins** are winglike structures used for balance and to control movement when swimming. Some types of fins occur in pairs, but other types occur singly.

The majority of fish have scales. Fish **scales** are overlapping, flat plates that cover the animal's body and provide protection. The number of scales a fish has remains the same throughout its life, but each scale grows larger as the fish grows. You can see in Figure 12-6 a fish scale that has growth rings. The growth rings are similar to those found in tree trunks.

Although the circulatory system of fish is advanced compared to those of invertebrates, it is the simplest of the vertebrates. The circulatory system includes the heart and blood vessels. Figure 12-7 shows the two chambers of the fish heart. One chamber is larger and more muscular than the other. This larger chamber pumps blood throughout the body.

You can follow the flow of blood through a fish by looking at Figure 12-8.

1. Blood is pumped from the large chamber of the heart through a large blood vessel to the gills. This blood is low in oxygen and contains the waste gas carbon dioxide.

2. The blood enters the gills. The **gills** are organs that absorb oxygen that is dissolved in water. The transfer of oxygen from the water to the blood occurs in the gills in tiny thin-walled blood vessels called *capillaries*. Carbon dioxide is given off to the water.

3. The blood, now rich in oxygen, moves from the gills to the rest of the body.

4. Blood from all parts of the body returns to the small chamber of the heart. This blood is low in oxygen and high in carbon dioxide. The blood then moves to the large chamber of the heart, completing the cycle of blood circulation.

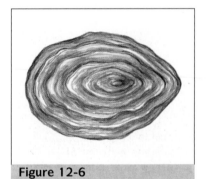

Figure 12-6

Some types of fish scales have yearly growth rings.

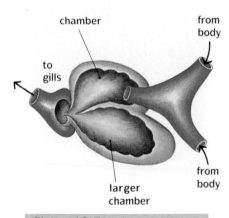

chamber

from body

to gills

larger chamber

from body

Figure 12-7

A fish heart has two chambers.

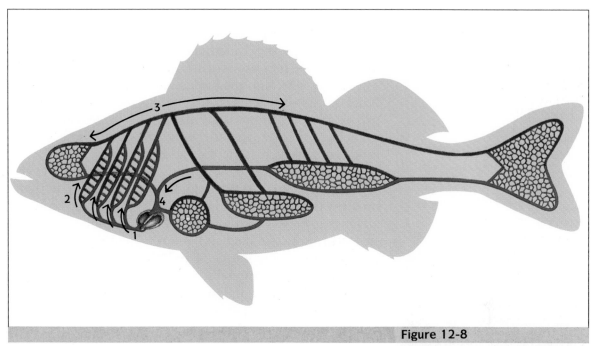

Figure 12-8

The circulatory system of a fish.

In most fish, reproduction begins with spawning. **Spawning** is the release of eggs into the water by the female fish. After the female spawns, the male releases sperm over the eggs. Some of the sperm join with the eggs. This joining of egg and sperm outside of the body of the female animal is called **external fertilization** (ehks TER nuhl fer-tuh luh ZAY shuhn). The fertilized eggs develop into young fish. Female fish release many thousands of eggs during spawning. How do the great numbers of eggs produced help to ensure the survival of fish? Frogs and other animals whose eggs are fertilized externally also tend to produce large numbers of eggs.

Scientists have grouped fish into three classes: *jawless fish, cartilage fish,* and *bony fish.* You are probably most familiar with bony fish. Trout, bass, and catfish are common examples of this class of fish.

Figure 12-9

A brook trout spawning. How do fish eggs compare in appearance with eggs laid by hens?

REVIEW

1. How do the fins of a fish and its shape help a fish swim?
2. Describe the blood circulation in fish, including the function of gills.
3. Describe reproduction in fish.

CHALLENGE   Why is water necessary for external fertilization?

12-4 JAWLESS FISH AND CARTILAGE FISH

JAWLESS FISH

The simplest of the three classes of fish are the jawless fish. **Jawless fish** are wormlike fish that have no jaws. These fish also lack the scales and paired fins that most other kinds of fish have. The endoskeleton of a jawless fish is made entirely of cartilage. The jawless fish has a notochord that remains throughout its life. There are two kinds of jawless fish: hagfish and lampreys.

The hagfish is found in salt water and is a scavenger. A **scavenger** is an animal that feeds on dead or dying organisms. The hagfish has a round mouth by which it attaches itself to a dead or dying fish. Toothlike structures that surround the hagfish's mouth opening are used to bore into the food source. The hagfish feeds on the contents of the other animal's body.

Lampreys are found in both fresh water and salt water. In the adult stage, most lampreys are parasites. Recall that a parasite is an organism that lives in or on another living thing and harms it. The lamprey attaches itself to another fish, as shown in Figure 12-11 (*right*). Like the hagfish, the lamprey has a round mouth but with many more toothlike structures than the hagfish. Figure 12-11 (*left*) shows the lamprey's mouth. Note the lack of a jaw. These features permit the lamprey to attach itself to another fish in a way much like the action of a suction cup. The toothlike parts are used to cut into the other fish, whose body liquids are sucked out by the lamprey.

Figure 12-10

A hagfish is a jawless fish.

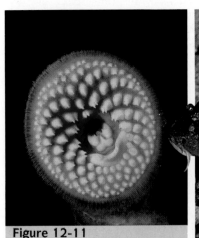

Figure 12-11

Mouth of a lamprey (*left*). Three lampreys (*right*) attached to a carp. How can you tell lampreys are parasites?

CARTILAGE FISH

Cartilage fish make up a second class of fish. As their name suggests, **cartilage fish** are fish that have endoskeletons composed entirely of cartilage. There are two types of cartilage fish: sharks and rays. Unlike jawless fish, sharks and rays have jaws, scales, and paired fins.

A shark has many rows of sharp, pointy teeth that are loosely attached to its jaws. As teeth in the front rows are lost, teeth in the rows behind them grow forward and replace the lost teeth. This is an important trait, since most sharks are meat eaters. Figure 12-12 (*top*) shows the rows of teeth in a shark's mouth. Notice that the teeth slant backwards, which helps a shark hold its prey. Some kinds of sharks eat microscopic plants and animals.

Sharks have a keen sense of smell. Even over great distances, they can sense blood from a wounded fish. Sharks have streamlined bodies and can swim quickly. A shark swims by moving its body and tail from side to side.

Rays look very different from sharks. The paired fins of the ray form large structures that extend from the ray's body. These fins look like large, flat wings. Rays swim by moving their fins in a wavelike motion. Most rays live on or near the ocean floor. They feed on small fish, mollusks, and crustaceans. Rays have a long, narrow tail. In some types of rays, the tail is used for defense. The sting ray, shown in Figure 12-13, has a poison spine in its tail.

Figure 12-12

A lemon shark (*top*) is a meat eater. A basking shark (*bottom*) feeds on microscopic organisms.

Figure 12-13

The sting ray has a poison spine in its tail. When threatened, the ray whips its tail, wounding its enemy. Poison enters the enemy and can cause its death.

REVIEW

1. Describe four traits of jawless fish.
2. In what way do hagfish and lampreys differ?
3. What are four traits of cartilage fish?

CHALLENGE How is the shape of a ray's body suited to the manner in which this fish lives?

12-5 BONY FISH

The bony fish make up the largest class of fish. A **bony fish** is a fish that has an endoskeleton made up mostly of bone. There is great variety among bony fish. Some of the varied body forms of bony fish are shown in Figure 12-14. Although there are about 20,000 species of bony fish, there are some traits that most bony fish have in common. These traits include scales and paired fins.

Figure 12-14

There is great diversity among bony fish. Examples of bony fish: sunfish (A), stonefish (B), surgeonfish (C), lionfish (D), butterfly fish (E), and sea horse (F).

Bony fish are found in both fresh and salt water throughout the world. Figure 12-15 shows a bony fish called a perch. The perch is a common freshwater fish that has traits typical of many bony fish. What is the body shape of the perch? Which of the fish you have studied thus far does the perch most look like?

The perch's body and tail move from side to side as the fish swims. This movement helps to propel the fish through the water. The fins are important for steering.

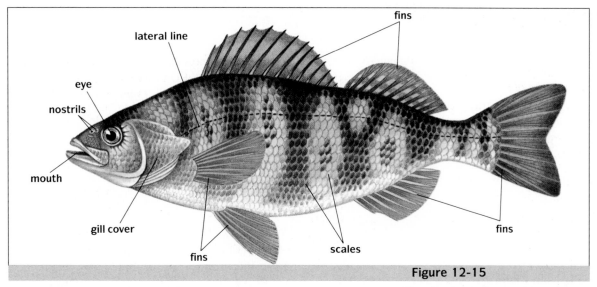

Figure 12-15

The structure of a perch.

One trait of bony fish can be seen by looking again at Figure 12-15. Each gill is covered and protected by a bony flap called a **gill cover**. In addition to protection, the gill cover aids in respiration. Water is taken into the body through the mouth. The opening and closing of the gill cover helps to move water over the gills and out of the body. As the water passes over the gills, dissolved oxygen in the water enters the blood through tiny capillaries.

An organ called the *lateral line* is usually found on each side of the fish. It begins above the gill cover and runs to the base of the tail. The lateral line is found in sharks as well as in bony fish. It is a line of specialized cells that detect vibrations in the water. What might cause the water to vibrate? How is detecting vibrations in the water helpful to fish? Bony fish also have a very sharp sense of smell. In the fish's snout are two openings called

SCIENCE PUZZLER

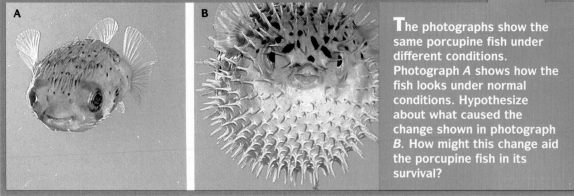

The photographs show the same porcupine fish under different conditions. Photograph *A* shows how the fish looks under normal conditions. Hypothesize about what caused the change shown in photograph *B*. How might this change aid the porcupine fish in its survival?

279

OBJECTIVE
Identify external features of a bony fish.

MATERIALS
preserved fish, tray, scissors, 2 slides of fish scales, microscope

PROCEDURE

A. Obtain a preserved fish. Hold the fish and observe the shape of its body. Place the fish on a tray. Count and record the number of fins. Note whether the fins on the top of the body are the same as or different from those on the bottom of the body. Observe which fins are paired. Make a drawing of the fish.

B. Run your fingers back and forth along the length of the fish's body. Note the shape and position of the scales.

C. Look for the lateral line, which appears as a series of dots running along the length of the body from the gill cover to the tail fin.

D. Lift up the gill cover. Use scissors to cut away one gill cover so that you can see the gills underneath. Count the layers of gills.

E. Obtain two prepared slides of fish scales of different types. Compare the scales.

F. Use a microscope to observe one scale under low power. Notice the series of rings that form the scale. Each dark ring represents one year of growth. Estimate the age of the fish from which the observed scale was taken. Draw the scale as you observed it under the microscope.

RESULTS AND CONCLUSIONS

1. Describe the shape of the fish.
2. How many fins does the fish have? How are the fins alike? How are they different? How is the shape of each fin related to its function?
3. Describe how the scales are arranged. How is this arrangement related to the function of scales?
4. How does the arrangement of the lateral line aid its function?
5. Describe the structure of the gills. How many layers of gills are there in the fish you observed?
6. Compare the structure of the two fish scales you observed. How are they alike? How are they different? You counted the rings on one fish scale. What is the age of the fish from which this scale was taken?

nostrils. The nostrils are lined with cells that are sensitive to odor. These cells are used in locating food. The sense of sight is not as well developed in bony fish as is the sense of smell.

Inside the perch is a long, saclike structure in the center of the body. This structure is called the *air bladder* or swim bladder. The air bladder contains gas and helps the fish stay at a certain depth in the water without using a great deal of energy. As the fish swims to different depths, the amount of gas in the air bladder increases or decreases.

REVIEW

1. What is one way in which bony fish differ from the other two classes of fish?
2. How does the gill cover function in respiration?
3. What is the function of the lateral line?

CHALLENGE As a fish swims from a greater to a lesser depth of the water, would the amount of gas in the air bladder increase or decrease? Explain your answer.

12-6 TRAITS OF AMPHIBIANS

One group of vertebrates can be described as leading a double life. These animals are the amphibians. An **amphibian** is a cold-blooded vertebrate that usually lives in water after hatching from an egg, but as an adult can live on land. Most amphibians have thin, moist skin. In the adult stage, they usually have two pairs of limbs. They have a circulatory system that includes a three-chambered heart, shown in Figure 12-16. Compare it with the fish heart shown in Figure 12-7.

As adults, most amphibians breathe with *lungs*. Lungs are organs through which animals get oxygen from air. Gases can also enter and leave an amphibian's body through the animal's thin skin. Although adult amphibians can live on land, most do not live far from water. Amphibians must return to water in order to reproduce. Fertilization occurs externally.

There are two major groups of amphibians: tailed and tailless. Legless amphibians make up a third, smaller group. Legless amphibians are wormlike animals that live in the tropics. The two major groups of amphibians will be discussed in this section.

TAILLESS AMPHIBIANS

The tailless amphibians include frogs and toads. As adults, frogs and toads have a short body, no neck, and no tail. They have four legs. The front legs are short. The large, powerful hind legs are used for jumping.

Frogs have smooth, moist skin and generally live near water. Toads, such as the one pictured in Figure 12-17, have dry, rough skin. A toad can live in moist places far

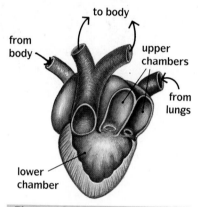

Figure 12-16

An amphibian heart has three chambers.

amphi- (double)
bios (life)

Figure 12-17

A black-spotted toad that is found in Asia. Toads have drier, rougher skin than do most frogs.

Figure 12-18

Leopard frog tadpoles (*top*) and a young adult leopard frog (*bottom*).

from water and usually does not return to water until it is ready to reproduce. The eggs of both frogs and toads are fertilized externally. Both animals lay their jelly-coated eggs in water, where the young hatch as tadpoles.

Figure 12-18 shows what a leopard frog looks like 1 week after hatching from an egg. The change from tadpole to adult leopard frog takes about 3 months. Figure 12-19 shows the changes that occur in this *metamorphosis*. Recall that metamorphosis is the series of distinct changes in form through which an organism passes as it develops from egg to adult. You learned about insect metamorphosis in Chapter 11. Refer to Figure 12-19 as you read about frog metamorphosis.

1. As the adult female frog lays a mass of many eggs in the water, the adult male frog releases sperm. The sperm fertilize the eggs.
2. Legless tadpoles hatch from the eggs.
3. Tadpoles have external gills and appear fishlike.
4. Hind legs and gill covers form. Lungs and front legs also form.
5. Lungs replace the gills, and the young frog moves onto land.

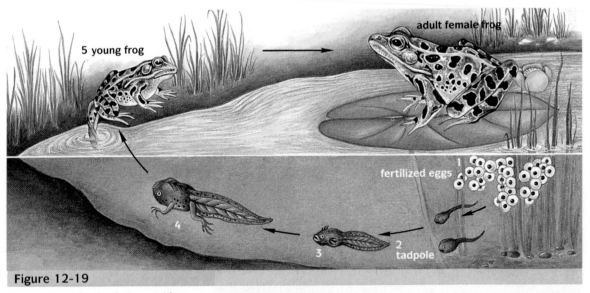

Figure 12-19

The metamorphosis of a leopard frog.

During the cold winter months, frogs and toads become inactive. This inactivity is in response to the decrease in temperature. Like all cold-blooded animals, an amphibian's body temperature changes with the external temperature. In cold months, frogs bury themselves in the mud at the bottom of lakes or ponds. Toads burrow into

ACTIVITY What Is the Structure of a Frog?

OBJECTIVES
Identify external features of a frog.
Hypothesize about the function of certain features of a frog.

MATERIALS
preserved frog, tray, probe, hand lens

PROCEDURE

A. Examine the skin of a preserved frog. Record any differences between the skin on the top and on the underside of the frog.

B. Use a probe to help you open the frog's mouth. Observe how the tongue is attached. Place your finger in the mouth of the frog. Record what you feel.
   1. Hypothesize about the relationship between the way a frog's tongue is attached to its mouth and the way a frog gets its food.

C. Observe the oval-shaped membrane just behind each eye of the frog. This is the tympanic (tihm PAN ihk) membrane.
   2. Using the location of this structure as a clue, what function do you think the tympanic membrane has?

D. Compare the front and hind legs of the frog. Record the differences in structure and size. Observe the toes.
   3. What structures between the toes suggest the frog spends time in water?

RESULTS AND CONCLUSIONS

1. Make a drawing of the frog. Label the following parts: head, front and hind legs, tympanic membranes, eyes, mouth, and nostrils.
2. Explain how the external features of the frog are helpful in living on land and in the water.

soft, moist soil. Body temperature is lower and metabolism slows down. This period of inactivity of animals during winter months is called **hibernation** (hī buhr NAY shuhn). Frogs and toads hibernate until the spring, when the outside temperature begins to rise.

TAILED AMPHIBIANS

The tailed amphibians include salamanders and newts. A salamander has a long body, a neck between the head and body, short legs, and a long tail. These animals are generally less than 20 cm long. A large salamander that lives in North America is the mud puppy, shown in Figure 12-20. The mud puppy can reach lengths of up to 48 cm. The largest amphibians in the world are the Japanese salamanders, which can reach 1.5 m in length.

Figure 12-20

A mud puppy is a salamander that spends its entire life in water.

DO YOU KNOW?

Most frog eggs are laid and fertilized in water, where many eggs are soon eaten by other animals. The foam-nesting frog of Africa, however, has a unique way of protecting its eggs. During the mating season, up to 40 adult frogs gather on a branch overhanging a pond. The females secrete a sticky substance on the branch. All the frogs beat their hind legs and whip the substance into a foam. The eggs are then laid and fertilized in this foam. Soon the foam hardens, protecting the eggs from drying out or being eaten. After hatching, the tadpoles drop into the water where they develop into adult frogs.

Another interesting behavior of frogs is seen in a small, poisonous frog found in South America. These frogs lay as few as two or three eggs. The eggs are laid and fertilized on the forest floor. One of the parent frogs protects the eggs. When they hatch, the female frog carries the tadpoles on her back and deposits each in a small puddle of water trapped on the leaf of a plant. The female frog returns to each tadpole laying additional, unfertilized eggs that the growing tadpoles eat.

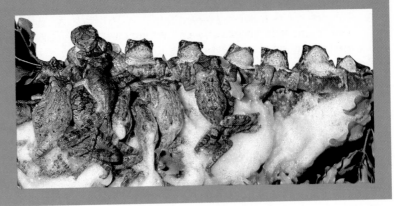

Figure 12-21

An adult newt (*top*) and a young newt (*bottom*). An adult newt may spend time both on land and in water. Why would an adult land-dwelling newt need to return to water?

Salamanders have thin, moist skin that is used in breathing. They are usually found near water or in damp places. Some salamanders, such as the mud puppy, live their entire life underwater. A mud puppy has feathery gills through which it breathes. Notice in Figure 12-20 how the gills extend from the mud puppy's body.

Newts begin their life underwater, using gills to breathe. As adults, newts breathe with lungs. Many kinds of newts spend time both in moist land areas and in water. In water, adult newts breathe through their skin. They also swim to the surface for air. Figure 12-21 shows two stages in the life cycle of a red-spotted newt. Notice the change in color that occurs in the adult stage.

REVIEW

1. What are some traits of amphibians?
2. Give two examples of tailless amphibians. Identify one way in which they differ.
3. What is hibernation?
4. Describe the metamorphosis of a frog.
5. Give two examples of tailed amphibians.

CHALLENGE During hibernation a frog is completely buried in mud. How do you think respiration occurs in a frog while it hibernates?

12-7 TRAITS OF REPTILES

There is a great deal of evidence that indicates large numbers of dinosaurs lived on the earth millions of years ago. Although they died out long ago, dinosaurs are probably the best-known reptiles. A **reptile** is a cold-blooded vertebrate that has dry, scaly skin and that lays eggs that have a leathery shell. When the dinosaurs were alive, many other kinds of reptiles were also present. As a result, this period of the past is called the Age of Reptiles.

Today, only four groups of reptiles remain. Turtles make up one group, alligators and crocodiles form a second group, and lizards and snakes are a third group. The fourth group has only one surviving species, called the tuatara (too uh TAH ruh). Tuataras live on islands off the coast of New Zealand. The modern tuatara, shown in Figure 12-23, is much like the tuatara that lived during the Age of Reptiles.

After completing this section, you will be able to

- **list** the four groups of reptiles and **describe** traits of reptiles.
- **compare** traits of amphibians with traits of reptiles.
- **compare** traits of the four groups of reptiles.

The key terms in this section are
internal fertilization
reptile

Figure 12-22

The term *dinosaur* comes from Greek words meaning "terrible lizard." But some dinosaurs, such as these hadrosaurs, were plant eaters.

Figure 12-23

The tuatara is sometimes called a living fossil. Can you explain why?

Reptiles have *adaptations* that make these animals suited for life on land. Recall that an adaptation is a trait that makes an organism better able to survive in its environment. The skin of a reptile is thick, dry, and covered by scales or plates. This waterproof skin holds moisture in and protects the animal from drying out. With the exception of snakes, reptiles have four limbs. The limbs usually have claws that are used for digging, climbing, and walking on land.

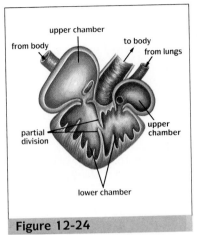

Figure 12-24

The heart of most reptiles has three chambers. The lower chamber is partially divided.

As you have learned, many water-dwelling vertebrates get oxygen from water, both through their gills and their skin. A reptile, however, breathes air; oxygen does not enter its body in either one of these ways. What adaptations do reptiles have that provide their cells with a constant supply of oxygen? One adaptation is the well-developed circulatory system of reptiles. In most reptiles the lower chamber of the three-chambered heart is partially divided, as seen in Figure 12-24. The oxygen-rich blood that returns from the lungs is thus separated from the blood that contains carbon dioxide. The respiratory system of reptiles is also well-developed for living on land.

Fertilization is internal in reptiles. **Internal fertilization** (ihn TER nuhl fer tuh luh ZAY shuhn) is the joining of egg and sperm inside the body of an animal. This trait is another adaptation of reptiles to life on land. Because sperm and egg join in the body of the animal, they are protected. The fertilized egg of a reptile has a leathery shell that protects against drying out but allows gases to enter and leave. The egg contains fluid and a large amount of stored food. This food is used by the reptile as it grows inside the egg.

Figure 12-25

A king snake hatching from its leathery-shelled egg.

A reptile's traits are very different from those of an amphibian. The reptile has adapted to life on land. Reptiles have dry, leathery skin. Amphibians have thin, moist skin. Unlike amphibians, reptiles do not have gills at any stage in their life. Amphibians must return to water to reproduce, but reptiles can reproduce on land. Why? Amphibians and reptiles also differ in their development. Most young amphibians look very different from their parents. Through metamorphosis, they change to the adult form. Newly hatched reptiles, however, look like small adults.

TURTLES

A turtle is a reptile that has two hard, bony shells that cover and protect its body. A dome-shaped shell covers the top of the body and a flat shell covers the bottom. When frightened, many kinds of turtles can pull their head and legs inside the shells for complete protection. Although turtles breathe air, many can live in water. But even water-dwelling turtles return to land to lay eggs. Turtles that live only on land are called land turtles, or tortoises (TAWR tehs ehz).

Compare the leg structure of the land and sea turtles in Figure 12-26. Land turtles have strong, short, clawed legs that are used for walking and digging. Sea turtles have clawless flippers that aid in swimming.

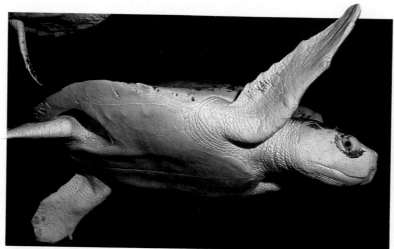

Figure 12-26

A sea turtle (*left*) and a land turtle (*right*). Land turtles are also known as tortoises.

CROCODILES AND ALLIGATORS

Crocodiles and alligators live in shallow waters of tropical streams, rivers, and swamps. These animals can reach lengths of over 6 m. Their long, muscular body is covered with thick, tough scales. They have large, strong jaws with very sharp teeth. Both animals have a large tail that is used for swimming. While their body is underwater, these reptiles are able to keep their eyes and nostrils above the water's surface. Another unusual feature of this group of reptiles is a four-chambered heart. The lower chamber of the heart is completely divided. This heart is similar to the heart of higher vertebrates.

Although crocodiles and alligators are often mistaken for one another, each can be identified by the shape of its snout. As you can see in Figure 12-27, an alligator has a broad, rounded snout. A crocodile has a narrower, pointed snout.

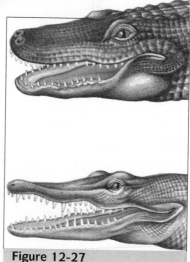

Figure 12-27

An alligator (*top*) has a rounded snout. A crocodile (*bottom*) has a more pointed snout.

287

SNAKES AND LIZARDS

Although snakes and lizards are in the same group, there are many differences in their body structure. Most lizards have four legs, movable eyelids, and ear openings. Snakes have no legs, eyelids that do not move, and no ear openings. Both types of animals have skin covered by scales. The skin is shed from time to time as the animals grow. This periodic shedding of skin is called *molting*.

Snakes and lizards both have the ability to eat prey that appear larger than their mouth opening. The lower jaw is loosely joined to the skull and can unhinge. This causes the mouth opening to become very large. This trait is best developed in snakes. It enables a snake, such as the one in Figure 12-28, to swallow whole a fairly large animal.

Figure 12-28

A snake molts as it grows (*left*). The unhinging of its lower jaw allows this snake to eat a large rat (*right*).

Figure 12-29

A Komodo dragon.

Snakes are found all over the world—living on the ground, in trees, and in water. Snakes are meat eaters. Many snakes are helpful to humans because these snakes eat insect and rodent pests. Most snakes are nonpoisonous. The poisonous snakes kill their prey by injecting them with a poison. The poison flows through long, hollow, pointed teeth called *fangs*. The fangs break the skin of the prey and the poison enters its body.

Most lizards live in hot, dry places, although some live in forests. A few species live in water. Most lizards are meat eaters that feed on insects and worms. Large lizards will also eat eggs, birds, and other lizards. Some lizards eat only plants. Most lizards grow no larger than 60 cm. The Komodo dragon, shown in Figure 12-29, is a lizard that grows as large as 3 m in length.

REVIEW

1. Describe traits of reptiles and give an example of an animal from each of the four groups of reptiles.
2. Describe the major differences between amphibians and reptiles.
3. Describe traits of turtles.
4. Describe traits of crocodiles and alligators.

CHALLENGE Suppose you were setting up a terrarium for a certain kind of lizard. What information would you need in order to provide a suitable environment for the lizard?

CHAPTER SUMMARY

The main ideas in this chapter are listed below. Read these statements before you answer the Chapter Review questions.

- Vertebrates are in a subphylum of phylum Chordata. Two other subphyla include the invertebrate tunicates and lancelets. Chordates have a notochord and gill slits at some time during development; they also have a nerve cord. (12-1)

- Most vertebrates have an endoskeleton made of bone and cartilage. The five classes of cold-blooded vertebrates include three classes of fish, amphibians, and reptiles. The two remaining classes are warm-blooded and include birds and mammals. (12-2)

- Fish are cold-blooded vertebrates that live in water, breathe with gills, and have a two-chambered heart. (12-3)

- Jawless fish are wormlike fish that lack jaws. Cartilage fish have jaws, scales, fins, and a skeleton made of cartilage. (12-4)

- Bony fish have gill covers, scales, fins, and a skeleton that is mostly bone. (12-5)

- Amphibians are cold-blooded vertebrates. They usually live in water and breathe with gills when young. As adults, most have lungs and live on land. (12-6)

- Legless amphibians are a small group of wormlike animals. Tailless amphibians include frogs and toads. Tailed amphibians include salamanders and newts. (12-6)

- Reptiles are cold-blooded vertebrates adapted to life on land. They have lungs and dry, thick, scaly skin. The female reptile lays eggs that have a shell. (12-7)

- The four groups of reptiles are the turtles, crocodiles and alligators, snakes and lizards, and a group with only one species, called the tuatara. (12-7)

The key terms in this chapter are listed below. Use each term in a sentence that shows the meaning of the term.

amphibian	external fertilization	reptile
bone	fins	scales
bony fish	fish	scavenger
cartilage	gill cover	spawning
cartilage fish	gills	vertebrate
chordate	hibernation	warm-blooded animal
cold-blooded animal	internal fertilization	
endoskeleton	jawless fish	

Chapter Review

VOCABULARY

Use the key terms from this chapter to complete the following sentences correctly.

1. Any animal that is in phylum Chordata and has a backbone is called a/an _____.
2. A/an _____ is a skeleton that is inside an animal's body.
3. An animal whose body temperature is not dependent on the external temperature is called a/an _____.
4. Fish release eggs into water by a process called _____.
5. The joining of egg and sperm inside the body of an animal is called _____.
6. Flat plates that cover the body of a fish are called _____.
7. The tough, flexible material that makes up the skeleton of some fish is called _____.
8. An animal that feeds on dead or dying organisms is called a/an _____.
9. A period of inactivity of some animals during winter is called _____.
10. A bony flap that protects the gills of bony fish is the _____.

CONCEPTS

1. What three traits do chordates have in common? (12-1)
2. How do tunicates and lancelets differ from other chordates? (12-1)
3. Describe vertebrates in terms of their skeleton, circulatory system, and nervous system. (12-2)
4. Distinguish between a cold-blooded animal and a warm-blooded animal. Give an example of each. (12-2)
5. Describe circulation and respiration in fish. (12-3)
6. Distinguish between internal and external fertilization. (12-3, 12-7)
7. How do fins and scales function in fish? (12-3)
8. Identify the three classes of fish and give one example of each. (12-3, 12-4, 12-5)
9. What are three ways in which jawless fish differ from the other two classes of fish? (12-4, 12-5)
10. Identify two types of jawless fish and describe how they obtain food. (12-4)
11. Describe four traits that sharks and rays have in common. (12-4)
12. What is the lateral line and what is its function? (12-5)
13. How does a gill cover function in respiration in bony fish? (12-5)
14. Describe the function of the air bladder. (12-5)

15. Why are amphibians described as leading a double life? (12-6)
16. Identify two major groups of amphibians and give two examples of animals in each group. (12-6)
17. Describe metamorphosis in a frog. (12-6)
18. Why do most adult amphibians tend to live near water? (12-6)
19. Identify the three major groups of reptiles. (12-7)
20. Describe how reptiles are adapted to life on land. (12-7)
21. How do reptiles and amphibians differ in development? (12-7)
22. What trait of snakes and lizards enables them to swallow their prey whole? (12-7)

APPLICATION/ CRITICAL THINKING

1. In many lizards the tail can be released from the body and a new tail will grow back. After it separates from the lizard's body, the tail may continue to move for a time. How are these traits helpful to the survival of a lizard?
2. For an animal in which fertilization is internal rather than external, why would producing large numbers of eggs not be as important to the survival of the species?
3. How does the lack of a jaw affect feeding habits of jawless fish?
4. Salamanders and lizards are similar in appearance. How could you easily distinguish between the two?
5. How does respiration occur in a frog swimming underwater? Why does a frog need to come to the surface from time to time?

EXTENSION

1. Lampreys feed on trout, whitefish, and other fish that people use as food. In the 1940s and 1950s, lampreys were the major cause of the death of most of the trout in the Great Lakes. Do research to find out what methods have been used to solve the lamprey problem. Write a report on your findings.
2. Find out which, if any, poisonous snakes live in your state. How can these snakes be identified?
3. Flounders as well as some other types of fish can change color, depending on their environment. Find out how this occurs and what benefit it is to the fish. Report your findings.

READINGS

Ballenger, Royce E., and John D. Lynch. *How to Know the Amphibians and Reptiles.* Dubuque, Iowa: William C. Brown, 1983.

Graham-Barber, Lynda. *Round Fish, Flatfish, and Other Animal Changes.* New York: Crown Publishers, Inc., 1982.

WARM-BLOODED VERTEBRATES

As you watch a bird in flight, you may be reminded of the way an airplane or a glider flies. But one type of bird moves like a helicopter. Not only can the hummingbird fly backward, it can also hover, or remain in one place, in midair! The hummingbird in the photograph is sucking nectar as it hovers near a flower. Its long beak and tongue are adapted for sucking nectar from flowers such as the one shown.

Due to their rapid movement, the wings of the hummingbird may appear as a blur. The wings beat so rapidly—up to 70 times per second—that they give off a humming sound. The hummingbird is named for this sound.

- *What traits of birds are helpful for flight?*
- *In what ways are birds like mammals?*
- *How do mammals differ from other animals?*

13-1 TRAITS OF BIRDS

Though birds and mammals do not appear to have much in common, they share some important traits. Unlike all other animals, birds and mammals are *warm-blooded*. A warm-blooded animal is able to maintain a constant body temperature, even when the outside temperature changes. Besides being warm-blooded, birds and mammals both have well-developed body systems.

A **bird** is a warm-blooded vertebrate that has wings and a body covering of feathers. Recall that a vertebrate is an animal that has a backbone. There are over 8500 species of birds. Birds are found all over the world, in a variety of environments. They live on land, and even in water. Since birds are warm-blooded, they are able to live in places where there are wide temperature ranges. Some species of birds live in places where the temperatures are extreme. For example, penguins live in the cold, ice-covered Antarctic. Other birds live in hot, humid jungles or in hot, dry deserts. Differences among birds enable them to live in these many kinds of places.

After completing this section, you will be able to

- **describe** traits of birds and **identify** traits that are adaptations for flight.
- **compare** down and contour feathers.
- **relate** the structure of beaks and feet to their functions.
- **define** the term *migration*.

The key terms in this section are

air sac	down feather
bird	migration
contour feather	
crop	

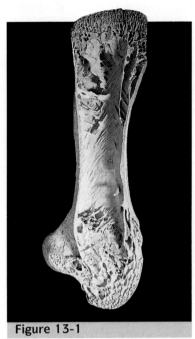

Figure 13-1

The crisscross structure of a bird bone.

LOW WEIGHT AND HIGH ENERGY

The most unique feature of birds is flight. Flight requires a low body weight compared with the size of the animal's body. Flight also requires a great amount of energy. Although birds differ in many ways, most birds have certain traits in common. Many of these traits are adaptations for flight. Recall that an adaptation is a trait that makes an organism better able to survive in its environment. The front limbs of birds are wings, and the hind limbs are legs. Most birds use their wings for flying. The legs are used for walking and for perching.

There are several traits of birds that result in their having a low body weight. Compared with the size of its body, the skeleton of a bird is very light. Many of the bones are filled with air spaces. Notice the crisscross structure inside the bird bone shown in Figure 13-1. This structure makes the bone strong but adds little weight.

Large amounts of oxygen are needed for flight. The oxygen is supplied by a complex respiratory system. Birds have well-developed lungs. Birds also have a series of air sacs. An **air sac** is a structure that is connected to the lungs of a bird and that helps to supply oxygen used in respiration. When a bird inhales, or takes in air, air enters the lungs and the air sacs. When a bird exhales, air goes out of its lungs. At the same time, air also moves from the air sacs to the lungs. Thus the lungs fill with air both when the bird inhales and when it exhales. Look at Figure 13-2 to see how much the air sacs increase the amount

Figure 13-2

The structure of a pigeon. How do air sacs affect the supply of air to the lungs?

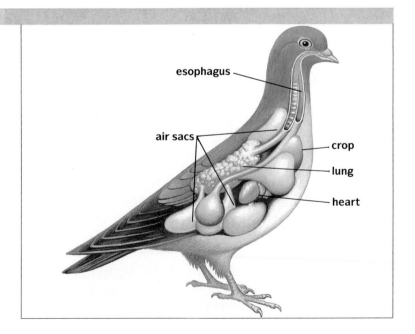

of air that is available to the lungs. The air sacs also function in cooling the bird's body during flight. The air sacs bring cool external air into close contact with the organs inside the body.

As you have learned, animals need food and oxygen for energy. Birds are able to eat large amounts of food at one time. After it is eaten, the food is stored in the crop. The **crop** is an organ in which food is moistened and stored before digestion. Locate the crop in Figure 13-2.

Birds have a well-developed circulatory system with a four-chambered heart. Look at the bird heart in Figure 13-3. Notice that in a four-chambered heart, there is a complete separation of oxygen-rich and oxygen-poor blood. The separation of oxygen-rich and oxygen-poor blood is an important feature. Because of it, the blood that is pumped throughout the body contains the large amounts of oxygen needed for flight.

FEATHERS

Birds are aided in flight by the streamlined shape of their body. Overlapping feathers cover a bird's body and help to give it this shape. There are two main types of feathers: contour (KAHN tawr) feathers and down feathers. A **contour feather** is one of the large feathers that help to give a bird its streamlined shape. Contour feathers also cover the wings. In flight the wings cut through the air

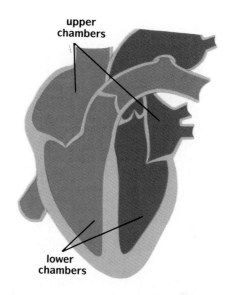

upper chambers

lower chambers

Figure 13-3

A bird heart has four chambers.

ACTIVITY   How Do Contour and Down Feathers Differ?

OBJECTIVE
Compare contour and down feathers.

MATERIALS
contour feather, scissors, hand lens, down feather

PROCEDURE
A. Examine a contour feather and locate the long central shaft.
B. Feel the vane along either side of the central shaft. Use scissors to cut about 2 cm off the end of the shaft. Look at the cut end. Record your observations.
C. Notice that the vane is soft yet firm. Hold the feather by the shaft and fan yourself. Describe what you feel.

D. Examine a down feather. Note the shape of the feather and how it feels. Hold the feather by the shaft and fan yourself. Describe what you feel.

RESULTS AND CONCLUSIONS
1. How is the shaft of the contour feather an adaptation for flight?
2. Does the down feather fan the air in the same way as the contour feather? Explain any differences you observed in the way the feathers fan the air.
3. As you have learned, down feathers function in insulation. How does the structure of a down feather serve this function?

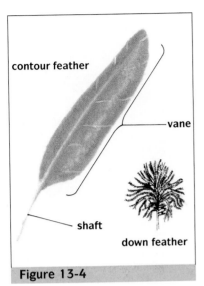

Figure 13-4

Contour and down feathers.

or glide on air currents. The light weight and smooth shape of contour feathers make them a good covering for the wings. Notice in Figure 13-4 that a contour feather has a main stem called a *shaft*. The flat part of the feather attached to the shaft is the *vane*.

A **down feather** is a short, fluffy feather found close to a bird's body. Compare the contour and down feathers shown in Figure 13-4. Down feathers are the main covering of young birds. In mature birds the down feathers are found between the bird's body and the contour feathers. Down feathers insulate the bird, or keep heat from being lost from the bird's body. These feathers trap air, which is then warmed by the bird's body. This warm layer of air helps to insulate the bird.

BEAKS AND FEET

Although birds lack teeth, they have a strong beak. The beak is used to pick up food, such as seeds. The structure of a bird's beak is adapted to the kind of food the bird eats. The shape of its beak can provide clues to the kind of food that a bird eats. Look at Figure 13-5. Notice the long, pointed beak of the woodpecker. This beak is used to bore into the trunks of trees as the woodpecker searches for insects. The cardinal breaks open seeds with its strong, thick beak. The meat-eating hawk tears the flesh of other animals by using its sharp, hooked beak.

Different types of birds' feet can also be seen in Figure 13-5. The structure of a bird's feet shows adaptations for food getting and for moving about in its environment. Most birds' feet have four toes—three in the front and one in the back. You can see this type of foot in the cardinal.

Figure 13-5

Notice the differences among the beaks and feet of the woodpecker, cardinal, hawk, and duck. Based on the shape of its beak, or bill, what kind of food might the duck eat?

The shape of its feet allows the cardinal to grasp tree branches. The hawk's grasping feet with sharp claws are used to strike at and then hold its victims. The duck has paddle-shaped, webbed feet that aid in swimming.

MIGRATION

Many birds cannot stay in the same place throughout the year. In some areas the weather gets very cold during winter months. The food supply of many birds becomes scarce. As winter nears, many species of birds fly to warmer locations.

The seasonal movement of animals from one location to another is called **migration** (mī GRAY shuhn). In the Northern Hemisphere many birds migrate southward in the fall and northward in the summer. They migrate to places where food, water, and suitable temperatures can be found. The bobolink breeds in North America during late spring and early summer. In fall the bobolink flies to the grasslands of South America. Trace the migration route of the bobolink shown in Figure 13-6.

Figure 13-6

A bobolink (A) and its migration route (B). The route covers a distance of 11,000 km.

REVIEW

1. Describe three traits of birds, and explain how these traits are adaptations for flight.
2. Describe the functions of contour and down feathers.
3. Give an example of how a bird's beak is related to the kind of food it eats. Give an example of how a bird's feet are related to where it lives.
4. Give two reasons why birds migrate.

CHALLENGE How does having a streamlined body aid a bird in flight?

13-2 REPRODUCTION IN BIRDS

albus (white)

In some ways, reproduction in birds is similar to that in reptiles. In both, fertilization is internal. This means that the egg and sperm join within the body of the female. Then the developing organism grows in an egg that is covered by a shell. But unlike the soft, leathery shell of a reptile egg, a bird egg has a hard, brittle shell.

Refer to Figure 13-7 as you read about the structure of a bird egg. At the center of the egg is the embryo (EHM-bree oh). The **embryo** is the organism in the early stages of its development. Attached to the embryo is the yolk. The **yolk** is food for the embryo. The yolk is surrounded by albumen (al BYOO muhn), also called egg white. **Albumen** is a watery substance that provides a liquid environment for the embryo. The albumen also acts as a cushion, protecting the embryo from injury.

A tough *shell membrane* surrounds the albumen. The hard *shell* protects the embryo from injury. The shell and the shell membrane both help to protect the egg from drying out. Also, both structures have tiny openings through which gases can pass. Thus, oxygen can pass into the egg, and carbon dioxide can pass out.

Figure 13-7

Structure of a bird egg. What part of the egg cushions the embryo?

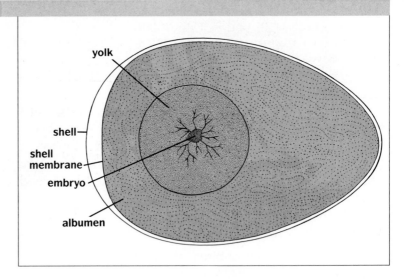

In most cold-blooded vertebrates, the parents do not take care of the eggs after they are laid. In birds, however, the eggs are usually protected by the parents. Either the male or the female parent sits on the eggs until they hatch. In some bird species the male and female take turns sitting on the eggs. Sitting on the eggs not only protects them but also warms them. A bird embryo can develop only if

Although most birds incubate their eggs by sitting on them, some birds have unusual nesting behavior. Some types of birds build mounds. Mound builders never sit on their eggs. Yet the eggs stay warm, and the embryos within them develop. How does this happen? The eggs of a mound builder are warmed by the nest.

For the megapode, a bird found in Australia and some Pacific islands, nest building begins in the early winter.

The bird first digs a very large hole. Sand and dried plant material are scraped into the hole, making a mound almost 1 m high and 4.5 m wide. The eggs are laid in the mound and covered. Spring rains cause the plant material to rot. The rotting process gives off heat and warms the eggs.

In the summer heat the nest becomes too warm. So the megapode opens the nest in the morning, letting heat escape. The bird then covers the nest at night.

Some mound builders check the temperature of their mounds by using their bill or tongue as a "thermometer." The bird sticks its bill into the nest.

incubation (ihn kyuh BAY shuhn) occurs. **Incubation** is the warming of an egg to a certain temperature over a period of time while the embryo develops. During incubation the egg must be kept humid and be turned.

in- (on)
cubare (lie)

Most birds incubate their eggs in a nest. The type of nest varies with the species. Nests vary in size and in the materials used to build them. Some birds that do not build nests lay their eggs on the ground. The color of the eggs matches the color of the surroundings.

The length of incubation varies with the species of bird. In general, the shorter the period of incubation the less developed are the baby birds when they hatch. Small birds, such as sparrows, wood thrushes, and robins, are incubated for 10–20 days. Figure 13-8 shows newly hatched wood-thrush chicks. These baby birds are weak, blind, and have few or no feathers. They are dependent on their parents. Larger birds, such as ducks and geese, incubate their eggs for 21–28 days. These birds are strong and independent soon after they hatch. They can feed themselves, walk, and swim. How do the baby ducks and wood thrushes shown in Figure 13-8 differ?

Figure 13-8

Wood-thrush chicks in their nest (A). One-day-old ducks and their mother (B).

REVIEW

1. What is an embryo?
2. Describe the structure of a bird egg.
3. Compare newly hatched birds having a short incubation with those having a long incubation.

CHALLENGE In what ways are birds' eggs more protected than eggs of cold-blooded vertebrates?

13-3 TRAITS OF MAMMALS

After completing this section, you will be able to

- **list** the major traits of mammals.
- **describe** the four types of teeth in mammals.
- **define** the term *instinct* and **give examples** of instincts.

The key terms in this section are
instinct   mammary gland
mammal

What do a dog, a bat, a monkey, and a whale have in common? They are all mammals. A **mammal** is a warm-blooded vertebrate that has hair and that feeds milk to its young. Mammals are a successful group of animals. A group of animals is successful if its members are found in many types of environments or in great numbers. Look at Figure 13-9. Where are mammals found?

Mammals are the only animals that have hair or fur. Though some mammals have little or no hair, most are covered with hair. Hair insulates mammals in much the same way that feathers insulate birds.

Figure 13-9

The mountain lions (*left*), the insect-eating bat (*middle*), and the dolphins (*right*) are mammals found in three different environments.

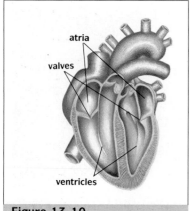

Figure 13-10

A mammal heart has four chambers.

Fertilization is internal in mammals. The young of nearly all mammals develop inside the mother's body. The amount of development at birth varies with the type of mammal. A mammal that is not fully developed at birth is dependent on its parents' care. The amount of care given to the young is greater in mammals than in any other class of animal. The mammary (MAM uh ree) gland is found only in mammals and is used in the care of their young. A **mammary gland** is a structure in female mammals that secretes milk. The milk provides food for the young.

Like birds, mammals have a four-chambered heart. Figure 13-10 shows these chambers. The upper chambers are called *atria* (AY tree uh). The atria receive blood from other parts of the body. The lower chambers, called *ventricles* (VEHN truh kuhlz), pump blood to other parts of the body. Structures called *valves* are found between the upper and lower chambers. The valves are flaps that open

OBJECTIVE

Observe the structure of a sheep heart.

MATERIALS

lab apron, dissecting pan, sheep heart cut in half, metric ruler, probe

PROCEDURE

A. Wear a lab apron during this activity. Place the two halves of a sheep heart together. Examine the exterior of the heart. Notice that the heart is firm and muscular. Make a drawing of the exterior of the heart.

B. Separate the two halves of the heart and examine the internal structures. Notice the four rounded chambers. Locate the upper chambers, or atria. Find the lower chambers, or ventricles.
  1. Which structures are larger—the atria or the ventricles?

C. Examine the walls of each chamber. Using a metric ruler, measure the thickness of the walls of each chamber. Record this number.

D. Locate the valves, or flaps, between the atria and ventricles. Touch a valve with your finger or a probe. Without using force, gently open the valve.
  2. Do the valves open toward the atria or toward the ventricles?

E. Examine the wall that separates the left and right sides of the heart.
  3. Are there any valves between the left and right sides of the heart?

F. Make a drawing of the internal structure of the heart. Label the atria and ventricles.

RESULTS AND CONCLUSIONS

1. Which chambers have the thickest walls? How does having thick walls serve the function of these structures?
2. Why is there no mixing of oxygen-rich and oxygen-poor blood in a four-chambered heart?

and close. They control the flow of blood between the upper and lower chambers.

Another important trait of all mammals is a well-developed nervous system that includes a complex brain. In general, the brain of a mammal is larger than that of other vertebrates. Mammals are more intelligent than most other vertebrates.

Mammals have very specialized teeth. There are four types of teeth in mammals: *incisors, canines, premolars,* and *molars.* The number and shape of each of these types of teeth are related to the kind of food the mammal eats. Meat-eating mammals, such as wolves and lions, have long, pointed canine teeth that are used for tearing. Their incisors are chisel-shaped and are used for cutting. Plant-eating mammals, such as horses and cows, have large, flat premolars and molars. These teeth are used for grinding plant materials.

The complex behavior of mammals is another trait of this class. Soon after a mammal is born, it finds its mother's mammary gland, or breast, and begins to feed on milk. Without being taught, the newborn seeks its mother's breast. This behavior is inborn. A complex, inborn pattern of behavior is called an **instinct**. Breast-feeding is one type of instinct. Mammals have many types of

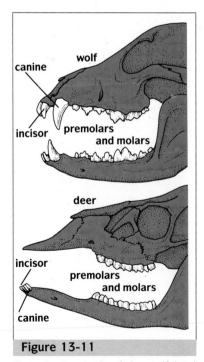

Figure 13-11

How do the teeth of the wolf (*top*) and the deer (*bottom*) differ?

instincts. Migration is an instinct of some mammals. The defense of a certain territory is another.

Hibernation is another instinct of mammals. You learned that frogs hibernate. Recall that hibernation is a type of deep sleep in which an animal has a lowered body temperature. Many mammals hibernate during winter. Food, needed to supply energy, is scarce in winter. A great amount of energy is needed to maintain a normal body temperature during cold weather. Since a hibernating animal maintains a low body temperature, it uses little energy.

in- (on)
sting- (urge)

Though many types of animal behavior are instinctive, mammals also learn behavior. An example of learned behavior is seen in bears. Figure 13-11 shows an Alaskan brown bear teaching her offspring to hunt salmon. Notice the young bears carefully watching their mother. After practice, the young bears will become skilled hunters.

Figure 13-12

An Alaskan brown bear teaching her young to hunt salmon. What food-related instinct do young bears have at birth?

REVIEW

1. What are three traits of mammals?
2. What structure in mammals functions in feeding the young?
3. How do the teeth of a plant eater differ from those of a meat eater?
4. What is an instinct? Give an example of an instinct in mammals.

CHALLENGE   Some mammals, such as elephants and whales, have little body hair. Suggest reasons why a lack of hair may be an adaptation in these mammals.

13-4 TYPES OF MAMMALS

There are about 4000 species of mammals. Although there is great variety among these many kinds of mammals, scientists classify them into three groups. These groups are based on how the young develop.

MONOTREMES

A **monotreme** (MAHN uh treem) is an egg-laying mammal. There are only two living species of monotremes. They are the spiny anteater and the duckbilled platypus. Compare these two monotremes, shown in Figure 13-13. How do their snouts and body coverings differ? These two species differ not only in the way they look but also in where they live and how they eat. The anteater, which is a good burrower, lives in rocky and sandy places. Its long snout and tongue are adapted for eating ants. The duckbilled platypus lives in a burrow along the banks of a lake or stream. It feeds by using its long snout to catch insects, worms, and crustaceans in the water. Look at the feet of the platypus shown in Figure 13-13. How are the feet adapted for moving in water?

Figure 13-13

The duckbilled platypus (*left*) and the spiny anteater (*right*) are the only two living species of monotremes.

Though these two monotremes are very different from each other, they do have traits in common. They are the only mammals that lay eggs. Like all mammals, monotremes have mammary glands. Though monotremes are warm-blooded, their body temperature varies much more than that of other mammals.

MARSUPIALS

marsipos (pouch)

A **marsupial** (mahr SOO pee uhl) is a mammal whose young complete their development in a pouch in the female's body. The kangaroo and the koala, two well-known marsupials, are shown in Figure 13-14. Like most marsupials, these animals are found in Australia, where they have few natural enemies. Only one marsupial—the opossum—is found in North America.

Figure 13-14

Like most marsupials, the koala (*left*) and the kangaroo (*right*) live in Australia.

Marsupials spend only a short time developing within the mother's body. At birth the tiny marsupial crawls into the mother's pouch, where it feeds on milk from the mammary glands. Notice in Figure 13-15 that opossums are very small and not well developed at birth. They are only about 1 cm in length when they are born. A young opossum spends about two months in its mother's pouch before it can be independent.

Marsupials differ from monotremes in several traits. Marsupials do not lay eggs but instead give birth to live young. The body temperature of these pouched animals is fairly constant.

PLACENTALS

Most of the mammals with which you are familiar are placentals (pluh SEHN tuhlz). A **placental mammal** is a mammal whose young are nourished through a placenta as they develop inside the female's body. A **placenta** is a structure through which the developing mammal receives food and oxygen and gives off wastes. In placental mammals the unborn young complete most of their develop-

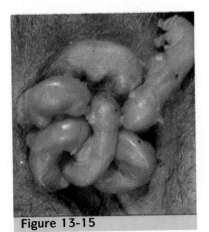

Figure 13-15

Baby opossums in their mother's pouch. These tiny marsupials are blind and helpless at birth.

ment within the mother's body. As with marsupials, the young are born live. Placentals are more fully developed at birth than are other mammals.

Placentals are found all over the world, in many kinds of places. There are 16 orders of placental mammals. The 10 most common orders are described in this section.

Insect eaters are small placental mammals. Shrews, moles, and hedgehogs are members of this insect-eating order. Many insect-eating mammals live in underground burrows. Notice the pointed snout of the shrew in Figure 13-16. This animal uses its snout to aid in its search for insects and worms.

Figure 13-16

The shrew is one of the smallest mammals. Some species are less than 3 g in mass when fully grown.

Figure 13-17

Like all bats, this hammerhead bat hangs upside down when at rest. It uses sight and smell to find fruit.

Bats are the only mammals that can fly. The wings of a bat are formed from long arms and fingers that are joined by a thin, smooth skin. Most bats sleep during the day and hunt for food at night. Many bats cannot see well in the dark, yet they can fly at night without bumping into objects. These bats have an unusual way of sensing objects around them. As it flies, a bat sends out high-pitched sounds that hit surrounding objects. Echoes return from the objects. Using its large ears, the bat detects the echoes and senses the location of the objects. Some bats also find insects and other types of food in this way.

Rodents are the largest group of mammals. Rats, mice, squirrels, beavers, and hamsters belong to the order of rodents. Rodents have sharp, chisel-shaped teeth that are used for gnawing and cutting. Some rodents eat parts of woody plants. An unusual trait of rodents is that their incisors continue to grow as long as the animal lives. The inset in Figure 13-18A shows the incisors of a beaver. What advantages might there be in having incisors that continue to grow?

Figure 13-18

The beaver is a rodent that uses its chisel-shaped teeth (inset) to obtain food — bark and twigs from trees (A). The rodentlike pika eats grasses (B).

Rodentlike mammals are an order of mammals that have well-developed hind legs. These animals, which include the pika shown in Figure 13-18B, are good at running and jumping. Rabbits and hares also belong to this order. They are all small, plant-eating mammals. One way they differ from rodents is in the number of cutting teeth. Rodents have only two upper incisors; rabbits and hares have four upper incisors.

Aquatic mammals are an order of mammals that have adapted to life in the water. Whales, porpoises, and dolphins belong to this group. The aquatic mammals have

Figure 13-19

Gray whale exhaling through blow-hole (*A*). A blue whale, like other aquatic mammals, lacks hair but has a thick layer of blubber below the skin (*B*). What function might this layer have?

streamlined bodies. Their hind limbs are fins or flippers. Although they live in water, these mammals breathe oxygen from the air. They return to the water's surface in order to breathe. While swimming at the surface, they exchange gases through one or two nostrils located at the top of their head. Figure 13-19A shows a whale exhaling through its nostril, or blowhole.

Toothless mammals are animals that have few or no teeth. These animals eat insects, worms, and leaves. Anteaters, armadillos, and tree sloths belong to this order. The armadillo is unusual because it is the only mammal that has tough bony plates covering its body. Notice this platelike body covering and the large front claws of the armadillo shown in Figure 13-20.

Figure 13-20

The armadillo, a toothless mammal, has plates that function like a suit of armor.

Meat eaters are mammals that have sharp teeth used for tearing and biting meat. Recall that meat eaters have large, pointed canines. Though they are called meat eaters, some members of this order, such as bears, also eat fruits and plants. Other members of this order are dogs, cats, and raccoons. Seals are meat eaters that live in water.

Hoofed mammals make up another order of mammals. The toes and nails of these animals form hoofs. Examples of hoofed mammals include horses, giraffes, deer, pigs, and cattle. The members of this order are all plant eaters.

Elephants are the only living members of an order of mammals that have a long trunk, or nose. Elephants are plant eaters. The males have tusks that are actually very long incisors. Elephants are the largest land mammals.

Primates make up another order of mammals. Apes, monkeys, and humans are primates. A **primate** is a mammal that has a well-developed brain and has an *opposable* (uh POHZ uh buhl) *thumb.* An opposable thumb is one that can be placed against each of the other fingers. With this arrangement of fingers, the animal is able to grasp objects. The opposable thumb of the ape in Figure 13-21 allows it to swing through trees, safe from its enemies. What human activities are possible because of opposable thumbs?

Figure 13-21

Gorilla (*A*), zebras (*B*), dog (*C*), and elephant (*D*). What four orders of mammals are represented by these animals?

REVIEW

1. Name the three major groups of mammals.
2. Describe the development of the young in each of the three groups of mammals.
3. Identify five orders of placental mammals, and give examples of each.

CHALLENGE   What disadvantages do the developing young of egg-laying mammals have when compared with the developing young of pouched mammals?

CHAPTER SUMMARY

The main ideas in this chapter are listed below. Read these statements before you answer the Chapter Review questions.

- A bird is a warm-blooded vertebrate that has wings and a body covering of feathers. The respiratory system of birds includes air sacs that increase the amount of oxygen that is available to the lungs. Birds have a well-developed circulatory system that includes a four-chambered heart. (13-1)

- Feathers insulate a bird's body and assist in flight. The shape of a bird's beak and feet are adapted to its food and where it lives. As cold weather approaches, some birds migrate to warmer places where there is more food. (13-1)

- Fertilization in birds is internal. The embryo develops within a hard shell outside the mother's body. A long incubation results in newly hatched birds that are well developed. (13-2)

- Mammals are warm-blooded vertebrates that have hair and that feed milk to their young. The milk is produced in mammary glands. A four-chambered heart circulates the blood. Mammals have a large, complex brain. Their teeth are adapted to the type of food the mammal eats. Mammal behavior may be instinctive or learned. (13-3)

- There are three groups of mammals. Monotremes are egg-laying mammals. Marsupials have a pouch in which the young complete their development. Placentals nourish their young through a placenta inside the female's body. (13-4)

- The ten most common orders of placental mammals include insect eaters, bats, rodents, rodentlike mammals, aquatic mammals, toothless mammals, meat eaters, hoofed mammals, elephants, and primates. (13-4)

The key terms in this chapter are listed below. Use each term in a sentence that shows the meaning of the term.

air sac	down feather	mammary gland	placenta
albumen	embryo	marsupial	placental mammal
bird	incubation	migration	primate
contour feather	instinct	monotreme	yolk
crop	mammal		

Chapter Review

VOCABULARY

Use the key terms from this chapter to complete the following sentences correctly.

1. A large feather that helps to give a bird its streamlined shape is called a/an _____ .

2. The seasonal movement of animals from one location to another is called _____ .

3. An organism in the early stages of its development is called a/an _____ .

4. In an egg, the watery substance that provides a liquid environment for the embryo is the _____ .

5. An animal that is warm-blooded, has hair, and feeds milk to its young is a/an _____ .

6. An egg-laying mammal is also known as a/an _____ .

7. Mammals that have a highly developed brain and an opposable thumb belong to the _____ order.

8. In birds, the chamber in which food is moistened and stored prior to digestion is called a/an _____ .

9. The process of warming an egg to a certain temperature over time while the embryo develops is called _____ .

10. A structure in birds that is connected to the lungs and that helps to supply oxygen is called a/an _____ .

11. Food for a developing bird embryo is supplied by the _____ .

12. Newborn mammals feed on milk from their mother's _____ .

13. A type of mammal that has a pouch in which its young complete their development after birth is called a/an _____ .

CONCEPTS

1. Describe how the skeletal and respiratory systems of a bird are adaptations for flight. (13-1)

2. What is the function of the crop? (13-1)

3. In what way does a four-chambered heart aid a bird's ability to fly? (13-1)

4. How does a contour feather differ from a down feather? (13-1)

5. Give two examples of birds to show how the beak is adapted to the type of food that a bird eats. (13-1)

6. Compare newly hatched ducks with newly hatched wood thrushes in terms of development and dependence. (13-2)

7. Describe two functions of the shell of a bird egg. (13-2)

8. Describe four traits of mammals. (13-3)

9. Compare the teeth of a wolf with the teeth of a cow. (13-3)

10. What is an instinct? (13-3)

11. Give an example of a learned behavior in mammals. (13-3)

12. Describe the major difference between monotremes, marsupials, and placentals. (13-4)

13. How does a newborn marsupial differ from a newborn placental? (13-4)

14. Describe how bats that cannot see in the dark can sense objects around them. (13-4)

15. How do aquatic mammals breathe? (13-4)

16. How does an opposable thumb function? Which order of mammals has this trait? (13-4)

1. Explain why air sacs are so important to birds.
2. Suggest reasons why it might be more important for a duck to incubate its young for a long period of time than it would be for a bird such as a robin or wood thrush.
3. The opposable thumb is an important trait of primates. Explain the role that this trait has played in developing human society as it is today.
4. Hoofed mammals tend to feed in herds. How might this behavior aid survival of these mammals?

1. Get permission from one of your parents to study wildlife in your area. Go to a local nature center, a natural history museum, or a zoo to learn which birds and mammals are found in your area. If possible, go to a national park or a wildlife preserve to observe animals in their natural habitats. Present your findings to your class.
2. Porpoises are aquatic mammals that have a highly developed brain. They use various sounds to communicate with each other. Do research to find out what scientists have learned about porpoise communication. Write a brief report on your findings.
3. If you have a pet bird or pet mammal such as a dog, cat, hamster, or gerbil, write a brief report on tasks that your pet has learned to perform.

Bartlett, Jen, and Des Bartlett. "Encounters With a Toothless Spineball." *International Wildlife*, November/December 1984, p. 30.

Cooke, Patrick. "How Do Birds Find Where They're Going?" *Science 84*, September 1984, p. 26.

Peterson, Roger Tory. *A Field Guide to the Birds*. Boston: Houghton Mifflin Company, 1980.

COMPARING ANIMALS

Look at the photographs. The animals shown differ greatly in the way they look. Which animals are invertebrates? Which are vertebrates? Notice what each animal is doing. The different animals shown are involved in the same activity. They are all eating. Each animal needs the energy in food to carry on life processes. But each animal has different structures for carrying on these same processes. For example, animals vary in the kinds of structures they have for obtaining and digesting food. Life scientists learn much about animals by comparing animal body structures and functions.

- *How are the basic needs of invertebrates and vertebrates similar?*
- *How do different animals meet these needs?*

14-1 SUPPORT AND MOVEMENT

SUPPORT

In Chapters 10 through 13, you learned about many kinds of animals. The body of each kind of animal is supported and protected in some way. For example, a sponge has hard, pointed internal structures called *spicules*, that help to give the sponge its form. The network of spicules also helps to protect the sponge from other animals. Coelenterates such as jellyfish are supported by the water surrounding them. Certain coelenterates, such as corals, are protected by a hard structure made of limestone. Mollusks have a hard shell that provides protection.

In many types of animals, the *skeleton* is the main structure of support. Besides supporting the body, a skeleton protects organs inside the body. The skeleton also assists in movement. There are two types of skeletons— an exoskeleton and an endoskeleton.

An **exoskeleton** is a skeleton that covers the outside of an animal's body. Arthropods, such as insects and crustaceans, are animals that have an exoskeleton. The exoskeleton is a hard structure that protects the organs inside

> *After completing this section, you will be able to*
> - **describe** the functions of a skeleton.
> - **compare** an exoskeleton with an endoskeleton.
> - **explain** how muscles cause movement in animals.
>
> *The key terms in this section are*
> endoskeleton   muscles
> exoskeleton

exo- (outer)

the body and keeps them from drying out. It also functions as a suit of armor that protects an animal's body from other animals. As an animal grows, its exoskeleton is molted.

An **endoskeleton** is a skeleton that is inside an animal's body. The endoskeleton protects organs inside the body from injury. It also gives the animal its shape. Because it is made up of living tissue, the endoskeleton grows as the animal grows. This type of skeleton also repairs itself. For example, if the animal breaks a bone, the broken parts will grow together.

Vertebrates, such as fish, birds, and mammals, have an endoskeleton. Most vertebrate skeletons are somewhat like the skeleton of the frog shown in Figure 14-1. Notice the backbone, which is made up of many small bones. Arms are attached to shoulder bones. Legs are attached to hipbones.

BODY MOVEMENT

Some animals, such as sponges, attach to objects and do not move from one place to another. However, most animals can move from place to place. Movement allows these animals to seek and obtain food and shelter. Animals that do not have a skeleton, such as worms, move from place to place by the action of muscles. **Muscles** are bundles of tissue that contract, or become shorter. The action of the muscles can cause movement. An earthworm has two groups of muscles, shown in Figure 14-2. One group of muscles is circular and surrounds the earthworm like a set of rings. The other group of muscles runs along the length of the body. When the circular muscles contract, the body gets longer and narrower. When the lengthwise muscles contract, the body gets thicker and shorter. The action of these two muscle groups causes a wavelike motion that moves the earthworm through the soil.

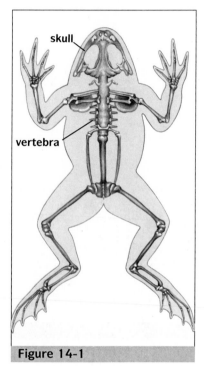

Figure 14-1

The frog skeleton is an endoskeleton.

endo- (inner, inside)

Figure 14-2

A cross section of an earthworm, showing the two types of muscles.

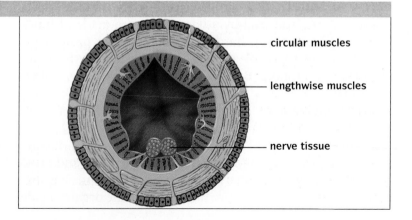

circular muscles

lengthwise muscles

nerve tissue

Arthropods have an exoskeleton that has joints. A joint is a place where two or more bones come together. Joints permit movement of the animal. Movement occurs because of the muscles attached to the exoskeleton. The contraction of the muscles causes movement of parts of the body. Figure 14-3A shows the relationship between the exoskeleton and the muscles of an insect.

Vertebrates, such as frogs, move by means of a complex system of muscles known as the *muscular system*. The muscular system of a frog is shown in Figure 14-3B. Vertebrates have pairs of muscles attached to the bones of the endoskeleton. One muscle of the pair contracts. At the same time the other muscle relaxes and lengthens. The action of these pairs of muscles attached to bones causes movement.

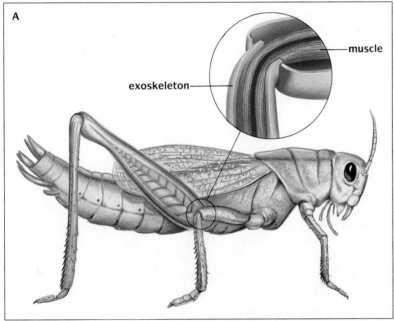

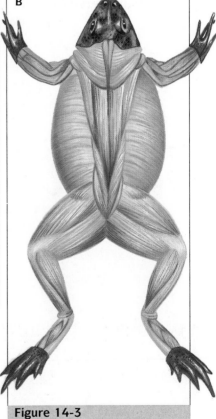

Figure 14-3

Exoskeleton of an insect, and relationship of the muscles and the exoskeleton (A). Muscular system of a frog (B).

REVIEW

1. What are the main functions of a skeleton?
2. Compare the structure and function of an endoskeleton with the structure and function of an exoskeleton.
3. Explain how an earthworm can move even though it lacks a skeleton.
4. Briefly explain the role of the endoskeleton and muscles in the movement of a vertebrate.

CHALLENGE A suit of armor is somewhat like an exoskeleton for humans. Suppose humans had an exoskeleton instead of an endoskeleton. List both the advantages and the disadvantages.

14-2 DIGESTION

digerere (to divide, distribute)

To carry on life processes, animals must have food from which they can obtain energy. Before food can be used by body cells, it must be digested. **Digestion** (duh-JEHS chuhn) is a series of steps in which food is broken down into simpler forms that are usable by the cells.

Simple animals such as sponges have a simple method of digesting food. Sponges are filter feeders. Along with water, sponges take in food through their pores. Food is digested within cells in the body wall and then passes to other body cells. Undigested food and wastes pass out of the sponge's body through a large opening at the top of the sponge. In Figure 14-4A, trace the movement of food into and the movement of wastes out of a sponge.

Coelenterates, such as the hydra, have one body opening — the mouth. Food enters and wastes leave the body through the same opening. The mouth opens into a saclike digestive cavity. Inside this cavity the food is acted upon by enzymes (EHN zīmz). An **enzyme** is a protein that controls the rate of chemical changes that occur in living things. It helps to break down food. The body wall of the hydra is only two cell layers thick. Thus, digested food easily diffuses from the inner layer to the outer layer of cells.

Figure 14-4

Movement of food into and wastes out of a sponge (*A*). A typical sponge (*B*).

- ■ movement of food
- ■ movement of wastes

Animals that are more complex have a *digestive system*. Their digestive system is made up of a digestive tube and digestive organs. Most often the digestive system has two openings. Food enters through a mouth. Wastes, such as undigested food, leave through an anus (AY nuhs). An **anus** is an opening of a digestive tube through which undigested food leaves an animal's body.

anus (ring)

316

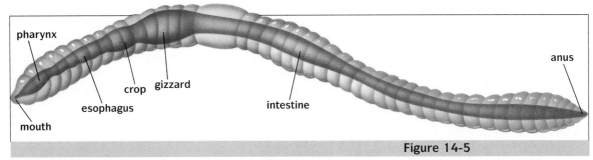

Figure 14-5

The digestive system of an earthworm. In which part of the digestive system is food stored?

An earthworm has a digestive system with two openings. Figure 14-5 shows the path of food through an earthworm's body. Food enters through the mouth. The food is then drawn farther into the digestive tube by the muscular action of the *pharynx* (FAR ihngks). The food then passes through a tube called the *esophagus* into the crop. The **crop** is a chamber that stores food in the digestive system.

From the crop, food is released into the gizzard. The **gizzard** (GIHZ uhrd) is a chamber in which food is broken down by muscular action. Food from the gizzard enters the intestine, which contains cells that produce enzymes. The action of these chemicals completes the digestive process. The digested food is absorbed by the cells lining the intestine. Undigested food passes out through the anus.

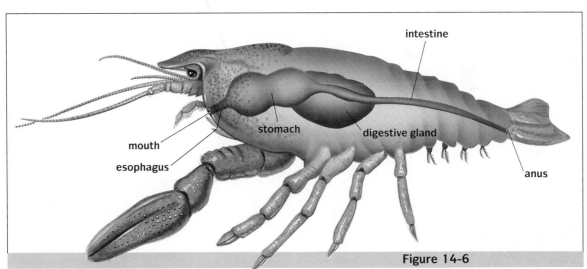

Figure 14-6

The digestive system of a crayfish.

Figure 14-6 shows the digestive organs of a crayfish. The jaws crush the food into smaller pieces before it is placed into the mouth. From the mouth, the food enters the esophagus and then passes to the *stomach*. The stomach is a large chamber in the digestive tube. The stomach contains toothlike structures that further crush the food.

Digestion is completed by the action of the digestive gland. A **digestive gland** is an organ that produces and releases digestive enzymes. In crayfish most of the digested food is absorbed by the digestive gland. Undigested food and other wastes enter the intestine. These materials pass out of the body through the anus.

ACTIVITY   What Makes Up a Frog's Digestive System?

OBJECTIVE
Observe the digestive system of a frog.

MATERIALS
lab apron, preserved frog, dissecting pan, dissecting pins, pointed scissors, probe, forceps

PROCEDURE

A. Wear a lab apron throughout this activity. Place a preserved frog in a dissecting pan. Use dissecting pins to hold down the limbs of the frog as shown.

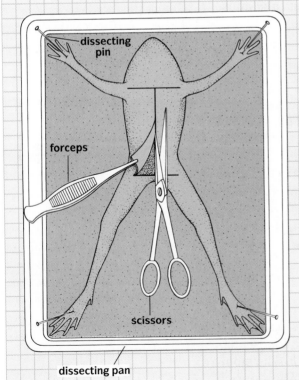

B. Using pointed scissors, carefully cut through the loose skin on the belly of the frog. Make the cuts in the shape of the letter I, as shown. Use the dissecting pins to pin the skin to the dissecting pan.

C. Under the skin is a layer of muscle. Below the muscle are the internal organs. Use the scissors to cut through the muscle in the same manner as you cut through the skin. Be careful not to cut or disturb the organs below the muscle.

D. Feel the bone in the middle of the chest. This bone protects the area of the heart. Using scissors, cut through this bone. Pin the muscle of the belly area to the dissecting pan.

E. Using a probe and forceps, or your fingers, move aside organs so that you can observe the parts of the digestive system. Refer to Figure 14-7 for help in locating and identifying the following parts of the frog's digestive system: *mouth*; *esophagus* — tube that leads from the mouth to the stomach; *liver* — large dark structure in the middle of the body cavity; *stomach* — long pale organ found under the liver; *gall bladder* — small round organ located in the middle of the liver; *pancreas* — thin flat organ next to the stomach; *small intestine* — small tube attached to the stomach; *large intestine* — large tube attached to the small intestine.

F. Make a drawing of the frog. Label the parts described in step **E**.

RESULTS AND CONCLUSIONS

1. Based on your observations of a frog's digestive system, describe the likely path of food after it enters the mouth.

2. Based on your observations, list the digestive organs that food does not pass through directly.

Look at the frog's digestive system in Figure 14-7. In a frog, food moves through the mouth and esophagus, and enters the stomach. Glands in the stomach walls give off enzymes that help to break down food. Food then passes to the small intestine. In the small intestine the food is acted upon by chemicals that are released by two organs—the *liver* and the *pancreas* (PAN kree uhs). The liver makes a substance called *bile*, which helps in the digestion of fat. Bile is stored in an organ called the *gall bladder*. The pancreas makes enzymes that also help to break down food.

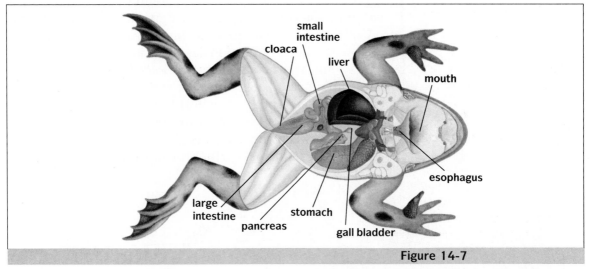

Figure 14-7

The digestive system of a frog. Through which structure do undigested foods leave the body?

From the small intestine, digested food is absorbed into the bloodstream. Undigested food passes into the large intestine. Unlike the crayfish, the frog has a *cloaca* (kloh AY kuh) into which the large intestine empties. A cloaca is a chamber that receives products of three different body systems. In the frog, undigested foods pass out of the body through the cloaca.

REVIEW

1. What is digestion?
2. Compare digestion in a hydra with that in an earthworm.
3. Compare the digestive system of a crayfish with that of a frog.

CHALLENGE In some animals, digestion occurs only within cells. In other animals, food is broken down outside of cells in a cavity or other structure. Which type of digestion does a sponge have? Which does a frog have? Explain your answers.

14-3 RESPIRATION AND CIRCULATION

RESPIRATION

Respiration (rehs puh RAY shuhn) is the process of releasing energy from food, usually sugar. The energy is used by the cells of an animal to carry on life processes. The breakdown of sugar occurs in the presence of oxygen. Carbon dioxide is given off. For respiration to occur, there must be an exchange of gases with the environment. Most animals have a *respiratory system* for the exchange of gases.

Many complex animals have special structures for getting needed oxygen. Land-dwelling arthropods, such as most spiders and insects, have spiracles (SPĪ ruh kuhlz). A *spiracle* is a small opening through which air enters the body. In spiders the spiracles open into *book lungs*.

Some arthropods, such as insects, have *tracheal* (TRAY-kee uhl) *tubes*. These tubes extend from the spiracles to all parts of the body. Tracheal tubes branch into smaller tubes that are in contact with body cells. Gas exchange occurs between the cells and these smaller tubes. Locate the spiracles and tracheal tubes of the insect in Figure 14-8B.

spirare (breathe)

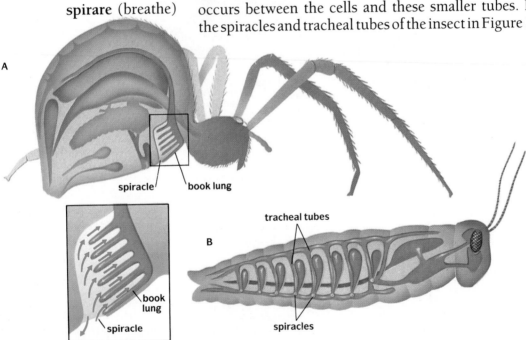

Figure 14-8

The book lungs of a spider (*A*), and the tracheal tubes and spiracles of an insect (*B*).

Gills are organs that allow for exchange of gases in many water-dwelling animals. As water passes over the gills, dissolved oxygen enters the bloodstream through tiny blood vessels in the gills. Carbon dioxide leaves these blood vessels and enters the water. Respiration in fish also occurs by means of gills. Compare the gills of a crayfish with those of a fish, shown in Figure 14-9.

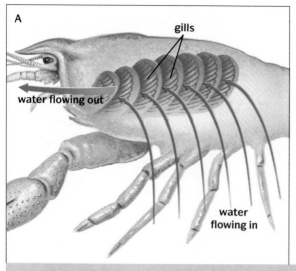

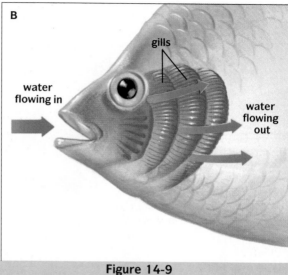

Figure 14-9

Gills of a crayfish (*A*) and gills of a fish (*B*).

Adult frogs and other land-dwelling vertebrates have respiratory organs called lungs. **Lungs** are the organs through which vertebrates get oxygen from air. Lungs are two elastic sacs formed of thin membranes. A tube leading from the mouth carries oxygen to the lungs. Exchange of gases occurs in the tiny blood vessels of the lungs. Oxygen is carried by the blood to body cells. Carbon dioxide given off by body cells is carried to the lungs by the blood.

CIRCULATION

Animals need water, oxygen, and food to survive. In most simple aquatic animals, water and oxygen diffuse into the cells directly from the water. Foods digested by special cells or in the central cavity diffuse to all cells of the body. In complex animals, transport of materials occurs by means of a *circulatory system*. The system often has a heart that pumps blood throughout the body.

SCIENCE PUZZLER

You have learned that a fish has gills that it uses for breathing. Unlike most other fish, the fish shown can drown in water. At intervals, this fish must come to the surface of the water to get air. Without this air, the fish would die. Hypothesize about what structures this fish has that most other fish lack.

Animals are often used to test new medical devices. Once the devices are proven safe, they can be used to treat people. Some of the technology that has helped people is now being used to save the lives of sick animals. Artificial pacemakers are being used in dogs to help their hearts beat more steadily.

In mammals a steady heartbeat depends on a region of the heart called the pacemaker. Heart disease can damage or stop the heart's natural pacemaker. When this happens, the heart cannot pump blood properly. An artificial pacemaker can take over the job of the natural pacemaker.

Dogs suffer from some of the same heart problems as humans. An artificial pacemaker made for humans works in a dog heart as well. The pacemaker is simply reset to match a dog's heartbeat.

Most of the pacemakers used in dogs are those that are no longer usable in humans.

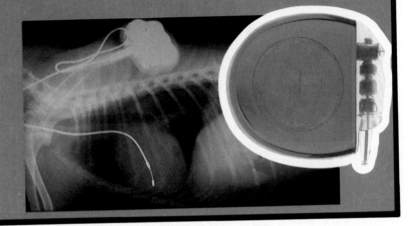

There are two basic types of circulatory systems — an open circulatory system and a closed circulatory system. Figure 14-10 compares these two systems. An **open circulatory system** is a transport system in which blood is not always contained within blood vessels. Blood flows into open spaces, where it is in direct contact with body cells. Exchange of gases occurs directly between the blood and the body cells.

A

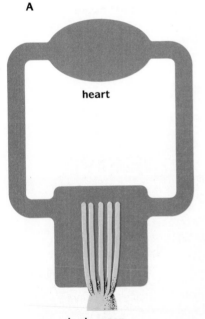

heart

body organ

Figure 14-10

General plan of an open circulatory system (A) and of a closed circulatory system (B).

B

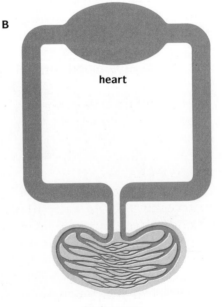

heart

body organ

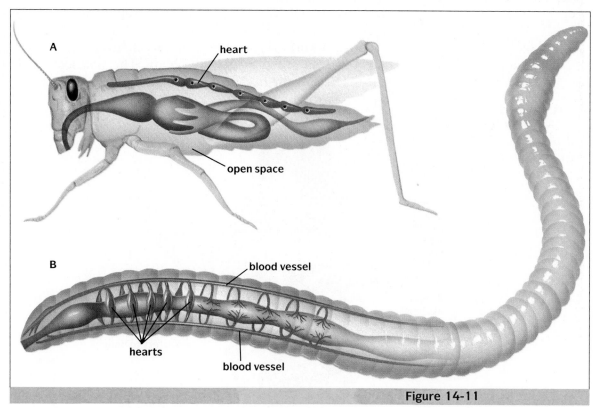

Figure 14-11

Open circulatory system of a grasshopper (A), and closed circulatory system of an earthworm (B).

An insect, such as the grasshopper in Figure 14-11A, has an open circulatory system. Notice that the main blood vessel in the grasshopper runs along its back. This blood vessel has several bulges that combine to form a tube-shaped heart. Blood from the heart passes into a main artery that leads into the insect's head. In the head, blood leaves this artery through an opening. The blood then flows into open spaces in the body, where it bathes the cells. Needed materials move into the cells and wastes move out. Locate the openings in the heart in Figure 14-11A. Blood returns to the heart through these openings.

A **closed circulatory system** is a transport system in which blood circulates within blood vessels. An earthworm has a closed circulatory system. Locate the two main blood vessels in an earthworm, shown in Figure 14-11B. These vessels are connected by five tubes, which are called hearts. Blood is pumped downward through these hearts to the main vessel near the lower surface of the earthworm. As the blood moves through this vessel, it enters tiny branching blood vessels. From these vessels nutrients and oxygen in the blood pass to the body cells. Blood containing wastes returns to the main blood vessel near the upper surface of the earthworm.

In vertebrates the heart is a complex organ. A fish has a heart that is made up of two chambers. The *atrium* (AY tree uhm) (pl., *atria*) is the heart chamber that receives blood from other parts of the body. The *ventricle* (VEHN-truh kuhl) is the heart chamber that pumps blood to other parts of the body.

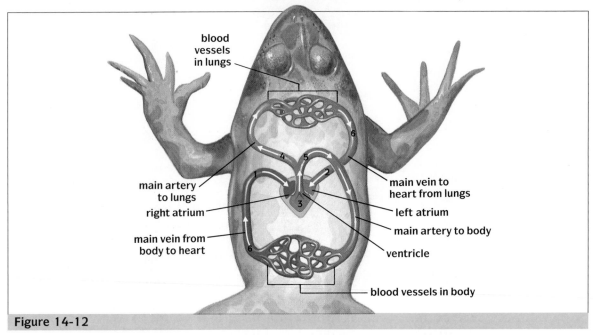

blood vessels in lungs

main artery to lungs

right atrium

main vein from body to heart

main vein to heart from lungs

left atrium

main artery to body

ventricle

blood vessels in body

Figure 14-12

General plan of the circulatory system of an amphibian.

Figure 14-12 shows the general plan of the circulatory system of an amphibian. An amphibian has a heart with three chambers: two atria and one ventricle. Refer to Figure 14-12 as you read about the flow of blood through the circulatory system of a frog.

1. Oxygen-poor blood from the body is carried to the heart through several large veins. The blood from the body enters the right atrium of the heart.
2. Oxygen-rich blood from the lungs enters the left atrium of the heart.
3. The heart contracts and pumps both oxygen-rich and oxygen-poor blood from both atria into the ventricle. The ventricle contracts, pumping blood out of the heart.
4. Much of the oxygen-poor blood is carried to the lungs and to the skin. Oxygen is picked up and carbon dioxide is given off in the lungs and through the skin.
5. Most of the oxygen-rich blood is carried to all other parts of the body.
6. Oxygen-poor blood from the body and oxygen-rich blood from the lungs return to the heart.

ACTIVITY   What Are the Organs of a Transport System?

OBJECTIVE
Observe the organs of the circulatory system of a frog.

MATERIALS
lab apron, preserved frog, dissecting pan, dissecting pins, hand lens, pointed scissors, probe, forceps, paper towels

PROCEDURE

A. Wear a lab apron during this activity. Use the same frog that you used in the activity on page 318. Place the frog in a dissecting pan. Pin the frog down as you did in step **B** of the previous activity.

B. Remove the digestive organs. Use a hand lens to look at the heart and the blood vessels that join the heart. These vessels have been injected with rubber to show the difference between veins and arteries. The veins are injected with blue rubber, and the arteries are injected with red rubber.

C. Examine the main blood vessels in the circulatory system. Note the thickness of these blood vessels. Locate the lungs and examine them with a hand lens.

D. Trace the main blood vessels from the heart to the head, lungs, limbs, and back to the heart.

E. Make a drawing of the heart, lungs, and major blood vessels. Refer to the drawing of the circulatory system of a frog shown here.

F. With the pointed scissors, cut all the blood vessels connected to the heart. Remove the heart from the body. Examine the heart with the hand lens. Using your scissors, make a lengthwise cut into the heart. Note the number of chambers and the number of blood vessels attached to the heart.

RESULTS AND CONCLUSIONS

1. Label the drawing you made in step **E**. Use colored arrows to show the path of blood through the body and heart.
2. How many chambers are there in the frog's heart?

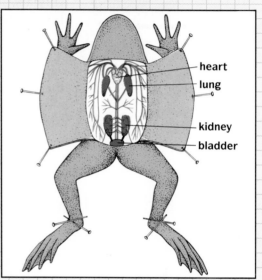

- heart
- lung
- kidney
- bladder

REVIEW

1. What materials are needed for body cells to carry out respiration?
2. Compare the structures involved in gas exchange in an insect with those in a frog.
3. Distinguish between an open circulatory system and a closed circulatory system. Describe how blood circulates in a grasshopper and in an earthworm.
4. How is heart structure related to the complexity of an animal? Use an earthworm, a fish, and a frog as examples.

CHALLENGE In warm-blooded animals, oxygen-rich and oxygen-poor blood do not mix. Hypothesize about the effect that the mixing of such blood would have on respiration in the cells of a warm-blooded animal.

14-4 EXCRETION

As a result of carrying on the processes of metabolism, the cells of all animals form waste products. These waste products of metabolism must be removed from the body or death occurs. The process of removing waste products of metabolism from the cells of the body is called **excretion** (ehk SKREE shuhn).

Animal cells produce several kinds of waste products of metabolism. These include excess water, carbon dioxide, salts, and compounds containing nitrogen. There are three kinds of wastes that contain nitrogen—*ammonia* (uh-MOHN yuh), *urea* (yu REE uh), and *uric* (YUR ihk) *acid.* Animals differ in the types of nitrogen-containing wastes they produce.

Ammonia is a poisonous waste produced by some animals. It is usually made by simple animals that live in water. A flatworm, such as a planarian, is an animal that produces ammonia. This waste is removed from the worm's body mainly by diffusion through the cells of the body wall. The simple *excretory system* of the planarian helps to remove excess water. The system is made up of a network of tubes. Some of these tubes connect to special cells called *flame cells,* which help to remove water.

excretus (sifted out)

Figure 14-13

The excretory system of a planarian, showing an enlargement of a flame cell. What is the function of a flame cell?

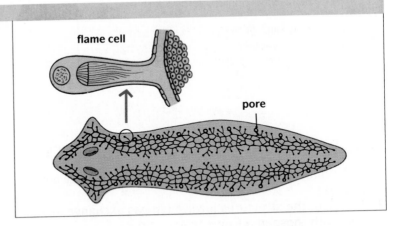

Vertebrates have special excretory organs that process wastes. The excretory organs of vertebrates are called kidneys. A **kidney** is an organ that removes wastes from the blood. The kidney is the main organ of excretion in vertebrates.

Fish produce the waste known as ammonia. This waste is released from the gills into the water that surrounds the fish. Fish have kidneys that function mainly in removing salts from the blood.

Birds produce wastes in the form of uric acid. In the kidneys, uric acid is removed from the blood. From the kidneys the uric acid enters the cloaca, where water in the uric acid is absorbed back into the bird's body. Uric acid is mixed with solid wastes in the cloaca. These wastes then pass out of the body.

Mammals produce nitrogen-containing wastes in the form of urea. Urea is excreted in the form of urine (YUR-uhn). Figure 14-14 shows the excretory system of a mammal. Notice a tube called a *ureter* (yu REE tuhr) leads from each kidney. In mammals the ureters carry urine from the kidneys to a bladder. The bladder is an organ that stores liquid wastes. From the bladder the urine that is produced leaves the body by means of a tube called a *urethra* (yu-REE thruh).

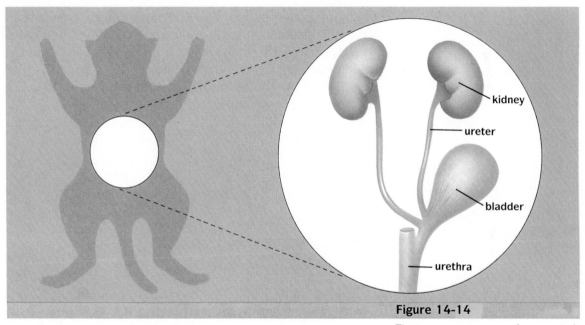

Figure 14-14

The excretory system of a mammal.

REVIEW

1. What process occurs during excretion?
2. List the three main nitrogen-containing wastes that animals produce.
3. Describe the excretory system of a planarian.
4. Compare the excretory system of a bird with the excretory system of a mammal.

CHALLENGE Birds lack a bladder for storing liquid wastes. They excrete wastes that are a mixture of solid wastes and uric acid. Hypothesize about how a bird's excretory system is an adaptation for flight.

14-5 NERVOUS CONTROL

After completing this section, you will be able to

- **describe** the need for nervous control in animals.
- **compare** the nervous systems of the hydra, planarian, and grasshopper.
- **explain** the functions of the three sections of the vertebrate brain.

The key terms in this section are

brain   nerve cell
ganglion   spinal cord

All animals receive and respond to *stimuli*. Recall that a stimulus is something that causes an organism to react. A stimulus may be something outside the animal's body, such as another animal ready to attack. A stimulus could also be something inside an animal's body. For example, it could be a bit of food that has just entered the mouth.

In very simple animals, all cells respond to stimuli. In animals that are more complex, a response is controlled by specialized cells, called nerve cells. A **nerve cell** is a cell that is specialized for receiving and conducting messages. Animals that are even more complex have a *nervous system*. The nervous system is made up of specialized structures that control an animal's responses to its environment.

Some simple animals, such as sponges, lack nerves but still respond to their environment. Other simple animals, such as the hydra, have a *nerve net*. A nerve net is a network of nerves that responds to stimuli. Figure 14-15A shows the nerve net of a hydra. Notice that the nerve net lacks a main control center.

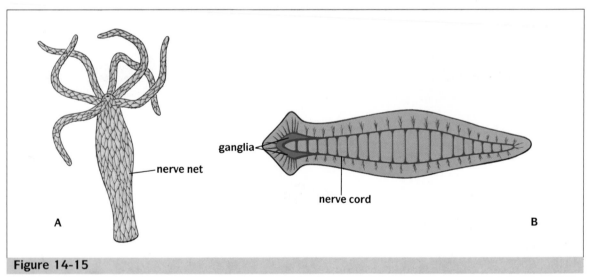

Figure 14-15

Nerve net of a hydra (A), and nervous system of a planarian (B).

ganglion (swelling)

The simple nervous system of a planarian is shown in Figure 14-15B. In the head region are two ganglia (GANG-glee uh) (sing., *ganglion*). A **ganglion** is a mass of nerve cells. In a planarian, the ganglia act as the main control center, or simple brain. The ganglia are attached to two main nerve cords that run the length of the flatworm's body. Branches of these nerve cords also run from one side of the body to the other.

An arthropod, such as a grasshopper, has a more complex nervous system than a flatworm. Compare the nervous system of the grasshopper shown in Figure 14-16 with that of the planarian in Figure 14-15B. Locate the three pairs of ganglia that join together to form the grasshopper's brain. Two nerve cords extend from the brain. These cords join in several places, where they form ganglia. Nerves from the ganglia branch out to all parts of the body.

Vertebrates have the most complex nervous system. A **brain** is the organ that is the central control center of the nervous system. The brain of a vertebrate is more complex than the brain of other groups of animals. A spinal cord is another trait of the nervous system of a vertebrate. A **spinal cord** is a nerve cord that extends from the brain and is enclosed and protected by a backbone.

The brain of a vertebrate is divided into three sections, as shown in Figure 14-17. What kinds of vertebrate brains are shown? The front part of the brain is called the *forebrain*. The forebrain controls the senses of smell, taste, hearing, touch, and pain. In complex vertebrates, such as mammals, the forebrain controls thought and memory. Behind the forebrain is the *midbrain*, which controls sight in most vertebrates. Behind the midbrain is the *hindbrain*, which controls actions such as breathing and heartbeat.

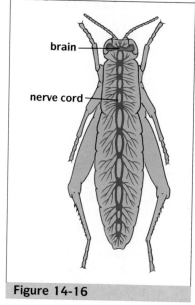

Figure 14-16

Nervous system of a grasshopper. Which structures join to form the brain?

Figure 14-17

Four vertebrate brains.

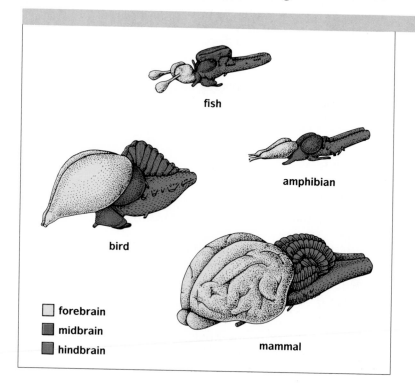

fish

amphibian

bird

☐ forebrain
■ midbrain
■ hindbrain

mammal

ACTIVITY How Do Animals Respond to Vinegar?

OBJECTIVES
Observe the responses of several different animals to vinegar.
Compare the responses of these animals.

MATERIALS
covered container of soil with live earthworms, 3 cotton balls, vinegar, metric ruler, container of live mealworms, 2-3 live land snails, paper towels

PROCEDURE
A. Make a data table like the one shown.
B. Remove the cover of a container that holds earthworms in soil. Observe the behavior of the worms. Record your observations under *Normal Behavior* in your data table.

Animal	Normal Behavior	Response to Vinegar
Earthworms		
Mealworms		
Snails		

C. Wet a cotton ball with vinegar. Place the ball 2 cm from the earthworms. Observe their behavior. Record your observations under *Response to Vinegar* in your data table.
D. Remove the cover of a container that holds mealworms. Observe and record the behavior of the worms.
E. Repeat step **C**, using mealworms instead of earthworms.

F. Place several land snails on moistened paper towels. Observe and record their behavior.
G. Repeat step **C**, using land snails instead of earthworms.

earthworm — cotton ball — soil — VINEGAR

RESULTS AND CONCLUSIONS
1. Describe the behavior of the earthworms, mealworms, and snails when you first observed them.
2. Does each type of animal respond to the vinegar in the same way? If not, explain how their responses differ.
3. How might the animals' responses help them to survive in their natural environment?

REVIEW
1. Compare the nervous system of a hydra with that of a planarian.
2. Describe the nervous system of a grasshopper.
3. Describe the three sections of a vertebrate brain and list the function of each.

CHALLENGE Suppose the tentacle of a hydra and the leg of a grasshopper were touched with a blunt probe. The entire body of the hydra would withdraw. Only the leg of the grasshopper would withdraw. Explain these responses in terms of differences in nervous control.

14-6 REPRODUCTION

For a species to survive, organisms of that species must reproduce. Reproduction is of two general types—asexual and sexual. **Asexual reproduction** (ay SEHK shoo-uhl ree pruh DUHK shuhn) is a form of reproduction in which a new organism is formed without the joining of a sperm cell and an egg cell. This type of reproduction occurs in simple animals, protists, and monerans.

There are different types of asexual reproduction. Look at Figure 10-7A on page 227, which shows how asexual reproduction occurs in a hydra by the process of *budding*. The bud is an outgrowth of the parent. It grows into a new hydra that is exactly like the parent. *Regeneration* is another type of asexual reproduction. Through regeneration, an entire new organism can grow from a body part.

> After completing this section, you will be able to
>
> - **distinguish** between asexual reproduction and sexual reproduction.
> - **compare** external fertilization and internal fertilization.
> - **compare** the types of reproduction that occur in a hydra, a frog, and a lizard.
>
> *The key terms in this section are*
> asexual reproduction
> external fertilization
> internal fertilization
> sexual reproduction

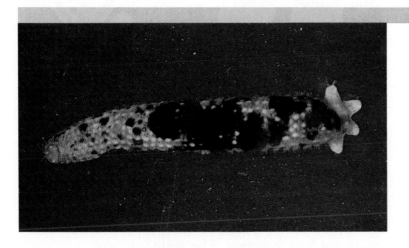

Figure 14-18

Regeneration in a starfish.

Sexual reproduction is a form of reproduction in which a new living thing is produced by the joining of an egg cell and a sperm cell. Females produce egg cells in organs called *ovaries* (OH vuhr eez). Males produce sperm cells in organs called *testes* (TEHS teez). Animals produced by sexual reproduction show traits of both parents.

Sexual reproduction occurs either outside or inside the body. **External fertilization** (ehk STER nuhl fer-tuh luh ZAY shuhn) is the joining of an egg cell and a sperm cell outside the body of an organism. In most fish and amphibians, this process takes place in water. A large number of eggs and sperm are produced. Many of the eggs are not fertilized. Also, only a small number of the developing young survive. Many of the young are eaten by other animals. The production of large numbers of eggs and sperm helps to ensure the survival of the species.

External fertilization occurs in frogs. Figure 14-19 shows the *reproductive system* of a female frog and of a male frog. In the female, large numbers of eggs travel through coiled tubes called *oviducts* (OH vuh duhkts). From the oviducts the eggs enter the cloaca and are released into the water. Sperm cells collect in the male's cloaca. As the eggs are shed by the female, the male releases the sperm over the eggs.

Figure 14-19

Reproductive structures in a male frog and in a female frog.

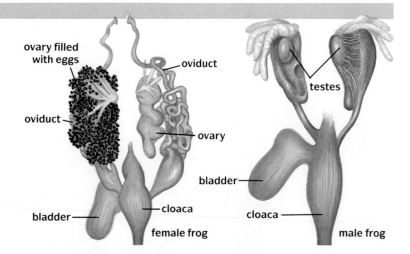

Internal fertilization is the joining of an egg and a sperm inside the body of an organism. This process usually occurs inside the female's body. Reptiles, birds, and mammals, as well as some fishes, reproduce in this way. The eggs produced by birds and most reptiles are fertilized inside the female's body. The young develop and hatch outside the female's body. In mammals, the development of the young occurs inside the female's body. Most mammals give birth to live young.

REVIEW

1. Describe the main difference between asexual reproduction and sexual reproduction.
2. Briefly describe how sexual reproduction occurs in frogs.
3. How do internal and external fertilization differ?
4. Frogs produce a great number of sex cells. How is this large number of cells related to the survival of the species?

CHALLENGE Describe the conditions under which asexual reproduction in an animal would be an advantage over sexual reproduction.

CHAPTER SUMMARY

The main ideas in this chapter are listed below. Read these statements before you answer the Chapter Review questions.

- A skeleton protects soft organs, supports an animal's body, and works with muscles to cause movement. An exoskeleton is a skeleton that covers the outside of an animal's body. An endoskeleton is a skeleton found inside an animal's body. (14-1)

- During digestion, food is broken down by enzymes into a form that can be used by body cells. In some simple animals, food is digested inside special cells. In more complex animals a digestive system changes food to a form that can be used by body cells. (14-2)

- During respiration, oxygen is used to release energy in food. Carbon dioxide is given off. Some simple animals exchange gases directly with their environment. More complex animals have a respiratory system with organs that are specialized for the exchange of gases. (14-3)

- Food, water, and oxygen are needed by the body cells of animals. In some simple animals these needed materials diffuse into body cells directly from the surrounding water or from the central body cavity. In more complex animals a circulatory system transports materials throughout the body. There are two main types of circulatory systems—an open system and a closed system. (14-3)

- During excretion, waste products of metabolism are removed from an animal's body. In very simple animals, wastes diffuse through the cells of the body wall. In more complex animals an excretory system removes these wastes. (14-4)

- All animals respond to stimuli. In very simple animals, all cells respond to outside stimuli. Some simple animals have a nerve net. More complex animals have a nervous system with a main control center—the brain. (14-5)

- There are two main kinds of reproduction—asexual and sexual. In sexual reproduction, fertilization may be external or internal. (14-6)

The key terms in this chapter are listed below. Use each term in a sentence that shows the meaning of the term.

anus	ganglion
asexual reproduction	gills
brain	gizzard
closed circulatory system	internal fertilization
crop	kidney
digestion	lungs
digestive gland	muscles
endoskeleton	nerve cell
enzyme	open circulatory system
excretion	respiration
exoskeleton	sexual reproduction
external fertilization	spinal cord

Chapter Review

VOCABULARY

Use the key terms from this chapter to complete the following sentences correctly.

1. Bundles of tissue that contract, or become shorter, are called _____.

2. A nerve cord that extends from the brain and is enclosed and protected by a backbone is a/an _____ .

3. The part of an earthworm's digestive system that acts as a storage chamber is the _____ .

4. A transport system in which blood is not always contained in blood vessels is a/an _____ .

5. The process of removing waste products of metabolism from the cells of the body is called _____ .

6. The process by which a new organism is formed without the joining of a sperm cell and an egg cell is _____ .

7. A mass of nerve cells is called a/an _____ .

8. Organs through which vertebrates get oxygen from the air are called _____ .

9. Organs through which some animals get oxygen from water are called _____ .

10. A skeleton that is on the inside of an animal's body is called a/an _____ .

CONCEPTS

1. Describe the main function of a skeleton. (14-1)

2. Distinguish between an exoskeleton and an endoskeleton. Give an example of an animal with an exoskeleton and one with an endoskeleton. (14-1)

3. Explain, in general terms, how movement occurs in a vertebrate. (14-1)

4. Using specific animals as examples, distinguish between a digestive system with one opening and a digestive system with two openings. (14-2)

5. Describe the main difference between digestion in a hydra and digestion in an earthworm. (14-2)

6. Which is more complex—digestion in a frog or digestion in a crayfish? Explain your answer. (14-2)

7. What is the function of a respiratory system? (14-3)

8. Describe the structures involved in gas exchange in an insect and those in a frog. (14-3)

9. What is the function of a circulatory system? (14-3)

10. Using specific animals as examples, distinguish between an open circulatory system and a closed circulatory system. (14-3)

11. Compare circulation in an earthworm with that in a grasshopper. (14-3)

12. Describe the main difference between the structure of the heart of a fish and the heart of a frog. (14-3)

13. Briefly describe the flow of blood into and out of a frog's heart. (14-3)

14. What is the function of an excretory system? (14-4)

15. What are the three types of nitrogen-containing wastes excreted by animals? (14-4)

16. Describe excretion in a fish. (14-4)

17. How does excretion in a bird differ from excretion in a mammal? (14-4)

18. What is the function of a brain? Name the three parts of a vertebrate brain. (14-5)

19. Using three animals as examples, show how the nervous system of a vertebrate is more complex than that of an invertebrate. (14-5)

20. What is the difference between asexual reproduction and sexual reproduction? Give an example of one animal that reproduces asexually and one that reproduces sexually. (14-6)

21. Distinguish between internal fertilization and external fertilization. (14-6)

APPLICATION/ CRITICAL THINKING

1. Many water-dwelling animals have no skeleton; yet, their bodies do not collapse. Hypothesize about how their bodies are supported.

2. A female frog lays from 500 to 5000 eggs in gelatinlike masses. A female sea turtle may lay about 100 rubbery-shelled eggs in a hole in the sand. Compare the frog and the turtle with regard to fertilization and chances for survival of the offspring.

EXTENSIONS

1. Build clay models of several vertebrate hearts.

2. If possible, visit a natural history museum. Go to the exhibits of the skeletons of various vertebrates. Note the similarities and differences in the arrangement of the bones.

READINGS

Billout, Guy. *Squid and Spider: A Look at the Animal Kingdom*. Englewood Cliffs, N.J.: Prentice-Hall, 1982.

Lambert, Mark. *Understanding Living Things*, Understanding series. Morristown, N.J.: Silver Burdett Company, 1986.

Have you ever trained a pet dog to do a trick? If you have, you know how much patience such a task takes. Dog trainers are patient people who enjoy working with animals.

Some dog trainers have a special job. They train dogs that aid people who are blind. The dogs must learn to move through crowds and in traffic without being afraid. It may take many months to train a dog to help a blind person.

The blind person who uses a trained dog also must have instruction in how to work properly with a dog. Trainers work with blind people and their dogs.

Some dog trainers work for schools and kennels that sell trained dogs. Others work for organizations that aid the blind. Trainers usually learn skills from other trainers. If you are interested in this career, you should take life science courses in high school.■

Dog Trainer

Have you ever taken a sick pet to a veterinarian? Veterinarians are doctors who care for animals. They diagnose and treat illnesses, give medicines, and perform surgery. Veterinarians also examine healthy animals. Sometimes they aid large animals in giving birth.

Many veterinarians work with pets such as cats, dogs, and birds. Others work with farm animals. Some veterinarians work with the animals in zoos and parks. Still others work in universities and teach courses there.

To become a veterinarian, you must have a four-year college degree in science. An additional degree from a veterinary school is required. If you care for animals and are interested in this career, you should take courses in biology and chemistry in high school.■

Veterinarian

Dr. Margaret M. Nice, Ornithologist

Dr. Margaret M. Nice was a world-famous ornithologist (awr-nuh THAHL uh jihst). An ornithologist studies birds. Dr. Nice began her studies of bird species in the 1920s.

Dr. Nice wrote many articles about the numbers of birds living in certain areas. She detailed exactly where they lived. Although she studied these topics for years, her real interest was in bird behavior.

In 1927, Dr. Nice moved to Columbus, Ohio, where she did a detailed study of the song sparrow. She used colored bands to mark individual birds. She was therefore able to name and number the birds she studied. This banding allowed Dr. Nice to follow the movements of the sparrows.

After her studies, Dr. Nice wrote the most comprehensive report ever done about a bird species. The title of her work is *Studies in the Life History of the Song Sparrow*. She later was honored for her outstanding contributions to the field of bird study.■

Issues and Technology

Although many kinds of insects are useful to humans, some insects cause serious problems. For centuries, people have tried to find ways to control the insects that spread diseases and destroy crops.

Insecticides are chemicals that are used to kill insects. One of the best-known insecticides is DDT. This chemical was first used to control the mosquitoes that carry malaria. DDT was so effective that it was soon being used to kill other insects that carry disease. By the 1950s, DDT was also widely used on farmlands.

Some insects sprayed with DDT were not affected by it. These insects survived to breed more insects with the same resistance. To overcome this new problem, people increased the amounts of DDT they used.

Insecticides like DDT are poisons. They can kill many species of animals in addition to insects. As more and more DDT was used, the chemical began to pollute waterways. Plants in rivers, lakes, and marshes took in the chemical. Some animals fed on the plants and took in DDT as they fed. These animals were food for larger animals. These food relationships among organisms make up a *food web*.

Figure 1 shows a food web in a marsh that had been sprayed with DDT for many years. The arrows show the transfer of DDT as the animals feed. The numbers show the level of DDT in each kind of animal.

APPLYING CRITICAL THINKING SKILLS

1. The DDT levels shown are measured in parts per million (ppm). What kinds of organisms had the lowest levels of DDT?
2. What was the DDT level in minnows? How did DDT get into these fish?
3. What kinds of organisms in the figure show the highest levels of DDT? Suggest a reason for these high levels of insecticide.
4. Blowfish eat clams and snails, yet the DDT level of blowfish is less than that of either of these other animals. Suggest a reason for this.
5. Do you think it would be hard to avoid getting insecticides

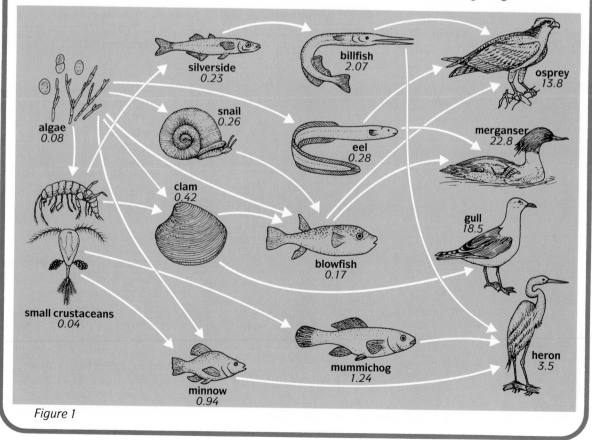

Figure 1

337

in your body once they are in the food web? Explain your answer, and suggest some ways to avoid taking in insecticides.

6. To control mosquitoes, the marsh was sprayed with DDT. Suggest another method that might have been used to control the mosquitoes. Discuss some advantages and disadvantages of your suggestion.

As scientists studied the DDT problem, they began to see some surprising effects. Large birds of prey, such as eagles and ospreys were decreasing in population. Adults were alive and breeding, but very few offspring were being raised. What was happening to the eggs of these birds?

Because DDT is poisonous, you might think that the baby birds were poisoned. This was one of the early hypotheses. However, when scientists looked at the nests of some of these birds, many broken eggs were found.

The baby birds were not poisoned. They had died because their eggs were crushed.

DDT interferes with the proper development of the eggshell. As a result, the eggshells were very thin. When the parents sat on the eggs to keep them warm, the weight of the parent birds broke the eggs. So many eggs were broken that only one out of every two or three nests was producing one living offspring.

In 1972 the use of DDT was banned in the United States. An increase in the populations of eagles and ospreys was not seen right away, because DDT remains in the soil, in the water, and in organisms for many years.

Figure 2 shows the offspring production of ospreys over nine years. It also shows the amount of DDE found in the eggs that failed to hatch. DDE is a chemical that is formed when DDT is broken down. A measurement of DDE levels in the eggs indicates the amount of DDT taken in by the parent birds.

APPLYING CRITICAL THINKING SKILLS

1. During which year was the amount of DDE highest? During which year was it lowest?
2. During which year was offspring production lowest? During which year was it highest?
3. Does the graph show a relationship between DDE levels and offspring production? If so, what is the relationship?
4. Eventually the increase in offspring production will level off, although the amounts of DDE found will probably continue to decrease. Why won't offspring production continue to increase as DDE levels decrease?
5. After DDT was banned, what do you think happened to the mosquito population in this marsh?

DDT is one of many insecticides that have been developed. Some, like DDT are banned in the United States. Others are still in use. Scientists are trying to find safer insecticides. They have rated insecticides on the basis of how poisonous they are to organisms other than insects, and how long they take to break down after they are used.

Figure 3 shows the ratings of some insecticides. On a scale of zero to four, four is the rating for the most poisonous pesticide, and zero is the rating for the least poisonous. On a scale of zero to four, four is the rating for the chemicals that last the longest, and zero is the rating for the chemicals that break down the fastest.

Insecticides are probably the fastest way to control insect pests, but they are not the only method available. One way to control insects is to find a natural enemy of that insect, and bring that enemy into the area. This

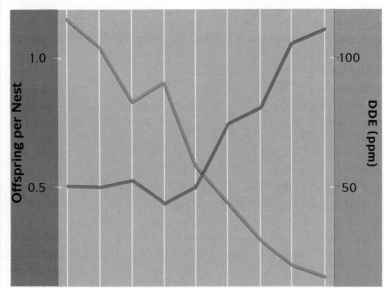

1969 1970 1971 1972 1973 1974 1975 1976 1977
Year

Figure 2

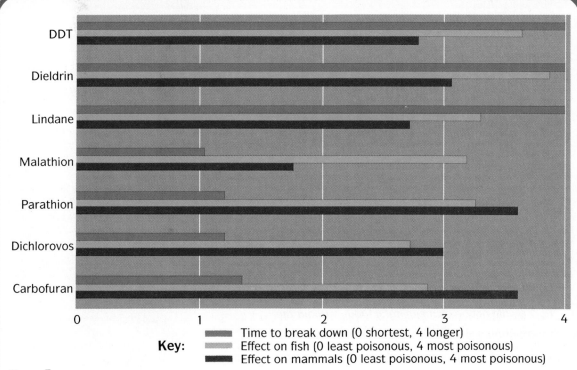

Key:
Time to break down (0 shortest, 4 longer)
Effect on fish (0 least poisonous, 4 most poisonous)
Effect on mammals (0 least poisonous, 4 most poisonous)

Figure 3

method is good because it does not pollute the environment and kill organisms other than the ones that are causing problems. But there are some problems with using natural enemies. Sometimes the organism that is introduced to control a pest cannot survive in the area. Sometimes the organism that is introduced eats other insects instead of the pest. A natural enemy should not be introduced into an area until its effects on the environment can be determined.

Scientists are trying to find viruses and other disease-causing organisms that will control insect populations. Like the natural-enemy method, control methods that use diseases must be tested very carefully before they are used.

Natural enemies and diseases will not completely destroy an insect population. They will only keep the insect population from becoming too large. Although these methods are slow to get started, once they are used they remain effective. In contrast, insecticides have to be reapplied every year.

APPLYING CRITICAL THINKING SKILLS

1. The chemical makeup of DDT, dieldrin, and lindane are similar. How else are these three insecticides similar?

2. Which insecticide shown in Figure 3 is the least poisonous to mammals? Is it also the least poisonous to fish?

3. Several of the insecticides that are banned in the United States are still made here and exported to other countries. Some of these countries are in Central America. Coffee and other foods are imported to the United States from these countries. What risks are there in importing these foods? What should we do to protect ourselves against these risks?

4. Insecticides produced in the United States are also exported to many countries where lack of food is a serious problem. Should insecticides that are known to be poisonous be used in these countries? Explain your answer.

5. More humans have been poisoned by insecticides in the countries that now use the dangerous insecticides than in the countries that now only export the insecticides. Suggest a reason for this difference.

6. Do you think control by natural enemies is better than control by insecticide? Compare the advantages and disadvantages of each.

7. Suppose you wanted to use a disease to control an insect population in a farming region. What reaction do you think there would be to your idea? How would you convince people that this is a good control method?

CONTINUITY AND CHANGE

▼ *Charles Darwin at age 31, after completing his around-the-world voyage.*

Over a century ago the English scientist Charles Darwin made a historic voyage around the world. Darwin's observations of plants and animals led to an important scientific theory — the theory of evolution. But Darwin's work would not be as meaningful today without the contribution of another scientist — Gregor Mendel. In this unit you will study principles of genetics and learn how and why organisms change over time. ■

▼ *A genetic abnormality causes this peacock, also called a peafowl, to lack coloration.*

► The principles of genetics were used to breed this prize-winning bull.

▼ Anthropologist Richard Leakey uncovered this 2.5-million-year- old skull of an early human.

► These dinosaur bones were found embedded in rock in Colorado.

▼ These marine iguanas from the Galápagos Islands exist nowhere else.

GENETICS

You have learned that living things come only from other living things of the same kind. There are a great many ways in which members of the same species are alike. But there is also great variety within a species.

Look at the children in the photograph. Think about the many ways in which they, and you, are alike. Now consider the many striking differences among the children. Notice that no two children look exactly like each other or like you. No two people in the world are exactly alike.

- *How are characteristics passed from parents to offspring?*
- *How can the passing of these characteristics be studied?*

15-1 HEREDITY

Have you ever noticed how babies look like their parents? People expect offspring, or young, to look like their parents. Animals, such as kittens or puppies, look like their parents. Plants even look like their parent plants. Farmers rely on the fact that offspring will be much like their parents. For example, a farmer might remove seeds from a tomato plant that produces large tomatoes. The farmer expects that the seeds will grow into new plants that will produce similar large tomatoes.

TRAITS

Organisms *inherit*, or receive, their characteristics from their parents. A characteristic, or feature, of an organism is also called a **trait**. There is much variety in the kinds of traits that living things have. The presence of five toes on a foot is an inherited trait of humans. A horse has just one toe on each foot. The presence of one toe on a foot is a trait of some hoofed mammals, such as horses and zebras. Winged seeds, shown in Figure 15-1A on the next page, is a trait of maple trees. Acorn-shaped seeds, shown in *B*, is a trait of oak trees.

After completing this section, you will be able to

- **give examples** of inherited traits.
- **define** the terms *heredity* and *genetics*.
- **describe** Mendel's experiments with pea plants.
- **distinguish** between dominant and recessive traits.

The key terms in this section are

dominant trait	purebred
genetics	recessive trait
heredity	trait
hybrid	

Figure 15-1

The traits of living things vary greatly.

Like plants and animals, protists also have inherited traits. Figure 15-1*C* and *D* shows two species of paramecia. Their different shapes are inherited traits of these protists.

The passing of traits from parents to young is called **heredity** (huh REHD uh tee). Many traits are passed to young when organisms reproduce. For example, humans inherit many traits other than toe number. Some of these traits can be seen easily. They include eye color, hair color, skin color, and ear shape. Many of the things that organisms do are also inherited. Making food is part of the heredity of plants. Migrating is an inherited trait of some species of birds.

hereditas (heirship)

MENDEL'S EXPERIMENTS

It was only about 120 years ago that heredity was first studied in a scientific way. The scientific study of heredity is called **genetics** (juh NEHT ihks). Gregor Mendel is often called the father of genetics. Mendel was a monk who lived in Europe in the nineteenth century. He had training in mathematics and biology. Mendel studied the heredity of pea plants that he grew in the garden of the monastery where he lived. Mendel's findings about the heredity of peas have been shown to apply to other organisms.

genes (breed)

Some of the methods used by Mendel are still used in the modern study of heredity. To study inherited traits, two organisms are mated. The mating of organisms to test for traits is called a *cross*. The results of a cross are the offspring. The traits of the offspring are studied.

Mendel made a good choice in using pea plants in his genetics experiments. There are several reasons why pea plants were a good choice. One reason is that it is easy to cross pea plants. Recall that pollination (pahl uh-NAY shuhn) is the transfer of pollen from the male to the female reproductive parts of a flower. A single pea flower usually pollinates itself in a process called *self-pollination*. Mendel found that he could transfer pollen from one flower to another. This process is called *cross-pollination*. Thus, Mendel could cause mating between different pea plants.

Another reason why peas are good plants for genetic study is that they reproduce quickly. Also, pea plants produce many offspring. A large number of offspring is needed for accurate results in genetics experiments.

The traits of pea plants may provide the best reason for using them in genetics. Peas have a number of traits that are easy to study. Many of these traits are shown in one of two forms. For example, pea plants are either tall or short. Pea pods are either smooth or wrinkled. Pea seeds are either green or yellow. Traits such as these are easy to observe.

Mendel began his work by using purebred pea plants. An organism is **purebred** for a trait if when self-pollinated the same form of a trait is shown in all of its offspring. Each generation of offspring that is self-pollinated will also produce purebred offspring. For example, look at Figure 15-2. A pea plant that is purebred for green peas produces only green peas each time it is self-pollinated. Likewise, all of its offspring produce only green peas when self-pollinated.

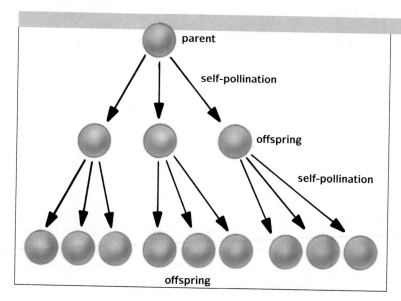

parent

self-pollination

offspring

self-pollination

offspring

Figure 15-2

The same trait appears in many generations when the organisms are purebred for that trait.

In one of his first experiments, Mendel crossed pure-bred tall and purebred short pea plants. This cross is shown in Figure 15-3A. What type of offspring came from the mating of tall and short pea plants? You may be surprised to see that all of the offspring were tall.

hybrida (mongrel)

The tall plants produced in this cross are called hybrids. A **hybrid** (HĪ brihd) is an organism that is produced by a cross of parents that have different forms of a trait. Each one of the hybrid plants was as tall as its purebred tall parent. Both purebred parent plants were the first cross and are called the *parent generation*. The tall hybrids were the first offspring and are called the *first offspring generation*.

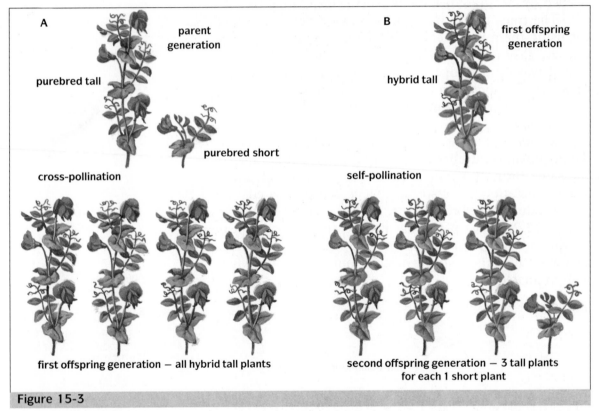

A parent generation

purebred tall

purebred short

cross-pollination

first offspring generation — all hybrid tall plants

B first offspring generation

hybrid tall

self-pollination

second offspring generation — 3 tall plants for each 1 short plant

Figure 15-3

First and second offspring generations of Mendel's cross of tall and short pea plants.

Why were all of the hybrids tall? What happened to the trait for shortness? Mendel hypothesized that the shortness trait must have been present in the tall hybrids but somehow hidden. He did another experiment to test his hypothesis.

In the next experiment, Mendel allowed the tall hybrids to self-pollinate. He then studied the plants produced by the tall hybrids. Those plants were the *second offspring generation*. Figure 15-3B shows this experiment. You can

In guinea pigs the trait for black fur color is dominant over the trait for white fur color. Yet both parents of the white guinea pig shown have black fur. What traits do the parents carry? Think about dominant and recessive traits. What if one parent was black and the other parent was white? Would it be possible for the guinea pig shown to be white? Explain.

see that there were about three tall plants for each short plant. The shortness trait had not disappeared. It was hidden in the tall hybrids.

Mendel concluded that each tall hybrid carried the traits of both its tall purebred and short purebred parents. He called tallness a dominant (DAHM uh nuhnt) trait. A **dominant trait** is one that prevents the showing of another trait. Tallness is a dominant trait in pea plants because it prevents shortness from showing in hybrid plants. Mendel called shortness a recessive (rih SEHS ihv) trait. A **recessive trait** is one that is hidden by the presence of a dominant trait.

Mendel grew thousands of pea plants over a period of eight years. The large number of plants grown, and the accurate records kept by Mendel made his work the first truly scientific study of heredity.

REVIEW

1. List some features that might be inherited traits of a cat or a dog.
2. Explain the difference between heredity and genetics.
3. Describe Mendel's first and second experiments with peas. Give the results of each experiment.
4. What is the difference between a dominant trait and a recessive trait? Give an example of each.

CHALLENGE A single hybrid tall pea plant is allowed to self-pollinate. Five of the seeds produced are planted. Is it possible that none of the resulting offspring will be short? Explain your answer.

15-2 INHERITANCE OF TRAITS

After completing this section, you will be able to

- **restate** Mendel's basic findings about traits.
- **distinguish** between phenotype and genotype.
- **describe** the use of a Punnett square.
- **explain** incomplete dominance.

The key terms in this section are
genotype
incomplete dominance
phenotype
Punnett square

MENDEL'S RESULTS

In his work with pea plants, Mendel studied pairs of contrasting traits. Figure 15-4 shows seven pairs of these traits. In each case, two purebred plants with contrasting traits were crossed to produce hybrid offspring. Then the hybrid offspring were self-pollinated to produce a second offspring generation. In this second generation, there were about three times as many plants with one trait as there were plants with the contrasting trait.

Mendel analyzed the results from his experiments with all the different pea plant types. He reported these conclusions about traits.

- Organisms inherit traits in pairs. An organism receives one trait from each of its two parents.
- Some traits are dominant; others are recessive. In hybrids, dominant traits cause recessive traits to be hidden. Recessive traits are shown only when no dominant trait is present.

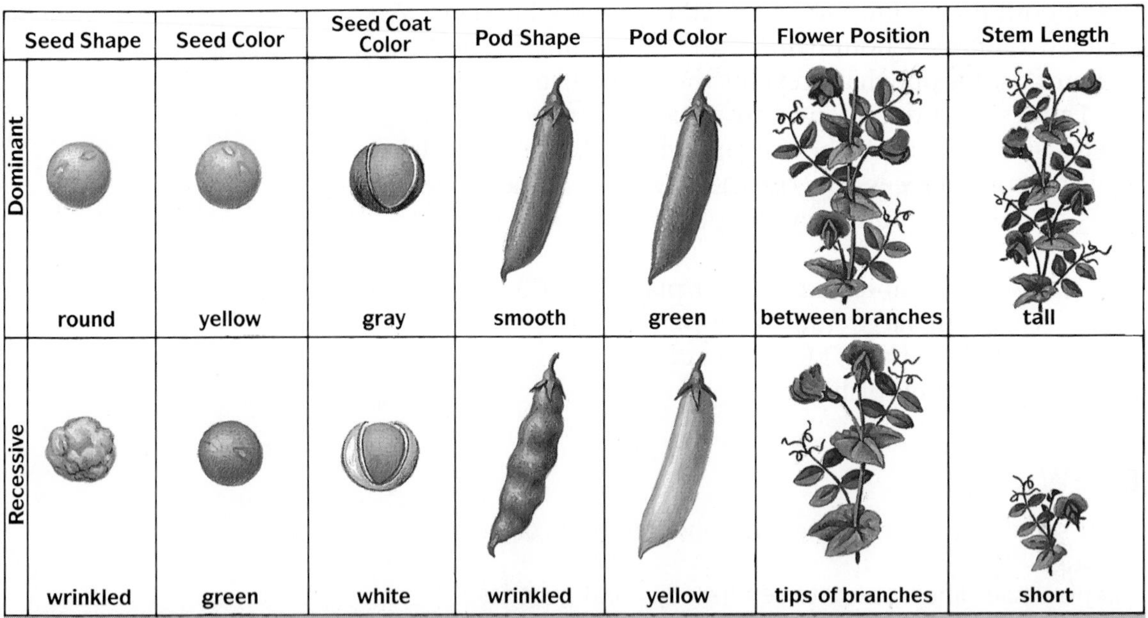
Seed Shape
Seed Color
Seed Coat Color
Pod Shape
Pod Color
Flower Position
Stem Length
Dominant
round
yellow
gray
smooth
green
between branches
tall
Recessive
wrinkled
green
white
wrinkled
yellow
tips of branches
short

Figure 15-4

Mendel studied these seven traits of pea plants.

Mendel used a system of symbols to show what traits an organism had and to show what traits were passed to offspring. Mendel's system is still in use. In this system, letters are used to represent traits. Capital letters stand for dominant traits. Small letters stand for recessive traits. For example, *T* stands for tallness and *t* stands for shortness. Notice that the same letter is used for the two contrasting forms of a trait. Using this system, *Y* stands for yellow peas and *y* stands for green peas. Which of these two traits is dominant?

Recall that organisms inherit traits in pairs. Therefore, letters are used in pairs to show the traits of an organism. For example, *Tt* stands for the two traits carried by a tall hybrid pea plant. What does *TT* represent?

Symbols also can be used to show crosses between organisms. An X represents a cross, or mating. The cross of a purebred tall pea plant with a purebred short pea plant can be shown as *TT* X *tt*. Recall that this cross produces all tall hybrid offspring. These tall hybrids are just as tall as the purebred parent. Thus, two organisms may have the same appearance but differ in their inherited traits.

The inherited appearance of an organism is its **phenotype** (FEEN uh tīp). Two organisms with different traits may have the same phenotype. Compare the two plants in Figure 15-7. They have the same phenotype. But they differ in their genotype (JEEN uh tīp). The genetic makeup of an organism is its **genotype**. The genotype of a purebred tall plant is *TT*. The genotype of a hybrid tall plant is *Tt*. *TT* and *Tt* are different genotypes. But plants with either of those genotypes will have the same phenotype—tall. What is the genotype of a plant whose phenotype is short?

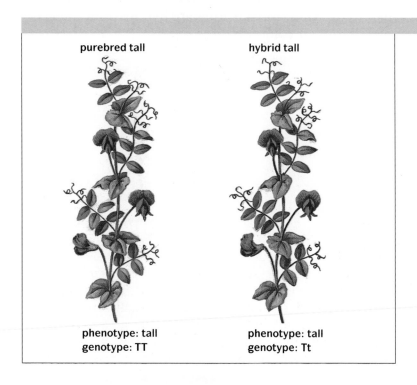

purebred tall   hybrid tall

phenotype: tall   phenotype: tall
genotype: TT   genotype: Tt

Figure 15-5

Plants that look the same have the same phenotype, but they can have different genotypes.

A

genotype of →
parents

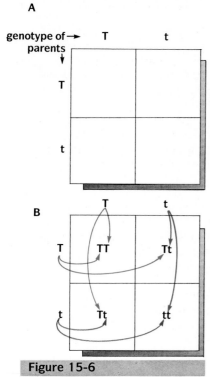

B

Figure 15-6

A Punnett square shows possible combinations of traits.

PUNNETT SQUARES

The cross of the hybrid tall plants can also be shown using a Punnett (PUHN iht) square. A **Punnett square** is a chart that shows all the possible combinations of traits among the offspring of a cross.

Examine the incomplete Punnett square in Figure 15-6A. Notice that the traits carried by one parent are shown at the top of the square. The traits of the other parent are shown at the left side of the square. Figure 15-6B shows the results of mating the two hybrid tall pea plants. Follow the colored arrows to see how the square is filled in. Each of the four boxes within the square shows a possible combination of traits in the offspring.

A Punnett square also shows the *ratio* of each type of offspring. A ratio is a comparison of two quantities. You can see in Figure 15-6B that one out of every four offspring is expected to be purebred tall. Two out of every four are expected to be hybrid tall. One out of every four is expected to be purebred short. A Punnett square does not show what will or must happen in a single cross. The Punnett square gives the results expected from many matings of the same type.

Another Punnett square is shown in Figure 15-7. This chart shows a cross between two purebred types of peas. A plant purebred for yellow seeds is crossed with a plant purebred for green seeds. Yellow seed color is the dominant trait. All of the offspring are hybrids with the genotype *Yy*. What color are these seeds?

Figure 15-7

A Punnett square showing the cross between two purebred types of peas.

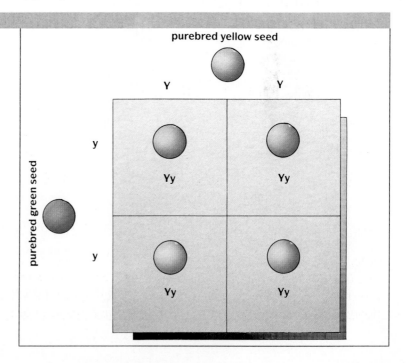

ACTIVITY   How Is a Punnett Square Used?

OBJECTIVES
Construct Punnett squares and **interpret** the results of crosses.

MATERIALS
paper, pencil, metric ruler

PROCEDURE
A. In this activity you will use Punnett squares to find the genotype of a tall pea plant. Draw two Punnett squares.

B. A tall pea plant of unknown genotype is crossed with a purebred short pea plant.
   1. What are the possible genotypes of the tall pea plant?
   2. What is the genotype of the purebred short pea plant?

C. In one Punnett square, write the genotype of each parent plant. Assume that the tall parent is purebred.

D. In the other Punnett square, write the genotype of each parent plant, but this time assume that the tall parent is hybrid.

E. Complete each Punnett square to show the possible genotypes of the offspring of each cross. See Figure 15-6, if you need help.

F. The cross of the purebred short pea plant with the tall pea plant resulted in 213 seeds. All the seeds were planted, and 114 tall and 99 short plants resulted.

RESULTS AND CONCLUSIONS
1. Are any short offspring shown in the first Punnett square? If so, how many?
2. Are any short offspring shown in the second Punnett square? If so, how many?
3. Which square better fits the data given in step **F**?
4. What is the genotype of the tall parent plant? How do you know?

INCOMPLETE DOMINANCE

You have learned about pairs of traits in which one trait is dominant over the other. Not all pairs of traits are like this. **Incomplete dominance** is a condition in which neither trait of a pair is dominant or recessive. Look at the Punnett square in Figure 15-8A. It shows flowers

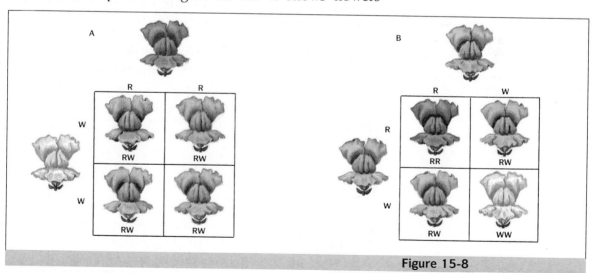

Figure 15-8

Incomplete dominance in snapdragons.

called snapdragons. Incomplete dominance occurs in these flowers. The Punnett square shows the cross between a purebred red (*RR*) flower and a purebred white (*WW*) flower. Notice that the symbols used for the traits are both

351

ACTIVITY   How Can Incomplete Dominance Be Shown?

OBJECTIVES
Construct Punnett squares and **interpret** the results of crosses.
Demonstrate incomplete dominance.

MATERIALS
metric ruler, 2 sheets of paper, pencil, transparent tape, 12 squares red cellophane (3 cm × 3 cm), 12 squares blue cellophane (3 cm × 3 cm)

PROCEDURE
A. Use a metric ruler to draw a Punnett square that is at least 16 cm on each side.
B. The genes for flower color in a certain plant show incomplete dominance. A purebred red flower (*RR*) is crossed with a purebred blue flower (*BB*). In your Punnett square, write the genotype of each parent plant.
C. Using colored cellophane to represent the genes for flower color, show the phenotype of each parent plant. Tape two squares of red cellophane, one on top of the other, above the genotype for red flower color. Tape two squares of blue cellophane, one on top of the other, next to the genotype for blue flower color.
D. Complete the Punnett square by writing the possible genotype of each offspring.
E. Show the phenotype of each offspring by taping the proper colored squares, one on top of the other, below each genotype. Thus, for a hybrid offspring, tape a blue square over a red square.

RESULTS AND CONCLUSIONS
1. What is the genotype of each offspring produced by the cross of the purebred red and purebred blue flowers?
2. What is the phenotype of each offspring from this cross?
3. Based only on its phenotype, it is not possible to know the genotype of a tall pea plant. In this activity the genotype of a flower can be determined from its phenotype. Explain why.

capitals but are different letters. How is this different from the symbols used in other crosses you have learned about?

All of the offspring produced by the cross of purebred snapdragons are hybrid pink. In a cross involving traits that show incomplete dominance, the offspring show a mixing of traits of the parents. In the case of snapdragon flowers, neither the trait for red nor the trait for white is dominant. The offspring show a mixing of these colors. This mixing produces pink flowers. Look back at the cross of two hybrid pink flowers in Figure 15-8B. What are the phenotypes of the offspring? What are the genotypes of the offspring?

REVIEW
1. What were Mendel's basic findings about traits?
2. Explain how symbols are used to represent traits.
3. What is the difference between genotype and phenotype?
4. What information does a Punnett square show?
5. Explain incomplete dominance, using snapdragon flowers as an example.

CHALLENGE If a purebred tall pea plant is crossed with a hybrid tall pea plant, can any of the offspring be short? Explain your answer.

15-3 CHROMOSOMES, GENES, AND HEREDITY

Mendel understood that organisms inherit traits from their parents. But he had no idea how the traits were passed on. Little was known about the nature of cells in Mendel's day. Inherited traits are carried by the chromosomes in a cell. Recall that a chromosome is a threadlike structure that is made up of DNA and protein. Information for traits is stored within the structure of the DNA molecules that make up the chromosomes. Many traits are carried by a single chromosome. Each section of a chromosome that carries the information for a specific trait is called a **gene**. The section of the pea plant chromosome that carries the tallness trait is the gene for tallness.

In Chapter 4, chromosomes were described as threadlike structures in a cell. There is another way chromosomes can be described. A **chromosome** is a series of genes. Think of a chromosome as a chain. The genes are the links that make up the chain. Each gene carries a piece of information. A chromosome carries many different pieces of information.

In cells of the body, chromosomes exist in pairs. Figure 15-9 shows a pair of chromosomes. Note that the same trait is carried on both chromosomes of a pair. Notice that the gene for a certain trait—height—is found in the same position on each chromosome. The two chromosomes of a pair can carry the genes for the same form or for contrasting forms of a trait. Think of one of Mendel's tall hybrid pea plants. The genotype of such a plant is *Tt*. The gene for tallness, *T*, would be on one chromosome of a pair. The gene for shortness, *t*, would be in the same position on the other chromosome of that pair.

After completing this section, you will be able to

- **identify** the roles of genes and chromosomes in inheriting traits.
- **describe** how chromosomes are passed from parents to offspring.
- **explain** the effect of meiosis on chromosome number.

The key terms in this section are
chromosome
gene

chromo- (color)
-soma- (body)

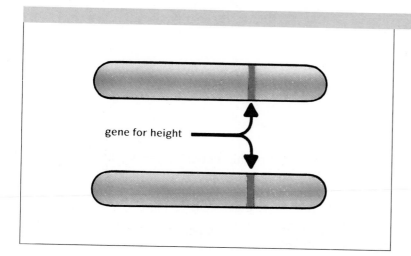

gene for height

Figure 15-9

A gene for a certain trait is at the same position on each chromosome of a pair.

How are chromosomes, and thus genes, passed from parents to offspring? Cells of multicellular organisms can be put into two groups. Those cells that function in reproduction are called *sex cells*. All other cells are called *body cells*. The sex cells of male organisms are called *sperm cells*. The sex cells of females are called *egg cells*.

The sex cells of both males and females are formed by a special kind of cell division called *meiosis* (mī OH-sihs). In meiosis, the number of chromosomes is reduced by half. The body cells of humans have 46 chromosomes, or 23 pairs of chromosomes. Each sex cell contains one chromosome from each pair. As you can see in Figure 15-10, human sperm cells and human egg cells each have half as many chromosomes as do human body cells.

When sex cells join during fertilization, they form the first body cell of the new organism. The cell formed from the joining of egg and sperm receives 46 chromosomes. The new body cell gets half its chromosomes from each parent. Thus, an organism gets half of its traits from each parent, just as Mendel had suggested.

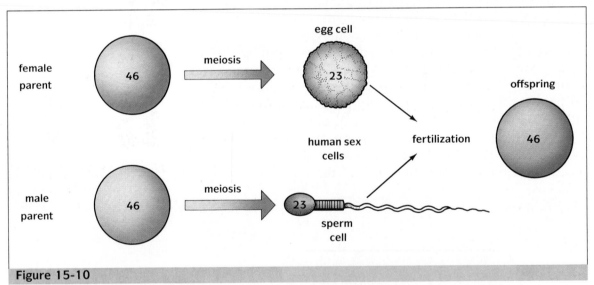

Figure 15-10

Sex cells have half the number of chromosomes as body cells have.

REVIEW

1. What is the relationship between genes and traits?
2. What is the difference between the number of chromosomes in body cells and sex cells?
3. By what process are sex cells formed?

CHALLENGE What would happen if sex cells contained the same number of chromosomes as in body cells?

15-4 SEX CHROMOSOMES

SEX DETERMINATION

The sex of an animal is determined by its chromosomes. The chromosomes of males differ from those of females. In humans, the difference occurs in one of the 23 pairs of chromosomes. The two chromosomes that determine sex are called the **sex chromosomes**. Look at the human chromosomes shown in Figure 15-11 (*left*). This photograph shows chromosomes that have been lined up by size. Chromosomes of a human male are shown. Locate the pair of chromosomes marked *X* and *Y*. The **Y chromosome** is a sex chromosome found only in the cells of males. The **X chromosome** is a sex chromosome found in the cells of both males and females. Each body cell of a male contains an X chromosome and a Y chromosome. Each body cell of a female contains two X chromosomes.

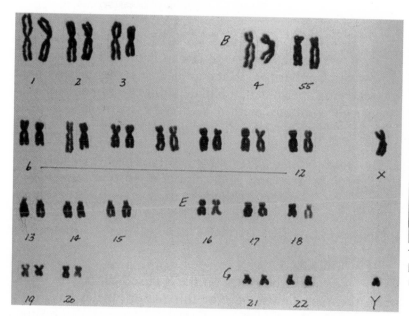

Figure 15-11

The 23 pairs of chromosomes in a human male (*left*), and sex chromosomes (*right*).

You may have noticed that unlike other pairs, the X and Y chromosomes are not the same size. The difference in the size of the sex chromosomes is shown more clearly in Figure 15-11 (*right*). Which chromosome is larger?

Recall that in meiosis the chromosome number is reduced by half. Half of the sperm carry an X chromosome and half carry a Y chromosome. Female body cells have two X chromosomes. Thus each egg cell, formed by meiosis, must contain an X chromosome.

Figure 15-12

The sex of the offspring is determined by the sex chromosome in the sperm.

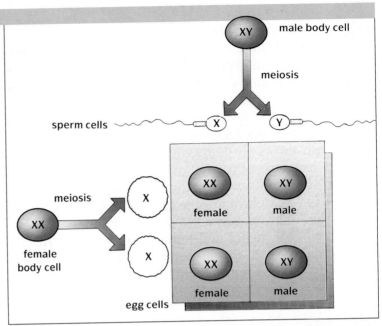

Look at the Punnett square in Figure 15-12. It shows how sex is inherited. When an egg cell combines with an X-carrying sperm cell, a female child is formed. When an egg cell combines with a Y-carrying sperm cell, a male child is formed. Thus it is the presence of an X or a Y chromosome in the sperm cell that determines the sex of the child. Notice that half the sperm produced carry an X chromosome, and half carry a Y chromosome. Thus there is a 50 percent chance that an egg will be fertilized by an X-carrying sperm cell. There is a 50 percent chance that an egg will be fertilized by a Y-carrying sperm cell.

SEX LINKAGE

Not all of the genes on the X chromosome are found on the Y chromosome. For this reason, males have only one copy of some genes. Females have two X chromosomes, which are the same size and carry the same group of genes.

A **sex-linked** trait is a trait that results from a gene that is found on the X chromosome but not on the Y chromosome. Sex-linked traits were first studied in fruit flies like the ones shown in Figure 15-13. Notice that there are two different eye colors. The eye color of fruit flies is a sex-linked trait. The gene for eye color is found on the X chromosome but not on the Y. The gene or trait for red eyes is dominant; the gene for white eyes is recessive.

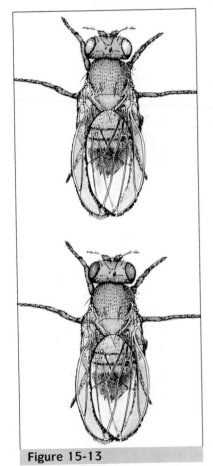

Figure 15-13

Eye color in fruit flies is a sex-linked trait.

OBJECTIVES

Demonstrate how chromosomes determine sex.

Identify differences in results using large and small samples.

MATERIALS

marking pencil, 2 large paper cups, 75 white beads, 25 colored beads, shoebox (or other large container)

PROCEDURE

A. Make a data table by writing numbers 1 through 50 on a sheet of paper.

B. Obtain two large paper cups. Label one cup *female parent*. Label the other cup *male parent*.

C. Use a white bead to represent an X chromosome. Use a colored bead to represent a Y chromosome.
  1. What two beads represent a female?
  2. What two beads represent a male?

D. Place 50 white beads in the cup labeled *female parent*. Place 25 white beads and 25 colored beads in the cup labeled *male parent*.

E. Without looking, take one bead from each cup. Look at the pair of beads and determine the sex of a child that has this combination of sex chromosomes. Record the sex of the child next to the number 1 on your data table. Then place the pair of beads in a shoebox.

F. Repeat step **E** until all beads have been removed from both cups. Record the sex of each child next to a different number in your data table.

G. Count the total number of females and the total number of males. Record these totals in your data table. This is a large sample.
  3. How many females and how many males are represented in the large sample?

H. Look at your data table to find the sex of the children for numbers 1 through 4. This is a small sample. Compare the results of your small sample with those of your classmates.

RESULTS AND CONCLUSIONS

1. What is the ratio of females to males in the large sample?

2. What is the ratio of females to males in the small sample?

3. Based on your results and your classmates' results, explain why it is important to use large samples in genetics experiments.

Sex-linked traits also occur in humans. One example is a kind of *color blindness*. Color blindness is the inability to see certain colors. Figure 15-14 is a chart used to tell if someone has red-green color blindness. Red-green color blindness is a condition in which a person cannot tell red and green from each other. Notice the pattern of dots in the chart. When a person with normal vision looks at the chart he or she will see the number 29. A color-blind person will see the number 70.

In humans, genes for color vision are found on the X chromosome, but not on the Y chromosome. The gene for normal color vision is dominant. The gene for color blindness is recessive. The trait for color vision is written as a smaller letter next to the X chromosome. Because there is no gene for color vision on the Y chromosome, no letter is written next to the Y. Thus the genotype of a normal male is written as $X^C Y$. The genotype of a color-blind male is written as $X^c Y$. What is the genotype of a color-blind female?

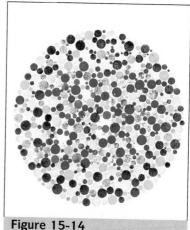

Figure 15-14

A test for color blindness.

The Punnett square in Figure 15-15 shows how color blindness is inherited. Both parents have normal vision. The father has one gene for normal color vision. His genotype is X^CY. The mother carries one gene for normal vision and one for color blindness. Her genotype is X^CX^c.

Figure 15-15

Color blindness is a sex-linked trait.

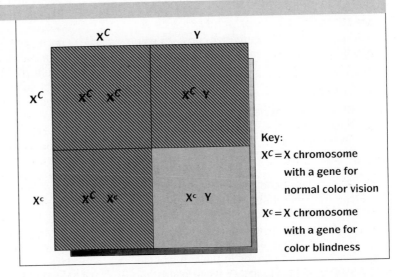

Key:
X^C = X chromosome with a gene for normal color vision

X^c = X chromosome with a gene for color blindness

Notice that the daughters are not color-blind. Do they have the same genotype? One of two sons is color-blind. Human males are more likely to have red-green color blindness than are females. A male need inherit only one gene for color blindness to be color-blind. It is usual in the inheritance of sex-linked traits for males to show the recessive traits more often than females. To be color-blind the female must inherit two genes for color blindness.

Hemophilia (hee muh FIHL ee uh) is another example of a sex-linked trait in humans. Hemophilia is a disorder in which the blood does not clot properly. It is caused by a recessive gene on the X chromosome. Hemophilia is inherited like other sex-linked traits. Why would a male be more likely to have hemophilia than would a female?

REVIEW

1. Describe differences between X and Y chromosomes.
2. How do chromosomes determine sex in humans?
3. What is a sex-linked trait? Give two examples of sex-linked traits.
4. Why do sex-linked traits show more often in males than in females?

CHALLENGE Is it possible for a son to inherit red-green color blindness from his father? Explain your answer.

15-5 APPLICATIONS OF GENETICS

It is thought that farmers in the Middle East began growing wheat about 10,000 years ago. At first they used a type of wild wheat. The garden wheat that the farmers grew years ago soon became very different from the wild wheat. Figure 15-16 shows wild wheat and a garden type of wheat. How do their seeds differ?

It is believed that garden wheat was produced from wild wheat by selective breeding. **Selective breeding** is the crossing of plants or animals with the most useful traits to produce offspring that have the combined useful traits of the parents. The farmers may have found that large seeds grew into plants that also produced large seeds. After many years of selecting the best seeds, the wheat produced was more useful than the original wild wheat.

Selective breeding has become even more successful in recent times. Figure 15-16 also shows some results of modern selective breeding. What useful or desirable traits might these organisms have?

Figure 15-16

In recent years a new procedure called genetic engineering has been developed. **Genetic engineering** is the transfer of genes from one organism to another. There are several different forms of genetic engineering. Moving genes from cells of other types of living things into cells of bacteria is the most common form of genetic engineering.

Compare wild wheat (*left*) and garden wheat (*top middle*). Selectively bred strawberries (*bottom middle*), corn (*top right*), and sheep (*bottom right*).

SCIENCE & TECHNOLOGY

You may have heard of some of the 1600 genetic diseases that are caused by a defect in a single gene. These include cystic fibrosis, muscular dystrophy, and hemophilia. One genetic disease that you may not know about is called ADA. ADA is a disease that makes the body unable to fight other diseases. A victim of ADA, such as the boy shown here, must not be in contact with other people. Even a minor illness can be fatal to a person born with ADA.

Researchers are developing techniques to cure some genetic diseases. One method, called gene therapy, involves replacing the defective gene with a healthy one.

Gene therapy may provide a cure for ADA. Researchers have identified the defective gene that causes ADA. Using genetic engineering, they have grown copies of the healthy human gene. Their goal is to transfer the healthy gene to the cells of people who have ADA.

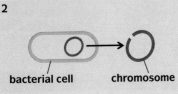

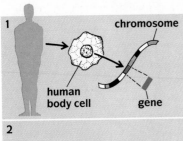

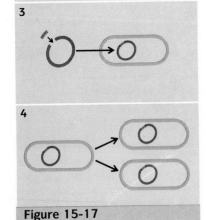

Figure 15-17

In one form of genetic engineering, a gene is removed from a human cell and attached to a bacterial chromosome.

You can see this form of genetic engineering in Figure 15-17. In this example, a human gene that makes a certain protein is being moved.

1. The desired gene is removed from a human chromosome.
2. The circular chromosome of a bacterial cell is removed and split open.
3. The human gene is attached to the bacterial chromosome at the opening. The bacterial chromosome, which contains the human gene, is returned to the bacterial cell.
4. Each time the bacterial cell divides, it copies the human gene along with its own chromosome.

Why would scientists want to put a human gene in a bacterium? Bacteria divide quickly, as often as every 20 minutes. In a short time there can be large numbers of bacteria that contain the human gene. If the gene makes a human protein, then all of these bacteria will be able to make that human protein. Thus the protein can be made quickly, in large amounts, and at low cost.

In Chapter 5 you learned that human insulin and human interferon are now being made by bacteria. The human genes for insulin and interferon are transferred to the bacteria by genetic engineering. Growth hormone is another human protein now being made by bacteria. Growth hormone is needed for normal growth during childhood. Children who lack growth hormone may fail to reach normal size. Such children can now be treated with human growth hormone made by bacteria.

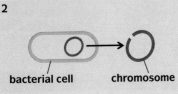
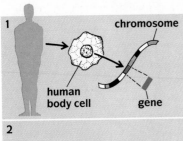
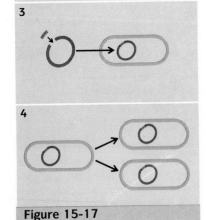

REVIEW

1. What is selective breeding? For what purposes has selective breeding been used?
2. Explain how human genes are transferred into bacteria. What is this process called?
3. What advantages are there in having bacteria that contain human genes?

CHALLENGE Most pea plants produce only a few peas in each pod. Devise a method to breed a new type of pea plant that makes more peas per pod.

CHAPTER SUMMARY

The main ideas in this chapter are listed below. Read these statements before you answer the Chapter Review questions.

• Heredity is the passing of traits from parents to their young. Genetics is the scientific study of heredity. (15-1)

• Gregor Mendel studied the traits of pea plants by carrying out certain crosses. Mendel found that some traits are dominant and some are recessive. (15-1)

• Mendel discovered that offspring inherit traits in pairs, one from each parent. In hybrids a dominant trait may prevent a recessive trait from showing. Two organisms with the same phenotype (appearance) may have different genotypes (genetic makeups). (15-2)

• The Punnett square is a method for showing all the possible combinations of genes that two parents can pass on to their off-spring. Incomplete dominance results in a mixing of traits, since neither trait of a pair is dominant. (15-2)

• A gene is a section of a chromosome. A gene carries the information for a specific trait. Sex cells have half the number of chromosomes found in body cells. Sex cells are formed by meiosis. (15-3)

• Sex of offspring is determined by the sex chromosomes. Sex-linked traits result from genes that are found on the X chromosome but are not present on the Y chromosome. (15-4)

• Some of the knowledge of genetics has been applied in selective breeding and genetic engineering. (15-5)

The key terms in this chapter are listed below. Use each term in a sentence that shows the meaning of the term.

chromosome	hybrid	sex chromosomes
dominant trait	incomplete dominance	sex-linked trait
gene	phenotype	trait
genetic engineering	Punnett square	X chromosome
genetics	purebred	Y chromosome
genotype	recessive trait	
heredity	selective breeding	

Chapter Review

VOCABULARY

Write the letter of the term that best matches the definition. Not all the terms will be used.

1. An organism that when self-pollinated will produce the same form of a trait in all its offspring
2. A section of a chromosome that carries information for one trait
3. A kind of chromosome found in the cells of both males and females
4. A characteristic, or feature, of an organism
5. An organism produced by a cross of parents that have different forms of a trait
6. A trait that is hidden by the presence of a dominant trait
7. The transfer of genes from one organism to another
8. The scientific study of heredity
9. A chart that shows all possible combinations of traits in offspring
10. A trait that prevents the showing of another trait

a. chromosome
b. dominant trait
c. gene
d. genetic engineering
e. genetics
f. genotype
g. hybrid
h. incomplete dominance
i. Punnett square
j. purebred
k. recessive trait
l. sex-linked trait
m. trait
n. X chromosome
o. Y chromsome

CONCEPTS

1. What is heredity? Identify two inherited traits—one that can be seen and one that cannot be seen. (15-1)
2. What is genetics? How did the study of genetics begin? (15-1)
3. Give three reasons why pea plants are good for use in genetics experiments. (15-1)
4. What is the difference between purebred and hybrid organisms? (15-1)
5. Which traits did Mendel call dominant and which ones did he call recessive? (15-1)
6. Mendel concluded that organisms inherit traits in pairs. Where do these traits come from? (15-2)
7. In a genetics experiment with pea plants, what do the following symbols mean: $TT \times tt$? (15-2)

8. What is phenotype and genotype? Explain how two organisms may have the same phenotype but different genotypes. (15-2)

9. What two things does a Punnett square show? (15-2)

10. What is incomplete dominance? Give an example of it. (15-2)

11. What is a gene? (15-3)

12. Describe a chromosome. (15-3)

13. Compare the number of chromosomes in human body cells and in human sex cells. (15-3)

14. Name the two sex chromosomes and describe how they differ. (15-4)

15. What sex chromosomes can an egg cell and sperm cell carry? What combination of sex cells produces a female offspring? A male offspring? (15-4)

16. Give two examples of sex-linked traits. (15-4)

17. Why is selective breeding done? Give two examples. (15-5)

18. What is genetic engineering? What are its benefits? (15-5)

APPLICATION/ CRITICAL THINKING

1. Explain why it is important that Mendel used thousands of plants in his experiments.

2. Describe the offspring that will be produced by crossing a tall hybrid pea plant (*Tt*) with a short pea plant (*tt*).

3. Green pea pods are dominant and represented by *G*. Yellow pea pods are recessive. What symbol is used to represent yellow pea pods? Explain why. Give the genotype of a plant which is hybrid for green pods.

4. What offspring will be produced by self-pollinating a pea plant hybrid for green pods?

EXTENSION

1. Hybrid seeds of peas that carry a recessive trait and a dominant trait are available. Ask your teacher to help you get these seeds. Use the seeds to repeat some of Mendel's experiments. Write a report on your results.

2. Prepare a short report about hemophilia. What famous people have been affected by this disease? How have treatments for this disease changed through history?

READINGS

Gonick, Larry, and Mark Wheelis. *The Cartoon Guide to Genetics*. New York: Barnes & Noble Books, 1983.

Lampton, Christopher. *DNA and the Creation of New Life*. New York: Arco Publishing, 1983.

Preuss, Paul. "Industry in Ferment." *Science 85*, July/August 1985, p. 42.

CHANGE OVER TIME

Look at the photograph. It shows the preserved remains, or fossil, of an animal. Can you identify the animal? Look closely at the body structure. Does this animal seem similar to any animals with which you are familiar? The fossil is that of a trilobite. Trilobites are animals that no longer exist. They are extinct. The last trilobites are thought to have died out about 230 million years ago. Scientists think that insects, spiders, crabs, and other similar creatures are distant relatives of trilobites.

- *How do fossils form?*
- *What do fossils tell us about the history of life on the earth?*
- *How do scientists explain the observation that different living things seem to be related?*

16-1 CHANGE AND MUTATION

It is thought that there are millions of species of living things on the earth. These many kinds of living things live in many different environments. Some live in wetlands and some in deserts. Others live in saltwater or freshwater environments. Some living things are found on the top of high mountains or in the depths of the oceans. Each species is suited for living in its environment.

ADAPTATIONS

Living things often have special features or traits that allow them to get along well in a certain environment. A trait that makes a living thing better able to live in an environment is an **adaptation** (ad ap TAY shuhn). There are different kinds of adaptations. Some are special structures. For example, monkeys have hands that have separate fingers. Such hands are useful for grasping. Monkeys spend much of their time in trees. Their hands are well adapted for grasping tree branches. A cactus has a thick waxy covering that helps to keep water inside the plant. Think about the kind of environment in which a cactus lives. How is this type of covering an adaptation?

> *After completing this section, you will be able to*
>
> - **define** the term *adaptation* and **give examples** of adaptations.
> - **distinguish** between harmful, neutral, and helpful mutations.
> - **describe** the kinds of changes that result in new adaptations.
>
> *The key terms in this section are*
> adaptation   mutation

ad- (to)
aptus (fitted)

Look at the large bird in Figure 16-1. This bird hunts for small fish while wading in shallow water. What adaptations does this bird have for wading?

In some animals, adaptations take the form of *camouflage* (KAM uh flahzh). Camouflage is an adaptation of special coloring or shape that allows an animal to blend in with its environment. This adaptation helps to conceal an animal from its enemies.

Adaptations include special ways in which living things act, or behave. Note that the musk oxen in Figure 16-2 (*left*) are standing close together. The parts of the animals that touch are not exposed to the cold air. The way the oxen stand together is a type of adaptation.

Some adaptations relate to the life processes or chemistry of organisms. Most grasses live on land and are harmed by salt. As you can see in Figure 16-2 (*right*), salt-marsh cordgrass lives with its roots in salt water. This plant survives by pumping salt out through its leaves. Because of this adaptation, cordgrass can survive in an environment where other kinds of grasses would die.

Figure 16-1

Look for the adaptations of this wading bird.

Figure 16-2

Types of adaptations. Note how the musk oxen stand close together (*left*). How can cordgrass live in salt water (*right*)?

MUTATIONS

How do adaptations occur? Species of living things change over time. Some changes are helpful. Other changes may have no effect on a living thing. Some changes may be harmful. A change that increases an organism's chances for survival is helpful. Helpful changes are those that lead to new adaptations.

Changes in living things occur in several ways. Sexual reproduction is one process that leads to change. In the last chapter you learned that when offspring are produced, genes from two parents are combined. Each generation that is produced by sexual reproduction has new combinations of genes. Offspring may have traits that did not appear in either of their parents. New adaptations may result from the new gene combinations.

Another source of change in living things is a mutation (myoo TAY shuhn). A **mutation** is a change in the genes or chromosomes of a cell. If a mutation occurs in a sperm cell or an egg cell, it can be passed along to offspring. Some of the causes of mutations are known. Some forms of radiation, such as X rays and ultraviolet rays, are known to cause mutations. Certain chemicals are also known to cause mutations. There may be other, unknown causes of mutations. Mutations occur suddenly. *Mutants*, or organisms that have mutations, can appear at almost any time.

mutare (to change)

Figure 16-3

A fruit fly with normal wings (*left*). A mutant fruit fly with tiny wings that cannot function (*right*).

Some mutations are small changes in the information contained in a gene. A gene changed in this way may show up in the offspring as a slightly changed trait. Often these mutations have no obvious effect. Such mutations neither help nor harm an organism. Other mutations may result from major changes in a gene or in a part of a chromosome. Some chromosomes may be absent, or extra ones may be present. Such mutations usually cause a major loss of function in an organism. These mutations usually are harmful.

A harmful mutation may cause death, or it may lower an organism's chances of surviving or reproducing. For example, one type of mutation produces an organism called an *albino* (al BĪ noh). An albino is a living thing that lacks coloring matter called pigment. Look at the two mice in Figure 16-4. Notice that one mouse is grayish-brown. The second mouse, an albino, is white. The albino mouse is the result of a mutation. Imagine that both of these mice were in a meadow of dry, brown grass. Which mouse would be more likely to be seen and attacked by a hawk flying overhead? Why? Is the mutation that produces an albino mouse harmful or helpful?

Figure 16-4

Deer mouse (*left*) and albino house mouse (*right*). The albino mouse is the result of a mutation.

Sometimes, mutations result in traits that help an organism survive. Suppose a mutation causes a plant to make more seeds than other similar plants. Such a mutation would be helpful. The mutant plant would be adapted for more successful reproduction.

Mutations as well as new combinations of genes may lead to new adaptations. Within a group, the organisms that are best adapted to their surroundings are most likely to reproduce. In time, the less-adapted organsims will die out. The group will contain more organisms that have favorable traits.

REVIEW

1. What is an adaptation? Give an example of a structure that is an adaptation. Give an example of a behavior that is an adaptation.
2. What are two ways that changes occur in organisms?
3. What is a mutation? Distinguish between a helpful mutation and a harmful mutation.
4. Explain how a mutation can result in an adaptation.

CHALLENGE Crop breeders sometimes treat plants with X rays, hoping to produce helpful mutations. How successful do you think such a procedure might be? Explain why.

16-2 EVIDENCE OF CHANGE OVER TIME

FOSSIL FORMATION

Earth scientists have evidence that the earth is about 4.6 billion years old. The oldest traces of life that have been found are about 3.5 billion years old. What traces of life of the past have been left behind? How do scientists know the age of such things? These are questions that cannot be answered by biologists alone. *Geologists* are scientists who study the earth and the rocks of which it is made. Biologists and geologists work together in studying the traces of life forms of the past.

Species of living things on the earth have changed a great deal over long periods of time. Direct evidence that life has changed comes from the study of fossils (FAHS-uhlz). A **fossil** is a trace or the preserved remains of an organism that lived in the past. Animals often leave tracks in mud or soil. The soil may later harden and become rock. The footprint may then be preserved in the form of a fossil. Such a fossil is evidence of an animal's activity.

> *After completing this section, you will be able to*
>
> - **describe** how sedimentary rock forms.
> - **describe** two types of fossils and **explain** how each forms.
> - **give an example** of how fossils can provide evidence that organisms have changed over time.
> - **describe** one hypothesis about how dinosaurs became extinct.
>
> *The key terms in this section are*
> extinct   fossil

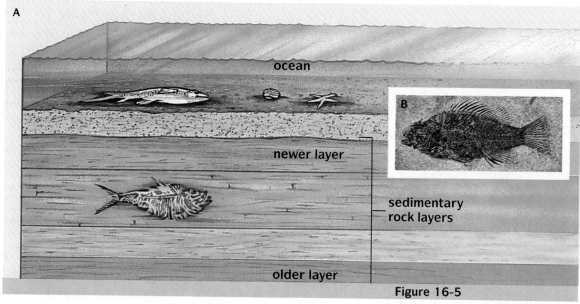

Figure 16-5

Layers of sedimentary rock (*A*). Fossil fish in sedimentary rock (*B*).

The bones of animals and the shells of sea animals sometimes become fossils. These fossils are often found in *sedimentary* (sehd uh MEHN tuhr ee) *rock*, as shown in Figure 16-5A. Such rock often forms from mineral particles that fall to the bottom of a body of water, such as an ocean or a lake. Over long periods of time, many layers of these particles may form at the bottom of lakes and

369

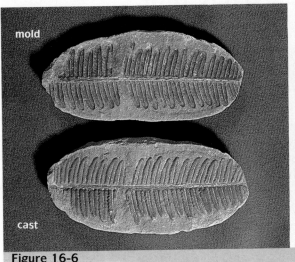
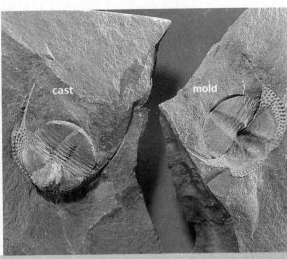

Figure 16-6

Examples of mold fossils and cast fossils. Notice how closely the molds and casts resemble the living things.

Figure 16-7

A fly preserved in amber.

oceans. The weight of the upper layers presses down on the lower layers. Under this weight, the lower layers of particles turn into sedimentary rock. Bones or shells of dead animals also may fall to the bottom of an ocean or a lake. Thus, they can become fossils in the sedimentary rock. What type of animal formed the fossil in Figure 16-5B?

Fossils found in rock may form in several ways. The soft body of an animal or plant may form one type of fossil. An organism dies and is buried by mud, which hardens into rock. As the organism's body decays, a hollow space is left in the rock. The space is in the shape of the organism or parts of it. This hollow space in the form of a once-living thing is called a *mold*.

A mold sometimes becomes filled by minerals that seep in through the rock. The solid object that forms is another type of fossil called a *cast*. A cast is a fossil that has the same outer shape as the animal or plant part that formed it. You can see examples of mold and cast fossils in Figure 16-6.

Sometimes, living things become trapped in substances such as sap or tar. Living trees sometimes ooze sap. Insects can be trapped in large drops of sap. When sap hardens, it turns into a substance called *amber*. Insects inside amber can be preserved as fossils over long periods of time. What type of insect can be seen inside the amber in Figure 16-7?

Many thousands of fossils have been found in a tar pit in California. The tar prevented the decay of the bones of animals that fell into this pit. Many complete skeletons of ancient animals have been taken from this tar pit.

Figure 16-8

Baby woolly mammoth preserved in ice (*left*). Skull of saber-toothed tiger found in tar pit (*right*).

A few complete fossil animals have been found trapped in ice in Siberia and Alaska. These animals lived many thousands of years ago. Because they have been frozen since that time, the bodies of these animals have been preserved. Such finds allow scientists to study the tissues and organs of extinct animals. These tissues and organs can then be compared to those of living animals.

ACTIVITY What Materials Are Best for Fossil Formation?

OBJECTIVE
Determine in which of two environments fossils are more likely to form.

MATERIALS
lab apron, sheets of newspaper, 2 pie plates, metric ruler, sand, modeling clay, sea shell, vegetable oil, plaster of Paris, container for mixing plaster, water, stick or stirring rod

PROCEDURE

A. Wear a lab apron throughout this activity. Spread several layers of newspaper over your work area.
B. Fill a pie plate with sand to a depth of about 2 cm. Place a similar amount of modeling clay in another pie plate.
C. Press a sea shell firmly into the sand.
D. Remove the shell from the sand. Spread a very small amount of vegetable oil over the surface of the shell. Press the shell firmly into the clay. Remove the shell and set it aside.

E. Your teacher will give you instructions on mixing plaster of Paris. Mix enough plaster to fill both pie plates.
F. Pour the plaster over the sand and over the clay in each pie plate.
G. Allow about one-half hour for the plaster to harden. Remove the plaster from the pie plates. Carefully separate the hardened plaster from the sand and from the clay.

RESULTS AND CONCLUSIONS
1. In what ways do the plaster fossils resemble real fossils?
2. What type of fossil do the plaster models represent?
3. Did one of the two plaster models more closely resemble the sea shell? If so, which one?
4. In which location do you think the best footprint fossils might form—desert sand or mud at the edge of a lake? Explain your answer.

FOSSIL EVIDENCE OF CHANGE

What has been learned from the many types of fossils that have been found? Fossils give evidence that life has changed during the history of the earth. For example, fossil evidence shows that, over time, there have been changes in the family of animals that includes the horse. Look at Figure 16-9. The leg bones of animals *A*, *B*, *C*, and *D* are fossils. The oldest animal shown is about 60 million years old. This dog-sized animal is thought to have been a distant ancestor of modern horses. How did the length of the leg bones and the overall body size change over time?

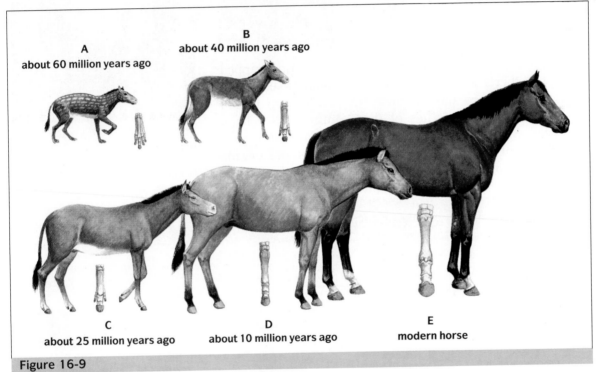

A
about 60 million years ago

B
about 40 million years ago

C
about 25 million years ago

D
about 10 million years ago

E
modern horse

Figure 16-9

Changes in the family of animals that includes the horse. How do the number of toes in *A* differ from the number of toes in *E*?

There are fossils of many species of organisms that no longer exist. Species of organisms of the past that no longer exist are said to be **extinct** (ehk STIHNKT). Dinosaurs are the best-known group of extinct organisms. Fossils of about 400 different species of dinosaurs have been found. These animals lived on the earth from about 200 million to 65 million years ago. However, not all species were alive at the same time. About 65 million years ago, those species that were living became extinct in a short time.

Biologists have long wondered what caused many species of dinosaurs to become extinct at one time. A number of hypotheses have been suggested. Some of these

Suppose you looked up in the sky and saw a flying reptile with an 11-m wingspan. What would you think? Millions of years ago such a sight was commonplace. Today, through technology, you might see a flying reptile called a pterosaur (TEHR uh-sawr). Pterosaurs have been extinct for 65 million years. Scientists believe that these reptiles were the largest animals ever to fly.

Paul MacCready, an engineer, has constructed a flying model of a pterosaur — *Quetzalcoatlus northropi* (keht sahl koh AHT luhs nawr THRAHP ee), QN for short. The design of QN is based on fossils of the animal. These fossils were discovered in Texas in 1972. They are the only known remains of the species.

The model not only looks much like the real pterosaur, it also flies like the real animal. QN has a special computerized brain. MacCready's creation can flap its wings and soar through the air.

involve the idea that an object from space might have struck the earth about 65 million years ago. Iridium (ih-RIHD ee uhm) has been found in many rock samples that contain fossils of the last dinosaurs. Iridium is an element that is usually rare on the earth. However, it is much more common in meteors and other objects from space.

Some scientists believe that a huge meteor hit the earth and exploded 65 million years ago. Such an explosion would have filled the air around the earth with dust. The dust is thought to have caused the death of many forms of life by keeping sunlight from reaching the earth. Dinosaurs and many other living things became extinct at about the same time.

The climate of the earth has changed many times in the past. Studies of fossils have shown that, over time, animals adapted to a changing environment. Organisms that were not well adapted became extinct.

REVIEW

1. Describe molds and casts. Explain how they form.
2. What do fossils show about life in the past? Use the horse as an example.
3. Describe the hypothesis that the extinction of dinosaurs was caused by an object from space. What evidence supports this hypothesis?

CHALLENGE Give reasons why bones and shells are the most common types of fossils found.

16-3 HISTORY OF THE EARTH

radius (ray, beam)

DETERMINING FOSSIL AGE

The ages of some fossils were given in the last section. How do scientists know how old a fossil is? There are several ways that scientists can find the age of a fossil. One important method involves the measurement of radioactive (ray dee oh AK tihv) elements in a fossil. A **radioactive element** is an element whose atoms change to other kinds of atoms, giving off energy and particles in the process. The energy and particles that are released are called *radioactivity*. The use of radioactive elements to find the age of a fossil is called **radioactive dating**.

As the atoms of a radioactive element release energy, the atoms are changed. Radioactive atoms decay, or change over time. They become atoms of a different element. The rate at which a radioactive element decays is given by its half-life. **Half-life** is the length of time it takes for one half of the atoms of a radioactive element to change. Carbon-14 is the radioactive form of carbon. The half-life of carbon-14 is 5730 years. In other words, half of a sample of carbon-14 will change in 5730 years. Half of the remaining amount will change in another 5730 years. Look at Figure 16-10. How much of the original sample of carbon-14 will remain after 11,460 years?

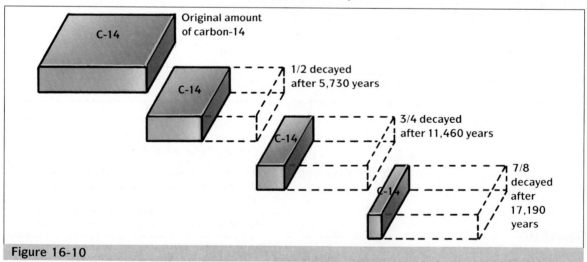

Figure 16-10

Carbon-14 is a radioactive substance that is used for measuring the age of fossils. You can see what happens to carbon-14 over thousands of years.

All living things have about the same percent of carbon-14. When a living thing dies, the amount of carbon-14 starts to decrease by decay. Scientists can find the age of a fossil by measuring the amount of carbon-14 in it. Because of the half-life of carbon-14, it is useful for measuring the age of fossils that are about 75,000 years old or less. Radioactive elements with longer half-lives are used for dating older fossils. Other radioactive elements are used in dating the rocks in which fossils are found. For example, potassium-40 has a half-life of over 1 billion years. Potassium-40 can be used to date very old rocks.

Radioactive dating is a direct method for measuring the age of rocks and fossils. Other methods of dating fossils are indirect. The properties of sedimentary rock are used in indirect dating. Recall that this type of rock forms in layers. The oldest layers are the deepest. The youngest layers are near the surface. All of the material in one layer of sedimentary rock formed about the same time in the earth's history. The age of one fossil in a certain layer of rock can be found. Other fossils in that same layer are then assumed to be about the same age. In general, fossils in deeper layers are older. Fossils in layers nearer the surface are younger.

GEOLOGIC TIME

Geologists have divided the history of the earth into four eras. An **era** (IHR uh) is a major division of geologic time. It is a very long period of time in the history of the earth. Major differences in the forms of life found on the earth divide the eras from each other. A description of each of the four eras, as well as how long ago each occurred, is presented in Table 16-1. Refer to Table 16-1 as you read about the eras.

era (number)

Table 16-1 *History of Life on Earth*

Era	Time (Years Before Present)	Important Events and Changes
Precambrian	4,600,000,000	No life on the earth. First cells appear. First cells with nuclei present. First multicellular organisms appear.
Paleozoic	600,000,000	Many simple animals and plants appear in the sea. Fish (first animals with a backbone) appear. Plants appear on land. Insects and amphibians (first land animals) appear. Many forms of animal life in sea become extinct.
Mesozoic	230,000,000	Dinosaurs and first warm-blooded animals, including birds, appear. Flowering and cone-bearing plants appear. Many life forms, including dinosaurs, become extinct.
Cenozoic	65,000,000	Many types of warm-blooded animals develop. Trees of modern types appear. Many mammals appear. Modern humans appear.

Figure 16-11

Some of the animals that lived during the Mesozoic Era. All the animals shown are now extinct.

The *Precambrian* (pree KAM bree uhn) *Era* began when the earth came into being, and it ended about 600 million years ago. During most of this era, only single-celled life forms existed.

The *Paleozoic* (pay lee uh ZOH ihk) *Era* began 600 million years ago and lasted for about 370 million years. Many of the major groups of plants and animals first appeared during this era. During the second half of this era, plants and then animals first appeared on land. The era ended with the extinction of many sea animals.

The *Mesozoic* (mehs uh ZOH ihk) *Era* began 230 million years ago and lasted for about 165 million years. Dinosaurs and other reptiles were the most important animals. Warm-blooded animals first appeared. Flowering plants became abundant later in the Mesozoic Era. This era ended with the extinction of the dinosaurs.

The *Cenozoic* (see nuh ZOH ihk) *Era* began about 65 million years ago and has continued to the present. The Cenozoic Era is the era in which we live. Mammals have been the most important animals of this era. Birds and insects also have been abundant during this era.

REVIEW

1. Explain how radioactive elements are used in finding the ages of fossils.
2. Describe an indirect way of finding the age of a fossil.
3. How is the history of the earth divided into eras? Give an example of one important event from each era.

CHALLENGE Some elements, such as carbon-14, are used to date the remains of organisms. Others, such as uranium-238, can only be used to date rocks. Explain why elements such as uranium-238 are not used to date living things.

16-4 THEORIES OF EVOLUTION

Fossils show changes that have occurred in living things. However, the study of fossils does not explain why those changes have taken place. The process of change that occurs over time in species of living things is called **evolution** (ehv uh LOO shuhn). A number of ideas about how evolution occurs have been presented.

LAMARCK'S THEORY

In the early 1800s the French scientist Jean B. Lamarck had an idea about how evolution occurs. He thought that he could explain how giraffes got their long necks. Note in Figure 16-12A that the giraffes are eating leaves high in a tree. Lamarck believed that a lifetime of eating this way would cause a giraffe's neck to get longer. Such giraffes would then pass on the trait of a long neck to their offspring. Over generations, giraffes' necks would get longer and longer.

After completing this section, you will be able to

- **describe** Lamarck's ideas about how evolution occurs.
- **explain** Charles Darwin's ideas about how evolution occurs.
- **give an example** of the theory of evolution by natural selection.

The key terms in this section are
  evolution
  natural selection

Figure 16-12

Lamarck's hypothesis on how organisms change over time. Short-necked giraffes stretch their necks to reach food (A). Over time the giraffes acquire a long neck (B).

Lamarck called a feature or a characteristic that an organism gets during its lifetime an *acquired characteristic*. He believed that evolution occurred by the passing on of these acquired characteristics from parents to offspring. His ideas are called the *theory of evolution by inheritance of acquired characteristics*. Lamarck formed his ideas before genetics came about. Modern genetics shows that characteristics acquired in one's lifetime cannot be passed on to offspring. Characteristics are inherited through the passing on of DNA contained in eggs and sperm. For this reason scientists today reject Lamarck's theory.

DARWIN'S THEORY

In the mid-1800s an English scientist presented his ideas about how evolution occurs. This man was Charles Darwin. In 1859, Darwin wrote a book called *The Origin of Species*. This book is the source of most of the modern thinking about evolution.

Charles Darwin was a biologist who wrote many science books. In the 1830s he took a job on a British naval ship. This ship, the H.M.S. *Beagle*, spent several years traveling around the world. The purpose of this long voyage was to collect samples of organisms and to prepare maps for the British government. Darwin was the ship's naturalist. He was in charge of describing and collecting samples of life forms from around the world.

After returning from the voyage, Darwin spent years reviewing his notes and ideas. Of special interest to him were the organisms he found on the Galápagos Islands. These islands are in the Pacific Ocean, about 950 km from the coast of Ecuador. Locate these islands on the map in Figure 16-14. Many of the organisms found on these islands are similar to species found in South America.

Figure 16-13

Plaque of Charles Darwin on the Galápagos Islands.

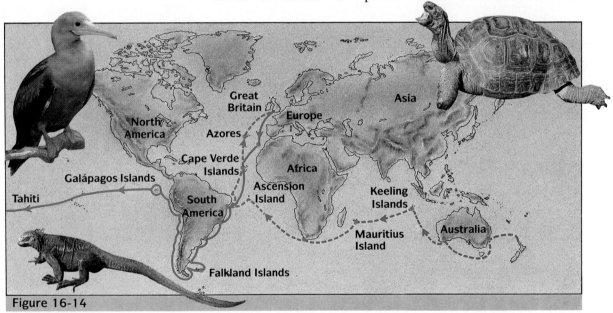

Figure 16-14

The route taken by Charles Darwin and his crew from 1831 to 1836 on the H.M.S. *Beagle*.

But Darwin was most interested in the differences. Darwin noticed that many of the living things on the islands had special adaptations to local conditions. Each of the Galápagos Islands is somewhat unique in its environment. Some are desertlike, but others have forests. Darwin observed that organisms on each island seemed to be well adapted to the conditions of their island.

OBJECTIVE

Determine how individual differences relate to natural selection.

MATERIALS

construction paper strips (15 each of green, light brown, and red), scissors, fresh grass clippings, watch or clock with second hand

PROCEDURE

A. Make a data table like the one shown.

B. Use green, light brown, and red strips of construction paper to represent three types of insects that live in grass. Some types of birds search the grass for insects to eat.

C. Have a classmate thoroughly mix the strips of colored paper with some grass clippings.

D. Your task is to pick up as many paper strips (insects) as possible in 15 seconds. Have a second classmate act as the timekeeper. Record your results in your table.

E. Repeat steps **C** and **D** two more times.

F. Complete the *Total* column in your table.

Color of Paper	Number of Insects Picked Up			
	First Person	Second Person	Third Person	Total
Green				
Brown				
Red				

RESULTS AND CONCLUSIONS

1. Which color insect was captured most often?
2. Which color insect was captured least often? What type of adaptation does this insect have?
3. Which color insect is most likely to survive and reproduce? Explain your answer.

Twenty-two years after he returned from the voyage, Darwin presented his ideas about how evolution occurs. His main points are listed here.

Overproduction   Most organisms produce more offspring than can be supported by the environment. Many of these offspring do not survive.

Variation   Many variations in traits or characteristics are found among the individuals within a species. Some variations make an organism better adapted for survival.

Selection   An organism with favorable variations has a better chance of surviving and reproducing than others of its species. Darwin called this process natural selection. **Natural selection** is the survival of those organisms best suited to their environment. This process also is known as *survival of the fittest*. However, reproduction is just as important as survival. Only through reproduction are favorable traits passed on to the next generation.

Change over time   If organisms with favorable traits reproduce more than others, then these traits will be present in more of the offspring. After many generations of natural selection, a species can have a different genetic makeup than it once had. The species also will be better adapted to its environment. If enough changes occur in a group of living things, a new species may develop.

Figure 16-15

A house spider with its many young is an example of overproduction.

Moths are often caught and eaten by birds. The photograph shows two kinds of peppered moths—a light-colored moth and a dark-colored moth. Both kinds of moths are resting on a dark-colored tree trunk. Which moth is more likely to be eaten by a bird? Which kind of moth would be likely to survive over time?

An English scientist, Alfred Wallace, studied evolution at the same time as Darwin. Although the two men did not work together, their ideas were similar. Wallace also formed the idea that natural selection caused evolution to occur. The explanation by Darwin and Wallace is known as the *theory of evolution by natural selection.*

The evolution of the horse is a good example of natural selection at work. Refer back to Figure 16-9. Animal *A* is the oldest animal shown. This animal is thought to have lived in forests. Notice how the animal changed over time. Modern horses live on flat, grassy areas known as prairies. As forests became prairies, longer, thinner legs and fewer toes became favorable, or naturally selected, traits of horses. This streamlining of the horse's leg seems to be an adaptation for running on flat, open ground. Unlike horses that lived in the forests of the past, horses living on prairies could not escape their enemies by hiding from them. Thus, those horses that could run better were more likely to survive and reproduce.

REVIEW

1. Describe the theory of evolution proposed by Lamarck. Why is this theory not accepted by most scientists?
2. Explain Darwin's ideas about how evolution occurs using the terms *overproduction, variation, selection,* and *change over time*.
3. Describe the theory of evolution by natural selection. Use the horse as an example.

CHALLENGE Reproduction of the fittest is a better description of natural selection than survival of the fittest. Explain why.

16-5 MODERN VIEWS OF EVOLUTION

GENETICS AND EVOLUTION

Most biologists today accept the idea that natural selection is an important cause of evolution. While many of Darwin's ideas are still accepted, most biologists agree that Darwin's ideas do not completely explain evolution. Much new information about evolution has been gathered since that time. This new information has brought about some changes in Darwin's theory.

Look at the mother pig and her piglets in Figure 16-16. What differences do you see among these animals? Darwin knew that such differences among the members of a species had to be present for change to occur. However, Darwin had no idea what caused such differences. The science of genetics came about after Darwin's time. Understanding genetics has aided scientists in their study of evolution.

> After completing this section, you will be able to
>
> - **explain** why theories of evolution continue to change.
> - **interpret** graphs showing patterns in the rate of evolution of species.

Figure 16-16

A mother pig and her litter of piglets. Notice how different the piglets are from the mother and each other.

You have learned that genes combine with other genes each time sexual reproduction occurs. Half of the male parent's genes are present in the sperm. Half of the female parent's genes are present in the egg. Each time sperm and egg join, new combinations of genes come about. Such new combinations of genes are one reason for the differences among organisms.

Mutations are another cause of the differences among organisms. Recall that mutations are changes in genes or

OBJECTIVES

Observe and **record** how traits vary within a species.

Construct a graph to show how often a trait occurs.

MATERIALS

20 leaves collected from several trees of the same species, metric ruler

PROCEDURE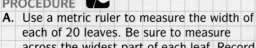

A. Use a metric ruler to measure the width of each of 20 leaves. Be sure to measure across the widest part of each leaf. Record each measurement to the nearest .25 cm. That is, record measurements such as 4.0 cm, 4.25 cm, 4.5 cm, and 4.75 cm.

B. Use the measurements to make a bar graph similar to the one shown.

C. Find the average width of all the leaves. To find the average add all of the measurements and divide by 20.

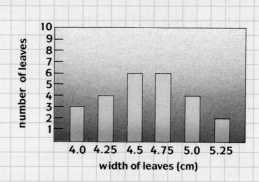

RESULTS AND CONCLUSIONS

1. What is the width of the narrowest leaf? Of the widest leaf? What is the average width of all the leaves?

2. What width occurs most often?

3. Under what conditions might small leaves be helpful to survival? Under what conditions might large leaves be an aid to survival?

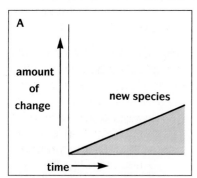

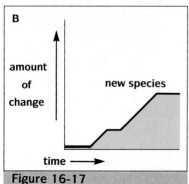

Figure 16-17

Gradual changes occur in a species over a long period of time (A). Sudden changes occur in a species over a short period (B).

chromosomes. Some mutations lead to new adaptations. Organisms with new adaptations may be naturally selected. They may be more likely to survive and reproduce than other members of their species. Thus the new adaptation will be passed on to future generations.

PATTERNS OF CHANGE

The theory of evolution by natural selection suggests that changes come about gradually, over time. In some cases, fossils seem to show that such gradual changes have occurred. The development of long-legged animals on prairies may be an example of gradual change. The graph in Figure 16-17A represents this pattern of evolution.

Other sets of fossils show a different pattern of change. Look at the graph in Figure 16-17B. Find a part of the graph that shows no change over a long period of time. Find another place on the graph where much change takes place in a short time. Some sets of fossils show this pattern of sudden change. A species may show little change over a period of many millions of years. Then in a short period of time, a major change occurs in the species. There is no sure explanation of why such rapid changes take place. Perhaps natural selection can explain both gradual and rapid changes in organisms. Perhaps conditions such as sudden changes in climate may also cause rapid change.

REVIEW

1. What two things about evolution did Darwin's theory not explain?
2. Describe two patterns in the rate of evolution of species.

CHALLENGE All the members of a certain species are identical. There is a sudden change in climate in the area in which this species lives. Predict two things that might happen.

CHAPTER SUMMARY

The main ideas in this chapter are listed below. Read these statements before you answer the Chapter Review questions.

- Living things have adaptations that allow them to survive in certain environments. New combinations of genes and mutations are causes of change that may result in adaptations. (16-1)

- Fossils, which are often found in sedimentary rock, are formed in a variety of ways. Some fossils are found in sap, in tar, in amber, and frozen in ice. Fossils give evidence that organisms have changed greatly or become extinct over time. (16-2)

- The age of fossils is found by radioactive dating and other methods. Learning the age of fossils allows scientists to describe the history of life on the earth. Geologists have divided the earth's his-

tory into eras based on differences in forms of life that existed in the past. (16-3)

- Jean B. Lamarck's theory of evolution by acquired characteristics has been rejected by modern scientists. After studying life forms all around the world, Charles Darwin proposed the theory of evolution by natural selection. (16-4)

- Darwin's theory of evolution by natural selection is accepted by nearly all biologists today. The study of genetics has explained why individuals in a species differ from each other. Fossils show different patterns in the rate of evolution of species. Some changes are gradual and some are sudden. (16-5)

The key terms in this chapter are listed below. Use each term in a sentence that shows the meaning of the term.

adaptation	evolution	fossil	mutation	radioactive dating
era	extinct	half-life	natural selection	radioactive element

Chapter Review

VOCABULARY

Use the key terms from this chapter to complete the following sentences correctly.

1. A major division of geologic time is called a/an _____ .

2. A/An _____ is an element whose atoms change to other kinds of atoms, giving off particles and energy in the process.

3. The process of change that occurs over time in species of living things is called _____ .

4. A/An _____ is a trait that allows an organism to get along better in its environment.

5. The time it takes for half of the atoms of a radioactive element to change is called its _____ .

6. A/An _____ is a change in an organism's genes or chromosomes.

7. The idea of evolution by _____ was developed by Darwin and Wallace.

8. _____ is a method for finding the age of fossils.

9. Species of organisms of the past that no longer exist are _____ .

10. A/An _____ is a trace of a once-living organism.

CONCEPTS

1. What is an adaptation? Give three examples. (16-1)

2. Explain why a mutation in a body cell cannot be passed on to an organism's offspring. (16-1)

3. How does sexual reproduction contribute to evolution? (16-1)

4. How do mutations contribute to evolution? (16-1)

5. What is the difference between a mold and a cast? (16-2)

6. What is sedimentary rock? Why is this type of rock important in the study of past life? (16-2)

7. Describe one current hypothesis of how dinosaurs became extinct. (16-2)

8. Why are fossils important in the study of evolution? What do fossils tell about life of the past? (16-2)

9. Identify one direct way and one indirect way of finding the age of a fossil. (16-3)

10. Why are different radioactive elements used in dating fossils of different ages? (16-3)

11. Name the four eras in the geologic history of the earth. (16-3)

12. How are the four eras of the geologic history of the earth distinguished from each other? (16-3)

13. Using giraffes as an example, explain Lamarck's theory of evolution.

14. Both Lamarck and Darwin lacked certain information when they proposed their theories. What information did they lack? (16-4)

15. Why were the Galápagos Islands important to Darwin's work? (16-4)

16. Explain how overproduction relates to evolution by natural selection. (16-4)

17. What has been learned from genetics that helps to explain differences among living things? (16-4)

18. Briefly describe the theory of evolution by natural selection. (16-4)

19. Explain how mutations may lead to the formation of organisms that are naturally selected. (16-5)

20. Describe two major patterns in the rate at which species change. (16-5)

---

1. How is the human hand adapted for using tools?

2. Fossil footprints often are found in places that were once the banks of rivers or the edges of lakes. Explain why.

3. What would Lamarck have predicted about the muscles of the children of a weight lifter? Why is this prediction incorrect?

EXTENSION

1. Use Table 16-1 as the basis for making a poster. Each of the four eras shown in Table 16-1 can be divided into smaller units of time called *periods* and *epochs*. Research the names and dates of the periods and epochs. In your poster include these dates and names, as well as drawings of organisms present in each time period.

2. Find out what is meant by the term *ice age*. How many ice ages have there been? What effect did ice ages have on humans and other life forms?

3. Write a brief biography of Charles Darwin. He wrote about many subjects in addition to evolution. Find out about the subject matter of some of his books and include this information.

READINGS

Colbert, Edwin. *Dinosaurs: An Illustrated History*. Maplewood, N.J.: Hammond, Inc., 1983.

Halstead, L. B. *The Search for the Past*. New York: Doubleday and Co., 1982.

Miller, Jonathan. *Darwin for Beginners*. New York: Pantheon Books, 1982.

Have you ever seen photographs of wild oxen? Through years of breeding, certain modern species of cows were developed from this older species. Animal breeders have developed several types of farm animals by studying the traits of many oxen and then carefully selecting which animals to breed.

Animal breeders work to improve animal breeds. Their work has produced cattle that yield more meat, cows that give more milk, chickens that lay more eggs, and animals that are resistant to some types of diseases.

Animal breeders work on farms and ranches. Some work on special farms run by the government. They also work at universities. Some animal breeders are trained on farms. Others receive a college degree and an advanced degree. If you are interested in this career, you should take biology and chemistry courses in high school.■

Animal Breeder

You have learned a lot about how traits are inherited. How are patterns of inheritance determined? Geneticists are researchers who study inheritance.

Many geneticists work with small organisms such as bacteria and yeasts. The information they obtain from these organisms can be applied to other organisms. Geneticists plan and carry out experiments, then record and analyze results. Geneticists working with crops have developed improved varieties of foods, such as corn and wheat.

New hybrid fruits and vegetables have also been produced.

Geneticists work for the government, for universities, and for industries. Their training varies but includes a four-year college degree in biology or genetics. An advanced degree is required for some jobs. If you are interested in how traits are inherited and in a career as a geneticist, you should take biology and chemistry courses in high school.■

Geneticist

Dr. Barbara McClintock, Geneticist

Dr. Barbara McClintock is a geneticist who won a Nobel Prize in 1983 for her work. Although she began her work about 40 years ago, many scientists did not accept Dr. McClintock's results and conclusions until recently.

Dr. McClintock studied mutations in corn. She noted that sometimes the color of offspring corn kernels was different from that of the parent kernels. She examined corn cells and found they contained small bits of chromosomes. Dr. McClintock hypothesized that the bits of chromosomes moved about. She suggested that the bits joined other chromosomes in the cells. She thought that the presence of the chromosome bits in cells resulted in the changed color of the corn.

These bits of chromosomes are now known as transposons. They are being studied by many geneticists. Dr. McClintock is a pioneer in the understanding of this aspect of genetics.■

Issues and Technology

For thousands of years, people have been breeding plants and animals for desired traits. This practice began long before the basis for heredity was known. Only in the last half century have scientists learned that an organism's traits are controlled by genes made up of DNA.

As they have learned more about genetics, scientists have developed techniques to change genetic material within cells. Scientists have been able to isolate genes. They also have been able to move genes from one cell to another and from one species to another. For example, in 1981, scientists moved a gene from a french bean seed into a sunflower.

This new technology, known as genetic engineering, shows great promise in areas such as medi-cine and farming. New drugs might be developed. Stronger, healthier animals might be bred. Better, more nutritious crops might be grown.

But some people are worried about genetic engineering. They wonder what would happen if sci-entists accidentally released a dangerous new organism into the environment. Because of such concerns, in 1976 the National Institutes of Health (NIH) began to control genetic engineering. Figure 1 shows a time line on the development of the control of traits in plants and animals.

APPLYING CRITICAL THINKING SKILLS

1. How long ago did the domes-tication of animals occur? How long ago did the domes-tication of plants occur?
2. When were the first rules of genetics established?
3. In which century did most advances in genetics occur?
4. How long after scientists learned that genes are made up of DNA was the first gene cloned?
5. Why did the National Insti-tutes of Health develop ge-netic engineering guidelines?
6. Many times, technologies be-come widely used before the problems they can cause are understood. Should the rate at which new developments are put into use be con-trolled? Why or why not?

Disease, insect pests, and sur-prise frosts destroy or damage millions of dollars worth of farm crops each year. Genetic en-gineering could reduce much of

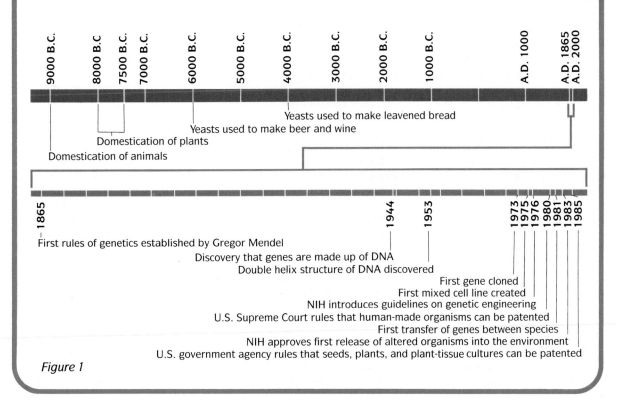

Figure 1

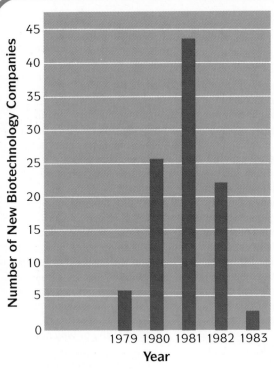

Figure 2A

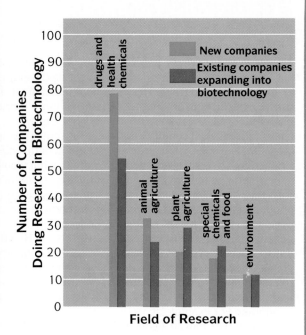

Figure 2B

this loss. For example, genetic engineers reported in May 1986 that they had given some plants hereditary resistance to viral infection. The researchers took a gene from a virus that attacks tomato and tobacco plants. They transferred the gene to some cells of these plants. These cells then grew into plants resistant to the virus. Scientists hope that the same process can be used to make other crops, such as potatoes and green peppers, resistant to viruses.

Scientists also are working on genetically altered microorganisms that can be used to kill insect pests. An insect pest called a rootworm lives on the roots of corn plants. A certain kind of bacteria also lives on these roots. Scientists have engineered the bacteria to produce a protein that is deadly to the rootworms.

Many different products could be made by using genetically al-tered organisms. Because of this, many companies have sprung up to produce and sell these products. Figure 2 shows the increase in the number of biotechnology companies from 1979 to 1983. *Biotechnology* refers to genetic engineering and other techniques that use microorganisms. The figure also shows the number of new and existing companies involved in different areas of genetic engineering. The same company may be involved in more than one field of biotechnology research.

APPLYING CRITICAL THINKING SKILLS

1. Look at Figure 2A. In which year did the greatest number of new companies form? In which year did the least number of new companies form?
2. Why, do you think, did the number of new companies formed after 1981 decrease?
3. Do you think the number of new companies will increase or decrease over the next 10 years? Explain your answer.
4. Look at Figure 2B. In which field is the greatest amount of research going on? Why, do you think, is this so?
5. Do you think the amount of research in each field is a good use of money and research time? Which fields should get more interest? Which should get less? Explain your answers.

Genetic engineering has many possible uses. In addition to improving farming, it may lead to cures for cancer, a vaccine for AIDS, new kinds of drugs, and new sources of chemicals. But some people worry that this technology could lead to serious problems if the work is not done slowly and carefully.

One concern about genetic engineering is that an altered bacterium or virus could get out of control in the environment. An organism made in the laboratory may have no natural enemies in the outside environment. Thus there would be nothing to control the population growth of such an organism. Most genetic engineers say that they are working with relatively weak and harmless organisms. And the researchers say that there are safeguards to prevent the escape of organisms from the laboratory into the environment.

But people who oppose genetic engineering point to past cases when foreign organisms were introduced with ill effects. Both the Japanese beetle and the gypsy moth were brought into the United States for useful purposes. The populations of these insects grew rapidly, and they became pests.

Many times in the past, the use of a new technology or substance has had unexpected effects. The development of resistance to insecticides among insects is one example of this. *Insecticides* are chemicals that are used to kill insects. Between 1970 and 1980, the number of species resistant to insecticides climbed from 224 to 428. Figure 3 shows the distribution of some insects that have become resistant to a certain insecticide. Some scientists fear that a similar problem could happen with genetically engineered organisms.

APPLYING CRITICAL THINKING SKILLS

1. Which resistant insect is more likely to spread out and cover new areas, the mosquito or the cattle tick? Explain your answer.

2. Suppose you were a farmer. If you were offered a choice between using insecticides or using genetically altered organisms to control pests, which method would you choose? Why? What are some of the factors you would consider before making a choice?

3. Consider the possible benefits and risks of genetic engineering. Do you think scientists should change the genes of living things? Why or why not?

4. The decisions about genetic engineering are being made by scientists, the government, and companies that have invested a lot of money in the process. Should the public be involved in the decision-making process? If so, who should represent the public interest?

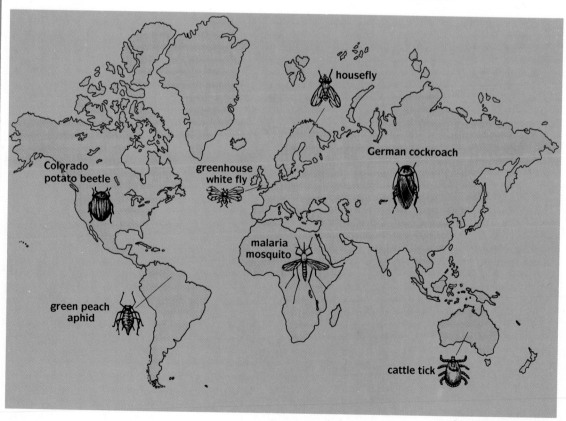

Figure 3

THE HUMAN BODY

*S*cience fiction movies sometimes show robots with human form. Often these machines are portrayed as having superhuman abilities. But the human body can do more than any machine. Can you think of a machine that can cook, paint, throw a baseball, sing, and play the violin? As you study this unit, you will learn about the many complex systems that make up the human body. You will also find out how these systems are coordinated. ■

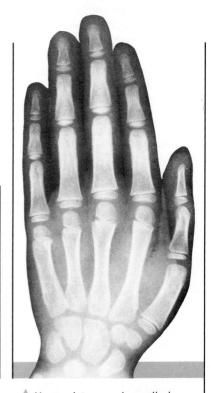

▲ *X-ray pictures, also called radiographs, have been widely used in medicine. This X-ray is of a human hand.*

▼ *This scanning electron micrograph shows human taste buds. These tiny projections cover the surface of the tongue.*

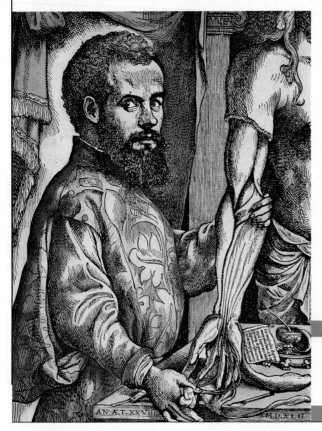

◄ *Andreas Vesalius, a sixteenth-century physician, was one of the first to study and describe human anatomy.*

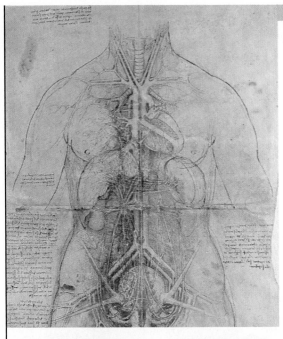

This drawing, done in 1510 by the famous Italian artist Leonardo da Vinci, shows the internal anatomy of a woman.

This modern-looking sculpture is a model of the twisted ladder structure of a DNA molecule.

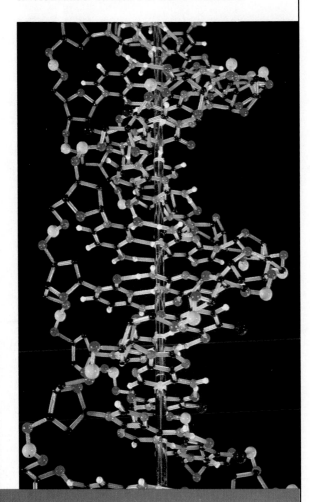

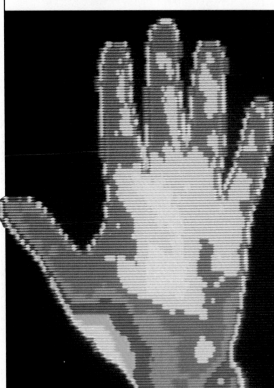

An infrared thermogram of a human hand records the heat given off by different types of tissue. The coolest areas appear in blue. The hottest areas appear red.

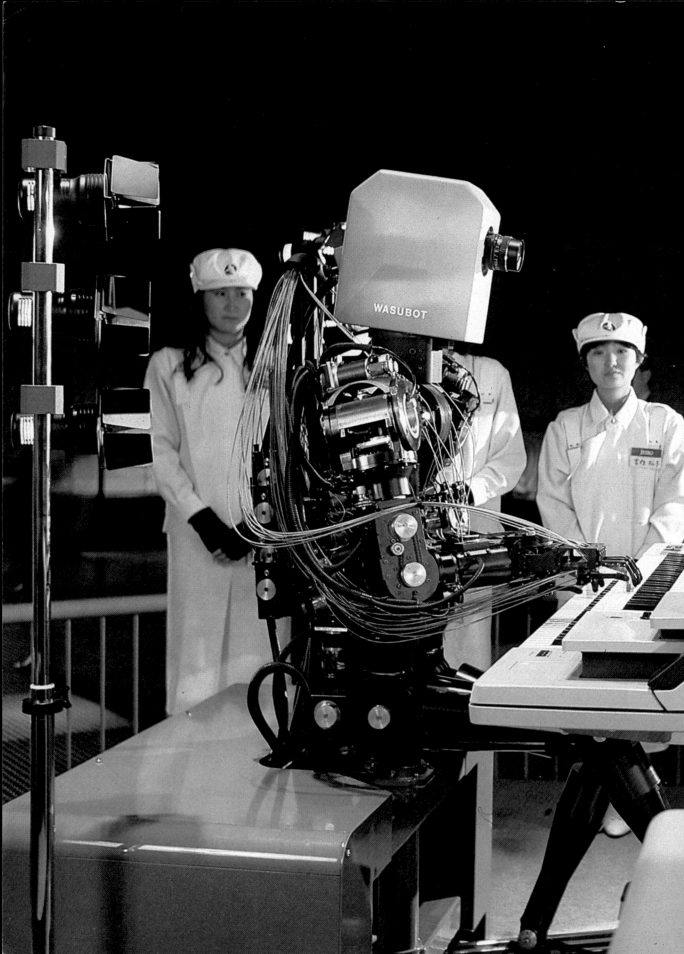

SUPPORT, MOVEMENT, AND BODY COVERING

Have you ever attended a concert given by a robot? The musician in the photograph is directed by an electronic brain. Its movements are controlled by electronic circuits. Do you think that music played by robots sounds as good as music played by humans?

There is still no machine that can do as many different things as a human being. The structure of the human body is very complex. No robot has been invented that can equal the abilities and skills of humans.

- *How is the human body organized?*
- *What gives the body its form?*
- *How does the body move?*

17-1 ORGANIZATION OF THE HUMAN BODY

The human body is made of trillions of cells. These cells have different shapes, sizes, and functions. The cells are organized into different types of tissues. A **tissue** is a group of cells that are similar in structure and function. The cells of a tissue work together to perform a specific job. The human body contains four basic types of tissues. Refer to Figure 17-1 on the next page as you read about each type of tissue.

Epithelial (ehp uh THEE lee uhl) **tissue** is made up of sheets of cells that cover and protect the inner and outer surfaces of the body. Epithelial tissue is made of epithelial cells that vary in structure, depending on where they are found. Your skin is made of many layers of epithelial cells. The inner surfaces of the intestines are lined with tall, columnlike epithelial cells.

Muscle tissue is made of muscle cells that can contract, or become shorter. Body movement is caused by the action of muscle tissue. All muscles in the human body are made of muscle tissue. Muscle tissue is also found in the heart, stomach, and other structures in the body.

Nerve tissue is made of long, branched nerve cells that carry messages throughout the body. Nerve tissue

---

After completing this section, you will be able to

- **distinguish** among tissues, organs, and organ systems.
- **describe** the four main kinds of tissues.
- **name** the major organ systems of the body.

The key terms in this section are

connective tissue
epithelial tissue
muscle tissue
nerve tissue
organ
organ system
tissue

---

epi- (on)

Table 17-1 *Organ Systems: Major Organs and Functions*

Skeletal System	Muscular System	Skin	Digestive System	Respiratory System
Major Organs	**Major Organs**	**Major Organs**	**Major Organs**	**Major Organs**
Bones	Muscles	Skin	Mouth, esophagus, stomach, liver, pancreas, intestines	Lungs, trachea, larynx, bronchi
Functions	**Functions**	**Functions**	**Functions**	**Functions**
Supports, permits movement, protects, stores minerals, produces blood cells	Produces movement of body parts, aids in digestion and circulation	Protects, prevents drying out, removes some wastes, helps to regulate body temperature	Breaks down food (prepares food for absorption into blood)	Exchanges oxygen and carbon dioxide

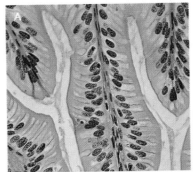
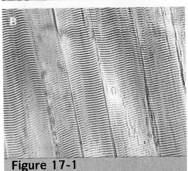
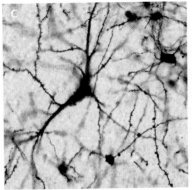
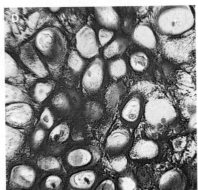

enables you to hear, smell, taste, touch, and see. The brain, nerves, and spinal cord are made of nerve tissue.

Connective tissue joins and supports different parts of the body. The human body has many different kinds of connective tissue. Connective tissue may be fluid or solid. Blood, bone, cartilage, and fat are four types of connective tissue. Each type of connective tissue is made of cells of various shapes and sizes.

Just as cells are organized into tissues, tissues are organized into organs. An **organ** is a group of two or more different tissues that work together and perform a certain

Figure 17-1

Four types of tissue: epithelial (*A*), muscle (*B*), nerve (*C*), and connective (*D*).

Circulatory System	Excretory System	Endocrine System	Nervous System	Reproductive System
Major Organs	**Major Organs**	**Major Organs**	**Major Organs**	**Major Organs**
Heart, blood vessels	Kidneys, lungs, skin	Endocrine glands	Nerves, brain, spinal cord	Ovaries, testes
Functions	**Functions**	**Functions**	**Functions**	**Functions**
Transports materials throughout body	Removes waste products	Regulates chemical activity in body	Receives and transports messages throughout body, coordinates body parts	Produces reproductive cells

function. The heart, liver, stomach, brain, and eyes are organs. The eyes, for example, are made of muscle, nerve, connective, and epithelial tissues. These same tissues working together enable you to lift your pencil off your desk and write your name.

Organs are arranged in organ systems. An **organ system** is a group of organs that work together and perform one or more specific functions. The human body has several organ systems. The organ systems, their functions, and the major organs in each system are shown in Table 17-1. Which organ systems allow movement?

REVIEW

1. How are cells, tissues, organs, and organ systems related to each other?
2. Describe the four types of tissues found in the human body.
3. Distinguish between an organ and an organ system.
4. Give three examples of organ systems and describe the function of each.

CHALLENGE Name every kind of tissue that is used in tossing a ball, and explain how you know these kinds of tissues are needed to perform this task.

17-2 THE HUMAN SKELETON

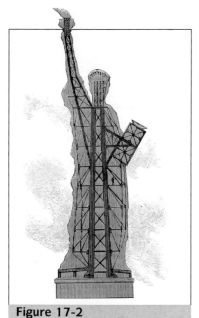

Figure 17-2

The iron framework inside the Statue
of Liberty. How is this framework like
a skeleton?

FUNCTIONS OF THE SKELETON

Figure 17-2 shows the iron framework inside the Statue of Liberty. To build the statue, the framework was constructed first and then was covered with a "skin" of copper. Like the statue, the human body also has a framework—the skeleton. The **skeleton** is the structural framework that supports the body and protects the internal organs. The human skeleton is made up of 206 bones. The bones of the skeleton are organized into a skeletal system. The **skeletal system** is made up of bones, joints, and connective tissue that help to support, move, and protect the body.

The skeleton has several important functions. The skeleton provides the support and basic shape of the body. Without a skeleton the body would be a shapeless mound of tissue. The skeleton also protects the soft organs of the body. For example, part of the skull forms an internal helmet that protects the soft tissue of the brain. The ribs are like a stiff vest that protects the lungs. The skeleton also functions in the movement of the body. The bones of the skeleton are the framework to which muscles are attached. Muscles and bones work together to move the parts of the body. Another function of some bones is to enclose *marrow,* which is a blood-forming tissue. Bones also store minerals, such as calcium and phosphorus. These minerals keep bones and teeth strong.

BONES OF THE SKELETON

Some of the major bones of the skeleton are shown in Figure 17-3. The skull is the part of the skeleton that surrounds and protects the brain. The skull is made up of the bones of the head and the face. The helmet-shaped part of the skull that encloses the brain is the *cranium.*

The *spinal column,* or backbone, is a series of small bones that enclose and protect the spinal cord. The spinal cord is made up of delicate nerve tissue. The 33 small ring-shaped bones that make up the spinal column are called *vertebrae* (VER tuh bree). The spinal column runs down the middle of the back from the base of the skull to the hip area. The main upright support for the body is provided by the spinal column.

The curved bones attached to the spinal column are the *ribs.* The human body has 12 pairs of ribs. Several pairs of ribs are joined by connective tissue to the *sternum,* or breastbone. The sternum is a narrow, flat bone in the

Figure 17-3

Bones of the human skeleton.

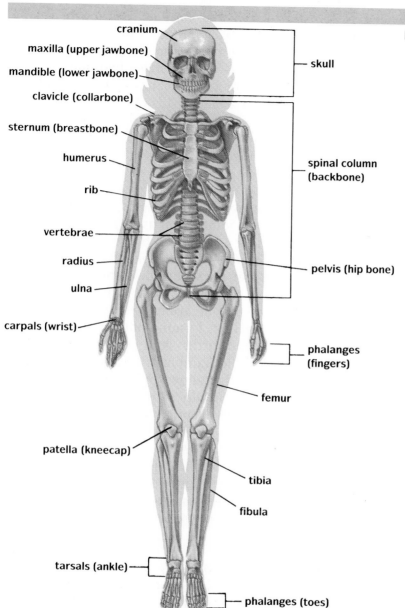

cranium

maxilla (upper jawbone)

mandible (lower jawbone)

clavicle (collarbone)

sternum (breastbone)

humerus

rib

vertebrae

radius

ulna

carpals (wrist)

patella (kneecap)

tarsals (ankle)

skull

spinal column (backbone)

pelvis (hip bone)

phalanges (fingers)

femur

tibia

fibula

phalanges (toes)

middle of the chest. Locate this bone in Figure 17-3. The ribs and sternum protect the heart and lungs.

The bowl-shaped bone at the hips is called the *pelvis.* The shape of the pelvis enables this bone to support the weight of the body. The pelvis also protects the reproductive organs inside the female body.

The bones of the arms and legs are called long bones because of their length. The long bones also help to support the weight of the body. Look again at Figure 17-3. What are the names of the long bones of the legs?

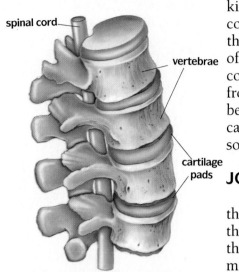

spinal cord

vertebrae

cartilage pads

Figure 17-4

Pads of cartilage between the vertebrae.

SCIENCE PUZZLER

You are asked to design a robot that can wash dishes. Decide which movements the robot must perform to complete the task of washing dishes. Then determine which kinds of joints the robot must have. Prepare a sketch of the robot, showing all movements that these joints can allow.

In addition to bone the skeleton also contains other kinds of tissue. Recall that cartilage is a tough, flexible connective tissue. Cartilage is found in several places in the body. The outer ear and the tip of the nose are formed of cartilage. Cartilage is found wherever two or more bones come together. It cushions the bones and prevents them from rubbing together. Small pads of cartilage are found between the vertebrae that form the spinal column. These cartilage pads, shown in Figure 17-4, act as shock absorbers in the spinal column.

JOINTS

A place where two or more bones come together in the skeleton is called a **joint**. What tissue at a joint prevents the bones from rubbing against each other? The body has three basic types of joints—fixed, partially movable, and movable. A joint that does not allow the movement of bones is called a *fixed joint*. A fixed joint is like a seam between two bones that lie against each other. Bones at fixed joints fuse together, forming one immovable bone. Fixed joints are found in the skull and the pelvis. How do the fixed joints of the cranium provide extra protection to the brain? A joint that allows only a small amount of movement is called a *partially movable joint*. Examples of such joints are found in the spinal column, where vertebra meets vertebra.

A joint that allows full movement of bones is called a *movable joint*. The movement possible is greater than that allowed by partially movable joints. Movable joints are found at the knees, elbows, wrists, ankles, neck, shoulders, and hips. Bones at movable joints are held together by ligaments. **Ligaments** are strong bands of connective tissues that hold two or more bones together at joints. Body parts can move in different ways because there are different kinds of movable joints. Figure 17-5 shows the location of some of the movable and fixed joints in your body.

A **ball-and-socket joint** is a joint that allows movement in almost all directions. The end of one bone in a ball-and-socket joint is rounded. This rounded end fits into the hollow part of the next bone. The shoulders and hips contain ball-and-socket joints. Look closely at the shoulder joint in Figure 17-5. Which bone contains the "ball" of the ball-and-socket joint?

A **hinge joint** is a joint that allows movement in only one direction. Knees and elbows are formed of hinge joints that allow bending movement. The movement of a hinge

Figure 17-5

Types of joints in the human body.

joint is similar to the movement of a door that is swinging on its hinges.

The skull is connected to the spinal column by a pivot joint. A **pivot joint** is a joint that allows rotating movement from side to side. The pivot joint in the neck is located between the first and second vertebrae. What movements does the pivot joint in the neck allow?

A **gliding joint** is a joint that allows sliding movements. The movement allowed is a simple gliding back and forth or sideways. These joints are found between the small bones of the wrists and ankles.

REVIEW

1. What are the main functions of the skeleton?
2. Which bone or bones protect the heart? The brain? The lungs? The spinal cord?
3. Explain the differences between a fixed joint, a partially movable joint, and a movable joint.

CHALLENGE Suppose a person had a disease in which the bones could not store calcium. What would be the effect on the skeleton?

17-3 STRUCTURE AND GROWTH OF BONE

After completing this section, you will be able to

- **describe** the structure of a long bone.
- **describe** the function of marrow.

The key term in this section is **marrow**

STRUCTURE OF BONE

Bone contains living tissue and nonliving material. The living tissue includes bone cells, cartilage, blood, blood vessels, nerves, and fat. The nonliving parts are water, protein, and minerals such as calcium and phosphorus.

The bones of the human body are of several different types. Long bones are found in the arms and legs. Short bones form the wrists and ankles. Flat bones are found in the ribs and shoulders. Irregular bones include the vertebrae and certain bones of the skull. Although bones in the skeleton have many different sizes and shapes, they all have the same basic structure. Figure 17-6 shows the structure of a long bone of the leg.

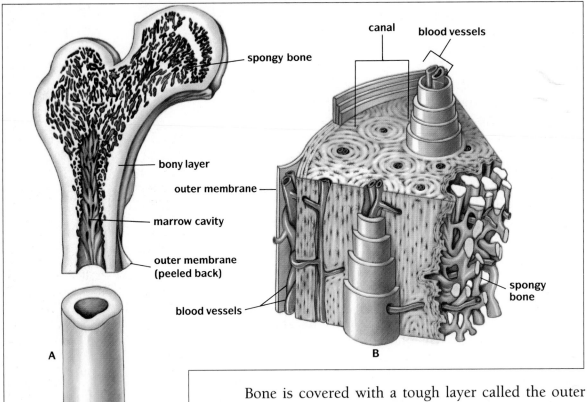

Figure 17-6

Structure of a long bone. Section of long bone (*A*); enlargement of a section of long bone (*B*).

Bone is covered with a tough layer called the outer membrane. The outer membrane contains many living blood vessels. Just beneath the outer membrane is the bony layer. The bony layer is very hard and strong. It contains living bone cells surrounded by deposits of calcium and phosphorus. At the ends of the bone, the bony layer contains many air spaces. The bony layer containing large air spaces is called *spongy bone*. In the center of the bone is a hollow space, or cavity. The cavity contains a tissue

OBJECTIVE

Observe the structure of a long bone.

MATERIALS

uncooked long bone of lamb cut in half along its length, hand lens

PROCEDURE

A. Examine a long bone of lamb with a hand lens. Look at the outer, uncut surface first. Notice the cartilage covering the ends of the bone.
  1. How does the cartilage function at the joint?

B. Turn the bone over and examine its internal structure. Most of the bone is composed of the bony layer. Find the area of spongy bone at each end.

C. Locate the marrow along the length of the bone.
  2. What color is it?

RESULTS AND CONCLUSIONS

1. Make a sketch of the cut surface of the bone you examined. Label the bony layer, spongy bone, marrow, and cartilage.
2. How does the tissue at the ends of the bone differ from the tissue in the middle?

called marrow. **Marrow** (MAR oh), a soft tissue inside bone, contains blood vessels and living blood-forming cells. Blood in the blood vessels carries food and oxygen to the bone cells. The blood also carries away wastes. The blood vessels reach the bone cells through a system of canals.

Two types of marrow are found within bone: *red marrow* and *yellow marrow*. In infants, all bones contain only red marrow. From about five years of age, the red marrow in some bones is replaced by yellow marrow. Red marrow is a tissue that produces red blood cells. In adults, red marrow is found in bones at the base of the skull, in the vertebrae, in the ribs and sternum, and at the ends of some long bones. The other bones of the skeleton contain yellow marrow. Yellow marrow is a tissue made of cells that store fat. After severe blood loss, yellow marrow can also produce blood cells.

GROWTH OF BONE

Before birth the body of the developing baby contains very few hard, rigid bones. Instead the skeleton is made up mostly of the strong, flexible connective tissue—cartilage. The cartilage in the body is slowly replaced by bone during the early years of life. Cartilage is replaced by bone as minerals such as calcium and phosphorus take the place of cartilage. The minerals fill in the spaces between the bone cells, making the bones hard and strong.

In an infant there are spaces between the bones of the cranium. The largest opening between the bones in the infant's skull is often referred to as the "soft spot." The bones of the front part of the cranium begin to join by two years of age. By the time a person is an adult, the bones are fully joined at fixed joints.

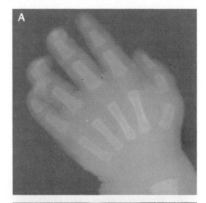

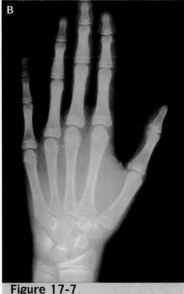

Figure 17-7

X rays of an infant's hand (*A*) and the hand of a 12-year-old (*B*). The white areas are bone. Which X ray shows more bone?

ACTIVITY How Can the Composition of Bone Be Tested?

OBJECTIVES
Compare untreated bone with bones from which components have been removed.
Draw conclusions about the functions of various components of bone.

MATERIALS
3 raw cleaned chicken leg bones, beaker, vinegar, balance, baking pan, oven, tongs

PROCEDURE

A. Examine a chicken bone. Try to bend it gently.
B. Place the bone you have just examined into a beaker. Add enough vinegar to cover the bone. Allow the bone to soak in the vinegar for 5 days. The vinegar removes calcium and other minerals from the bone.
C. After 5 days, rinse the vinegar-soaked bone in water. Try to bend this bone. Note and record its texture.
D. Examine another chicken bone. Using a balance, find the mass of the bone. Note and record its mass, texture, and color.

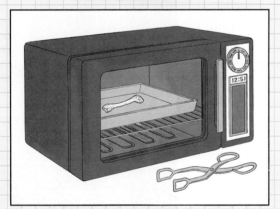

Place this bone in a pan and put it in an oven set at 400°F. Keep the bone in the oven for 4 hours. Heating the bone removes water, which makes up a large part of the membranes, blood vessels, and marrow.
E. Use a pair of tongs to remove the bone from the oven. Allow the bone to cool. When it has cooled, examine the bone. Note and record its color and texture. Using a balance, find the mass of the bone. Record this figure.
F. Now examine an untreated bone. Try to bend it gently. Note and record its color and texture.
G. Compare the vinegar-soaked bone with the untreated bone examined in step **F**. Note and record any differences between the two bones.
H. Compare the heated bone with the untreated bone. Note and record any differences.

RESULTS AND CONCLUSIONS
1. Describe how the bone looked after it had been soaked in vinegar. How did the vinegar-soaked bone compare with the untreated bone?
2. How did the vinegar change the composition of the bone?
3. Describe how the bone looked after it had been heated and then cooled. How did the mass of the heated bone compare with that of the untreated bone?
4. How did heating change the composition of the bone?
5. Why did this activity include one bone that was not treated in any way?
6. How are calcium and other minerals important to the function of bone?

REVIEW
1. Describe the parts of a long bone.
2. Distinguish between the function of red marrow and yellow marrow.
3. How does bone replace cartilage?

CHALLENGE Why is it important for children, including babies, to have foods that contain calcium and phosphorus? Considering the diet of most infants, what food is high in these minerals?

17-4 THE MUSCULAR SYSTEM

In everything you do, you use muscles. When you run, muscles move your arms and legs. When you breathe, muscles cause your lungs to fill with air and then to expel carbon dioxide and water vapor. When blood flows through your body, heart muscle provides the push. When you sit quietly in a chair reading a book, eye muscles move your eyes from side to side as you read. When you eat, muscles help you chew, swallow, and move food through your digestive system.

The human body has over 600 different muscles. The **muscular system** is made up of all the muscles in the body that produce movement of body parts. The major muscles of the body and their functions are shown in Figure 17-8. In an adult female, muscles make up about 30 percent of the total body mass. In an adult male, muscles make up about 40 percent of the total body mass.

> *After completing this section, you will be able to*
>
> - **compare** and **contrast** voluntary muscle and involuntary muscle.
> - **distinguish** between skeletal muscle, smooth muscle, and cardiac muscle.
>
> *The key terms in this section are*
> cardiac muscle
> involuntary muscle
> muscular system
> skeletal muscle
> smooth muscle
> voluntary muscle

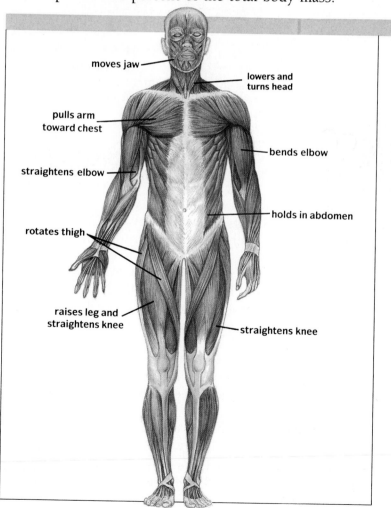

moves jaw

lowers and turns head

pulls arm toward chest

bends elbow

straightens elbow

holds in abdomen

rotates thigh

raises leg and straightens knee

straightens knee

Figure 17-8

Major muscles of the human body and their functions.

VOLUNTARY AND INVOLUNTARY MUSCLE

The muscles in the body can be divided into two major groups—voluntary muscles and involuntary muscles. A **voluntary muscle** is a muscle that is under conscious control. For example, you can control the muscles in your arms and legs when you run, walk, jump, swim, or ride a bicycle. The muscles of your arms and legs are voluntary muscles.

An **involuntary muscle** is a muscle that is not under conscious control. Such a muscle works without your thinking about it. Your heart beats all the time without your ever having to think about it. Heart muscle is an example of involuntary muscle.

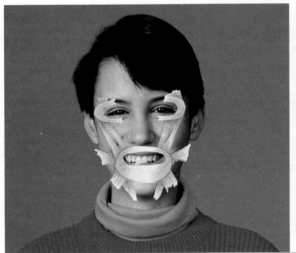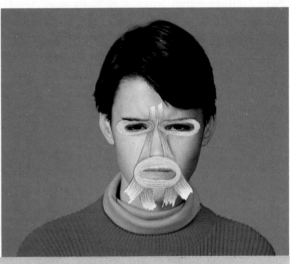

Figure 17-9

Muscles that cause a smile or a frown. Are these muscles voluntary or involuntary?

Some movements controlled by voluntary muscles are not always under conscious control. Blinking your eyes, for example, is caused by the action of voluntary muscles. When you consciously think about blinking, you can control the muscles that cause these movements. At other times you cannot consciously control the muscles that cause blinking. You continue to blink your eyes even when you do not think about these movements. The muscles that cause these movements are controlled by two sets of nerves. One set of nerves regulates conscious control of the muscles. The other set regulates unconscious control.

TYPES OF MUSCLE

Muscles in your body are made of three types of muscle tissue. All three types of muscle tissue are made of muscle cells. The three types of muscle tissue are skeletal muscle, smooth muscle, and cardiac muscle.

Skeletal muscle is the muscle that is attached to and that moves the skeleton. Skeletal muscles, such as those in your arms and legs, are voluntary muscles and are under conscious control. Skeletal muscle has dark bands, or striations, running across the muscle. Locate the dark bands in the skeletal muscle in Figure 17-10A. Each long fiber is a muscle cell.

Smooth muscle is the muscle that makes up the wall of many organs inside the body. Smooth muscles are involuntary muscles. Organs of the digestive system are lined with smooth muscle. The walls of some blood vessels also contain smooth muscle. Notice in Figure 17-10B that smooth muscle does not have striations. The fibers that make up smooth muscle are long and narrow at the ends.

Cardiac (KAHR dee ak) **muscle** is the muscle that makes up the heart. In fact, cardiac muscle is found only in the heart. Cardiac muscle, like smooth muscle, is involuntary. Like skeletal muscle, cardiac muscle also has striations. In Figure 17-10C you can see that cardiac muscle has many light-colored striations, which are separated by darker bands. The short fibers of cardiac muscle are connected to each other, forming a network.

cardio- (heart)

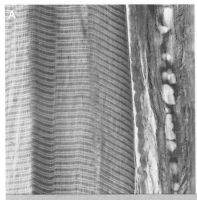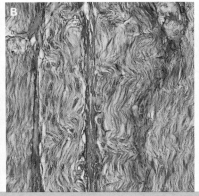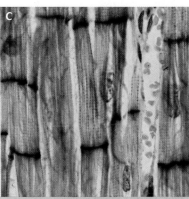

Figure 17-10

Three types of muscle tissue: skeletal (*A*), smooth (*B*), and cardiac (*C*). Which type of muscle is found in the heart?

REVIEW

1. Explain the difference between voluntary and involuntary muscles.
2. Name and describe the three types of muscle tissue.
3. Where is each type of muscle tissue found?
4. How is cardiac muscle like skeletal muscle? How is it different from skeletal muscle?
5. How is cardiac muscle like smooth muscle? How is it different from smooth muscle?

CHALLENGE Identify the problems that would result if cardiac muscle were voluntary instead of involuntary muscle.

17-5 BODY MOVEMENT AND DISORDERS

BODY MOVEMENT

The body moves because of the action of muscles, which are made up of muscle cells. Muscle cells are unique because they are the only cells in the body that can *contract,* or shorten, and *relax,* or lengthen. When a muscle cell relaxes, it returns to its original size. This ability of muscle cells to contract and relax causes movement in the body. Body movements are the result of bones and muscles working together. Bones cannot move by themselves. Only muscles have the ability to move.

Figure 17-11A shows the major muscles in the arm. These muscles are voluntary skeletal muscles. Skeletal muscles are attached to bones by tough bands of connective tissue called **tendons**. Locate the tendons in Figure 17-11A. Identify the hinge joint at the elbow and the biceps muscle in the same figure. Notice that the tendons attach the biceps muscle to the bones on either side of the joint at the elbow. Now locate the triceps muscle. To which bones are the tendons of the triceps muscle attached? Refer back to Figure 17-3, if needed.

ACTIVITY   How Does a Chicken Wing Move?

OBJECTIVE
Examine a chicken wing to **infer** how the muscles, tendons, joints, and bones work together.

MATERIALS
uncooked chicken wing with skin removed, paper towels

PROCEDURE
A. Place the chicken wing on a paper towel.
B. Refer to the drawing to help you locate the muscles, tendons, bones, joints, and cartilage of the chicken wing.
C. Hold the chicken wing at both ends. Slowly bend and straighten the wing several times. Carefully observe the movement of the muscles in the wing.

RESULTS AND CONCLUSIONS
1. Make a drawing of the chicken wing. Label the following parts of the wing: muscles, joint, tendons, bones, and cartilage.
2. Describe the appearance of the tendons.
3. What kind of joint is in the wing?
4. On the drawing of the wing, label which muscles are flexors and which muscles are extensors.
5. Do muscles in a chicken wing work together in pairs to bend and straighten the wing? Make a drawing to explain your answer.

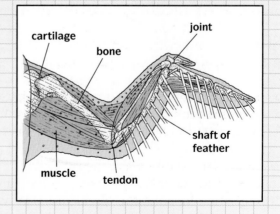

Skeletal muscles usually work in pairs to cause movement. The biceps muscle and triceps muscle work together as a pair to raise and lower the arm. To bend the elbow and raise the lower arm, the biceps muscle contracts, as shown in Figure 17-11A. The contraction, or shortening, of this muscle pulls the lower arm upward. At the same time that the biceps contracts, the triceps relaxes and thus lengthens. To straighten the arm, the triceps muscle contracts. The shortening of the triceps pulls the lower arm downward, as shown in Figure 17-11B. The biceps relaxes at the same time that the triceps contracts. Notice that the pull of muscles on bones causes movement. Muscles always move bones by contracting, never by relaxing.

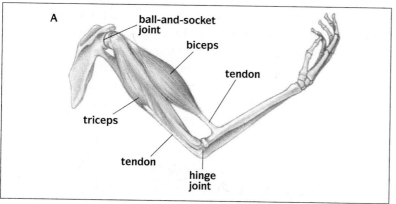

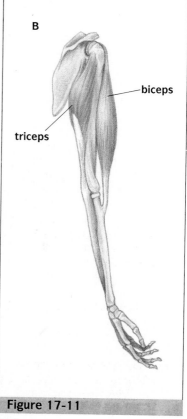

Similar pairs of muscles work together to bend and straighten the legs. A muscle that contracts and causes a part of the body to bend toward the body is called a **flexor** (FLEHK suhr). A muscle that contracts and causes a part of the body to straighten, or move away from the body, is called an **extensor** (ehk STEHN suhr). Look again at Figure 17-11A. Is the biceps a flexor or an extensor?

BONE AND MUSCLE DISORDERS

Injuries to bones and muscles occur quite often. A **sprain** is an injury that occurs when a ligament is stretched or torn away from a joint. Recall that ligaments hold bones together at a movable joint. Sprains often result when the bones at a joint are twisted or pulled suddenly.

Another common injury to the skeleton is a fracture. A **fracture** (FRAK chuhr) is a crack or break in a bone. The most serious type of fracture is an *open fracture*. In the past an open fracture was called a compound fracture. An open fracture occurs when the broken bone is pushed through the skin. In a *closed fracture*, once called a simple fracture, the bone is not pushed through the skin.

Figure 17-11

Major muscles of the arm: arm bent (*A*) and arm extended (*B*). Which muscle contracts when the arm is bent?

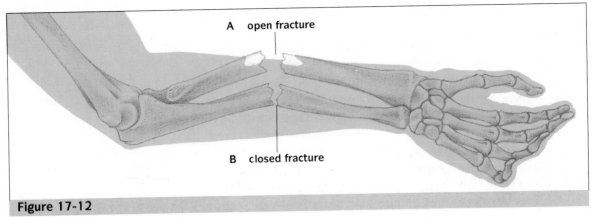

A   open fracture

B   closed fracture

Figure 17-12

Broken arm bones: open fracture (*A*) and closed fracture (*B*).

Figure 17-13

A field hockey player wearing protective equipment.

Suppose a leg or arm is injured near a joint. It is sometimes difficult to determine if the damage is caused by a sprain or by a fracture. Doctors use X rays to locate the cause of the swelling and pain.

Sprains are usually treated by applying ice to the injured area. The ice reduces the swelling and lessens the pain. Ice should be used on and off for 24 to 72 hours. Then heat is applied to speed healing. The area that is sprained should not be used until the pain is gone.

If a bone is fractured, a cast is put around the area. The cast prevents the broken ends of the bone from moving and thus allows proper healing. The cast usually stays on for several weeks until the fracture is healed.

A muscle **cramp** is a painful and involuntary contraction of a muscle. Too much exercise can sometimes cause muscles to cramp. Cramps may also be caused by failing to warm-up before exercising. Rubbing the cramped area can reduce the pain. Muscle cramps usually disappear in a few minutes.

A good way to prevent injury to muscles and bones is to wear the right equipment when playing sports. How does the equipment in Figure 17-13 protect the muscles and bones of the field hockey player?

REVIEW

1. Describe how the action of muscles allows you to bend your arm. Describe how muscle action allows you to straighten your arm.
2. Is the triceps a flexor or an extensor? Explain your answer.
3. What is the difference between a sprain and a fracture?
4. Compare the treatments for a sprain and a fracture.

CHALLENGE Which type of fracture causes the greatest danger to the body? Explain your answer.

17-6 SKIN

The skin is the outer covering of the body. As you read about the parts of the skin, look at the drawing in Figure 17-14. The skin, which consists of several types of tissue, is made of two main layers. The tough outer layer of the skin is the **epidermis** (ehp uh DER mihs). The epidermis is made of epithelial tissue. It consists of two layers of cells. Cells in the outer layer are either dead or dying and are always falling or being rubbed off. This outer layer contains keratin (KEHR uh tihn)—a material that waterproofs the skin.

The inner layer of cells of the epidermis is made of living cells. These living cells contain melanin (MEHL uhnihn). **Melanin** is a brown pigment that colors the skin. People of different races have different amounts of melanin in their skin.

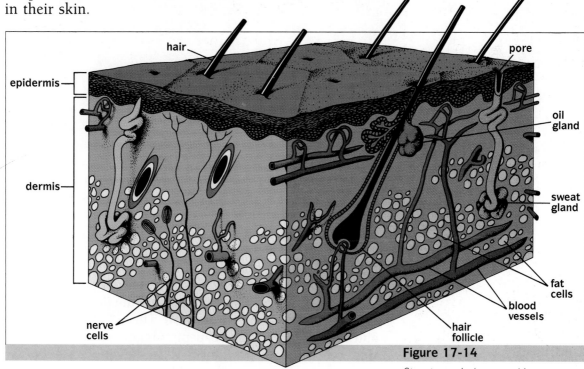

Figure 17-14

Structures in human skin.

All people have a certain amount of melanin in their skin. When the skin is exposed to sunlight, extra melanin is produced. This darkens, or tans, the skin. Melanin helps to protect the skin against the harmful rays of the sun.

The thicker, inner layer of the skin is the **dermis** (DER mihs). The dermis is made of connective tissue. Most of the structures in the skin are found in the dermis. *Sweat glands* are coiled tubes that help to cool the body by giving off moisture. The sweat glands open to the outside of the

SCIENCE & TECHNOLOGY

Each year, about 10,000 people die of severe burns. A burn victim faces two main threats to life: infection and loss of fluids. In a healthy person the skin keeps out disease organisms and keeps in body fluids. A person without a covering of skin lacks this protection.

In the past, burn victims have had some of their skin replaced by skin grafts. These grafts are patches of skin taken from unburned parts of their body. A person with extensive burns, however, does not have enough good skin to supply these grafts. Such a person needs another source of skin.

For years, scientists have worked toward making a material that acts like skin. The artificial skin has to have several important qualities. It must be thin and elastic. It has to allow just the right amount of moisture to enter and leave.

Scientists have made a material that is nearly as good as real skin. From the photograph you can see that the artificial skin looks like moist, elastic paper toweling. It has three main parts — fibers from cowhide, cartilage from sharks, and a rubber called silicone. When joined together in the right way, these substances behave almost like skin. But unlike real skin, artificial skin does not have sweat glands and hair. Artificial skin has already saved the lives of many burn victims.

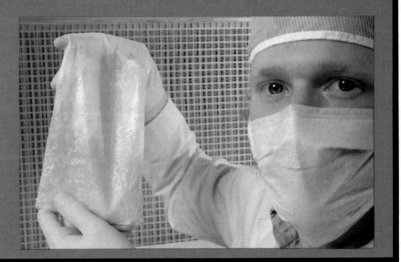

epidermis at openings called *pores*. Locate a pore and a sweat gland in Figure 17-14. The dermis also contains *hair follicles*. Hair follicles are long, deep pockets from which hair grows. Oil glands in the dermis are connected to the hair follicles. Oil from these glands keeps the hair and skin soft. The dermis also contains many blood vessels and nerves. Below the dermis is a layer of fatty tissue.

The skin has many important functions. The main function of the skin is protection. The skin keeps bacteria and many other disease-causing organisms from entering the body and causing illness. The skin protects internal organs by acting as a cushion. Melanin in the skin protects the body from the harmful rays of the sun.

Skin helps to control body temperature. Sweat glands in the skin carry sweat to the surface. Sweat is a liquid that contains water, salt, and some body wastes. When sweat evaporates from the skin, the skin is cooled. At the same time, wastes are removed from the body through the skin. The skin is a sense organ. Nerve cells in the skin allow you to feel heat, cold, pressure, and pain. They also allow you to sense the texture of objects.

REVIEW

1. Describe the two layers of the epidermis.
2. Describe three structures in the dermis.
3. How does sweat help to cool the body?
4. List three functions of the skin.

CHALLENGE   During which season of the year would people in North America produce the most melanin? Explain your answer.

CHAPTER SUMMARY

The main ideas in this chapter are listed below. Read these statements before you answer the Chapter Review questions.

- Cells in the human body are organized into tissues, organs, and organ systems. (17-1)

- The four main types of tissues in the body are epithelial tissue, muscle tissue, nerve tissue, and connective tissue. (17-1)

- The functions of the skeletal system are support, protection, movement, production of blood cells, and the storage of minerals. (17-2)

- The three main types of joints — fixed joints, partially movable joints, and movable joints — allow for movement and protection of the body. (17-2)

- The ball-and-socket joint, gliding joint, hinge joint, and pivot joint are the main types of movable joints. (17-2)

- The human body contains several different types of bones; all bones contain both living and nonliving material. (17-3)

- The muscular system is made up of three main kinds of muscle tissue — skeletal, smooth, and cardiac — that cause the movement of body parts. (17-4)

- Movement of body parts is caused by skeletal muscles working in pairs. (17-5)

- Cramps, sprains, and fractures are injuries of muscles and bones. (17-5)

- The main types of fractures are closed fractures and open fractures. (17-5)

- The functions of the skin are protection, waste removal, temperature regulation, cushioning, and sensation. (17-6)

The key terms in this chapter are listed below. Use each term in a sentence that shows the meaning of the term.

ball-and-socket joint	flexor	melanin	skeletal system
cardiac muscle	fracture	muscle tissue	skeleton
connective tissue	gliding joint	muscular system	smooth muscle
cramp	hinge joint	nerve tissue	sprain
dermis	involuntary muscle	organ	tendon
epidermis	joint	organ system	tissue
epithelial tissue	ligaments	pivot joint	voluntary muscle
extensor	marrow	skeletal muscle	

VOCABULARY

Use the key terms from this chapter to complete the following sentences correctly.

1. The part of a skeleton where two or more bones meet is a/an _____.

2. _____ connect muscles to bones.

3. _____ hold bones together at movable joints.

4. A/An _____ is a group of two or more tissues that work together to perform a specific function.

5. The type of muscle making up the heart is _____ muscle.

6. _____ tissue joins and supports different parts of the body.

7. _____ is a pigment in skin.

8. _____ tissue carries messages throughout the body.

9. _____ is the soft tissue inside bones that contains blood vessels, nerves, and living bone cells.

10. A/An _____ muscle is attached to and moves bones.

CONCEPTS

1. Describe the functions of nerve and connective tissues. (17-1)

2. Compare the functions of epithelial and muscle tissues. (17-1)

3. What is the difference between a tissue, an organ, and an organ system? (17-1)

4. List and briefly describe the functions of the organ systems of the body. (17-1)

5. What are the main functions of the skeleton? (17-2)

6. Give an example of a partially movable joint and a fixed joint. Compare the functions of the two joints named. (17-2)

7. Describe the main structures of a long bone. (17-3)

8. Compare red marrow and yellow marrow. (17-3)

9. Compare the amount of cartilage in an unborn baby's skeleton to the amount of cartilage in an adult's skeleton. (17-3)

10. How does voluntary muscle differ from involuntary muscle? (17-4)

11. Compare the structure of cardiac muscle with the structure of skeletal muscle. (17-4)

12. How do muscle cells differ from other cells in the body? (17-5)

13. Distinguish between a flexor and an extensor. (17-5)

14. Explain how muscles work in pairs. (17-5)

15. Describe how the triceps and biceps muscles work together to bend the arm up and straighten it. (17-5)
16. What is a sprain and what causes it? (17-5)
17. Describe one way to treat a sprain. (17-5)
18. Compare an open fracture and a closed fracture. (17-5)
19. Distinguish between the dermis and the epidermis. (17-6)
20. What are some of the important functions of the skin? (17-6)
21. Explain the function of melanin. (17-6)
22. Compare the functions of sweat glands and oil glands. (17-7)

APPLICATION/
CRITICAL
THINKING

1. The amount of calcium in the bones decreases as a person grows older. How can this information explain why older people suffer many broken bones?
2. Pregnant women are encouraged to eat diets rich in calcium and phosphorus. Give reasons for this type of diet.
3. The thickness of the outer layer of the epidermis varies a great deal from one part of the body to another. Give an example of a part of the body where the outer epidermis is thick and a part where it is thin. Give reasons for these differences.
4. Cardiac muscle, unlike smooth or skeletal muscle, has fibers that form a network. What is the advantage of this structure in cardiac muscle?
5. The casts used to treat fractures were normally made of plaster. Today, casts are often made of plastic, fiberglass, or even air-filled plastic tubes. Give reasons why the new casts are better than plaster casts.

EXTENSION

1. Acne is a common skin disorder among teenagers. Find out the cause of acne, and how it can be prevented or reduced. Describe different treatments for acne.
2. Find out how artificial joints are made and used. What materials are used to make artificial joints? How long will an artificial joint last?
3. What is osteoporosis? Find out its cause and prevention. Who is most likely to suffer from this disorder?

READINGS

Crump, Donald J. *Your Wonderful Body,* Books for World Explorers, Series 4. Washington, D.C.: National Geographic Society, 1982.

Hancock, Ralph. *Understanding Movement.* Morristown, N.J.: Silver Burdett Co., 1984.

NUTRITION AND DIGESTION

Have you ever cooked food over a campfire or eaten food that was cooked on an outdoor grill? The odors produced by food as it cooks can sharpen your appetite. Even some of the sounds made as food cooks—the sizzling and crackling, for instance—seem to increase hunger. Such aromas and sounds bring people to the table. But eating does more than satisfy hunger.

Living things differ in the kinds of food they use, but all living things need food. What are some of your favorite foods? Do you enjoy many different kinds of foods, or just a few kinds? The kinds of foods people eat can affect their health in many ways.

- *Why must people, and other living things, have food?*
- *Do different foods meet different needs of the body?*
- *What happens to food after it enters the body?*

18-1 NUTRITION

Your body needs food. Food is needed because it supplies the body with nutrients (NOO tree uhnts). A **nutrient** is any substance that the body needs to live and grow. Some nutrients provide energy. The energy from nutrients is the fuel that allows your body to run, jump, walk, and swim. Energy from nutrients keeps your heart beating and your brain working. Each cell in your body needs the energy supplied by nutrients.

Nutrients have two other main functions. They provide material for cell growth and repair, and they help the body use other nutrients. To use nutrients, the body must first get food. Then the food must be broken down. The process by which the body obtains and uses nutrients is called **nutrition** (noo TRIHSH uhn).

Nutrients are divided into six main classes. The six classes of nutrients are carbohydrates (kahr boh HĪ drayts), fats, proteins (PROH teenz), vitamins (VĪ tuh mihnz), minerals (MIH nuh ruhlz), and water. These six classes of nutrients have many different functions and are found in a variety of foods.

> *After completing this section, you will be able to*
>
> - **define** the term *nutrient*.
> - **identify** the six main classes of nutrients.
> - **list** the functions of carbohydrates, fats, and proteins.
> - **give examples** of foods that contain carbohydrates, fats, and proteins.
>
> *The key terms in this section are*
> carbohydrates   nutrition
> fats   proteins
> nutrient

nutrire (nourish)
-tion (process)

CARBOHYDRATES

carbo- (carbon)
hydr- (water)
-ate (having)

Carbohydrates are nutrients that provide the body with its main source of energy. Two important kinds of carbohydrates are *sugars* and *starches*. Sugars and starches are found in many foods. Starch is found in bread, crackers, noodles, and cereal. These foods are all made from grains. Grains contain large amounts of starch. Some examples of grains are wheat, corn, rice, and oats. Vegetables such as peas, beans, potatoes, and beets also contain starch. Sugar is found in fruits, such as plums, apples, peaches, grapes, and raisins. Honey, syrup, and jams contain large amounts of sugar.

There are two types of sugars—simple and complex. Table sugar is an example of a complex sugar. As shown in Figure 18-1, a complex sugar is made up of two simple sugars linked together. Based on Figure 18-1, how would you describe a starch? In the body, complex sugars and starches are broken down, forming simple sugars such as glucose (GLOO kohs). Glucose is broken down in cells during respiration. In this process, energy is released.

complex sugar

starch

Key:

= simple sugar

= many simple sugar units

Figure 18-1

Table sugar and starch are both carbohydrates that are made up of simple sugars.

FATS

Fats are nutrients that provide energy and building materials for the body. Gram for gram, fats contain about twice as much energy as do carbohydrates. In addition, fats are used to build cell membranes. Fats are found in foods such as oils, butter, margarine, whole milk, cheese, eggs, meat, poultry, nuts, and olives. The body not only takes in and uses fats but also makes fats from food. Such fats are stored in the body. When the body takes in less food than it needs, it uses these stored fats. Stored fats also insulate and protect some organs of the body.

ACTIVITY   How Can Food Be Tested for Starch?

OBJECTIVE
Identify foods that contain starch.

MATERIALS
lab apron, safety goggles, 2 test tubes, starch solution, test-tube rack, water, iodine solution in dropper bottle, paper towels, paper cup, food samples (bread, crackers, cooked egg white, cooked chicken, apple, potato, pear, milk)

PROCEDURE

A. Wear a lab apron and safety goggles during this activity.

B. Make a data table with headings like the one shown.

Food	Color Change	Food Contains Starch (Yes or No)

C. Add starch solution to a test tube until it is half full. Place the test tube in a test-tube rack. Add tap water to another test tube until it is half full. Place this test tube in the test-tube rack.

D. Place 5 drops of iodine solution in the test tube containing the starch solution and in the test tube containing water. Observe the contents of each test tube. **Caution:** Iodine is a stain. Be careful not to spill the iodine or get it on your hands or clothing. If you spill the iodine, tell your teacher at once.

E. Iodine changes from yellow to blue-black in the presence of starch. Under the column headed *Food,* list the starch solution and the water. Complete the table for the results of testing starch and testing water, noting any changes in color.

F. Place pieces of several different foods on paper towels. If you are testing a liquid, place a small amount in a paper cup. Place one or two drops of iodine solution on each food. Look for a color change in each food. Record the results in your data table.

RESULTS AND CONCLUSIONS
1. Describe how iodine solution is used to test foods for starch.
2. Which foods that were tested contain starch?
3. Which foods that were tested do not contain starch?

Fats are a type of *lipid.* Recall that lipids are organic compounds that store energy. As shown in Figure 18-2, fats are large molecules that are made up of smaller molecules called *fatty acids* and *glycerol* (GLIHS uh rohl). Fatty acids and glycerol can be broken down to release energy. This energy can be used by cells.

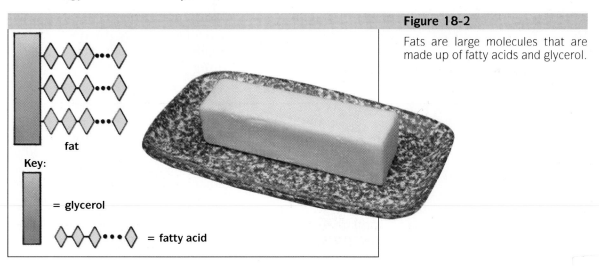

Figure 18-2

Fats are large molecules that are made up of fatty acids and glycerol.

fat

Key:

= glycerol

= fatty acid

OBJECTIVE

Identify foods that contain fats.

MATERIALS

lab apron, brown paper bag, scissors, food samples (apple, potato, carrot, bacon, cooked egg white, uncooked ground beef, peanut butter, mayonnaise, margarine, butter, salad oil, bread), paper towels

PROCEDURE

A. Wear a lab apron during this activity. Cut a large section from a brown paper bag. Divide it into sections and label each section with the name of one food sample.

B. One at a time, rub each food on its labeled section of the brown paper. Wait a few seconds, then wipe away any excess food.

Use a clean paper towel for each food.

C. Set aside the brown paper to dry overnight.

D. The next day hold the brown paper up to a light source or a sunny window. Look for a transparent spot in each section. Foods that contain fats leave a transparent spot on the brown paper.

E. In a table, record the name of each food and whether or not it contains fats.

RESULTS AND CONCLUSIONS

1. Which foods that were tested contain fats?
2. Which foods that were tested do not contain fats?
3. Why was it necessary for the brown paper to dry overnight?
4. Why was it necessary to use a clean paper towel to wipe away the excess food?

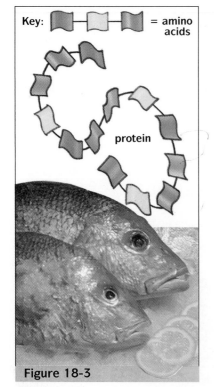

Figure 18-3

Proteins are made up of chains of amino acids.

PROTEINS

Proteins are nutrients that provide the body with materials for cell growth and repair, and that control body functions. Proteins are the main building material of cells. Enzymes (EHN zīmz) are proteins. Recall that enzymes control chemical changes in living things. Beef, pork, poultry, fish, eggs, milk, and nuts contain protein.

Recall that proteins are very large molecules that are made up of many smaller molecules called *amino* (uh MEE-noh) *acids*. Based on Figure 18-3, how would you describe a protein? There are 20 kinds of amino acids that link together in different combinations to form thousands of different proteins. When proteins are used by the body, they are broken down into amino acids. The body then uses these amino acids to form new proteins that the body needs. Some amino acids can be made by the body. Other amino acids cannot be made by the body and must be supplied by foods containing protein.

REVIEW

1. Give three reasons why the body requires nutrients.
2. What are the main types of nutrients needed by the body?
3. List the main functions of carbohydrates, fats, and proteins.
4. Give examples of foods that contain at least one of each of the following nutrients: sugar, starch, fat, and proteins.

CHALLENGE What might happen to the body if the amino acids that the body cannot make were not in food?

18-2 VITAMINS, MINERALS, AND WATER

VITAMINS

Two types of nutrients help the body to function normally and to use other nutrients. These nutrients are vitamins and minerals. Unlike most nutrients, vitamins and minerals cannot be used by the body as a source of energy. A **vitamin** is an organic substance that helps to control the chemical functions of the body. Without vitamins, the body cannot grow or function normally.

Table 18-1 lists six vitamins and the foods in which they are found. Vitamins are found in many foods, but no single food contains all the vitamins that the body needs. Eating a variety of foods provides all the vitamins needed. What foods are good sources of the B vitamins? What foods provide the body with vitamin C?

After completing this section, you will be able to

- **give examples** of vitamins and their functions and sources.
- **give examples** of minerals and their functions and sources.
- **explain** how water is used by the body.

The key terms in this section are
mineral   vitamin

vita (life)

Table 18-1 *Vitamins*

Vitamin	Needed For	Sources
A	Healthy eyes, hair, and skin	Green and yellow vegetables, fruit, egg yolk, liver, milk, butter
B-complex	Obtaining energy from glucose, proper functioning of heart and nerves; healthy skin	Meat, milk, liver, eggs, grains
C	Healthy bones, teeth, and gums; resisting infection	Citrus fruit, tomatoes, potatoes, green leafy vegetables, alfalfa sprouts
D	Healthy bones and teeth	Fortified milk, eggs, tuna, liver; made by skin in presence of sunlight
E	Healthy cell membranes	Vegetable oils, milk, grains
K	Blood clotting; proper liver functioning	Leafy green vegetables, tomatoes, grains

Only small amounts of each vitamin are needed by the body. When the body takes in more vitamins than it needs, the excess vitamins may be removed from the body as wastes. However, excess amounts of the vitamins A, D, E, and K can be stored in the body. Because these vitamins are stored in the body, large amounts of them can accumulate and harm the body.

When the body does not get enough of a given vitamin, the result is disease. Diseases caused by a lack of vitamins can be prevented and be cured by eating foods rich in the needed vitamins.

MINERALS

A **mineral** is an element that helps the body to function normally and to use other nutrients. Minerals provide material for the growth and development of bones and teeth, the growth of cells, and the formation of red blood cells. Minerals are also important for the proper functioning of the circulatory system and nervous system. Some of the minerals needed by the body are shown in Table 18-2. How is iron used by the body?

Table 18-2 *Minerals*

Mineral	Needed For	Sources
Calcium	Strong bones, teeth, and muscles; blood clotting; nerve function	Milk and milk products, fish, eggs, leafy green vegetables
Phosphorus	Development and growth of bones and teeth; nerve and muscle function	Milk and milk products, beans, meat, whole grains, nuts, broccoli
Potassium	Nerve and muscle function	Bananas, other fruits, meat, vegetables, milk
Sodium	Nerve function; control of amount of water in body	Table salt, most foods
Magnesium	Nerve and muscle function; making proteins	Green leafy vegetables, milk, meat, potatoes, whole grains
Iron	Carrying oxygen in red blood cells	Liver, red meat, egg yolk, nuts, beans, green leafy vegetables
Iodine	Controlling the rate at which food is used	Fish, shellfish, iodized table salt
Zinc	Healing wounds; making proteins	Meat, eggs, dried beans and peas, milk, green vegetables, eggs, seafood

Minerals are found in many foods. Table 18-2 lists some of these foods. Which minerals are found in milk? As with vitamins, no single food contains all the needed minerals. As you can see in Figure 18-4, eating a wide variety of foods provides the minerals needed by the body.

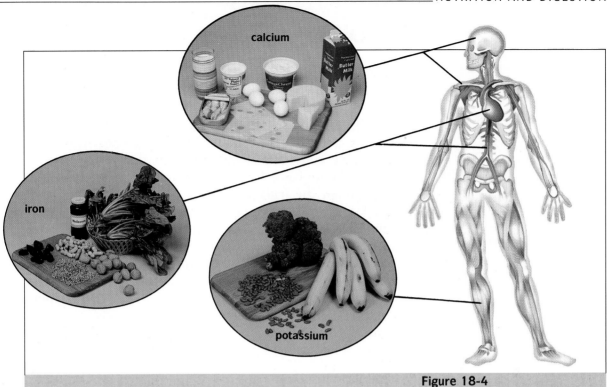

Figure 18-4

Minerals have many uses in the body.

WATER

Water is a nutrient needed for most body functions. Water is found in most foods. It is the nutrient needed in the greatest quantity. Figure 18-5 compares the amounts of water and other substances that make up the body. About what percent of the body's mass is water? Water has many functions in the body. The chemical changes that take place in the body must happen in water. Blood, which is 90 percent water, carries food, oxygen, and other materials throughout the body. Water carries wastes from the body.

The average adult loses about 2.5 L of water each day. Only about 1 L of water is replaced by drinking water and other fluids. The remaining amount is replaced by eating foods that contain water.

REVIEW

1. Give three examples of vitamins and their functions.
2. Give three examples of minerals and their functions.
3. What foods are good sources of vitamin C? What foods are good sources of potassium?
4. Describe two important functions of water in the body.

CHALLENGE What might be some of the characteristics of a disease that results from a lack of vitamin A?

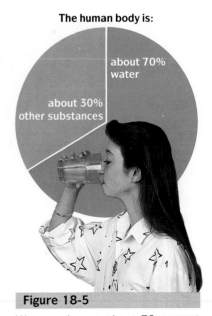

Figure 18-5

Water makes up about 70 percent of the body's mass.

18-3 THE BALANCED DIET

After completing this section, you will be able to

- **identify** foods in the four basic food groups.
- **plan** a balanced diet.
- **identify** Calories as a measurement of energy in food.

The key terms in this section are
Calorie   fiber

FOOD GROUPS

How do you know if you are getting all the nutrients that your body needs? Foods are divided into four basic food groups. Each group contains some of the nutrients that are needed by the body. By eating foods from each group, the body gets all the nutrients that it needs.

The four basic food groups are the *milk group,* the *meat group,* the *fruit and vegetable group,* and the *grain group.* The milk group provides proteins, minerals, vitamins, fats, and water. Though milk is the best source of nutrients in the milk group, foods such as yogurt and cheese also supply the body with many nutrients.

The meat group provides proteins, fats, and some vitamins and minerals. Notice in Figure 18-6 that the meat group contains not only meat and eggs but also peas and beans. Peas and beans are *legumes* (LEHG yoomz). Legumes are a good source of protein, so they are included in the meat group.

Figure 18-6

The milk group (*left*) and the meat group (*right*).

The fruit and vegetable group supplies the body with carbohydrates, vitamins, minerals, and water. Fruits and vegetables are also a good source of fiber, or roughage. **Fiber** is the part of plants that the body cannot digest. Fiber is important to the proper functioning of the *digestive system*—the system that breaks down food.

ACTIVITY   What Nutrition Information Is on Food Labels?

OBJECTIVE

Interpret the nutrition information listed on cans and boxes of food.

MATERIALS

5 or more food labels from different foods

PROCEDURE

A. Make a data table with headings like those shown.

B. Locate the list of ingredients on several food labels. The ingredients are listed in order from the greatest amount to the smallest amount.
   1. What ingredient is first on each label?
   2. What ingredient is last on each label?

C. Locate the nutrition information on each label. Complete your data table, using the nutrition information listed on each label.

RESULTS AND CONCLUSIONS

1. Of the foods that you studied, which contain protein?
2. Which food has the most Calories per serving?
3. Which food has the fewest Calories per serving?
4. Which foods contain fat?
5. What information *not* listed in your data table is given on the food labels?
6. How can reading food labels help you plan a balanced diet?

Food	Serving Size	Calories	Protein	Carbohydrates	Fat	Vitamins	Minerals

Figure 18-7

The fruit and vegetable group (*left*) and the grain group (*right*).

The grain group supplies starches, proteins, and B vitamins. The grain group also supplies fiber. This group contains many foods that are made from whole grains. These foods include bread, cereal, crackers, tortillas, and pasta. What foods in the grain group can you identify in Figure 18-7?

Eating the proper amounts of food from the four basic food groups provides a *balanced diet*. A balanced diet is a daily intake of food that supplies enough of all the basic nutrients. Look at Figure 18-8. A balanced diet each day includes a minimum number of servings from the following food groups: four servings from the milk group, two servings from the meat group, four servings from the fruit and vegetable group, and four servings from the grain group.

Figure 18-8

The recommended daily servings of the four food groups.

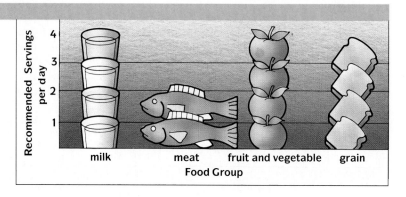

CALORIES

You have probably heard the term *Calorie* (KAL uh-ree) used in discussion of food. A **Calorie** is a measure of the energy available in food. Different foods contain different amounts of Calories, or supply different amounts of energy. Many kinds of food have packages with labels that show how many Calories are contained in the food.

Every activity of the body uses energy. In general, teenagers and young adults require the greatest number of Calories. Most males require more Calories than do

calor (heat)

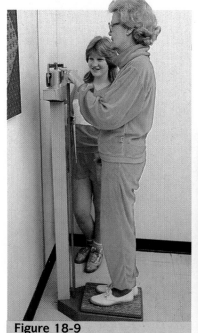

Figure 18-9

The combination of exercise and a good diet can help you maintain a healthy weight.

WARNING: *Obesity is hazardous to your health.* Will you one day see this type of warning label? Scientists at the National Institutes of Health in Washington, D.C., have studied obesity. They have found that an overweight person is more likely than a person of normal weight to have heart disease, high blood pressure, diabetes, and even some kinds of cancer.

But what is the cause of obesity? It has been long known that eating too much and exercising too little lead to obesity. Scientists have found that obesity may be linked to characteristics of fat cells in the body.

In an overweight person the fat cells are up to two and a half times as large as the fat cells of an average-weight person. Some scientists believe that fat cells are "programmed" to maintain a given size. Once fat cells have grown to a large size, they tend to quickly regain this size. When an overweight person diets, or takes in small amounts of food, the fat cells shrink. However, when this person takes in an amount of food that would be normal for most other people, the fat cells grow to their former large size.

Although scientists continue to study fat cells and their role in obesity, the best way to control and avoid obesity is to eat a balanced diet and to exercise regularly.

females. People who are very active use more Calories than do people who are less active. If a person takes in the same number of Calories that are used, that person's weight will remain the same. When a person takes in more Calories than are used, that person gains weight.

Obesity (oh BEE suh tee) is a condition in which a person's weight is at least 10 percent more than normal for his or her height. Treatment of obesity includes increased physical activity and a diet low in Calories. When activity increases, the body needs more Calories. If the person consumes fewer Calories than are used, the body needs extra Calories. How does the body get these extra Calories? Before going on a special diet or exercise program, you should always check with your doctor.

REVIEW

1. Give examples of foods from each basic food group.
2. List foods in a balanced diet for a day's meals.
3. How are Calories in food related to body weight?

CHALLENGE Before athletic events, many runners and other athletes eat large amounts of food from the grain group. Why do athletes eat these foods?

18-4 THE DIGESTIVE SYSTEM

After completing this section, you will be able to

- **describe** the function of the digestive system.
- **compare** mechanical digestion and chemical digestion.
- **trace** the path of food through the digestive system.

The key terms in this section are
chemical digestion
digestive system
esophagus
large intestine
mechanical digestion
peristalsis
small intestine
stomach

Food must be broken down before it can be used by cells of the body. *Digestion* (duh JEHS chuhn) is the process that breaks the food into substances that can be used by cells. Digestion takes place in the digestive system. The **digestive system** is a system made up of organs that function together to digest, or break down, foods. Figure 18-10 shows the organs of the digestive system.

TYPES OF DIGESTION

There are two types of digestion that function together. **Mechanical digestion** is the process that breaks food into small pieces. Chewing is the first step of mechanical digestion. Food is broken into smaller pieces as it travels through the digestive system.

Mechanical digestion prepares food for chemical digestion. **Chemical digestion** is the process that chemically changes food into simpler substances. These simpler substances can then be used by cells. For example, chemical digestion breaks down fats into the simpler molecules of fatty acids and glycerol. Only after food has been digested by both processes can it be used by cells.

Figure 18-10

The digestive system.

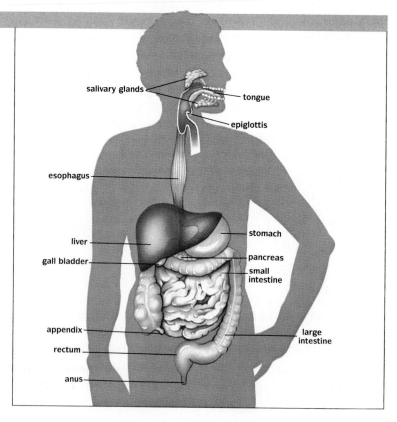

salivary glands — tongue — epiglottis — esophagus — liver — gall bladder — stomach — pancreas — small intestine — appendix — rectum — anus — large intestine

426

DIGESTIVE ORGANS

Refer to Figure 18-10 as you read about the path of food through the digestive system. Both kinds of digestion begin in the mouth. In the mouth, food is broken into pieces as it is chewed by the teeth. The tongue pushes food around the mouth and helps to break food into smaller pieces. The food is mixed with a liquid called *saliva*. Saliva contains a substance that begins chemical digestion. Saliva also moistens the food, which helps to move it through the digestive system. The tongue pushes the food to the back of the mouth, where it is swallowed.

Food moves from the mouth to the esophagus (ee-SAHF uh guhs). The **esophagus** is a long muscular tube that connects the throat to the stomach. Notice in Figure 18-11A that the esophagus lies behind the windpipe. As food is swallowed, a flap of tissue called the *epiglottis* (ehp-uh GLAHT ihs) moves down as the top of the windpipe moves up. These structures cover the windpipe and keep food from going into it. After swallowing, the structures move back in place allowing air into the windpipe.

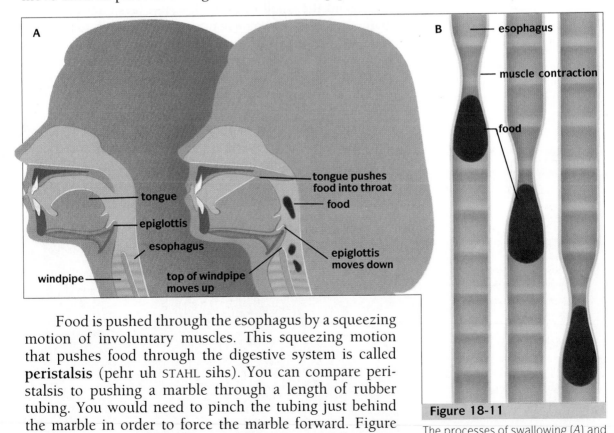

Figure 18-11

The processes of swallowing (A) and peristalsis (B) move food to the stomach.

Food is pushed through the esophagus by a squeezing motion of involuntary muscles. This squeezing motion that pushes food through the digestive system is called **peristalsis** (pehr uh STAHL sihs). You can compare peristalsis to pushing a marble through a length of rubber tubing. You would need to pinch the tubing just behind the marble in order to force the marble forward. Figure 18-11B shows peristalsis in the esophagus. In relation to the food, where do the muscles of the esophagus contract?

From the esophagus, food moves into the stomach. The **stomach** is a J-shaped, muscular sac that stores food and helps to digest it. Food stays in the stomach for about four to six hours. The stomach can hold about 1.5 L of food. There is a sphincter (SFIHNGK tuhr) muscle at each end of the stomach. A sphincter muscle is a ring of muscle that contracts to close off an organ. Sphincter muscles control the flow of substances from one digestive organ to the next.

The walls of the stomach are made of several layers of muscle. These muscles contract and relax, causing the stomach to twist and turn. As the stomach twists and turns, bits of food are broken into smaller pieces. The small pieces are mixed with liquids and are broken down further by chemical digestion.

From the stomach, food moves into the small intestine. The **small intestine** is a long, narrow tube in which food is digested and absorbed. Notice the many coils of the small intestine shown in Figure 18-12. If the small intestine were uncoiled, it would be more than 6 m long. It is called the small intestine because it is only 2.5 cm in diameter. Most of the chemical digestion of food takes place in the small intestine. This is also where most food is absorbed into the bloodstream. Food remains in the small intestine for about five to eight hours.

Near the place where the small intestine joins the large intestine, there is a small pouch called the *appendix* (uh PEHN dihks). The appendix has no known function in humans. Sometimes the appendix becomes infected and causes pain. This condition is called appendicitis (uh pehn-duh SĪ tuhs). In severe cases, the appendix is removed.

SCIENCE PUZZLER

When astronauts were first sent up in space, scientists wondered how the body would function without gravity. On the ground, in the presence of gravity, food travels down the esophagus to the stomach. It was found that the astronauts had no problems swallowing their food. Even if they were upside down, food went through the esophagus to the stomach. Explain why.

Food that has not been absorbed into the bloodstream moves to the large intestine. Notice in Figure 18-12 that the large intestine looks like an upside down U surrounding the small intestine. The **large intestine** is a short, wide tube that absorbs water from the remaining undigested food. Food remains in the large intestine for about eight to ten hours but no digestion takes place here. The large intestine is about 1.5 m long and about 6 cm in diameter. Why, do you think, is it called the large intestine?

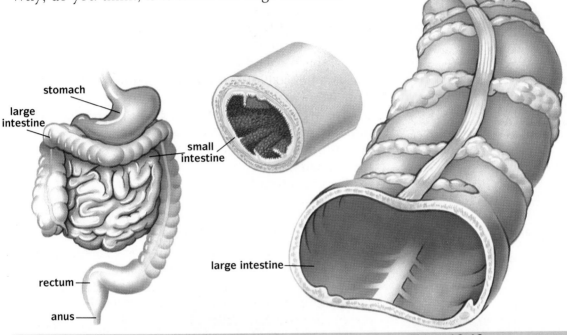

Figure 18-12

The stomach, small intestine, and large intestine (*left*). Notice the differences in the cross sections of the small intestine (*middle*) and the large intestine (*right*).

Look at Figure 18-12. Locate the *rectum*, the last part of the large intestine. The rectum is a muscular pouch that stores solid wastes until they are removed from the body. Solid wastes that are the end product of digestion are called *feces* (FEE seez). Feces are removed from the body through an opening called the *anus*. The anus is located at the lower end of the rectum.

REVIEW

1. What is the function of the digestive system?
2. How do mechanical digestion and chemical digestion differ?
3. List the organs through which food moves as it passes through the digestive system.

CHALLENGE Suppose a person is on a liquid diet. This diet does not allow bread, cereal, fruits, or vegetables. Describe the possible effect of this diet on digestion.

18-5 DIGESTION AND ABSORPTION

You have learned that mechanical digestion breaks food into very small pieces. But cells cannot use most nutrients until they are further broken down by chemical digestion. Figure 18-13 shows which type of digestion takes place in each of the main digestive organs. Chemical digestion changes food into simpler substances. According to Figure 18-13, what are fats broken down into? What are proteins broken down into? What are carbohydrates broken down into?

Chemical digestion takes place in the presence of special liquids called digestive enzymes. A **digestive enzyme** is a substance that chemically breaks down a nutrient. There are many different digestive enzymes. Each digestive organ contains a different set of enzymes. Look again at Figure 18-13. Which organs contain enzymes that digest protein? Each enzyme acts only on certain nutrients. For example, digestive enzymes that act on proteins do not act on fats.

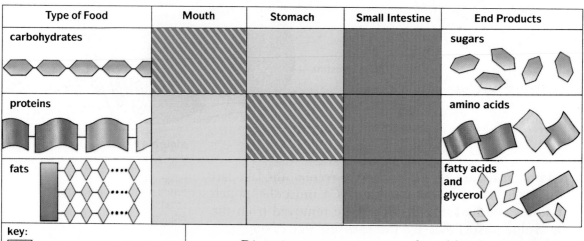

Type of Food	Mouth	Stomach	Small Intestine	End Products
carbohydrates				sugars
proteins				amino acids
fats				fatty acids and glycerol

key:
- mechanical digestion
- chemical digestion
- mechanical and chemical digestion

Figure 18-13

The digestion of carbohydrates, fats, and proteins.

Digestive enzymes are produced by the stomach and the small intestine. Other glands also produce digestive enzymes. Glands that produce digestive enzymes are called **digestive glands**. These glands are attached to other digestive organs by small tubes, or ducts. Food does not move through these ducts. Instead, the enzymes move through the ducts to the organs in which the food is digested.

Recall that mechanical digestion begins in the mouth. With the action of saliva, chemical digestion also begins in the mouth. **Saliva** is a liquid that contains the digestive enzyme that begins the chemical digestion of starch. Saliva is produced by the **salivary** (SAL uh vehr ee) **glands**. These glands are shown in Figure 18-14. Saliva breaks down starch into sugar. If you have ever chewed a cracker for several seconds before swallowing, you may have noticed a sweet taste. The sweet taste is the result of saliva breaking down starch into sugar.

Chemical digestion continues in the stomach. Within the stomach are many gastric glands. Gastric glands produce a substance called _gastric juice._ Gastric juice is a mixture of enzymes and strong acids that chemically digests food in the stomach. Gastric juice begins the chemical digestion of proteins. Recall that proteins are broken into amino acids. As food is churned and mixed with gastric juice in the stomach, the partly digested food is changed to a thick liquid.

This liquid food moves into the small intestine. This is where most chemical digestion and absorption takes place. In the small intestine, fats are acted upon by a liquid from the liver. Locate the liver in Figure 18-15. The **liver** is a large lobed organ that produces _bile._ Bile is a liquid that helps to digest fats but it is not a digestive enzyme. Bile breaks fats into small drops. The droplets of fat are easier for the enzymes to digest. Why is bile not a digestive enzyme? Bile is stored in a saclike organ called the _gall bladder._ From the gall bladder, bile moves to the small intestine.

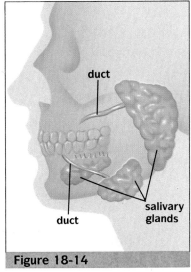

Figure 18-14

The location of the salivary glands.

Figure 18-15

The liver, gall bladder, and pancreas.

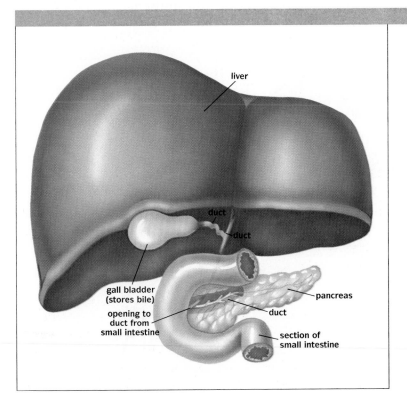

The pancreas (PAN kree uhs) is found below the stomach. The **pancreas** is a digestive gland that produces pancreatic juice. *Pancreatic juice,* which is released into the small intestine, is a mixture of three types of digestive enzymes. One type of enzyme breaks down protein into groups of amino acids. A second type of enzyme breaks down undigested starch into sugars. A third type of enzyme breaks down fats into glycerol and fatty acids.

The small intestine also produces digestive enzymes. Enzymes produced by glands in the small intestine make up *intestinal juice.* Intestinal juice breaks down proteins, fats, and carbohydrates into simpler substances.

villus (tuft of hair)

After food has been digested, it is absorbed into the bloodstream. This process takes place in the small intestine. The inner walls of the small intestine are folded and are covered with millions of tiny fingerlike structures called **villi** (sing., *villus*). Each villus contains tiny blood vessels. Nutrients in the small intestine diffuse through the villi into these blood vessels. Figure 18-16 shows villi in the wall of the intestine. The many villi provide a large surface area through which nutrients can be absorbed. The twists and turns of the small intestine, plus its folded inner surface, also help to increase surface area for absorption. If the walls were smooth, much less food could be absorbed into the blood. Blood carries the nutrients to cells throughout the body.

Figure 18-16

Villi in the small intestine as seen with a scanning electron microscope (A). Close-up of one villus shows the blood vessels in the villus (B).

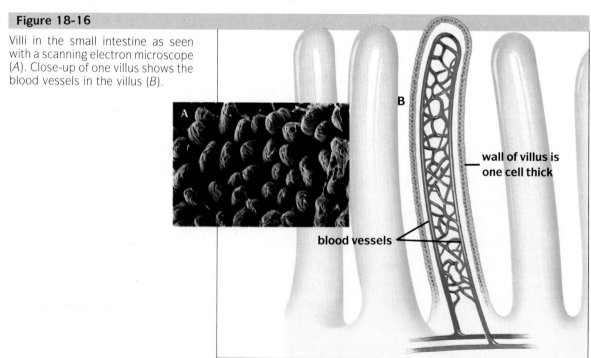

wall of villus is one cell thick

blood vessels

REVIEW

1. Describe what happens to fats, proteins, and carbohydrates in the digestive system.
2. What is the role of the pancreas in digestion?
3. What happens to food in the small intestine?

CHALLENGE   Do you think it is possible for a person to live without a stomach? Give reasons for your answer.

CHAPTER SUMMARY

The main ideas in this chapter are listed below. Read these statements before you answer the Chapter Review questions.

- Nutrients provide the body with energy and materials for growth and repair. Nutrients also help the body use other nutrients. (18-1)

- Carbohydrates and fats provide energy; proteins provide materials for growth and repair. Proteins are also needed to make up enzymes, which control body functions. (18-1)

- Vitamins and minerals are nutrients that help the body to function normally and to use other nutrients. These nutrients are not used as a source of energy for the body. (18-2)

- Water is a nutrient needed for chemical changes and many other functions in the body. Water makes up the greatest part of the body mass. (18-2)

- The four basic food groups are the milk group, the meat group, the fruit and vegetable group, and the grain group. (18-3)

- A balanced diet provides the body with the correct amounts of all the basic nutrients. Eating a variety of foods from the four basic food groups provides a balanced diet. (18-3)

- Mechanical digestion and chemical digestion work together to break down nutrients into substances that can be used by cells. (18-4)

- In the digestive system, food moves from the mouth through the esophagus, through the stomach, and through the small intestine. Undigested food moves into the large intestine. (18-4)

- Various digestive enzymes break down nutrients throughout the digestive system. (18-5)

- Most chemical digestion takes place in the small intestine. Digested food is absorbed into the bloodstream through the walls of the small intestine. (18-5)

The key terms in this chapter are listed below. Use each term in a sentence that shows the meaning of the term.

Calorie	fiber	peristalsis
carbohydrates	large intestine	proteins
chemical digestion	liver	saliva
digestive enzyme	mechanical digestion	salivary glands
digestive glands	mineral	small intestine
digestive system	nutrient	stomach
esophagus	nutrition	villi
fats	pancreas	vitamin

Chapter Review

VOCABULARY

Use the key terms from this chapter to complete the following sentences correctly.

1. A long, tubelike organ in which food is digested and absorbed is the _____ .
2. Nutrients that provide the body with its main source of energy are _____ .
3. Elements that help the body to function normally and to use other nutrients are called _____ .
4. A J-shaped muscular sac that stores food is the _____ .
5. The liquid that contains the digestive juice that begins the digestion of starch in the mouth is called _____ .
6. Any substance that the body needs to live and grow is a/an _____ .
7. The process that chemically changes food into simpler substances is called _____ .
8. A large, lobed organ that produces bile is the _____ .
9. The squeezing movement that pushes food through the digestive system is called _____ .
10. Nutrients that provide the body with materials for cell growth and repair, and that control body functions are called _____ .
11. The process that breaks food into smaller pieces is called _____ .
12. Fingerlike structures through which food is absorbed in the small intestine are called _____ .

CONCEPTS

1. Why does the body need nutrients? (18-1)
2. List the main nutrients needed by the body. (18-1)
3. Compare the functions of carbohydrates and fats. (18-1)
4. What foods are good sources of proteins? (18-1)
5. Identify the functions of the following vitamins and list food sources for each: A, D, and K. (18-2)
6. Identify the functions of the following minerals and list food sources for each: calcium, magnesium, and iodine. (18-2)
7. Why is water needed by the body? (18-2)
8. Identify the four basic food groups and give three examples of foods from each group. (18-3)
9. Make up a menu for a day's meals to provide the recommended number of servings from the basic food groups. (18-3)

10. Explain the importance of fiber in the diet. (18-3)

11. Explain how the number of Calories eaten and the number of Calories used are related to body weight. (18-3)

12. Describe the function of the digestive system. (18-4)

13. How do mechanical digestion and chemical digestion work together to break down food? (18-4)

14. Trace the path of food through the organs of the digestive system. (18-4)

15. What is a digestive enzyme? (18-5)

16. Describe what happens to proteins in digestion. (18-5)

17. In which digestive organs is starch digested? (18-5)

18. Which digestive gland produces enzymes for the digestion of carbohydrates, fats, and proteins? (18-5)

19. What is the role of the liver in the digestive process? (18-5)

20. What is the function of the villi in the small intestine? (18-5)

APPLICATION/ CRITICAL THINKING

1. Give several examples of healthful snacks that can be part of a balanced diet.

2. How can reading food labels help a person plan a balanced diet?

3. Why would a person with a physically active job require a higher intake of food than a person with a less active job?

4. The small intestine is long and coiled, and its inner surface is folded and covered with villi. How is the structure of the small intestine related to its function?

5. Imagine that food was not broken into small pieces by physical digestion. How would this situation affect chemical digestion?

EXTENSION

1. Go to the library to research Alexis St. Martin. How did he contribute to the study of digestion?

2. Find out which diseases are caused by too little of the vitamins C, D, and B_1. Report on the symptoms and treatment of each disease.

3. What is cholesterol? Find out how cholesterol functions in the body. Why is it important to limit the intake of cholesterol?

4. A vegetarian diet contains no meat. Plan a vegetarian menu that includes sufficient protein.

READINGS

"Anorexia Nervosa: A Hormonal Link." *Newsweek,* May 23, 1983, p. 69.

Dusheck, Jennie. "Fish, Fatty Acid and Physiology." *Science News,* October 19, 1985, p. 252.

Katz, Susan. "Getting Sick on Vitamins." *Newsweek,* May 10, 1986, p. 80.

TRANSPORT, RESPIRATION, AND EXCRETION

Have you ever competed in a race? Perhaps you have been part of some other sports activity that required you to push yourself as hard as you could. Intense physical activity causes certain body systems to work very hard. For example, you have probably noticed that your breathing rate increases when you run fast. The system that transports needed materials to the muscles and other body tissues must also work harder than usual. Many waste products are produced by the body all the time. The quantities of some of these wastes increase with physical exercise. These waste products must be removed from the body by another hard-working body system.

- *What body system transports materials to body tissues?*
- *How does breathing relate to the exchange of gases in cells?*
- *How are waste products removed from the body?*

19-1 THE BLOOD

FUNCTIONS OF BLOOD

In an adult, about one sixteenth of the body weight is blood. Blood flows through tubes called blood vessels. The heart is the pump that moves blood through the blood vessels. Together the blood, blood vessels, and heart are known as the **circulatory** (SER kyuh luh tawr ee) **system.**

Blood has many important functions. These functions include transporting materials through the body, helping to maintain a constant body temperature, and defending against disease. Blood carries oxygen and digested food to the cells of the body. Wastes from all parts of the body are carried by the blood to the organs that remove these wastes. Chemical messengers known as hormones are transported from one organ to another by the blood.

Blood also helps to cool the body. Heat from the warm internal organs is carried by the blood to the cooler surface of the body. Blood helps the body stay free of disease. Special cells in blood fight disease-causing organisms that invade the body.

After completing this section, you will be able to

- **describe** the functions of blood and **identify** its parts.
- **explain** the role of red blood cells in transporting oxygen.
- **describe** the process of blood clotting.
- **explain** why blood types must be matched for transfusion.

The key terms in this section are

blood types	plasma
circulatory	platelet
system	red blood cell
hemoglobin	white blood cell

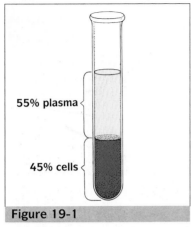

Figure 19-1

Blood separated into plasma and cells. What are some materials carried in the plasma?

COMPOSITION OF BLOOD

Blood is a mixture of several types of cells in a large amount of liquid. The pale yellow liquid portion of the blood is called **plasma**. Figure 19-1 shows blood that has been separated into plasma and cells. Notice that more than half of the volume of blood is plasma. Plasma is made up mostly of water. Wastes, digested food, and other substances are transported in the plasma.

The most numerous cells in the blood are the red blood cells. A **red blood cell** is a cell that transports oxygen. Observe the red blood cells in Figure 19-2. Notice that they are disk-shaped and are thinner in the center than at the edges. This shape allows red blood cells to be flexible. They can bend when moving through very narrow blood vessels. Why is it important that these blood cells be able to bend?

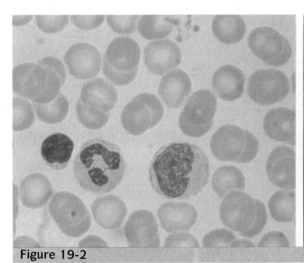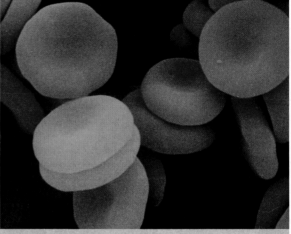

Figure 19-2

Red blood cells: as seen through a light microscope (*left*); as seen through an SEM (*right*).

hemato- (blood)
globus (globe)

A mature red blood cell lacks a nucleus. It consists mainly of the red substance called hemoglobin (HEE muh-gloh buhn). **Hemoglobin** is a protein in red blood cells that joins with oxygen. Hemoglobin molecules contain atoms of iron. When blood passes through the lungs, oxygen from the lungs attaches to the iron in the hemoglobin of the red blood cells. In other parts of the body, hemoglobin releases oxygen. The oxygen is used by body cells to release energy from food.

Also found in the blood are white blood cells. A **white blood cell** is a cell that helps defend the body against disease. A white blood cell has a nucleus and is larger than a red blood cell. Blood contains fewer white blood cells than red blood cells.

White blood cells, shown in Figure 19-3A, change shape as they move. They resemble amoebas in the way they move. Some white blood cells capture bacteria and foreign particles in much the same way as an amoeba takes in food. A white blood cell surrounds and then takes in a particle. Many white blood cells may surround a large foreign particle. The white blood cells release substances that destroy the particle. Some white blood cells release chemicals into the blood. These chemicals fight infections caused by bacteria and viruses.

Platelets are also part of the blood. A **platelet** is a cell fragment that functions in blood clotting. The *clotting* of blood is a process that seals off cuts and breaks in blood vessels. Platelets are formed from large cells in the bone marrow. When these bone marrow cells mature, they split into many pieces. The pieces are released into the blood as platelets. Follow the steps in Figure 19-4A as you read about the process of clotting.

1. When a blood vessel is cut, blood leaks out of it. Platelets stick to the cut edges of the blood vessels.
2. The platelets release chemicals that cause proteins in the plasma to form fibers. The chemicals also cause other platelets to stick to each other and the cut edges.
3. The cut in the blood vessel soon becomes filled with a mesh of fibers. Many platelets and some red blood cells become stuck in this mesh.
4. The cut finally is plugged with a solid mass of platelets, fibers, and red blood cells.

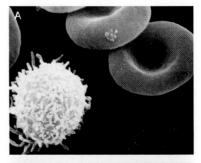

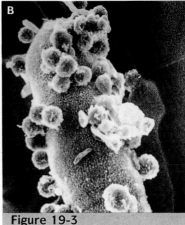

Figure 19-3

White blood cell among red blood cells (A). Many white blood cells attack a foreign particle (B).

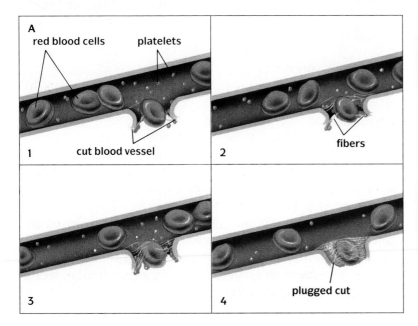

A
red blood cells   platelets

1   cut blood vessel

2   fibers

3

4   plugged cut

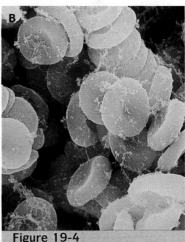

Figure 19-4

The process of blood clotting (A). Red blood cells caught in the mesh of fibers (B).

BLOOD TYPES

When a person is seriously injured, clotting cannot occur rapidly enough to stop the blood flow. So a lot of blood may be lost. Lost blood can be replaced with blood from another person. The process by which blood is transferred from one person to another is called *transfusion* (tranz FYOO zhuhn). Blood from different people has different characteristics. **Blood types** are groups into which blood is classified based on its characteristics.

The most important set of blood types are the ABO blood types. This set includes four blood types known as *A, B, AB,* and *O.* These blood types result from substances called *antigens* (AN tuh juhnz) on the surface of red blood cells. Type A blood has red blood cells with antigen A on their surfaces. Type B blood has red blood cells with antigen B. Type AB blood has red blood cells with both antigens A and B. Type O blood has red blood cells with neither antigen.

Figure 19-5

A patient receiving a blood transfusion.

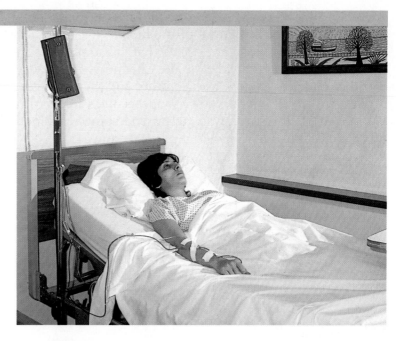

The *Rh factor* is another antigen found on the surface of some red blood cells. About 85 out of every 100 people have Rh factor on the surfaces of their red blood cells. These people are said to be Rh-positive. They have the blood type Rh+. People who do not have this factor are said to be Rh-negative. They have the blood type Rh−.

Although transfusion has become a routine process, it must be done with great care. Before a transfusion, blood must be matched for both the ABO types and the Rh factor.

Often when people are injured or are having surgery, they need a blood transfusion. But before receiving a transfusion, patients have to wait for their blood type to be matched. To solve this problem, researchers have been developing artificial red blood cells. With artificial red blood cells, matching would not be necessary. Patients could receive transfusions right away.

One kind of artificial red blood cell that is being studied is made by mixing hemoglobin with two fatty compounds. When mixed together, the fatty compounds form a membrane around droplets of hemoglobin. The result is small cell-like structures that can carry oxygen. Artificial red blood cells are smaller than natural cells. This could make artificial cells useful for patients who have blocked blood vessels. Normal cells cannot get past the blockages. So the tissues do not receive enough oxygen. The artificial cells could carry oxygen past the blockages and into these tissues.

The synthetic membrane of artificial cells is stronger than the membrane around natural red blood cells. This property would make the artificial cells useful in open-heart surgery. While the heart is being operated on, special pumps circulate blood through the patient. The pumps put a lot of pressure on the blood cells and blood vessels. Cells with stronger membranes could better withstand these pressures. Because of their special properties, the use of artificial red blood cells could save the lives of many people.

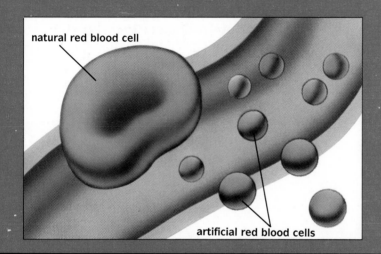

natural red blood cell

artificial red blood cells

Matching is done by mixing two small blood samples. One sample is taken from the person who is to receive the transfusion. The other sample is taken from the person who will donate the blood for transfusion. If the two blood samples do not match, the red blood cells clump together. If this clumping were to occur within a person's blood vessels, serious illness or death might result.

REVIEW

1. Describe the composition and function of blood.
2. What is the main protein in red blood cells? What does it do?
3. What are the functions of white blood cells?
4. Describe the process of clotting.
5. Why must blood be matched before transfusion?

CHALLENGE   There are about one-thousand times more red cells than white cells in blood. Relate this difference in number to the function of each type of cell.

19-2 BLOOD VESSELS AND LYMPH

TYPES OF BLOOD VESSELS

Blood travels through blood vessels in all parts of the body. There are several different types of blood vessels. An **artery** (AHR tuhr ee) is a blood vessel that carries blood away from the heart. Arteries have thick, muscular walls. You can see the wall of an artery in Figure 19-6.

Blood is pumped out of the heart and into the arteries in spurts, or surges. Elastic material in the walls of arteries allows them to stretch as blood surges through them. The muscle in the walls of arteries controls how much blood can flow through. The blood flowing within an artery is under pressure. The pressure is due to the surging of blood each time the heart pumps. The thick, flexible wall of the artery can withstand this pressure.

Figure 19-6

Cross section of an artery and a vein. How does the wall of the artery differ from the wall of the vein?

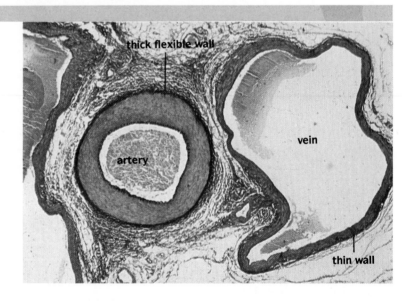

thick flexible wall

vein

artery

thin wall

capillus (hair)

Two large arteries carry blood out of the heart. The arteries divide into smaller branches away from the heart. These smaller arteries carry blood to the body's organs. Within organs, these arteries branch into even smaller blood vessels. The smallest blood vessels are called capillaries (KAP uh lehr eez). A **capillary** is a blood vessel whose wall is only one cell thick. Examine the structure of the capillary in Figure 19-7. Some capillaries are only a few micrometers in diameter. Blood cells move through these tiny capillaries in single file. Notice in Figure 19-8 that a single small artery branches into many capillaries. The capillaries form a network or *capillary bed.*

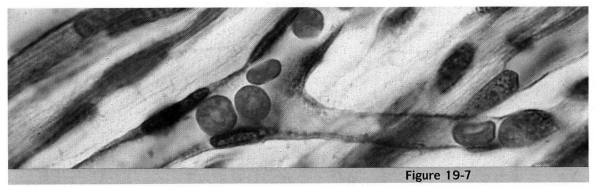

Figure 19-7

Red blood cells in a capillary. Notice that the capillary is only wide enough for cells to pass through one at a time.

Much of the work of the circulatory system occurs in the capillary beds. Because the walls of capillaries are thin, materials can pass through them. Oxygen, food substances, and other materials move out of the blood through the capillary walls. These materials move into the surrounding tissues, where they are used in metabolism. Carbon dioxide and other wastes are produced in the tissues. These wastes pass through the capillary walls into the blood and are carried away.

Note in Figure 19-8 that blood flows from the capillary bed into a small vein. A **vein** is a blood vessel that carries blood toward the heart. The walls of veins are much thinner than the walls of arteries. Compare the wall of the vein with the wall of the artery in Figure 19-6. What might happen if the walls of an artery were as thin as those of a vein? Many small veins join to form larger veins. Veins from all the organs of the body join to form a few large veins that empty blood into the heart. As blood moves through the capillaries, it loses pressure. Blood that enters the veins is under low pressure. Veins have valves that keep blood flowing toward the heart.

Figure 19-8

An artery and a vein joined by a capillary bed. The arrows show the movement of blood. What occurs in the capillary bed?

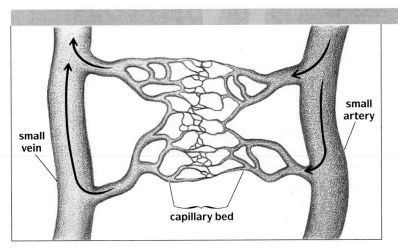

small vein

small artery

capillary bed

THE LYMPHATIC SYSTEM

Small amounts of plasma leak out of the capillaries. This liquid, called **lymph** (lihmf), surrounds the body tissues and bathes the cells. As lymph collects around cells, the excess moves into a system of vessels. The vessels make up the *lymphatic system*. You can see the vessels of the lymphatic system in Figure 19-9. Lymph is filtered in masses of tissue called *lymph nodes*. Special cells in these nodes destroy bacteria and other foreign particles. Lymph flows from lymph vessels into two veins in the neck. Thus, the liquid lost from the blood in the capillaries is returned to the blood by the lymphatic system.

Figure 19-9

Structure of the lymphatic system. Where can you find clusters of lymph nodes?

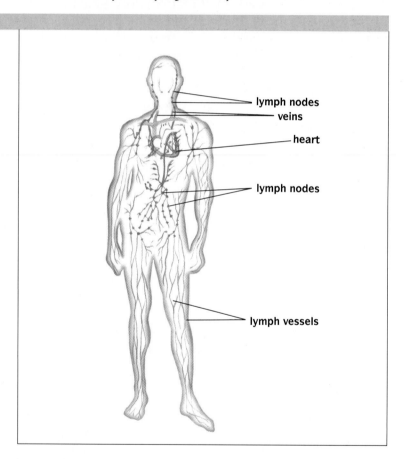

REVIEW

1. Distinguish between the structures of arteries, capillaries, and veins. What is the function of each?
2. What exchanges of materials occur in the capillaries?
3. Where does lymph come from? Where does it go?

CHALLENGE Blockage of a lymphatic vessel causes the surrounding tissue to swell. Explain why.

19-3 THE HEART AND CIRCULATION

STRUCTURE OF THE HEART

The heart is a pump that keeps blood flowing through the many kilometers of blood vessels in the body. Most of the heart consists of muscle tissue. The muscle tissue of the heart does not tire. It begins to contract long before birth and continues throughout life. Study Figure 19-10 as you read about the structure of the heart. The heart contains four cavities, or chambers. Each of the two upper chambers of the heart is called an **atrium** (AY tree uhm) (pl., *atria*). Each of the two lower chambers of the heart is called a **ventricle** (VEHN truh kuhl).

Notice in Figure 19-10 that the walls of the atria are much thinner than those of the ventricles. The atria collect blood from veins and pump it only a short distance, into the ventricles. Now compare the walls of the two ventricles. You can see that the wall of the left ventricle is much thicker than that of the right. The right ventricle pumps blood to the lungs. The thick-walled left ventricle pumps blood throughout the body.

> After completing this section, you will be able to
> - **describe** the structure of the heart.
> - **describe** the pattern of blood flow through the body.
> - **identify** the causes of the heartbeat and the pulse.
>
> *The key terms in this section are*
> atrium   valve
> pulse   ventricle

atrium (entrance room)

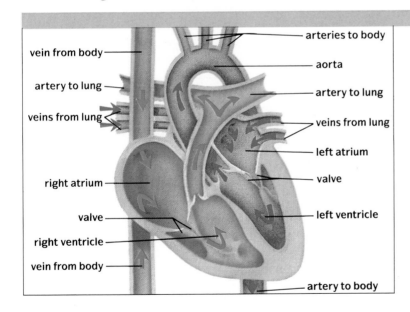

vein from body

artery to lung

veins from lung

right atrium

valve

right ventricle

vein from body

arteries to body

aorta

artery to lung

veins from lung

left atrium

valve

left ventricle

artery to body

Figure 19-10

Structure of the human heart. How does the wall of the left ventricle compare with the wall of the right ventricle?

CIRCULATION

As has been said, the heart pumps blood through the body. Refer to Figure 19-11 on the next page as you read about the circulation of blood. Find the two blood vessels (veins) labeled *vena cava* (VEE nuh   KAY vuh) (pl., *venae cavae*). One vena cava carries blood from all parts of the body that are above the heart. The other vena cava carries

Figure 19-11

Main structures of the circulatory system.

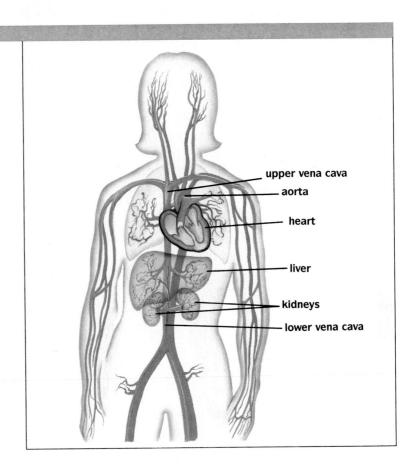

upper vena cava
aorta
heart
liver
kidneys
lower vena cava

blood from all parts below the heart. Both of these large veins empty blood into the right atrium. This blood has little oxygen. The oxygen was used by cells as the blood flowed through the tissues of the body.

The right atrium pumps blood through a valve and into the right ventricle. A **valve** is a flap of tissue that allows blood to pass in only one direction. Look back at Figure 19-10 to see a valve. The right ventricle pumps blood through another valve into a large artery. This artery divides, sending a branch to each lung. As blood flows through the lungs, it absorbs oxygen from the air inside the lungs and releases carbon dioxide.

The oxygen-rich blood from the lungs returns to the heart through veins. The veins empty blood into the left atrium. The left atrium pumps blood through a valve into the left ventricle. The strong contraction of the left ventricle pumps blood through a valve into the body's largest artery. This artery is called the *aorta* (ay AWR tuh). Blood moves to all organs of the body except the lungs by way of arteries that branch from the aorta.

As the blood passes through capillaries, oxygen and nutrients are delivered to cells. Wastes from cells enter the blood. Carbon dioxide is removed by the lungs. Other wastes are removed from the blood as it passes through the kidneys. When resting, up to one fifth of all the blood in the body is in the kidneys.

After passing through capillaries in the body, blood enters veins. Blood that passes through capillaries in the intestines picks up digested nutrients. This blood is carried by a vein to the liver. Some nutrients are removed from the blood and stored in the liver. Blood from the body returns to the right atrium through one of the venae cavae.

Look back at Figure 19-10. Notice that the right atrium and the right ventricle are shown in blue. The blue color is to show that the blood in these chambers lacks oxygen. Oxygen-rich blood returns from the lungs to the left atrium and ventricle. Notice that both of these chambers are colored red. The red color is to show that this blood is rich in oxygen.

HEARTBEAT AND PULSE

Not all of the heart muscle contracts at the same time. The two atria contract first, forcing blood into the ventricles. The two ventricles contract a fraction of a second later. For this reason, each heartbeat can be heard as two parts. The weak contraction of the atria makes one sound. This sound is followed by the much stronger sound caused by contraction of the ventricles. As shown in Figure 19-12, a doctor hears this two-part heartbeat when using a device called a stethoscope (STEHTH uh skohp) to listen to your heart.

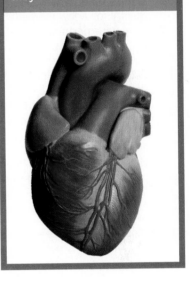

Figure 19-12

Use of the stethoscope for listening to heart sounds.

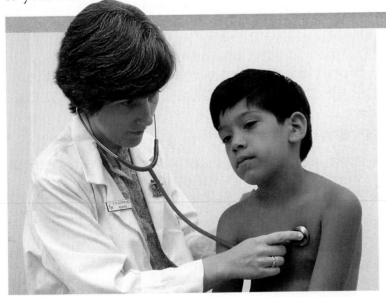

447

OBJECTIVES

Determine factors that cause the pulse to change.
Construct a graph to show variations in pulse.

MATERIALS

clock or watch with second hand, graph paper

PROCEDURE

A. Make a data table with headings as shown.

Resting Pulse	After Exercise			
	Immediately	1 min	4 min	6 min

B. Work with a partner. Have your partner sit quietly for a few moments.
C. Take your partner's pulse by placing two fingers on the inside of your partner's wrist near the base of the thumb. See Figure 9-13. Move your fingers until you can feel the beating. Using a clock or watch, count the number of pulse beats in 30 seconds. Multiply the result by 2 to find the number of pulse beats in 1 minute. Record this number as the resting pulse.
D. Have your partner jog in place for 2 minutes and then sit down. Immediately

take your partner's pulse as in step **C**. Record the result.
E. Have your partner continue sitting. Take his or her pulse again after 2, 4, and 6 minutes of sitting. Record each of these results.

RESULTS AND CONCLUSIONS

1. Prepare a graph similar to the one shown. Make a bar graph of your results.

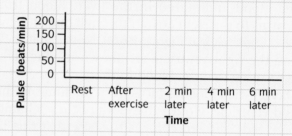

2. Did exercise cause the pulse to increase or decrease? What change occurs in muscles during exercise? How is this change in the muscles related to the change in pulse?
3. Did the pulse return to its resting level after exercise? If it did, how long did it take? If it did not, how much longer do you think it would have taken?

When the left ventricle contracts, blood moves into the aorta and branching arteries under high pressure. The walls of the arteries are stretched by this pressure. When the ventricle relaxes, the pressure in the arteries goes down. The arteries return to their original size. The stretching and relaxing of the arteries with each heartbeat is felt as a throbbing called the **pulse**. At the wrists and at the sides of the neck, arteries pass near the surface of the skin. It is easy to feel the pulse at either of these places. Figure 9-13 shows the proper way to take the pulse at the wrist.

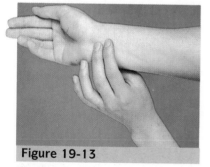

Figure 19-13

Method for taking the pulse.

REVIEW

1. List in order all the structures that blood must pass through to get from the right atrium to the aorta.
2. Relate the thickness of the ventricle walls to the function of each ventricle.
3. What causes the pulse?

CHALLENGE In what way is the vein that carries blood from the intestines to the liver different from other veins?

19-4 DISORDERS OF THE CIRCULATORY SYSTEM

Disorders of the circulatory system are one of the main causes of death among Americans. Many of these disorders can be prevented. One of the most common problems of circulation is known as atherosclerosis (ath-uhr oh skluh ROH sihs). **Atherosclerosis** is the buildup of fatty materials on the inner walls of arteries. There are several types of fatty materials in these buildups. One fatty material is *cholesterol* (kuh LEHS tuh rohl). Cholesterol is a normal part of many body tissues, but it is abnormal for it to be on the inner walls of arteries.

Compare the two arteries shown in Figure 19-14. Notice that one artery is partly blocked due to atherosclerosis. Such blockage reduces the flow of blood, and less oxygen reaches the tissues. This decrease in oxygen can lead to many problems because tissues cannot live without oxygen. A *heart attack* is one problem that can result from atherosclerosis. Heart attacks often involve death of part of the heart muscle due to lack of oxygen in blood vessels supplying the heart. If arteries in or leading to the brain get clogged, a *stroke* may result. Strokes occur when brain cells die from lack of oxygen.

> *After completing this section, you will be able to*
>
> - **describe** the causes of several disorders of the circulatory system.
> - **identify** ways to reduce chances of developing circulatory disorders.
>
> *The key terms in this section are*
> anemia
> atherosclerosis

skleros (hard)

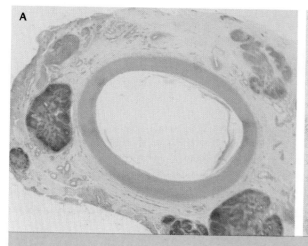
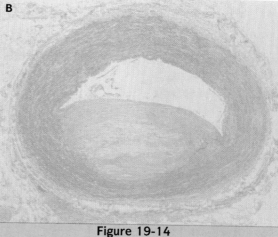

Figure 19-14

Cross section of a normal artery (A). Cross section of an artery from a person who has atherosclerosis (B). What material has built up on the walls of the artery in B?

When arteries become clogged, the opening through the artery becomes smaller. Thus, the heart must work harder to push the blood through. The pressure of the blood within the arteries is increased. Abnormally high blood pressure is called *hypertension* (hī puhr TEHN shuhn), or high blood pressure. High blood pressure puts a strain on the heart. This increased pressure is dangerous because it can lead to heart disease as well as other problems. Hypertension can be detected by a blood pressure check. This problem is easier to treat if it is found early.

Bypass surgery is used to treat heart disease that is caused by blocked arteries in the heart. A piece of a healthy blood vessel is taken from some other part of the body. Each end of the healthy vessel is connected to an unclogged part of the blocked artery. This procedure, shown in Figure 19-15, allows blood to bypass the blocked artery.

Figure 19-15

Technique used in bypass surgery.

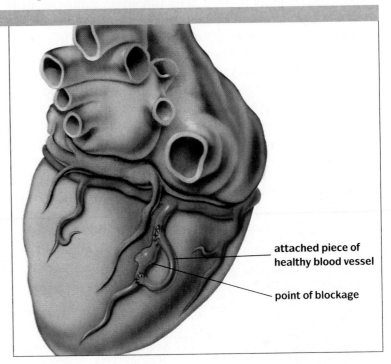

attached piece of healthy blood vessel

point of blockage

Several factors are thought to cause atherosclerosis and hypertension. These factors include lack of exercise, a diet high in animal fats, and cigarette smoking. Scientists have shown that regular exercise, a balanced diet, and not smoking will greatly reduce the chance of developing circulatory disorders.

Some circulatory disorders affect the blood cells rather than the blood vessels or the heart. **Anemia** (uh NEE mee-uh) is a disorder in which there are too few red blood cells or too little hemoglobin. With too few red blood cells, not enough oxygen is carried to the body's tissues. There are many forms of anemia. Some forms are caused by poor diet. For example, a lack of iron in the diet causes one form of anemia. Why would a lack of iron cause anemia?

an- (without)
haima (blood)

Other forms of anemia are inherited disorders. *Sickle cell disease* is an inherited anemia. Observe the red blood cells in Figure 19-16B. How might sickle cell disease have received its name? Sickle cell disease creates many problems. As with other forms of anemia, not enough oxygen is carried by the blood. The abnormally-shaped sickle cells get stuck in small capillaries. These trapped cells may block off blood flow in the capillaries, causing pain and weakness. Transfusions of normal blood cells can help in treating patients with this disease. There is no known cure for it.

One form of blood disorder affects the white blood cells rather than the red blood cells. *Leukemia* (loo KEE-mee uh) is a blood disorder in which many immature white blood cells are produced. These white blood cells cannot work properly in defending the body against disease. Why does a person who has leukemia get infections easily? The disease can be treated with certain kinds of drugs and with radiation.

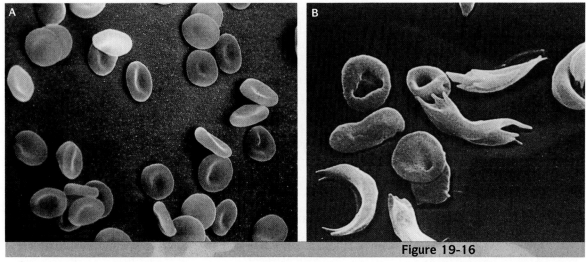

Figure 19-16

Normal red blood cells (*A*). Blood cells from a person with sickle cell disease (*B*). The sickle-shaped cells sometimes block blood vessels.

REVIEW

1. What is atherosclerosis? What problems does this disorder create?
2. What do heart attacks and strokes have in common?
3. Why is hypertension dangerous? How can it be detected, and how might the risk of developing it be reduced?
4. Describe how sickle cell disease affects the body.

CHALLENGE Sometimes, persons with severe atherosclerosis appear to be healthy. Why might they suddenly have a heart attack after heavy exercise?

19-5 THE RESPIRATORY SYSTEM

re- (again)
spirare (to breathe)

All cells in the body need oxygen to carry on their life processes. Oxygen is used in getting energy from food. The process of obtaining energy from food in the form of glucose is called *respiration* (rehs puh RAY shuhn). Carbon dioxide and water are given off as wastes of this process. Note in Figure 19-17 that *breathing* is part of respiration. Breathing is the process in which oxygen is taken into the body from the air, and carbon dioxide and water are given off. Oxygen is taken in each time you *inhale*. Carbon dioxide and water vapor are given off each time you *exhale*. The structures and organs used in breathing make up the **respiratory** (REHS puhr uh tawr ee) **system**.

PARTS OF THE RESPIRATORY SYSTEM

Refer to Figure 19-18 as you read about the path air takes during breathing. A person normally breathes through the nose. Air passes through the spaces inside the nose and is changed in several ways. The air is warmed, dust is filtered out, and moisture is added. Changing the air in these ways helps to protect the cells that line the lungs.

After passing through the spaces inside the nose, the air enters the *pharynx* (FAR ihngks). The pharynx is the region behind the nose and mouth leading down the throat. The lower part of the pharynx leads to the *larynx* (LAR-ihngks), or voice box. The larynx contains two folds of tissue called *vocal cords*. Vocal cords vibrate, or move back and forth. These vibrations produce the sounds of human speech.

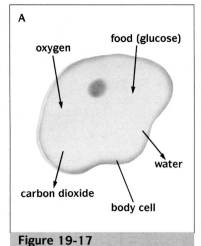

Figure 19-17

Respiration in body cells (*A*). Breathing (*B*).

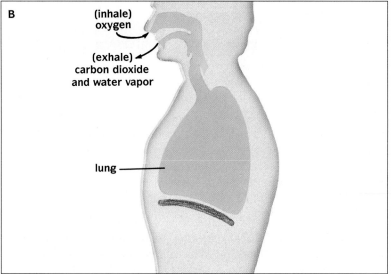

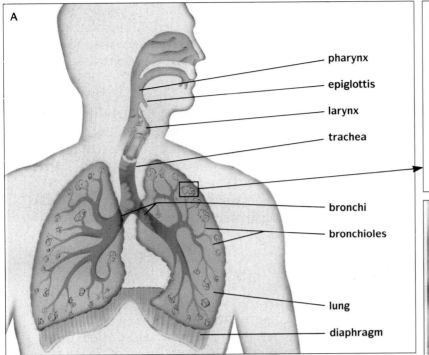

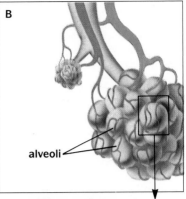

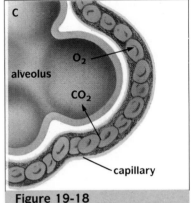

Figure 19-18

The structure of the human respiratory system (*A*). Enlargement of alveoli (*B*). The exchange of gases between an alveolus and a capillary (*C*).

Note in Figure 19-18*A* that the larynx leads into the windpipe, or trachea (TRAY kee uh). The **trachea** is a tube in the throat that carries air from the larynx toward the lungs. The walls of the trachea contain rings of cartilage. These rings keep the trachea open. A flap of tissue called the *epiglottis* (ehp uh GLAHT ihs) is located at the top of the larynx. When food is swallowed, the epiglottis moves down to cover the larynx. This action keeps food out of the respiratory system.

The trachea divides into two branches within the chest. The two branching tubes of the trachea are called **bronchi** (BRAHNG kī) (sing., *bronchus*). One bronchus leads into each lung. Within the lung, the bronchi divide into smaller and smaller branches called *bronchioles* (BRAHNG-kee ohlz). The smallest bronchioles end in groups of tiny air sacs called **alveoli** (al VEE uh lī) (sing., *alveolus*). Notice the grapelike cluster of air sacs shown in Figure 19-18*B*. The exchange of gases between the air and the blood occurs in the alveoli.

Look at Figure 19-18*C*. Notice that a capillary passes along the wall of an alveolus. The blood in the capillary has come from the right ventricle of the heart. This blood contains much carbon dioxide and little oxygen. The air within the alveolus contains much oxygen but little carbon

bronchos (windpipe)

alveus (cavity or hollow)

dioxide. As the blood flows past the alveolus, oxygen diffuses from the air into the blood. Carbon dioxide diffuses from the blood into the air. This oxygen-rich blood returns from the lungs to the left atrium of the heart.

BREATHING

Fresh air must constantly be brought into the alveoli. Inhaling brings in more oxygen, which diffuses into the blood. Exhaling carries away carbon dioxide that has diffused out of the blood. Inhaling and exhaling require the action of several muscles. The most important of the muscles used in breathing is the diaphragm (DĪ uh fram). The **diaphragm** is a sheet of muscle that separates the chest cavity from the other internal organs. Look back at Figure 19-18 and locate the diaphragm. The lungs are surrounded by the ribs. Muscles attached to the ribs work along with the diaphragm during breathing.

Refer to Figure 19-19 as you read how breathing occurs. In part A notice that before inhaling, the diaphragm curves upward into the chest cavity. Now look at part B. You can see that the diaphragm contracts and moves downward. Muscles cause the ribs to move outward

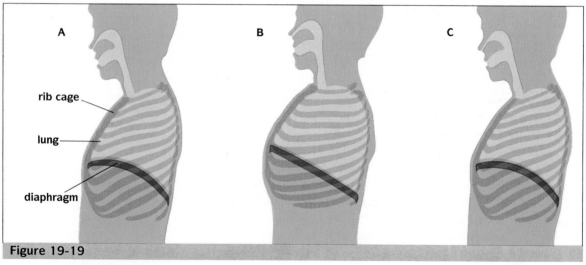

A

B

C

rib cage

lung

diaphragm

Figure 19-19

Position of diaphragm before a person inhales (A). Inhaling: diaphragm moves down and chest cavity increases (B). Exhaling: diaphragm moves up and chest cavity decreases (C).

and upward as the diaphragm contracts. These actions increase the size of the chest cavity. As a result, air flows into the lungs. In other words, contraction of the diaphragm and rib muscles causes you to inhale.

In part C notice that the diaphragm moves upward again as it relaxes. The ribs move inward and downward as the muscles attached to them relax. Compare the size

ACTIVITY   How Can You Use a Model to Show Breathing?

OBJECTIVES
Construct a model of the respiratory system.
Demonstrate how air moves into and out of the lungs.

MATERIALS
sharp scissors, 1-L plastic bottle, 1 large round balloon, 1 small balloon, short length of plastic tubing, masking tape, one-hole rubber stopper, large rubber band

PROCEDURE

A. Use scissors to carefully cut a plastic bottle in half around its center. Use the upper half for this activity.
B. Place the neck of a small balloon over one end of a length of plastic tubing. Use tape to seal the balloon around the tube. Pass the tubing through the neck of the bottle so that the end with the balloon is within the bottle. Pass the free end of the plastic tubing through the hole in a rubber stopper. Push the stopper into the neck of the bottle as shown.

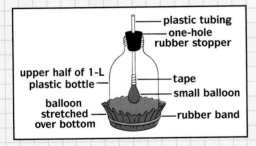

C. Cut the neck off a large balloon. Discard the neck. Stretch the balloon across the wide bottom opening of the bottle. Secure the balloon in place with a rubber band.
D. Pull down on the stretched balloon. Observe what happens to the balloon inside the bottle. Release the balloon. Again observe what happens to the balloon inside the bottle.

RESULTS AND CONCLUSIONS
1. What happened to the balloon inside the bottle as you pulled down on the stretched balloon? What happened when you released the stretched balloon?
2. Make a chart like the one shown. Complete the chart to show which parts of the real respiratory system match the parts of the model.

Parts of Model	Respiratory System
Balloon inside bottle	
Plastic tubing	
Bottle	
Stretched balloon	

3. How did the volume of the bottle change when you pulled down on the stretched balloon? What effect did this have on the balloon inside the bottle?
4. The lung contains many elastic fibers. How do they help you exhale?

---

of the chest cavity in parts *B* and *C*. You can see that the chest cavity is made smaller when these muscles relax. Air is pushed out of the lungs as the chest cavity becomes smaller. Thus, relaxation of the diaphragm and rib muscles causes you to exhale.

DISORDERS OF THE RESPIRATORY SYSTEM

There are several disorders that cause problems in breathing. One of the more common disorders is *asthma* (AZ muh). Asthma is a condition in which the bronchi and bronchioles become narrowed. Asthma may occur as a reaction to foreign substances in air that is breathed. Pollen from plants is among the substances that can cause asthma. The narrowing of the bronchi in this disorder makes it much harder to get air in and out of the lungs.

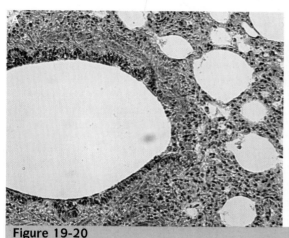
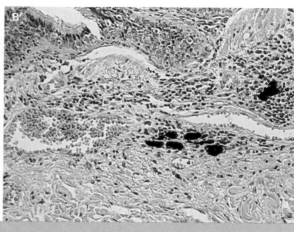

Figure 19-20

Normal alveoli (*A*). Alveoli damaged by emphysema (*B*). What is the main difference between the normal alveoli and the damaged alveoli?

Breathing can become very difficult. The diaphragm and rib muscles must work much harder in breathing.

Emphysema (ehm fuh SEE muh) is a disorder in which the walls of the alveoli are destroyed. In Figure 19-20 you can see tissue damage from this disorder. Recall that oxygen is absorbed into the blood through the walls of the alveoli. As the walls of the alveoli are destroyed, less oxygen can be absorbed into the blood. A person with emphysema becomes weak and easily tired. Smoking is a major cause of emphysema. Some forms of air pollution are also thought to be factors that help cause this disease.

Lung cancer is another respiratory system disorder thought to be caused by smoking. Cancer is a disorder in which cells divide in an abnormal way. Cancer cells within the lungs do not perform the jobs of normal, healthy lung cells. Although cancers may occur in any organ, lung cancer has become more common in recent decades. This increase may be related to increases in the number of people who smoke.

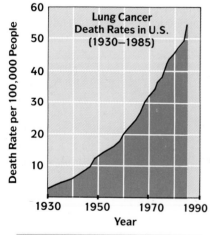

Figure 19-21

The number of people developing lung cancer has risen in recent years.

REVIEW

1. How does air change as it passes through the nose?
2. List in order the structures that air passes in getting from the nose to the capillaries within the lung.
3. What muscles are used in breathing? How do these muscles cause you to inhale? To exhale?
4. Identify two respiratory problems thought to be caused by smoking.

CHALLENGE Persons with emphysema are unable to do any sort of physical exercise. Explain why.

19-6 THE EXCRETORY SYSTEM

EXCRETION OF WASTES

Some of the processes of metabolism release waste products that must be removed from the body. *Excretion* (ehk SKREE shuhn) is the process by which the wastes of metabolism are removed from the body. The organs that help in excretion—the lungs, skin, and kidneys—make up the **excretory system**.

Recall that the process of getting energy from sugar releases carbon dioxide and water as waste products. Heat is another waste product of this process. The carbon dioxide and much of the water are removed by the lungs. Excess heat is lost from the body through the skin.

The breakdown of excess proteins in the body produces a waste product called *urea* (yu REE uh). Urea is a poison and must be removed. Other processes in the body release *salts* as waste products. While salts are not poisons, they, too, must be excreted so that they do not build up in the body. Small amounts of urea and salts are excreted by the skin. These substances are carried in the water that passes out of the skin as sweat.

After completing this section, you will be able to

- **identify** the sources of wastes in the body and the organs that eliminate these wastes.
- **describe** the process by which urine is formed.
- **describe** disorders of the excretory system.

The key terms in this section are

bladder	nephron
excretory system	ureters
kidneys	urethra

excretus (sifted out)

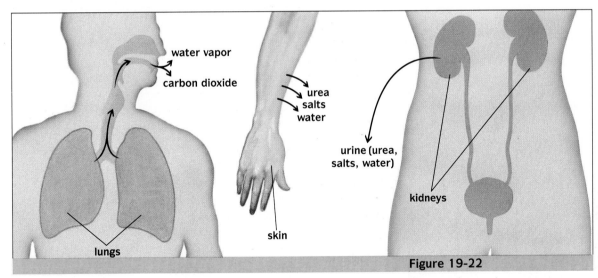

Figure 19-22

Organs of excretion.

While some urea and salts are removed by the skin, these substances are excreted mainly by the kidneys. The **kidneys** are the main organs of excretion in humans and other vertebrates. Two kidneys lie at the back of the body cavity, above the hipbones. The kidneys form a liquid called *urine* (YUR uhn), which contains wastes and water from the blood. Locate the kidneys in Figure 19-22. What other organs of excretion are shown?

457

nephros (kidney)

Each kidney contains about a million microscopic units called nephrons (NEF rahnz). A **nephron** is a structure in the kidney that filters the blood and forms urine. Look at the nephron shown in Figure 19-23A. Notice that it is made up of a coiled tube around which many capillaries are wrapped. Extra water passes from the blood into the nephron. Urea, salts, and other substances are carried along with the water. Urine forms from these substances within the nephron. The urine flows through the nephron to a collecting area in the kidney.

The kidneys control the amount of water and salts in the body. When there is excess water in the body, more water passes from the blood into the urine. The same is true for salts. The kidneys can excrete almost any substance that is in oversupply. Thus, the kidneys not only excrete wastes but also serve to balance the supply of many materials in the blood.

Notice in Figure 19-23B that each kidney is connected to a large artery and a large vein. A great amount of blood flows through the kidneys. Notice also that a tube leads out of each kidney, near these large blood vessels.

Figure 19-23

Enlargement of a nephron (A). Main structures of the excretory system (B).

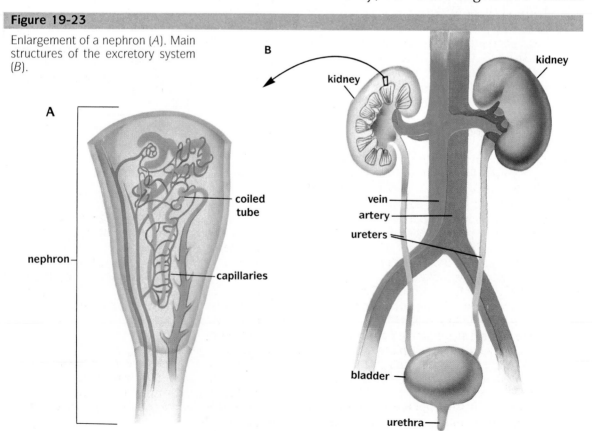

The **ureters** (yu REE tuhrs) are the tubes that carry urine out of the kidneys. If you trace the ureters downward you will see that they lead to the bladder. The **bladder** is a saclike organ that stores urine until it is excreted. Observe in Figure 19-23B that a third tube, called the urethra (yu-REE thruh), leads out of the bladder. The **urethra** is the tube that carries urine out of the body.

ACTIVITY   How Can You Make a Model of a Nephron?

OBJECTIVE
Demonstrate how a nephron functions.

MATERIALS
lab apron, safety goggles, dialysis tubing (20–25 cm in length), 3 250-mL beakers, distilled water, graduate, yellow food coloring, dropper, stirring rod, potassium permanganate solution, string, small funnel, clock or watch

PROCEDURE
A. Wear a lab apron and safety goggles during this activity. Obtain a piece of dialysis tubing and place it in a beaker containing distilled water. Soak the tubing in the water for a few minutes.
B. Use a graduate to measure and pour 25 mL of distilled water into another beaker. Add yellow food coloring, drop by drop, while stirring. Continue until the water is a bright yellow color.
C. Add 25 mL of potassium permanganate solution to the yellow water. **Caution:** Potassium permanganate is a stain. Be careful not to spill the solution or get it on your hands or clothing. If you spill the potassium permanganate, tell your teacher at once.
   1. What color is the potassium permanganate solution?
   2. What color is the mixture formed by the yellow food coloring and the potassium permanganate solution?
D. Remove the dialysis tubing from the water. Twist one end of it. Tie a piece of string about 5 cm from the twisted end. Tie it as tightly as possible. Open the other end of the tubing and insert the narrow end of a funnel into it. While you hold both the funnel and the tubing, have a classmate pour the colored mixture through the funnel into the tubing. Remove the funnel.
E. Twist and tie the remaining open end of the tubing. Rinse off the outside of the tube if any of the solution is on it. Bend the tubing into a U shape. Put the U-shaped tubing into a beaker of distilled water so that the two tied ends are above the surface of the water, as shown. Record the time.

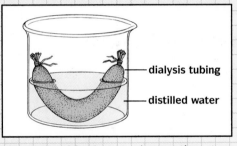

dialysis tubing

distilled water

F. After about 20 minutes, observe the mixture inside the tubing and the water around the tubing. Record your observations.

RESULTS AND CONCLUSIONS
1. In step **F** was there any change in the mixture inside the tubing? Describe any change you observed.
2. In step **F** was there any change in the water around the tubing? Describe any change you observed.
3. Give reasons for any changes you observed.
4. How are the changes you observed related to the way the kidneys work?
5. Suppose that the tubing represents a capillary and the mixture in the tubing represents blood. Suppose also that the beaker and water represent a nephron. What substance acted the way urea acts in the kidneys?

DISORDERS OF THE EXCRETORY SYSTEM

Many people suffer from disorders of the kidney. *Kidney stones* are crystals of minerals that form in the body and block the passage of urine. Kidney stones sometimes are passed out of the body with the urine. In other cases, surgery is needed to remove them.

Nephritis (nih FRĪ tihs) is a condition in which the nephrons are swollen and damaged. Nephritis sometimes is caused by bacterial infection. Damage to the nephrons slows down the filtering process. As a result, poisonous wastes build up in the blood. Also, needed substances may escape from the blood into the urine.

Kidney failure is a condition in which the kidneys fail to filter the blood. Urea and other wastes may build up to poisonous levels in the blood. If only one kidney fails, a person can still function normally. But, if both kidneys fail, the person must have his or her blood filtered by a kidney machine. Sometimes patients with kidney failure have kidney transplants.

Figure 19-24

The portable kidney machine carried by this woman allows her to move around as wastes are filtered from her blood.

REVIEW

1. What processes produce wastes that must be excreted?
2. What organs are involved in excretion?
3. Explain how urine is formed and trace its path out of the body.
4. Name and describe one disorder of the excretory system.

CHALLENGE During heavy exercise, about half as much blood is in the kidneys as when the body is at rest. Explain why.

CHAPTER SUMMARY

The main ideas in this chapter are listed below. Read these statements before you answer the Chapter Review questions.

- Blood transports many kinds of materials through the body. Red blood cells, which contain hemoglobin, carry oxygen. White blood cells protect against disease. Platelets are involved in blood clotting. (19-1)

- Blood types include A, B, AB, and O. Blood types must be matched before blood is transfused. (19-1)

- Arteries carry blood away from the heart; veins carry blood toward the heart. Capillaries allow exchange of substances between blood and tissues. (19-2)

- Lymph flows throughout the body. Bacteria and foreign particles are destroyed in the lymph nodes. (19-2)

- The heart is made up of two atria and two ventricles. The right side of the heart receives blood from all parts of the body and pumps it to the lungs. The left side of the heart receives blood from the lungs and pumps it to all parts of the body. (19-3)

- The pulse results from the alternate stretching and relaxing of arteries with each heartbeat. (19-3)

- Disorders of the circulatory system include atherosclerosis and hypertension, which can result in heart attack, stroke, and heart disease. Anemia results from too few red blood cells or too little hemoglobin. (19-4)

- Breathing is part of respiration—the process of using oxygen to obtain energy. Gas exchange between the air and the blood occurs in the alveoli of the lungs. The diaphragm and rib muscles help to move air into and out of the lungs. (19-5)

- Respiratory disorders that cause problems in breathing include asthma and emphysema. Lung cancer, thought to be caused by smoking, has become a common respiratory disorder. The death rate from lung cancer is now ten times as great as it was 60 years ago. (19-5)

- Wastes produced by metabolism are excreted by the lungs, skin, and kidneys. Nephrons are small structures in the kidneys that form urine by filtering wastes from the blood. (19-6)

The key terms in this chapter are listed below. Use each term in a sentence that shows the meaning of the term.

alveoli	diaphragm	respiratory system
anemia	excretory system	trachea
artery	hemoglobin	ureters
atherosclerosis	kidneys	urethra
atrium	lymph	valve
bladder	nephron	vein
blood types	plasma	ventricle
bronchi	platelet	white blood cell
capillary	pulse	
circulatory system	red blood cell	

Chapter Review

VOCABULARY

Write the letter of the term that best matches the definition. Not all the terms will be used.

1. A blood vessel whose wall is only one cell thick
2. A disorder resulting from too few red blood cells or too little hemoglobin
3. A tube in the throat that carries air from the larynx toward the lungs
4. Pale yellow liquid portion of the blood
5. Saclike organ that stores urine until it is excreted
6. A blood vessel that carries blood toward the heart
7. One of the upper chambers of the heart
8. The buildup of fatty materials in the walls of arteries
9. The tube that carries urine out of the body
10. A sheet of muscle that separates the chest cavity from other internal organs
11. Tiny air sacs in the lungs
12. One of the lower chambers of the heart

a. alveoli
b. anemia
c. artery
d. atherosclerosis
e. atrium
f. bladder
g. bronchi
h. capillary
i. diaphragm
j. kidney
k. plasma
l. trachea
m. ureters
n. urethra
o. vein
p. ventricle

CONCEPTS

1. Identify three functions of the blood. (19-1)
2. What substance in the blood carries oxygen? Where is this substance found? (19-1)
3. What cells function as a defense against disease? How do they perform this function? (19-1)
4. Describe clotting of blood. Mention the function of platelets in your description. (19-1)
5. What must be done before blood can be transfused from one person to another? Why? (19-1)
6. Why is it important that the walls of arteries be flexible? (19-2)
7. What is the function of capillaries? How does their structure aid their function? (19-2)
8. Describe the lymphatic system and its functions. (19-2)
9. In terms of their structure and function, how do atria differ from ventricles? (19-3)
10. How does the right ventricle differ from the left ventricle? (19-3)

11. What is the function of valves in the heart? (19-3)

12. What causes the pulse? (19-3)

13. How do arteries change in atherosclerosis, and what substances cause these changes? What can result from it? (19-4)

14. What is sickle cell disease? Identify two problems caused by this disorder. (19-4)

15. Describe how breathing occurs. (19-5)

16. Where is sound produced in the respiratory system, and how is it produced? (19-5)

17. Describe what occurs in the alveoli. (19-5)

18. What muscles are used in breathing? How do these muscles cause you to inhale? (19-5)

19. Describe emphysema and its causes. (19-5)

20. What substances are excreted by the skin? In what form are they excreted? (19-6)

21. Distinguish between urea and urine. (19-6)

22. Describe the function of a nephron. (19-6)

23. Trace the path of urine from the kidneys out of the body. (19-6)

24. What is kidney failure, and how is it treated? (19-6)

APPLICATION/ CRITICAL THINKING

1. The heart can be thought of as two pumps. What parts of the heart form each of these pumps? To which parts of the body does each pump direct blood?

2. Some disorders cause abnormal blood clots to form within blood vessels. Such clots are more likely to form in veins than in arteries. Explain why.

3. Explain why the pulse can only be felt in certain places in the body.

EXTENSION

1. The Heimlich maneuver and cardio-pulmonary resuscitation (CPR) are used to revive people who are choking or who have stopped breathing. Find out how to perform these life-saving actions and what conditions each is used for.

2. Smoking is thought to cause several diseases of circulation and respiration. Get information on this topic from the library or from health organizations. Present a report on your findings.

READINGS

Hull, Nancy R., and others. *High Blood Pressure*. Atlanta, Ga: Pritchett & Hull, 1983.

Silverstein, Alvin, and Virginia Silverstein. *Heartbeats: Your Body, Your Heart*. New York: Harper & Row, 1983.

Ward, Brian. *The Lungs & Breathing*. New York: Franklin Watts, Inc., 1982.

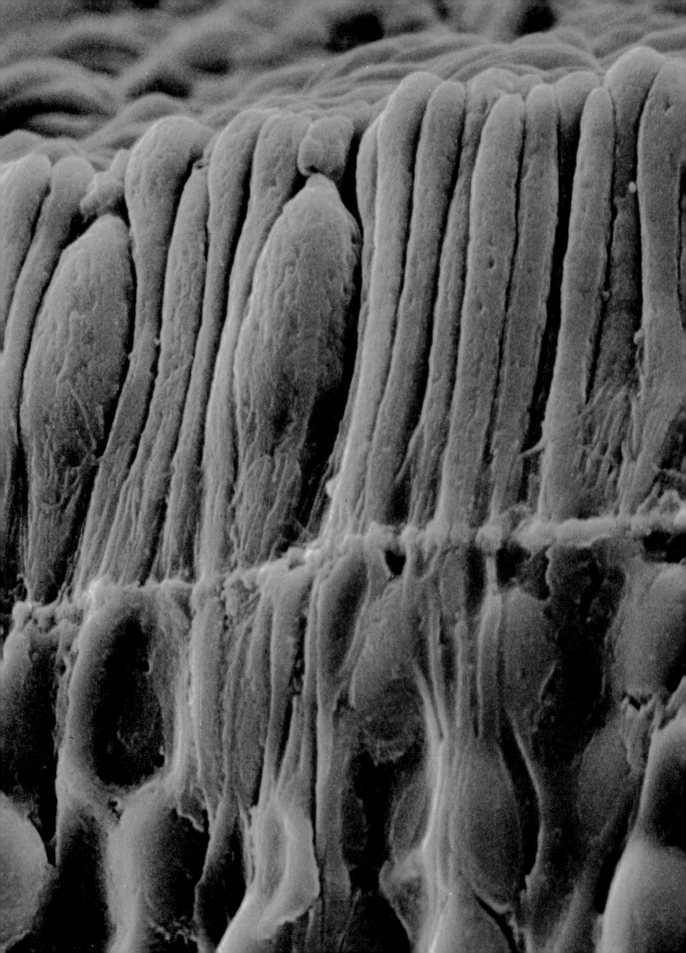

CONTROL SYSTEMS

What do you see when you walk down the street? You probably see many different objects, such as people, trees, street signs, and cars. When you look at each of these objects, you also see shapes, sizes, and colors. An object might also be moving. You can see its motion as it moves toward or away from you. Your ability to see all of these things depends mainly on your eyes. Each eye has special cells that are stimulated by light. These cells are shown in the photograph. Some of these cells allow you to see shape and movement. Some allow you to see color.

- *How does the body receive information from the outside world?*
- *How does the body process and respond to information?*

20-1 SENDING ELECTRICAL MESSAGES

When you are frightened, your heart may beat faster. When you are cold, your body may shiver. What causes these changes in the body? How are the different body systems involved in these changes controlled?

Most of the responses of the body to the outside world are controlled by the nervous system. The **nervous system** is a control system made up of the brain, spinal cord, and nerves. The coordination of actions such as walking and breathing is also controlled by the nervous system.

The nervous system receives stimuli from outside the body. Recall that stimuli are events or conditions that cause an organism to react. Stimuli move through the nervous system as electrical signals. The nervous system then sends electrical messages to parts of the body, causing them to respond to the stimuli.

The nervous system is made up of neurons (NUR ahnz). **Neurons** are nerve cells that carry electrical messages. The central part of the neuron is the *cell body*. Look at the

After completing this section, you will be able to

- **identify** the functions of the nervous system.
- **describe** how an impulse moves from one neuron to another.
- **identify** three types of neurons.

The key terms in this section are

impulse	neurons
nervous system	synapse

465

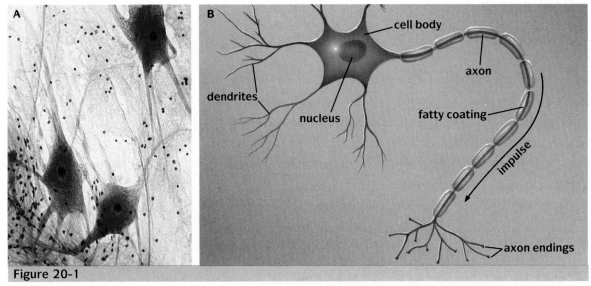

Figure 20-1

Neurons as seen through a microscope (A). The structure of a neuron (B).

syn- (together)

neuron shown in Figure 20-1B. Note the many fibers that extend from the cell body. The shorter fibers on one side of the cell body are called *dendrites* (DEHN drīts). Dendrites are parts of a neuron that carry messages toward the cell body. The single long fiber that extends from the other side of the cell body is called an *axon*. The axon is the part of a neuron that carries messages away from the cell body. Most neurons have only one axon.

The electrical message that travels along a neuron is called an **impulse**. An impulse moves along a neuron from dendrites to cell body to axon. The dendrites and axons of neurons are sometimes covered by a fatty coating. The fatty coating helps to prevent impulses from jumping randomly from one neuron to another. It also increases the speed at which impulses can be carried along the nerve cell.

Impulses move through the body by passing from one neuron to another. The neurons do not actually touch each other. Between any two neurons is a gap called a **synapse** (sih NAPS). Locate the synapses shown in Figure 20-2A.

How do impulses move across the synapse between nerve cells? Look at Figure 20-2B. Suppose an impulse is moving along a neuron. When the impulse reaches the end of the axon, it causes chemicals to be released from the end of the axon. These chemicals move across the synapse to the dendrites of the next neuron. The chemicals cause an impulse to start in that second neuron. Thus, the impulse moves from nerve cell to nerve cell.

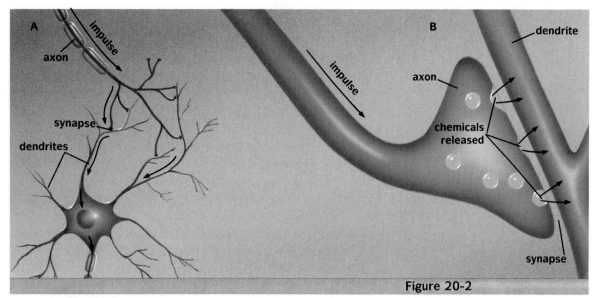

Figure 20-2

Neurons showing axon and dendrite endings (A). Notice that a message crosses a synapse from the axon to the dendrite (B).

Neurons vary in the number of dendrites they have. Most nerve cells have many dendrites. Some have only one. Nerve cells also vary in shape and size. Some have axons over 1 m long. Others have axons that are very short.

There are three kinds of neurons—sensory, motor, and association. *Sensory neurons* carry impulses from outside the body to the spinal cord or the brain. For example, when you stroke a cat, impulses are carried from your fingers to your brain by sensory neurons. Sensory neurons also carry impulses from body organs to the spinal cord or the brain. *Motor neurons* carry impulses from the spinal cord or the brain to the body. For example, impulses from a motor neuron cause a muscle to contract. *Association neurons* are found inside the spinal cord and the brain. These neurons serve as links between sensory and motor neurons.

REVIEW

1. What are the functions of the nervous system?
2. How does an impulse pass from one neuron to another?
3. Distinguish between motor, sensory, and association neurons in terms of their functions.

CHALLENGE The following kinds of wires are found in a computer system: wires that run from a keyboard to the computer box; wires that are contained within the computer box; and wires that run from the computer box to the printer. Explain how each of these types of wires is similar to one of the three types of neurons.

20-2 THE NERVOUS SYSTEM

CENTRAL NERVOUS SYSTEM

The **brain** is the main control center of the nervous system. It is found within the skull. The brain is made up of billions of neurons. This complex organ is connected to the spinal cord. The **spinal cord** is a structure that carries messages between the brain and other parts of the body. It contains nerve tissue and is enclosed by the backbone. The brain and the spinal cord together make up the *central nervous system,* shown in Figure 20-3A.

The brain is divided into three regions. You can see the parts of the brain in Figure 20-3B. The cerebrum (suh-REE bruhm) is the uppermost and largest part of the brain. It fills most of the skull. The **cerebrum** is the part of the brain that functions in learning, memory, and reasoning. It also functions in interpreting messages from many parts of the body.

Figure 20-3C shows a "map" of the cerebrum. You can see that different parts of the cerebrum have different functions. Where is information that comes from the eyes received? Locate the part of the cerebrum that controls the muscles. Notice that just behind this part is a region that receives information about the sense of touch. Other

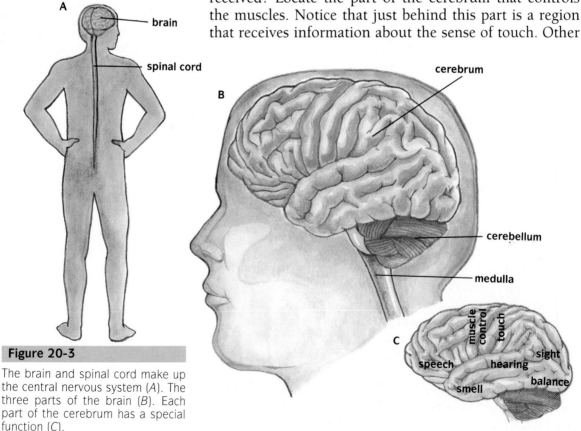

Figure 20-3

The brain and spinal cord make up the central nervous system (*A*). The three parts of the brain (*B*). Each part of the cerebrum has a special function (*C*).

parts of the cerebrum are involved in hearing, smelling, and speaking. If a section of the cerebrum is destroyed, the function controlled by that area is lost.

The cerebrum is divided into right and left halves. Each half of the cerebrum controls the opposite half of the body. That is, the left half of the cerebrum controls the right half of the body. The right half of the cerebrum controls the left half of the body. The left half of the cerebrum is usually larger in right-handed people. The right half is usually larger in left-handed people.

The **cerebellum** (sehr uh BEHL uhm) is the part of the brain that is involved in muscle coordination and body balance. Locate this part of the brain in Figure 20-3. Movements such as riding a bicycle or walking a tightrope require action of many muscles working together. Impulses to the muscles begin in the cerebrum. These impulses pass through the cerebellum. The result is the smooth movement of the body.

Figure 20-4

What part of the brain allows these athletes to maintain their balance?

The medulla (mih DUL uh) is at the top of the spinal cord. The **medulla** is the part of the brain that controls many involuntary functions necessary for life. Involuntary functions are those that are not under conscious control. Breathing, heartbeat rate, and muscle movements in the digestive system are controlled by the medulla. The medulla also controls such things as coughing and sneezing.

The brain and spinal cord are covered with protective membranes. The central nervous system is also surrounded by fluid. This fluid is called *cerebrospinal* (sehr-uh broh SPĪ nuhl) *fluid.* It cushions the brain and spinal cord and protects them from injury. Some scientists think that this fluid may also transport chemicals.

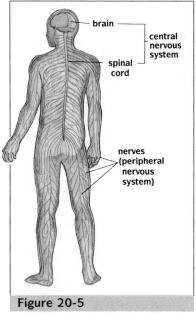

Figure 20-5

The peripheral nervous system.

PERIPHERAL NERVOUS SYSTEM

Notice in Figure 20-5 that many nerves pass from the central nervous system to all parts of the body. A nerve is a group of neuron fibers. The nerves that connect the central nervous system with the parts of the body form the *peripheral* (puh RIHF uhr uhl) *nervous system*. The peripheral nervous system carries messages to and from the central nervous system.

The peripheral nervous system, together with the spinal cord, controls some actions that do not involve the brain. For example, suppose you step on a sharp object while walking barefoot on the beach. Almost instantly, your foot is lifted and your weight is shifted to your other foot. These reactions happen automatically. You do not have to think about what to do. Lifting your foot in response to stepping on a sharp object is an example of a reflex. A **reflex** is a quick, automatic response to a stimulus.

The path that an impulse takes in a reflex is called a *reflex arc*. The reflex arc shown in Figure 20-6 involves three neurons—sensory, association, and motor. Note that the path the impulse takes in a reflex does not include the brain. Look at Figure 20-6 as you read about a reflex.

Figure 20-6

The association neuron of a reflex arc is found in the spinal cord.

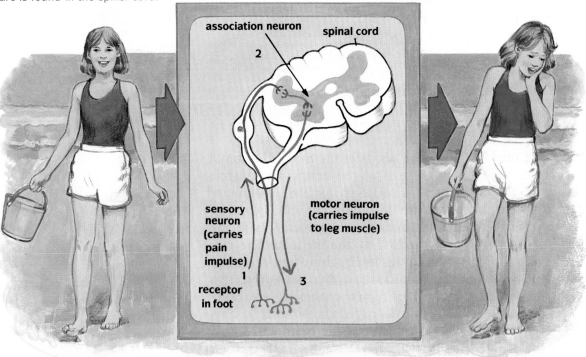

OBJECTIVE

Identify some defensive reflexes of humans.

MATERIALS

small flashlight, watch or clock, desk

PROCEDURE

A. Work with a partner. Cover your eyes with your hands. Do not press on your eyes, but keep out as much light as possible. Your partner will tell you when 3 minutes have passed.

B. When the time is up, uncover your eyes and have your partner observe the size of your pupils. Record any observations.

C. Have your partner shine light from a small flashlight into one of your eyes. Again, have your partner observe the size of your pupils. Record what happens to each pupil.

D. Have your partner observe your eyelids. Let your partner clap his or her hands close to your face. Record any changes.

E. Sit on the edge of a desk and let your legs dangle. Have your partner use the edge of his or her hand to strike your leg gently just below your kneecap. Record what happens to your leg.

F. Change places with your partner and repeat steps **A** through **E**.

RESULTS AND CONCLUSIONS

1. How do the pupils change size in response to light and dark? Do both pupils respond together or do they respond separately?

2. What reflex action occurred in the eyelid?

3. What is the protective value of each of the reflexes observed in steps **B** and **D**?

4. Suppose you walk into a dimly lit room. Which reflex would be useful in this situation? Explain why.

1. The contact of the foot with a sharp object starts a pain stimulus. The pain stimulus is received by a receptor in the skin of the foot. A **receptor** is a structure that receives a stimulus from the environment. An impulse then travels from the receptor through a sensory neuron to the spinal cord.

2. In the spinal cord the impulse passes through an association neuron. The association neuron causes an impulse in a motor neuron.

3. The impulse travels along the motor neuron to the muscles of the leg. The impulse causes the leg muscles to contract. When the muscles contract, the foot is lifted off the sharp object.

receptor (receiver)

LEARNING

Think about some of the skills you have acquired since you were born. What things do you remember learning? You may remember learning how to swim, to ride a bicycle, or to do some other activity. When you began, you had to think about many parts of the task at one time. As you practiced, the activity became more automatic. Finally you could perform the task without thinking about it. *Learning* is a complex process by which the ability to do a new task is acquired. Learning is a function of the nervous system.

OBJECTIVES

Determine how repetition affects learning.
Construct a graph to show how repetition affects learning.

MATERIALS

15 cardboard squares (3 cm × 3 cm), watch or clock with second hand

PROCEDURE

A. On squares of cardboard, write the first 15 letters of the alphabet, one letter on each square.
B. Scramble the squares and lay them out on your desk, letter side up.
C. Have a classmate keep time with a watch or clock. When your classmate says "go," use your index finger to touch each of the squares in *alphabetical order*. Record the number of seconds it took to touch all the letters in order.
D. Repeat step **C** four more times.

E. Draw a graph like the one shown below, and graph your results.

[Graph: vertical axis labeled "Time (s)", horizontal axis labeled "Trial" with values 1 2 3 4 5]

RESULTS AND CONCLUSIONS

1. How long did it take to touch the letters the first time? Did the amount of time increase or decrease with each trial? Explain why this change occurred.
2. Predict what the graph would look like if you repeated the task ten more times.

Figure 20-7

Practice is an important part of learning.

Practicing and repeating steps seem to be important to learning. Some scientists think that practicing a task affects synapses. Do you play basketball? Each time you practice, you repeat a set of actions. These actions always involve the same neurons and synapses. Practice seems to cause messages to move across synapses more quickly. Learning also involves forming a memory of how to do an activity. It is thought that memories are stored in the cerebrum. Scientists are not sure in what form memories are stored.

REVIEW

1. What are the parts of the central nervous system?
2. What is the cerebrum? What functions does it have?
3. Describe the functions of the cerebellum and the medulla.
4. Distinguish between the central nervous system and the peripheral nervous system.
5. What is a reflex? Explain how reflexes work.

CHALLENGE Describe the reflex involved in touching a hot stove. Explain why your saying "ouch" and shaking your hand afterward are not part of the reflex. After you have had experiences with hot stoves, it becomes automatic for you not to touch them. Why is this automatic behavior not a reflex?

20-3 THE SENSES

Heat, sound, and light are examples of the many kinds of stimuli that act on the nervous system. Each of these stimuli is detected by a different kind of receptor. Some receptors are the endings of dendrites. Other receptors are structures attached to the dendrites. Some receptors are contained within *sense organs*. For example, the eye is a sense organ that contains light receptors.

Each sense organ sends impulses along nerves to the brain. These impulses are interpreted in various parts of the cerebrum. For example, receptors in the eye detect light. You are aware of the light only when impulses from the eye reach the sight center of the cerebrum.

SIGHT

Study the drawing of the eye in Figure 20-8. Light enters the eye through the cornea (KAWR nee uh). The **cornea** is the clear area at the front of the eye. Behind the cornea is the colored part of the eye, called the iris. The **iris** is a ring of muscle that expands or contracts in response to light. This action, which is a reflex, causes the pupil to change size. The **pupil** is the opening in the middle of the iris. The size of the pupil controls the amount of light that enters the eye. When would the pupil be small?

Light passes through the pupil into the lens. The **lens** is a clear, flexible structure that focuses light. Muscles attached to the lens cause it to get thicker or thinner. As

After completing this section, you will be able to

- identify the sense organs.
- explain how the eyes and ears function.
- describe the processes of smelling and tasting.
- identify the kinds of receptors in the skin.

The key terms in this section are

cochlea	lens
cones	pupil
cornea	retina
eardrum	rods
iris	semicircular canals

Figure 20-8

The structure of the eye.

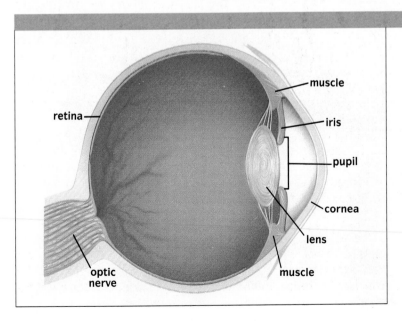

retina

muscle

iris

pupil

cornea

lens

muscle

optic nerve

the lens changes shape, it focuses light from near or far objects onto the back of the eye. At the back of the eye is a layer of receptor cells called the **retina** (REHT uh nuh). The retina contains two kinds of receptor cells—rods and cones. **Rods** are receptors that detect the presence or absence of light. Rods allow you to see in dim light. Rods do not detect color. **Cones** are receptors that allow you to see color. Cones function well in bright light but not in dim light. Which receptors do you make most use of at night?

The rods and cones are connected to sensory neurons that form the *optic nerve*. The optic nerve connects the eye to the brain. When light stimulates the rods and cones, nerve impulses are sent along the optic nerve to the brain. The brain interprets these impulses and forms an image.

HEARING AND BALANCE

The sounds you hear are caused by vibrating objects. For example, if you pluck a guitar string, it vibrates. As it vibrates, it sends sound waves through the air. The sound waves are picked up by receptors in the ear. The receptors change the waves into impulses. These impulses go to the brain, where they are interpreted as sound.

SCIENCE & TECHNOLOGY

A mechanical hand may soon help people who are both blind and deaf to communicate. The hand is run by a computer and can spell out letters of the manual alphabet. The manual alphabet is a series of hand signals used by deaf people to spell words.

The mechanical hand is connected to a small computer. Words typed into the computer keyboard are spelled out in the manual alphabet by the mechanical hand. A blind-deaf person "reads" the words by touching the hand as it spells. It may be possible someday to link the hand to a telephone.

Another computer device allows severely paralyzed people to type just by moving their eyes. The typewriter looks like a pair of welding goggles. A person wearing the goggles sees a display of letters inside the goggles. The display looks like the keys on a normal typewriter. The person types by looking at one letter at a time for a second or two. A special sensor picks up which letter the eye is looking at. A small computer helps the sensor display the letter.

One day this typewriter may be connected to a voice synthesizer. This would allow the wearer to talk by using an artificial voice.

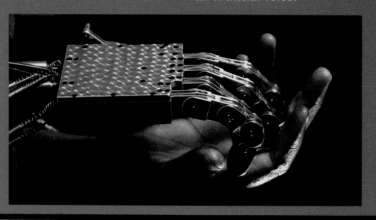

Look at Figure 20-9, which shows the structure of the ear. The *outer ear* gathers sound waves. The outer ear is made up of two parts—the visible part of the ear, on the outside of the head, and a canal. The canal carries sound to the eardrum. The **eardrum** is a circular membrane that vibrates when sound waves strike it. The eardrum is stretched across the inner part of the canal. It separates the outer ear from the *middle ear*. The middle ear contains three tiny bones. The first bone is attached to the eardrum. Vibrations of the eardrum pass through the three bones.

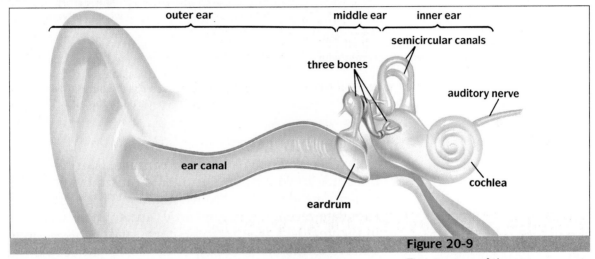

Figure 20-9

The structure of the ear.

The third bone in the middle ear rests on the cochlea (KAHK lee uh), a structure in the *inner ear*. The **cochlea** is a fluid-filled tube that contains hairlike receptors for sound. Sound vibrations are carried through this fluid. The vibrations cause the hairlike structures to bend. These receptors send impulses through sensory neurons in the *auditory* (AW duh tawr ee) *nerve*. The auditory nerve connects the inner ear to the brain. Impulses from the cochlea are interpreted in hearing centers in the cerebrum. Loud noise can damage structures in the ear. How is the worker in Figure 20-10 preventing such damage?

Notice in Figure 20-9 that the inner ear also contains three semicircular canals. **Semicircular canals** are structures that help the body maintain balance. Like the cochlea, these canals contain fluid and hairlike receptor cells. When the head moves, the fluid in the canals moves. Movement of the fluid causes the receptor cells to send impulses to the brain. The brain interprets these impulses and uses the information to control the body's motion. The brain also uses the information to maintain balance.

Figure 20-10

Some workers wear protective ear covering.

OBJECTIVE

Compare the ways in which sounds are received by the ear.

MATERIALS

tuning fork, rubber hammer, metric ruler

PROCEDURE

A. Have your partner strike a tuning fork with a rubber hammer and hold the vibrating tuning fork directly in front of you, about 20 cm away.
   1. Describe the sound you hear.
B. Have your partner strike the tuning fork and hold it by the side of your head, about 20 cm from your left ear. Repeat this test with your right ear.
   2. How do the sounds you hear compare with the sound you heard in step **A**?

C. Have your partner strike the tuning fork and hold the base of it against your forehead.
   3. How does this sound compare with the sounds you heard in steps **A** and **B**?
D. Repeat step **C**, but cover both ears.
   4. How does what you hear compare with the sounds you heard in step **C**?

RESULTS AND CONCLUSIONS

1. Which sound was softest? Suggest a reason.
2. Which sound was loudest? Suggest a reason.
3. Sound waves usually reach your ear by moving through the air. In which steps did this occur?
4. In which steps were sound waves not able to reach your ear by moving through the air? Why was this not possible?
5. How did sound waves reach your ear when they could not travel through the air?

SMELL AND TASTE

When you open a bottle of perfume, odor rises from the bottle to your nose. The odor is caused by molecules of perfume diffusing through the air. These molecules stimulate receptors in your nose. Locate these receptors in Figure 20-11. The receptors then send impulses along a nerve to the brain. A part of the cerebrum behind the nasal cavities interprets the impulses as a particular smell. It is believed that the brain can distinguish thousands of different odors.

Figure 20-11

Receptors for smell are located in the nose.

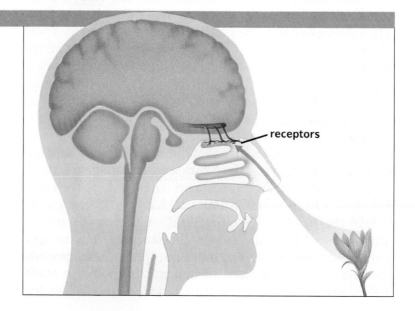

receptors

The tongue is the sense organ of taste. Within the tongue are many receptors called *taste buds*. Like the receptors for smell, taste buds respond to molecules of different substances. As you eat, food molecules are released into saliva. These molecules cause the taste buds to send impulses to the brain, where they are interpreted.

TOUCH

Touch is one of five stimuli that the skin detects. You can see receptors of the skin in Figure 20-12 (*left*). The ends of dendrites of sensory neurons are thought to act as pain receptors. Other receptors in the skin are special structures attached to dendrites. Notice that the skin has separate receptors for light touch and strong pressure. Pressure receptors are found deep in the skin. What are the other types of receptors in the skin? Skin receptors are not spread evenly over the body. For example, there are more receptors in the skin of the fingers than in the skin on most other parts of the body.

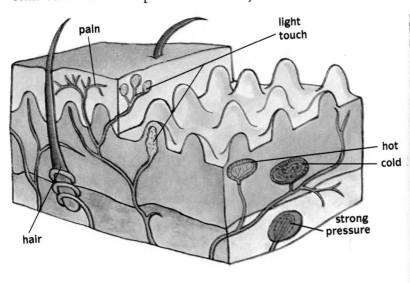

Figure 20-12

The skin contains five kinds of receptors (*left*). Touch receptors make it possible to read Braille (*right*).

REVIEW

1. Give three examples of sense organs.
2. Describe the path of light through the eye.
3. Explain how sound vibrations move from the outer ear to the receptors in the inner ear.
4. Describe the function of taste buds.
5. What kinds of receptors are found in the skin?

CHALLENGE Fish have receptors that detect moving objects by their vibrations in the water. These receptors are similar to a type of receptor found in humans. Which type? Explain your answer.

20-4 CHEMICAL REGULATION

You learned in Section 20-1 that most control functions of the body are carried out by the nervous system. Control functions are also carried out by the endocrine (EHN doh krihn) system. The **endocrine system** is a control system made up of glands. Glands are special organs that make chemicals that control certain body functions. *Endocrine glands* release their chemicals directly into the blood. Thus endocrine glands are different from digestive glands, which release their chemicals through special tubes, or ducts.

The chemicals produced by endocrine glands are called **hormones.** Hormones travel more slowly than nerve impulses. A nerve impulse may travel the length of the body in less than a second. A hormone may take many minutes to travel through the blood. Therefore, chemical control takes longer than nerve control. However, the effects of chemical control last longer. The body's endocrine glands are shown in Figure 20-13. Refer to the figure as you read about each endocrine gland.

Figure 20-13

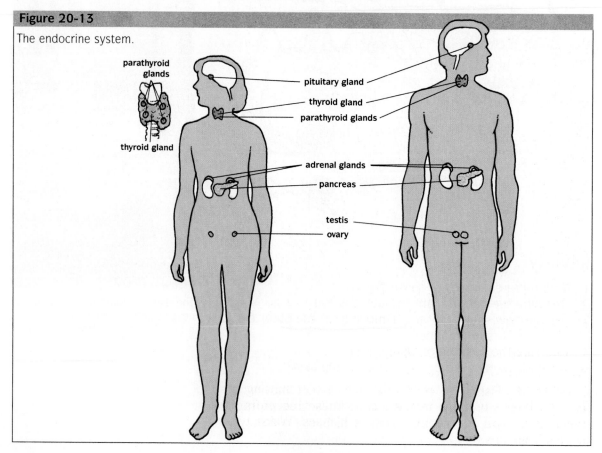

The endocrine system.

Pituitary Gland   The pituitary (pih TOO uh tehr ee) gland is a small gland at the base of the brain. The pituitary gland releases many hormones. Some of these hormones control other glands, so the pituitary gland is often called the master gland.

One of the hormones released by the pituitary gland is called *growth hormone.* Growth hormone causes growth in many of the body tissues. For example, growth hormone causes bones to grow and protein to form within muscles. In some children the pituitary gland may release too little or too much growth hormone. With too little growth hormone, a child will not grow enough. With too much growth hormone, a child may grow beyond normal size. Such problems can be treated if they are found early in life.

Adrenal Glands   An adrenal gland is found just above each of the two kidneys. Each adrenal gland has two layers. The outer layer produces several hormones that help to control the body's use of sugar and minerals. The inner layer of the adrenal glands produces the hormone *adrenaline* (uh DREHN uh lihn). Adrenaline is released when a person is under stress or involved in intense exercise. Adrenaline causes the heart to beat faster. It also increases the flow of blood to the brain and muscles. These changes help the body respond to stress.

Figure 20-14

How do the adrenal glands help these fire fighters respond to stress?

Thyroid and Parathyroid Glands The thyroid (THĪ roid) gland lies on the trachea, or windpipe. The thyroid gland produces a hormone that controls the rate of metabolism. If the thyroid gland releases too little of this hormone, metabolism will slow down. What will happen if the thyroid releases too much of this hormone?

The thyroid gland also releases a hormone that helps to control the amount of calcium and phosphorus in the blood. Calcium and phosphorus make up bones and teeth and are also used in many body processes. This second thyroid hormone works together with a hormone released by the parathyroid (par uh THĪ roid) glands. The parathyroid glands are four small glands attached to the thyroid gland, shown in Figure 20-13.

Pancreas   You learned about the pancreas (PAN kree-uhs) when you studied the digestive system. The pancreas is really two glands in one. Part of the pancreas releases digestive enzymes into a duct that leads to the small intestine. The pancreas also contains endocrine tissue, shown in Figure 20-15. This tissue releases hormones into the blood. One of these hormones is *insulin* (IHN suh lihn).

Figure 20-15

These cells of the pancreas release insulin.

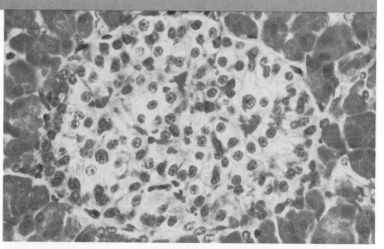

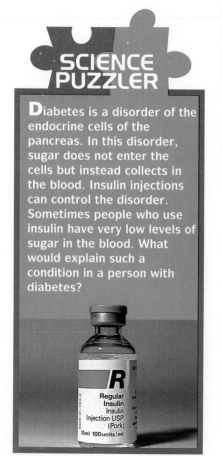

SCIENCE PUZZLER

Diabetes is a disorder of the endocrine cells of the pancreas. In this disorder, sugar does not enter the cells but instead collects in the blood. Insulin injections can control the disorder. Sometimes people who use insulin have very low levels of sugar in the blood. What would explain such a condition in a person with diabetes?

Insulin controls the amount of glucose in the blood. Recall that glucose is a sugar the body uses for energy. After eating, glucose enters the blood from the digestive system. This action causes insulin to be released from the pancreas. Insulin causes glucose to move from the blood into cells, where it is used. Insulin also causes extra glucose to enter the liver, where it is stored. As the amount of glucose in the blood decreases, the pancreas stops making insulin.

The release of insulin in response to glucose in the blood is an example of *feedback control*. In feedback control the last step of a process controls the first step of that process. Look at Figure 20-16. In the first step the pancreas releases insulin. In the last step the amount of glucose in the blood decreases. This last step then causes the first

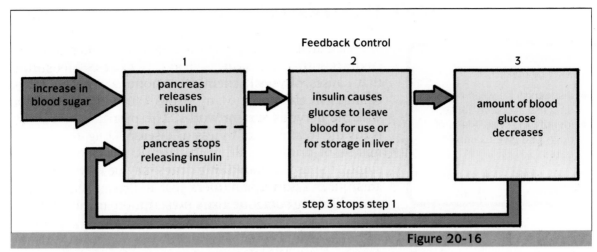

Feedback Control

Figure 20-16

Feedback control of insulin production.

step to stop. What do you think happens after the pancreas stops releasing insulin? The release of hormones by other endocrine glands also depends on feedback control.

In some people the pancreas does not make enough insulin. This disorder is called *diabetes* (dī uh BEE tihs). Without insulin, glucose cannot enter cells. Instead, the glucose collects in the blood. The nervous system and the circulatory system can be damaged by this condition. Diabetes can be treated by taking insulin and by reducing the amount of sugar that is eaten.

Ovaries and Testes   Ovaries (OH vuhr eez) are the female reproductive organs. Testes (TEHS teez) are the male reproductive organs. These organs produce sex cells. However, both of these organs are also endocrine glands. These glands produce sex hormones. Sex hormones prepare the body for reproduction. As the body matures, these hormones also cause development of sex characteristics. These changes include the growth of facial hair in males and the development of breasts in females. You will learn more about sex hormones when you read about human reproduction in Chapter 21.

REVIEW

1. Name the glands that make up the endocrine system.
2. List one hormone produced by each endocrine gland and state the function of that hormone.
3. Describe how the release of insulin is controlled.
4. Describe the disorder that results from lack of insulin.

CHALLENGE Compare the feedback control in the body to the way a thermostat works.

20-5 DRUGS AND THE BODY

addictus (give over to)

Scientists have discovered or made thousands of chemicals that are used as drugs. A **drug** is a chemical that causes physical, chemical, emotional, or behavioral changes in the body. Many drugs cause changes in the way the nervous system works. The proper use of drugs is for the treatment of illness or disease. *Drug abuse* is the misuse of drugs, resulting in harm to the body. For example, the use of painkilling drugs may be necessary after an injury. Taking painkillers just to "feel good" is drug abuse. Taking someone else's prescription medicine is also drug abuse.

A person who abuses a drug over a period of time may become *dependent* on the drug. The body becomes used to the presence of the drug. The person feels a need to keep taking the drug. With some drugs, dependence may lead to addiction. **Addiction** is a condition in which the body requires a drug. The person addicted to the drug cannot easily stop its use. When a person stops taking an addictive drug, he or she may have chills, headache, nausea, or other problems. Drug abusers sometimes die or are disabled by overdoses of drugs.

Many drugs are abused. Although each drug has its own effects, and some are more harmful than others, most drugs fall into one of the four groups listed in Table 20-1. These groups are stimulants (STIHM yuh luhnts), depressants (dih PREHS uhnts), narcotics (nahr KAHT ihks), and hallucinogens (huh LOO suh nuh jehnz).

Figure 20-17

It is important to be aware of the dangers of addictive drugs.

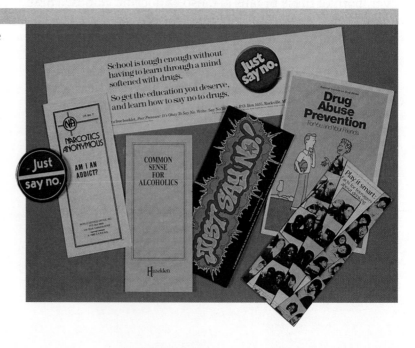

482

Table 20-1 *Some Abused Drugs and Their Effects*

Type of Drug	Examples	Effects
Stimulants	Amphetamines Caffeine Cocaine Nicotine	Increased activity in the nervous system; nervousness and overactivity; increased heartbeat rate and breathing; increased alertness and decreased tiredness.
Depressants	Alcohol Barbiturates	Decreased activity in the nervous system; drowsiness or sleepiness; decreased heartbeat rate and breathing; reduced worry or stressful feelings.
Narcotics	Codeine Heroin Morphine	Reduced sensitivity to pain; drowsiness or sleepiness; decreased activity in the nervous system; decreased heartbeat rate and breathing.
Hallucinogens	LSD Marijuana PCP	Changed pattern of thoughts and emotions; user sees, hears, smells, or feels things that are not real.

STIMULANTS

Drugs that increase the activity of the nervous system are called *stimulants*. A stimulant may increase the number of impulses passing along a neuron in a given period. Increased action in the nervous system can also affect other organs. Stimulants generally cause the heart to beat faster and the breathing rate to increase. These drugs may also cause increases in blood pressure.

Caffeine and *nicotine* (NIHK uh teen) are widely used stimulants. Nicotine is a drug in tobacco. Heartbeat rate and blood pressure are increased by nicotine use. Smokers become dependent on nicotine. Caffeine is a drug found in coffee, tea, cocoa, and some cola drinks. It is harmful to the body to take in large quantities of caffeine.

Amphetamines (am FEHT uh meenz) and *cocaine* (koh-KAYN) are also stimulants. Amphetamines are sometimes used as diet pills or to increase alertness. Overuse of these drugs can lead to dependency. Cocaine is a very dangerous stimulant that leads to dependency. A form of cocaine called *crack* causes rapid addiction. Using crack increases heartbeat rate and blood pressure. Crack can also affect the brain and can cause death.

DEPRESSANTS

Drugs that reduce activity of the nervous system are called *depressants*. Depressants may reduce the number of impulses passing along neurons in a given period. These drugs also change the movement of chemicals across the synapses between neurons. Heartbeat and breathing are usually slowed by depressants. Depressants reduce feelings of worry and stress. Why do these drugs usually make the user sleepy?

The most often abused depressant is *alcohol*. It is found in drinks such as beer, wine, and liquors. Small amounts of alcohol may act as a stimulant for a short time. Large amounts of alcohol cause a person to become sleepy or to even lose consciousness. Loss of coordination and slurred speech are also effects of this drug.

Many people are able to use alcohol in small amounts without ill effects. But, some people develop a dependence on alcohol, called *alcoholism*. Alcoholism is a major health problem in some countries.

Alcoholism that goes on for a long time can lead to serious illness. A large intake of alcohol over a period of time causes changes in the liver. After a while, the liver cannot function normally. It becomes diseased. Liver cells die and are replaced by deposits of fats and fibers, as shown in Figure 20-18. This liver disease, called *cirrhosis* (suh-ROH sihs), is a major cause of death among alcoholics.

Alcoholics often do not eat properly. They do not get the vitamins and minerals contained in a balanced diet. Therefore, alcoholism can also lead to vitamin shortages and other nutrition problems.

Sometimes people who are not alcoholics abuse alcohol. For example, some people drink and then drive. Drunk driving is a major cause of deaths and injuries due

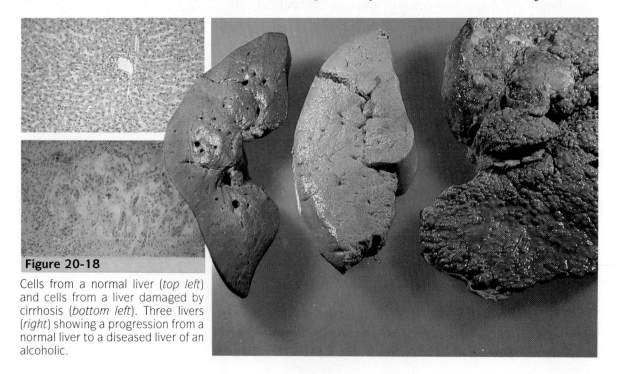

Figure 20-18

Cells from a normal liver (*top left*) and cells from a liver damaged by cirrhosis (*bottom left*). Three livers (*right*) showing a progression from a normal liver to a diseased liver of an alcoholic.

to traffic accidents. Groups such as Mothers Against Drunk Driving (MADD) work to make people more aware of these dangers. They also work to get stronger penalties for drunk drivers. The police in many places have begun to check for drunk driving, as shown in Figure 20-19B.

Figure 20-19

Drunk driving causes accidents.

Barbiturates (bahr BIHCH uh rayts) are depressants used medically by people who have trouble sleeping. Barbiturates are also used to reduce nervousness and worrying. These drugs slow the rate of breathing. With large doses, breathing may stop. Overuse of barbiturates can lead to unconsciousness and death.

NARCOTICS

Narcotics are drugs that reduce pain and produce a feeling of well-being. Opium, morphine, codeine, and heroin are narcotics. They are made from a certain type of poppy plant. These drugs often lead to dependence and addiction. As the body adjusts to these drugs, larger and larger doses are taken to get the same effect. The dose may finally become so large that it is fatal.

Addiction to narcotics can sometimes be overcome. But this process is very difficult. It often means that the user must be in a hospital for a long time. A lot of time must also be spent in a treatment program.

HALLUCINOGENS

Drugs that cause hallucinations are called *hallucinogens*. Hallucinations are things that a person sees, hears, feels, or smells that are not real. Hallucinogens may cause a person to have visions of unusual colors or patterns. These drugs may cause a person to hear music when none is playing.

Marijuana (mar uh WAH nuh) is a hallucinogen. In low doses, marijuana acts as a depressant. In higher doses it causes hallucinations. LSD, also called acid, and PCP, known as angel dust, are strong hallucinogens. Both of these drugs have been known to cause brain damage when taken in large doses.

SMOKING

You have learned that nicotine is a stimulant in tobacco. But nicotine is not the only harmful substance that is inhaled when tobacco is smoked. Carbon monoxide, a poisonous gas, is also present in tobacco smoke. This gas damages the hemoglobin in red blood cells. Thus, the ability of red blood cells to carry oxygen is reduced. Smoking is a major cause of heart disease and other problems of circulation.

Tobacco smoke also contains a great deal of tar. Tar is a substance that is thought to be the cause of several lung diseases. The most serious of these diseases is lung cancer. Chronic bronchitis (brahng KĪ tihs) and emphysema (ehm fuh SEE muh) are other lung diseases thought to be caused by the tar in tobacco smoke.

A

B

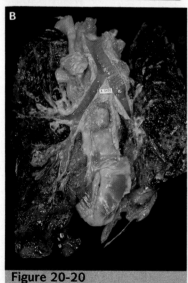

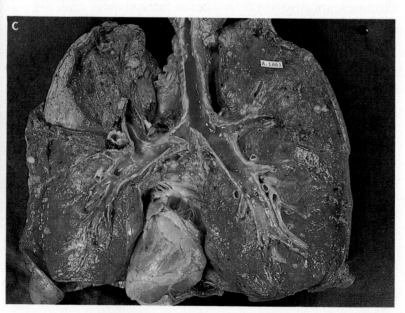

Figure 20-20

Cigarette packages must have warning labels (*A*). How are the lungs of a smoker (*B*) different from those of a nonsmoker (*C*)?

486

REVIEW

1. What is the difference between proper drug use and drug abuse?
2. Name two kinds of drugs. Give an example of each.
3. What health problems are caused by alcoholism?

CHALLENGE   A chewing gum containing nicotine is sometimes prescribed to help people quit smoking. Explain how such a gum might work for this purpose.

CHAPTER SUMMARY

The main ideas in this chapter are listed below. Read these statements before you answer the Chapter Review questions.

- The nervous system is one of the body's control systems. It is made up of neurons, which carry impulses from place to place in the body. (20-1)

- The brain and spinal cord make up the central nervous system. The main parts of the brain are the cerebrum, cerebellum, and medulla. The cerebrum is responsible for conscious control of many parts of the body. The cerebellum controls coordination and balance. The medulla controls involuntary functions necessary for life. (20-2)

- The peripheral nervous system carries messages to and from the central nervous system. The peripheral nervous system and the spinal cord control reflex actions. (20-2)

- Learning is a function of the nervous system by which the ability to do a new task is acquired. (20-2)

- Sense organs contain receptors that receive stimuli from the environment. Impulses are sent from sense organs to the brain, where the information is interpreted. Receptors are found in the eye, ear, nose, tongue, and skin. (20-3)

- The endocrine system is the second of the body's control systems. Endocrine glands secrete hormones into the blood. Hormones work by feedback control and regulate the functions of many organs. (20-4)

- The misuse of drugs resulting in harm to the body is drug abuse. Drug abuse may lead to dependence and addiction. Abused drugs include stimulants, depressants, narcotics, and hallucinogens. (20-5)

- Smoking leads to a number of health problems, including heart disease and lung cancer. (20-5)

The key terms in this chapter are listed below. Use each term in a sentence that shows the meaning of the term.

addiction	drug	lens	reflex
brain	eardrum	medulla	retina
cerebellum	endocrine system	nervous system	rods
cerebrum	hormones	neurons	semicircular canals
cochlea	impulse	pupil	spinal cord
cones	iris	receptor	synapse
cornea			

Chapter Review

VOCABULARY

Use the key terms from this chapter to complete the following sentences correctly.

1. The _____ is the part of the brain that functions in learning, memory, and reasoning.
2. The _____ is the part of the brain that controls muscle coordination and body balance.
3. A quick, automatic response to a stimulus is called a/an _____ .
4. An eye receptor that detects colors is a/an _____ .
5. Hairlike receptors for sound are found in the _____ .
6. The clear area at the front of the eye is called the _____ .
7. A/An _____ is an electrical message that travels along a neuron.
8. The _____ contain receptors for the sense of balance.
9. A chemical that causes physical, chemical, emotional, or behavioral changes in the body is called a/an _____ .
10. The _____ is a circular membrane that vibrates when sound waves strike it.
11. The chemicals made by endocrine glands are called _____ .

CONCEPTS

1. What does the nervous system do? (20-1)
2. What is an impulse? In which direction does an impulse move along a neuron? (20-1)
3. Name three kinds of neurons and describe their functions. (20-1)
4. What structures make up the central nervous system? (20-2)
5. What are the functions of the cerebellum? (20-2)
6. What are the functions of the medulla? (20-2)
7. What is the peripheral nervous system? What are its functions? (20-2)
8. List in order the structures through which an impulse travels in a reflex arc. (20-2)
9. What is learning? (20-2)
10. Where is information from sense organs interpreted? (20-3)
11. State the function of each of the following parts of the eye: iris, lens, retina, optic nerve. (20-3)
12. Explain the difference between the two kinds of receptors found in the retina. (20-3)
13. Explain how sound vibrations are passed from the outer ear to the inner ear. (20-3)

14. What structures make up the inner ear? What are their functions? (20-3)
15. Identify five types of receptors found in the skin. (20-3)
16. In what ways is the endocrine system similar to the nervous system? In what ways do the two systems differ? (20-4)
17. What are the effects of the growth hormone made by the pituitary gland? (20-4)
18. Where is the thyroid gland located? What are the effects of its hormones? (20-4)
19. Where does adrenaline come from? What is its function? (20-4)
20. Describe the feedback control of insulin release. (20-4)
21. How does proper drug use differ from drug abuse? (20-5)
22. How do stimulants and depressants differ in their effects on the nervous system? (20-5)
23. Give one example each of a narcotic and a hallucinogen. (20-5)
24. Name two health problems caused by alcohol abuse. Name two health problems caused by smoking. (20-5)

APPLICATION/ CRITICAL THINKING

1. How is the eye similar to a camera?
2. Identify a device in your home that works by feedback control and explain how it works.
3. When the light is dim, are colors easier or more difficult to see? Explain your answer in terms of receptors in the eye.
4. An injury to the brain might be fatal if the medulla rather than the cerebrum were damaged. Explain why.

EXTENSION

1. Caffeine is found in coffee, tea, and some other foods. Go to the supermarket and read the list of ingredients on different foods. Make a list of the kinds of foods that contain caffeine. Some headache medications also contain caffeine. Find out which ones contain caffeine. Explain why they do.
2. Write a report on the difference between *sensation* and *perception*. Include a discussion of *optical illusions*. How do optical illusions relate to the difference between sensation and perception? Include drawings of some optical illusions.
3. Find out about an organization called Students Against Drunk Driving (SADD) in Marlborough, Massachusetts. Report to your class on your findings.

READINGS

Gilling, Dick, and Robin Brightwell. *The Human Brain*. New York: Facts on File, Inc., 1982.

Silverstein, Alvin, and Virginia Silverstein. *The Sugar Disease: Diabetes*. Philadelphia: F.B. Lippincott, 1980.

REPRODUCTION

You may have seen photographs of yourself as a newborn baby. How has your appearance changed? You probably think that you have changed a great deal since the time that you were born. You passed through many stages of development, from infant to toddler to young child to older child to teenager. Although you changed much during that time, you changed even more during the nine months before you were born. In this period you changed from a single cell to an organism with working body systems. Your body is still changing. Usually between the ages of 9 and 16, the body becomes able to produce special cells for reproduction.

- *How are these special cells produced?*
- *What structures are involved in reproduction?*
- *How does a baby develop?*

21-1 REPRODUCTIVE SYSTEMS

The process by which organisms make more of their kind is called *reproduction* (ree pruh DUHK shuhn). Recall that in sexual reproduction, *sex cells*—egg and sperm—join. The process in which egg and sperm join is called **fertilization** (fer tuh luh ZAY shuhn). The organs that produce sex cells and bring them together make up the **reproductive system**.

THE MALE REPRODUCTIVE SYSTEM

The sex cells of the male are sperm. **Testes** (TEHS-teez) are the reproductive organs that produce sperm. Figure 21-1 on the next page shows the parts of the male reproductive system. Find the testes. They are located outside of the body, in a saclike structure called the *scrotum* (SKROH tuhm). Sperm are made within tubes inside the testes. When sperm leave the testes, they pass from these tubes into a long tube called the *sperm duct*.

Three kinds of glands release fluids into the sperm duct. The fluids from these glands provide a liquid in

After completing this section, you will be able to

- **describe** the structure and function of the male and female reproductive systems.
- **identify** changes in the male body and female body at puberty.
- **describe** the major events in the menstrual cycle.

The key terms in this section are

fertilization	penis
menstrual	reproductive
cycle	system
ovary	testes
oviduct	uterus
ovulation	vagina

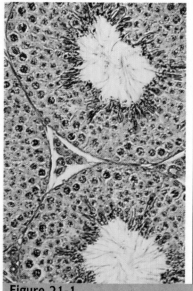

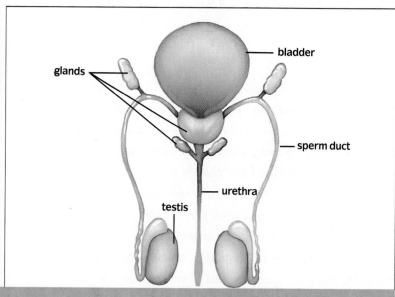

Figure 21-1

The male reproductive system. The photograph shows a cross section of a testis. The two large spaces are tubes in which sperm are made.

which the sperm swim. The mixture of sperm and fluid from these glands is called *semen* (SEE muhn). The semen passes from the sperm duct into the *urethra* (yu REE thruh), a tube located inside the penis. The **penis** is the male organ through which semen passes to the outside of the body.

Besides producing sperm, the testes also make sex hormones. These hormones cause changes in a boy's body at *puberty* (PYOO buhr tee). Puberty is the time when the body becomes sexually mature and can reproduce. At puberty the testes begin to make sperm. Hair begins to grow on a boy's face and body. The voice deepens, and body fat is reduced. Most boys also get taller at this time.

THE FEMALE REPRODUCTIVE SYSTEM

The female reproductive system is shown in Figure 21-2. Find the parts in the drawing as you read about them. An **ovary** (OH vuhr ee) is a reproductive organ that produces eggs. Each of the two ovaries is about 3 cm long and is located within the abdomen. The **oviduct**, or *Fallopian* (fuh LOH pee uhn) *tube,* is the tube through which an egg passes from an ovary to the uterus. The **uterus** (YOO tuhr uhs) is a hollow pear-shaped organ with thick muscular walls. It is the organ in which a baby develops.

The narrow neck of the uterus, called the *cervix,* connects with the vagina (vuh JĪ nuh). The **vagina** is the passageway from the uterus to the outside of the body. The vagina is the place where sperm enter the body of the

ovum (egg)
ductus (to lead)

492

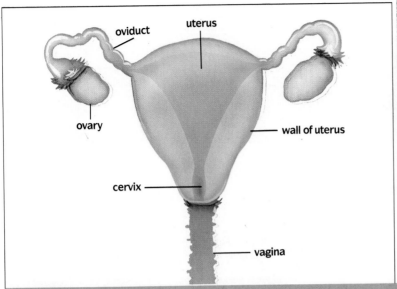

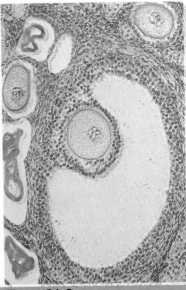

Figure 21-2

The female reproductive system. The photograph shows a cross section of an ovary. The circular structure near the center is a mature egg cell.

female. It is also the passageway through which a baby is born. Why is the vagina also called the birth canal?

Besides producing eggs, the ovaries make sex hormones. These hormones cause changes in a female's body at puberty. Hair begins to grow on the body. The breasts grow larger and the hips widen. Also, the ovaries begin to release eggs. Most girls grow taller at this time.

A major change in females at puberty is the start of the menstrual (MEHN stroo uhl) cycle. The **menstrual cycle** refers to the monthly changes in the body of a female that occur with the release of an egg from an ovary. This cycle usually takes about 28 days. However, menstrual cycles vary from woman to woman.

The release of an egg from an ovary is called **ovulation** (oh vyuh LAH shuhn). Ovulation occurs on Day 14 of a typical cycle. Usually only one egg is released from one of the ovaries each cycle. Changes that occur in the body prepare for the possible fertilization of that released egg.

During the cycle the lining of the uterus becomes thickened. It also develops an increased blood supply. If the egg is fertilized, this lining will support the growth of the new individual in the uterus.

If the egg is not fertilized, the lining of the uterus breaks down. Blood and tissue are released from the uterus and flow out of the body through the vagina. This passage of blood and cells from the uterus is called *menstruation* (mehn stroo AY shuhn). Figure 21-3 shows the major events of a typical menstrual cycle.

mensis (month)

493

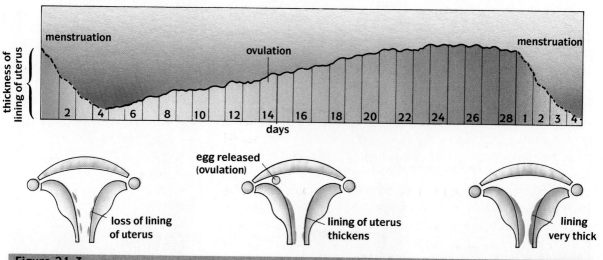

Figure 21-3

The menstrual cycle. Notice that one complete cycle and the beginning of the next cycle are shown.

Notice that the day on which menstruation begins is Day 1. Menstruation usually lasts from 3 to 7 days. An egg will be released a week to 10 days after the end of menstruation. If the egg is not fertilized, menstruation begins again about 14 days later.

If the egg is fertilized, the menstrual cycle stops. Neither menstruation nor ovulation occurs during this time. Why is it important that these events cease during the development of a baby?

The menstrual cycle continues from puberty until a woman reaches *menopause* (MEHN uh pawz). Menopause is the time at which eggs are no longer released from the ovaries and a woman can no longer reproduce. This change usually occurs between ages 45 and 55.

REVIEW

1. What are the two products of the testes?
2. Describe the changes that occur in the body of a male when he reaches puberty. Describe the changes in a female at this time.
3. Name the main structures of the female reproductive system and give the function of each.
4. Describe the major events that take place during the menstrual cycle.

CHALLENGE To develop properly, human sperm must be kept cooler than the normal body temperature of 37°C. Explain how the structure of the male reproductive system keeps sperm cooler than body temperature.

21-2 PRODUCING SEX CELLS

As your body grows, new cells are made. Body cells produce new cells by *mitosis*. Recall that each cell that divides by mitosis produces two daughter cells that each have a full set of chromosomes.

MEIOSIS

The sex cells—sperm and eggs—are made by a different division process. **Meiosis** (mī OH sihs) is cell division in which sperm or eggs are made. Meiosis produces cells that have half the number of chromosomes as the original cell. It is sometimes called *reduction division* because the chromosome number is reduced.

Recall that an individual's body cells have pairs of chromosomes. Notice that the first cell shown in Figure 21-4 contains four chromosomes. How many pairs of chromosomes are there? Refer to the numbered pictures in Figure 21-4 as you read about the stages in meiosis.

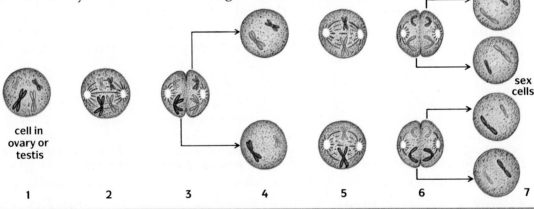

cell in ovary or testis

sex cells

1   2   3   4   5   6   7

Figure 21-4

Meiosis produces cells with half the number of chromosomes as the original cell.

1. At the start of meiosis each chromosome is doubled.
2. These doubled chromosomes line up in pairs in the center of the cell.
3. One doubled chromosome of each pair moves to one side of the cell. The other doubled chromosome of the pair moves to the opposite side of the cell.
4. Two cells are formed. Each of these cells has two doubled chromosomes. This is the division in which the chromosome number is reduced.
5. Each of the two new cells begins to divide.
6. In this division the doubled chromosomes separate.
7. Each cell formed has two single chromosomes, one from each pair. Meiosis results in four cells, each with half the number of chromosomes as the original cell.

ACTIVITY   What Are the Events in Meiosis?

OBJECTIVE
Demonstrate the movement of chromosomes in meiosis.

MATERIALS
colored pencils

PROCEDURE
A. Look at the drawing of the cell.
  1. How many doubled chromosomes does it have?
  2. How many pairs of chromosomes does it have?

B. At the top of a piece of paper, copy the drawing of the cell. Use a different color for each pair of chromosomes. Label this drawing *1*. You will add six drawings below this one.
C. Drawing *2* should show one cell. This time, show the doubled chromosomes in pairs along a line in the middle of the cell. The pairs should be drawn close together.
D. Drawing *3* should show one cell. Show one doubled chromosome from each pair at one side of the cell, and the other doubled chromosome from each pair at the other side of the cell.
E. Drawing *4* should show two cells, each smaller than the ones above them. Each of these cells should have one doubled chromosome from each pair.
  3. How is this cell similar to the one shown in drawing *1*? How is it different?
F. Drawing *5* should show two cells. In each cell, show the doubled chromosomes along a line in the middle of the cell.
G. Drawing *6* should show two cells. Show that each of the doubled chromosomes has separated into two single chromosomes, which are at opposite sides of the cell.
H. Drawing *7* should show four cells, each smaller than the ones above them. Show each cell with one single chromosome from each pair.
I. Now add arrows to connect your drawings from top to bottom. The drawings now show the order of the events in meiosis.

RESULTS AND CONCLUSIONS
1. Which drawings show cell divisions?
2. In which division does the reduction in chromosome number take place?
3. In meiosis, how many cells are produced from one cell? How do these cells differ between males and females?

SPERM AND EGGS

The reduction of chromosome number in sperm and egg during meiosis is very important. In humans, sperm cells and egg cells each have 23 chromosomes. When they join, the fertilized egg has 46 chromosomes. This is the normal chromosome number for human body cells. If a reduction division did not take place, sperm and eggs would each have 46 chromosomes. When they joined, the fertilized egg would have too many chromosomes.

A mature sperm is one of the smallest cells in the body. Its total length is only about 0.05 mm. A sperm is made up of a head, a middle region, and a tail. Locate these structures in Figure 21-5A. The head contains the genetic material. The middle region contains a large mitochondrion, which releases energy used in movement. The tail is a whiplike structure used in movement.

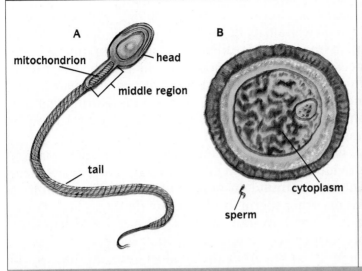

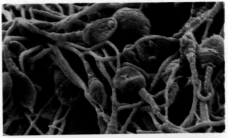

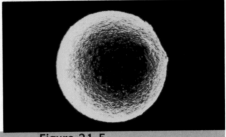

Figure 21-5

Drawings of human sperm cell (A) and human egg cell with sperm to show size difference (B). Photographs of human sperm cells (*top*) and human egg cell (*bottom*).

Recall that four cells are produced from each cell that undergoes meiosis. When sperm are produced, all four of those cells can become mature sperm. However, when eggs are produced, only one of the four cells becomes an egg. The other three cells are tiny and soon die.

The cell that becomes the egg is a large cell, as shown in Figure 21-5B. It is about 10,000 times larger than a sperm. An egg contains a great deal of cytoplasm. The cytoplasm contains substances used in development.

Sperm production begins at puberty and continues throughout a male's lifetime. At birth a female's ovaries contain all of the eggs she will have as an adult. The eggs will mature and be released, one at a time, about once a month. This process continues from puberty to menopause. In total, only about 400 eggs will ever be released from the ovaries.

REVIEW

1. How is meiosis different from mitosis?
2. Explain why the reduction of chromosome number in meiosis is important.
3. Describe the process of meiosis.
4. Compare the structure of a sperm with that of an egg.

CHALLENGE When cells divide by meiosis, the chromosomes are divided equally among the resulting four cells. When meiosis occurs in females, the cytoplasm is not divided equally among the resulting four cells. What have you read that supports this?

21-3 FERTILIZATION AND DEVELOPMENT

zygo (paired)

A new human begins to develop if sperm and egg join in the process called fertilization. In humans this process is also called *conception*. The time between fertilization and birth is called *pregnancy*. In humans, pregnancy lasts about 280 days, or 9 months. During that time a single cell, the fertilized egg, changes into a complex living thing made up of billions of cells.

Fertilization of a human egg usually takes place in the oviduct. One sperm enters the egg. Then a new membrane forms around the outside of the egg. This membrane prevents other sperm from entering the egg. The fertilized egg is called a **zygote** (ZĪ goht). What would happen if more sperm were able to enter the zygote?

As it moves from the oviduct into the uterus, the zygote begins to divide by mitosis. It forms a hollow ball of cells. About 10 days after fertilization, this ball of cells attaches to the lining of the uterus. The cells in the hollow ball continue to divide.

Figure 21-6

Only one sperm fertilizes the egg.

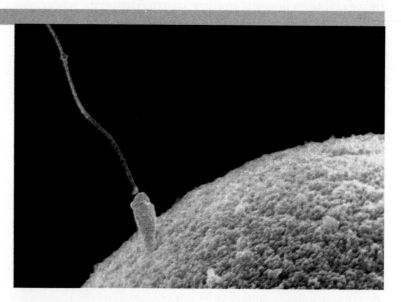

DEVELOPMENT

From about the third week of development until the end of the second month, the developing organism is called an **embryo** (EHM bree yoh). The embryo is attached to the uterus by a special structure called the placenta (pluh SEHN-tuh). The **placenta** is a structure through which materials can pass between the embryo and the mother. Look at Figure 21-7, which shows a six-week-old embryo and its placenta.

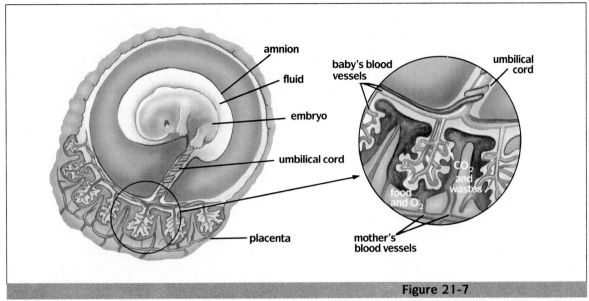

Figure 21-7

A 6-week-old embryo is attached to a fully developed placenta (*left*). Enlargement of section of placenta (*right*).

The placenta has many blood vessels that are part of the embryo's blood supply. The mother's blood comes very close to the blood vessels of the embryo. However, the blood from the mother and the embryo do not mix. Nutrients and oxygen pass from the mother's blood into the embryo's blood. Carbon dioxide and other wastes pass from the blood of the embryo into the mother's blood.

The **umbilical** (uhm BIHL uh kuhl) **cord** is a ropelike structure containing blood vessels that connects the embryo to the placenta. Locate this structure in Figure 21-7. Notice that the embryo is surrounded by a clear membrane called the **amnion** (AM nee uhn). The amnion forms a sac containing a fluid that cushions the embryo. During the embryo stage, all of the major body systems begin to form. Table 21-1 lists some of the changes that take place as the embryo develops. What happens during the fifth week of development?

Table 21-1 *Development of the Embryo*

Week	Development
4	The embryo is 0.6 cm long. The circulatory system develops.
5	The embryo is about 1.3 cm long. The heart beats and the stomach is developing.
6	The embryo is about 2 cm long. The digestive, nervous, and excretory systems are developing. The skeleton contains only cartilage.
8	Bone begins to replace cartilage.

From the beginning of the third month until birth, the developing baby is called a **fetus** (FEE tuhs). Figure 21-8 shows a fetus at 11 weeks and at 16 weeks of development. Note that after 11 weeks, arms and legs are fairly well developed. Facial features, such as the eyes, have also formed. The fetus is about 7 cm long at this time.

By 16 weeks of age, the fetus begins to move actively. These movements can be felt by the mother. The heartbeat can be heard with a stethoscope. The fetus is about 20 cm long at this time. During the last three months of development, the fetus grows quickly.

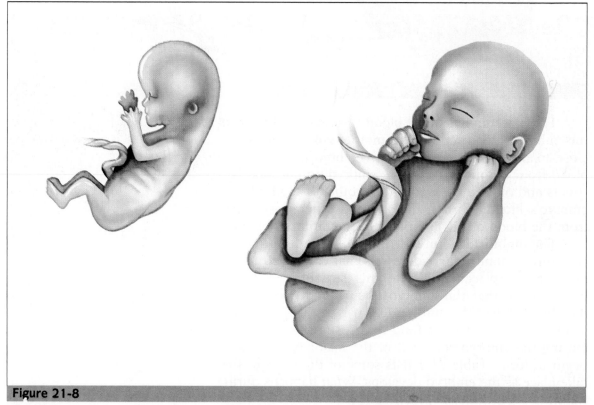

Figure 21-8

A fetus at 11 weeks of development (*left*) and at 16 weeks of development (*right*).

BIRTH

Near the time of birth, the fetus usually turns within the uterus. Its head points down toward the cervix, the neck of the uterus. At birth the fetus is about 50 cm long and has a mass of about 3 kg. Birth begins when the muscles of the mother's uterus begin to contract. These contractions of the muscles of the uterus are called *labor*. The period of labor can be divided into three stages.

The *first stage of labor* usually lasts about 10 to 12 hours. During this time, contractions push the baby toward the cervix. The cervix *dilates*, or opens wider.

During the *second stage of labor*, the baby emerges. At this time the contractions of the uterus become stronger and last longer. The baby usually is born head first. Figure 21-9 shows this stage. When the baby is born, the umbilical cord is still attached to the placenta inside the uterus. The cord is clamped and cut so that the baby does not lose blood from the blood vessels inside the cord. The short piece of the cord that is still attached to the baby falls off in a few days. The navel, or belly button, is the scar that shows where the umbilical cord was attached.

Figure 21-9

The second stage of labor includes the birth of the baby.

The *third stage of labor* occurs shortly after the baby is born. More contractions of the uterus force the placenta and the amnion out of the mother's body. This mass of tissue is called the *afterbirth*. Release of the afterbirth is the third and last stage of labor.

Changes in the mother's body continue after the birth of a baby. Hormones cause milk to be formed in the breasts. The baby can feed on this milk by nursing.

REVIEW

1. Describe the changes that occur in development from a zygote to a 2-month-old embryo.
2. Distinguish between an embryo and a fetus.
3. Explain the importance of the amnion, placenta, and umbilical cord to the embryo or fetus.
4. Briefly describe the three stages of labor.

CHALLENGE Explain how harmful substances could reach an unborn baby if his or her mother smoked, drank alcohol, or took drugs while pregnant.

21-4 HUMAN HEREDITY

INHERITANCE OF TRAITS

People who are expecting a baby often wonder what the baby will look like. They may try to predict such traits as eye color and hair color. Think of how many human traits there are—freckles, dimples, curly hair, and so on. Think how these traits vary among your friends.

Some human traits, such as dimples, are controlled by a single dominant gene. Recall from Chapter 15 that a *dominant trait* is one that prevents another trait from showing. A *recessive trait* is one that is hidden by the presence of a dominant trait. A person will have dimples if a dominant gene for dimples is present.

Remember that genes are inherited in pairs. Let *D* represent the gene for dimples. Let *d* stand for the recessive gene of the pair. *Genotype* is the term used to refer to the genes an organism has. In this case, the genotype of an individual with two dominant genes is shown as *DD*. The genotype of someone with two recessive genes is shown as *dd*. A hybrid is shown as *Dd*.

Figure 21-10

The traits of humans vary greatly.

In Chapter 15 you learned the use of the Punnett square. Recall that a Punnett square is a chart that shows the possible gene combinations that result from a cross between two individuals.

Look at the Punnett square in Figure 21-11A. It shows the possible genotypes of the children of a man with two recessive genes and a woman with two dominant genes for dimples. Each sperm carries a recessive gene and each

ACTIVITY   Are Human Traits Related?

OBJECTIVES
Determine if the presence of one trait can predict the presence of another.
Construct a graph to show the frequency with which certain traits occur.

MATERIALS
colored pencils, graph paper

PROCEDURE
A. Make a data table like the one shown. Under *Student*, write a number for each classmate.
B. Determine if you are able to roll your tongue upward at the sides.
C. Determine if your earlobes are attached to the side of your head. This trait is called attached ear lobes. If the ear lobe is not attached, the trait is called free ear lobes.
D. Record your results in your data table. Indicate whether you are male or female.

Your teacher will list the results for the class on the chalkboard. Record all the data.

Student	Male or Female?	Tongue Roller?	Attached Ear Lobes?

RESULTS AND CONCLUSIONS
1. For the two traits listed, there are four different possible combinations. List these four combinations.
2. How many males show each of the combinations?
3. How many females show each of the combinations?
4. Prepare a bar graph to display your data. Your graph should show the eight numbers from questions **2** and **3**.
5. Do your results indicate any relationship between the traits you studied? Explain.

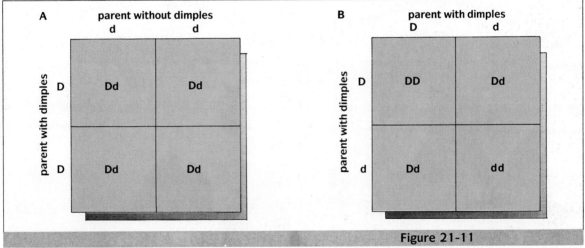

Figure 21-11

Punnett squares showing the inheritance of dimples.

egg carries a dominant gene. All of the couple's children, therefore, will be hybrid for this trait. What will their genotypes be? The inherited appearance of an organism is its *phenotype*. The children will have the dimple phenotype because the gene for dimples is dominant.

What gene combinations would be possible if parents who were both hybrids (*Dd*) for the dimple trait had children? The Punnett square in Figure 21-11*B* shows the results of this cross. How many of the offspring shown have dimples?

The inheritance of most human traits is more complex than that of dimples. Traits such as height, skin color, and eye color are controlled by more than one pair of genes. Many shades of skin color occur in humans. Skin color is determined by several different pairs of genes. These genes affect the amount of coloring matter, or pigment, in the skin. Several genes also control the amount of pigment in the iris of the eye. Because many different combinations of traits are possible, there is great variety among humans.

TWINS

No one has your exact combination of traits, unless you have an identical twin. **Identical twins** are twins formed from a single fertilized egg. As it divides, the zygote separates into two parts. Because identical twins are formed from the same zygote, they have the same genes. They will be the same sex and will be alike in appearance.

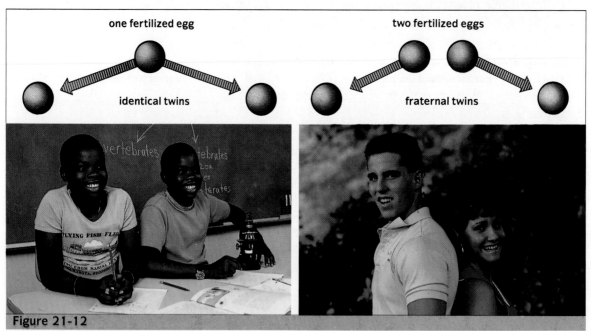

Figure 21-12
Identical twins form from one fertilized egg (*left*). Fraternal twins form from two fertilized eggs (*right*).

Compare the development of identical twins with that of fraternal twins in Figure 21-12. **Fraternal twins** are twins formed when two eggs are released at the same time and fertilized by two sperm. The two zygotes produced develop into two individuals. Because fraternal twins are formed from different sperm and eggs, they do not have identical sets of genes. Fraternal twins are no more alike than other brothers and sisters. They may be of different sexes and may be different in appearance.

Emperor Maximilian I and his family (*right*) lived in the fifteenth century. Holy Roman Emperor Charles V (*far right*) lived during the sixteenth century. Charles was a descendant of Maximilian. Both men were Hapsburgs.

Since the Hapsburgs were important, family members had their portraits painted. Because these paintings exist, scientists can study the family's features.

Both Maximilian and Charles had a condition called the *Hapsburg lip*. Note that each had a lower lip that jutted out and a slightly opened mouth. These features are believed to be caused by a dominant gene.

Environment can affect how traits will appear. The genes that you inherit determine what traits you can have. Your environment can determine whether or not these traits will show. For example, you may have genes for a certain height. But if you have poor nutrition or are very ill during the early years of your life, you may not grow to that height.

Scientists do not agree on the extent to which environment affects traits. Identical twins who have been raised in different places have been studied to find out about the effect of the environment. These twins have the same genes. Any differences between them are believed to be the result of their environments. The studies have shown that twins raised apart still look like one another. However, they may show some differences. What differences might you expect in such twins?

REVIEW

1. Use a Punnett square to show the possible genotypes of children whose father has black hair (*Bb*) and whose mother has red hair (*bb*).
2. Give the phenotypes of the children in question **1**.
3. Explain how identical twins differ from fraternal twins.
4. Name some environmental factors that might affect how traits will appear.

CHALLENGE Even if identical twins are raised in the same home, one twin may be much shorter than the other. How would you account for this difference?

21-5 GENETIC DISORDERS

CAUSES OF GENETIC DISORDERS

Some traits that are inherited cause disorders. Disorders that are inherited are called **genetic disorders**. A genetic disorder can be inherited from one or both parents. It can be caused by the wrong number of chromosomes. It can also result from chromosomes or genes that are abnormal.

One way that scientists can detect genetic disorders is to study a *karyotype* (KAR ee oh tīp) of a person's chromosomes. A karyotype is a picture of chromosomes. A karyotype is shown in Figure 21-13 (*right*). The chromosomes of a cell are photographed. This photograph is cut into pieces so that paired chromosomes can be shown together. Remember that the normal number of chromosomes for humans is 46, or 23 pairs. Scientists can look at the karyotype to find out if the person has the normal number of chromosomes. The scientists can also see if any chromosomes have missing or added pieces.

Count the chromosomes in the karyotype shown in Figure 21-13. If you counted carefully, you found that the person has 47 chromosomes. Note that there are three number 21 chromosomes instead of two. During meiosis, one of the sex cells—either the sperm or the egg—received an extra chromosome. When fertilization took place, the resulting zygote received 47 chromosomes. As the zygote divided by mitosis, all of the cells that formed also got 47 chromosomes.

Figure 21-13

People with Down's syndrome competing in a race (*left*). Down's syndrome is caused by an extra chromosome (*right*).

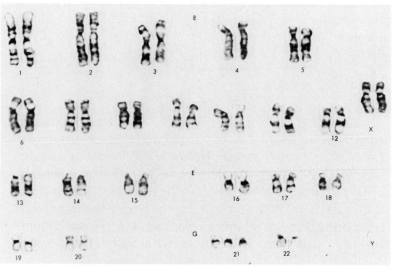

506

The presence of this extra chromosome causes *Down's syndrome*. Down's syndrome is one of the most common genetic disorders. People with Down's syndrome often are mentally retarded. They may also have defects of the heart or other organs. However, many people with this genetic disorder are still able to lead active lives.

Phenylketonuria (fehn uhl kee tuh NYUR ee uh), or *PKU,* is a genetic disorder caused by the presence of two recessive genes. A person with PKU lacks an enzyme that is needed to break down one of the amino acids that is found in many proteins. In people with PKU, this amino acid is only partly broken down. Waste products from this partial breakdown collect in the bloodstream. They cause improper brain development. The collection of waste products also results in severe mental retardation.

Today there are ways to prevent mental retardation due to PKU. The disorder can be detected by taking a sample of a newborn baby's blood. A baby with PKU can be placed on a special diet limiting the amount of the amino acid. By reducing this amino acid in the baby's diet, the effect of PKU on the baby is lessened.

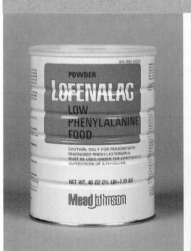

Figure 21-14

A special formula is used for babies who have PKU. This formula contains very little of the amino acid that cannot be broken down.

Tay-Sachs disease is another genetic disorder caused by the presence of two recessive genes. It occurs most often among Jewish people. Babies with Tay-Sachs disease cannot make an enzyme that breaks down fatty material. A few months after birth, fatty materials begin to collect around the brain cells. The result may be blindness, mental retardation, and loss of muscle control. There is no known cure for this disorder. Children with Tay-Sachs disease usually die before age 4.

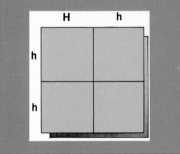

Cystic fibrosis (SIHS tihk   fī BROH sihs) is a genetic disorder that affects mucous glands in the body. Large amounts of mucus are produced in the lungs and digestive system. This problem leads to pneumonia and other infections. People with cystic fibrosis receive special treatments to clear their respiratory systems. They also need to be treated for digestive disorders. People with cystic fibrosis rarely live beyond early adulthood. Like Tay-Sachs disease, cystic fibrosis is caused by the presence of two recessive genes.

Huntington's disease is a rare genetic disorder that is caused by a dominant gene. The disorder causes brain damage, which leads to death. The effects of most genetic disorders show early in life. In Huntington's disease the effects do not begin to show until the person is over 40 years old. How else is Huntington's disease different from other genetic disorders?

GENETIC COUNSELING AND TESTING

As you have seen, in many genetic disorders the genes that cause the disorder are recessive. A person who inherits only one such recessive gene is called a *carrier*. Carriers do not have the disorder, but they can pass on the gene for the disorder to their children.

People who have a history of a genetic disorder in their family worry that they may be carriers of the disorder. Carriers of some genetic disorders can be identified by special blood tests. There are tests for carriers of PKU, Tay-Sachs disease, and cystic fibrosis. Scientists are trying to find carrier tests for other genetic disorders.

Figure 21-15

A genetic counselor can help a couple determine if their children might inherit a genetic disorder.

People who are carriers are concerned that their children may inherit a disorder. A *genetic counselor* is a person who can help couples predict whether their children may have a genetic disorder. The counselor asks questions about the medical history of their family. The counselor also looks at the results of any carrier tests that are done. The counselor uses this information to draw a *pedigree* (PEH-duh gree). A pedigree is a diagram that shows how a trait is passed from one generation to the next.

The pedigree in Figure 21-16 shows the inheritance of the trait for PKU in three generations. Males are shown as squares and females are shown as circles. Horizontal lines between shapes show marriages. Vertical lines lead to the offspring of a marriage. A colored shape stands for someone who has PKU. A half-colored shape stands for a carrier. How many carriers are shown in the pedigree? What is the sex of the child who has PKU?

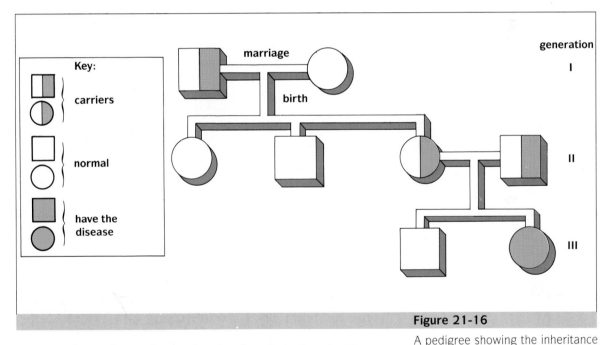

Figure 21-16

A pedigree showing the inheritance of PKU in three generations of a family.

Look at the male in the third generation in Figure 21-16. He does not have PKU. According to the pedigree, he is not a carrier of the disorder. How can two carrier parents have a child who is not a carrier?

Pedigrees can be used to show the inheritance of many other genetic disorders. A pedigree may be very useful to a scientist who is studying a genetic disorder. The pedigree helps a scientist find out if a certain trait is dominant or recessive. A pedigree can also show if a trait appears in one sex more often than in the other.

ACTIVITY   How Is the Gene for Left-handedness Inherited?

OBJECTIVE
Analyze a pedigree to find out how the gene for left-handedness is inherited.

MATERIALS
none

PROCEDURE
A. The descriptions given below show the inheritance of right-handedness and left-handedness in three generations. As you read the descriptions, prepare a pedigree to show these generations. Use circles to stand for females and squares to stand for males. Use Figure 21-16 as a guide. Do not shade in any shapes until you have drawn all of them.

B. Draw the shapes for the first generation. A man and a woman married. Both were right-handed.

C. The man and woman had three offspring: two girls and one boy. Draw the shapes for these offspring.

D. One daughter was left-handed. She married, and had two children—a boy and a girl. Both children were right-handed. Add the shapes for these individuals.

E. The other daughter was right-handed. She did not marry.

F. The son was left-handed. He married, and had two daughters. One daughter was right-handed; the other was left-handed. Add the shapes for these individuals.

G. Read steps **B** through **F** again, to identify left-handed individuals. Shade in each shape that stands for a left-handed person.

RESULTS AND CONCLUSIONS
1. The pedigree in Figure 21-16 shows genotypes. Does your pedigree show genotypes or phenotypes?
2. Is the gene for left-handedness dominant or recessive? How do you know?
3. What are the genotypes of the man and woman described in step **B**? Use *R* for the dominant gene and *r* for the recessive gene.
4. What is the genotype of the daughter who was left-handed? Explain your answer.
5. What are the possible genotypes of the daughter who was right-handed? Explain your answer.
6. Is the wife of the son described in step **F** left- or right-handed? How do you know?
7. What is the genotype of each of the son's two children? How do you know?
8. What is the phenotype of the husband of the left-handed daughter? How do you know?

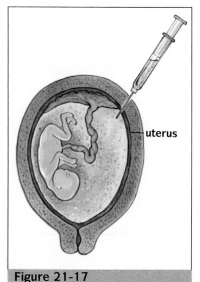

Figure 21-17

In amniocentesis some of the fluid surrounding the fetus is removed.

Scientists are finding ways to detect genetic disorders before offspring are born. One procedure allows doctors to study the cells of a fetus. This procedure is called *amniocentesis* (am nee oh sehn TEE sihs). A long needle is inserted through the wall of the abdomen into the uterus. Notice in Figure 21-17 that the needle does not touch the fetus. A small sample of the fluid that surrounds the fetus is removed. This fluid can be used for many different tests.

The fluid that surrounds the fetus contains cells from the fetus. The cells that are removed with the fluid can be grown and examined. Some genetic disorders can be identified by studying the chromosomes of the cells. Others can be identified by chemical tests. Some genetic disorders can be treated before the baby is born. For example, doctors can now give a developing fetus vitamin treatments or other medicines. It is even possible to operate on a developing fetus and correct a problem.

REVIEW

1. What is a genetic disorder? Give at least three examples of genetic disorders.
2. Describe how a karyotype is useful in identifying genetic disorders.
3. What is the cause of Down's syndrome? What are the effects of the disorder?
4. Describe amniocentesis and explain why it is a useful procedure.

CHALLENGE Suppose both parents are carriers of PKU. What are the chances that they will have a child with PKU? What are the chances if only one parent is a carrier and one is normal?

CHAPTER SUMMARY

The main ideas in this chapter are listed below. Read these statements before you answer the Chapter Review questions.

- In sexual reproduction in humans, sex cells join to form a new individual. The sex cells are formed in the male and female reproductive systems. (21-1)

- Puberty is the time at which the body becomes sexually mature. In females the menstrual cycle begins. The menstrual cycle includes menstruation, the buildup of the uterine lining, and ovulation. (21-1)

- Sperm and eggs are produced by meiosis. Meiosis results in the formation of sex cells that have half the number of chromosomes as the original cell. (21-2)

- When an egg is fertilized, the embryo, later called the fetus, develops inside the uterus. After about 9 months, contractions of the uterus force the baby out of the body of the mother. (21-3)

- Some human traits are controlled by one gene pair; other traits are controlled by more than one gene pair. (21-4)

- Identical twins have identical sets of genes. Fraternal twins do not have identical sets of genes. Environment plays a role in how traits appear. (21-4)

- Genetic disorders may result from the wrong chromosome number or from abnormal chromosomes or genes. Genetic counselors advise couples about the possibility of genetic disorders among their offspring. (21-5)

The key terms in this chapter are listed below. Use each term in a sentence that shows the meaning of the term.

amnion	meiosis	reproductive system
embryo	menstrual cycle	testes
fertilization	ovary	umbilical cord
fetus	oviduct	uterus
fraternal twins	ovulation	vagina
genetic disorders	penis	zygote
identical twins	placenta	

Chapter Review

VOCABULARY

Write the letter of the term that best matches the definition. Not all the terms will be used.

1. The reproductive organ in which eggs are produced
2. A membrane that surrounds the developing fetus
3. The pear-shaped organ in which the embryo develops
4. The process by which sperm and egg join
5. The tube through which the egg passes from the ovary to the uterus
6. The structure through which sperm leave the body
7. A ropelike structure containing blood vessels that connects the embryo to the placenta
8. A fertilized egg
9. The reproductive organs in which sperm are produced
10. The passageway through which the baby leaves the body of the mother during birth

a. amnion
b. embryo
c. fertilization
d. fetus
e. genetic disorder
f. menstrual cycle
g. ovary
h. oviduct
i. penis
j. placenta
k. testes
l. umbilical cord
m. uterus
n. vagina
o. zygote

CONCEPTS

1. Compare the functions of the testes and the ovaries. (21-1)
2. Compare the body changes that take place in females during puberty and menopause. (21-1)
3. On what day of a typical 28-day menstrual cycle does ovulation usually occur? (21-1)
4. What kind of cells are produced by mitosis? What kind of cells are produced by meiosis? (21-2)
5. Describe the process of meiosis. (21-2)
6. If a body cell of an organism has 32 chromosomes, how many chromosomes would its sex cells have? (21-2)
7. Compare the sizes of eggs and sperm. (21-2)
8. What is the function of the amnion? (21-3)
9. Explain why the placenta is important to the development of the fetus during pregnancy. (21-3)
10. Before birth, when do all the major body systems begin to form? (21-3)

11. Describe the major events during the stages of labor. (21-3)

12. The gene for right-handedness (R) is dominant over the gene for left-handedness (r). Using letter symbols, show the genotype of a hybrid for this trait. What is the phenotype of a person with the hybrid genotype? (21-4)

13. Why are human traits so varied? (21-4)

14. Which are more likely to look the same—identical twins or fraternal twins? Why? (21-4)

15. The average height of Americans has increased several centimeters over the last 200 years. How might environment have influenced this trait? (21-4)

16. What is the difference between the cause of Down's syndrome and the cause of PKU? (21-5)

17. How is genetic counseling helpful to couples planning to have children? (21-5)

18. In amniocentesis, whose cells are present in the fluid that is removed from the uterus? How are these cells used? (21-5)

---

1. Write the names of the following structures in the order in which sperm would pass through them: sperm duct, penis, testes.

2. Is fertilization likely to occur on Day 1 of the menstrual cycle? Explain your answer.

3. Your friend Tom tells you that he has an identical twin sister named Toni. How do you know that his story is not accurate?

4. If a pedigree shows that both parents are carriers of a recessive gene for a disease, will their children have the disorder?

APPLICATION / CRITICAL THINKING

---

1. Investigate the types of fertility drugs. Why might they cause multiple births?

2. Write a report on ultrasonography. Include information about the kinds of problems that can be detected by this procedure.

3. Investigate a genetic disorder other than those discussed in this chapter. Report to the class on the incidence of the disorder in the human population. Describe the cause of the disorder and its treatment, if any.

EXTENSION

Clark, Matt, and Mary Hayer. "A Breakthrough Against CF?" *Newsweek,* May 12, 1986, p. 69.

Gold, Michael. "The Baby Makers." *Science 85,* April 1985, p. 26.

READINGS

Science in Careers

Have you ever seen a respirator? It is a machine that is used to aid people who have breathing problems. It is the job of a respiratory therapist to use the respirator with the patients who have these difficulties. The use of respirators has saved the lives of many people.

Besides using respirators, respiratory therapists also use other breathing equipment. They test breathing and give therapy. They also teach patients who have respiratory system disorders, such as emphysema and cystic fibrosis, to do exercises. Over time, the exercises can help to strengthen a patient's respiratory system.

Respiratory therapists must have a high school diploma and two years of additional training. Most also have special certification. If you are interested in this career, you should take courses in biology and chemistry in high school.■

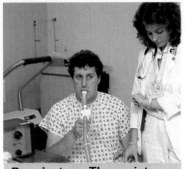
Respiratory Therapist

Have you read about the artificial heart? It was designed and built by biomedical engineers. Biomedical engineers combine their knowledge of engineering, biology, and medicine in their work.

Biomedical engineers have developed the pacemaker, artificial heart valves, kidney machines, and artificial arteries. They have also developed several kinds of bone and joint replacement parts, among other medical devices.

Biomedical engineers usually have a four-year college degree in engineering and additional training in biology. Some have a degree in biology and training in engineering. If you are interested in a career as a biomedical engineer, you should take courses in biology, chemistry, physics, and mathematics in high school.■

Biomedical Engineer

People in Science

Dr. Angella D. Ferguson, Medical Doctor

Dr. Angella D. Ferguson is a medical doctor. For many years she has studied the effects of sickle cell disease.

Sickle cell disease usually affects black people. The red blood cells of someone with the disease do not have the usual disc shape. Instead, they are shaped like a sickle. These sickle-shaped red blood cells do not carry oxygen well. Also, the disease is a very painful one for the patient.

Dr. Ferguson, along with other scientists, studied how the disease affects children of different ages. Her studies revealed a pattern in which the symptoms varied with the age of the patient. She developed treatments that made the symptoms of the disease less severe. These treatments included having the patient exercise, drink large amounts of water, and eat a balanced diet. Although many of her ideas seem simple, Dr. Ferguson's methods of treatment have reduced the pain and suffering of many children with sickle cell disease.■

Issues and Technology

There has been a revolution in the way Americans prepare and eat foods. Fifty years ago, dinner might have been a roast baked in the oven, whole potatoes cooked and mashed by hand, and fresh vegetables. Dessert might have been a homemade pie or cake. All of this food would have taken hours to prepare.

The family today is different than it was years ago, when people often had hours to spend preparing meals. Today, women and men often work, raise families, and want to have leisure time. They do not want to spend a large part of the day in the kitchen, baking roasts, mashing potatoes, chopping vegetables, and rolling pie crusts.

Modern technology has changed people's eating habits. Foods can be precooked and frozen. They can be dried or freeze-dried. The processed convenience foods served in many homes come already prepared, precooked, powdered, canned, or frozen. Instant mashed potatoes often are used in place of fresh potatoes. Frozen pies are advertised as tasting like homemade pies.

Technology has made it possible for foods to be prepared quickly. Chains of fast-food restaurants make use of technology to serve hot meals to many people very quickly. Each day, one out of every five Americans eats at least one meal at a fast-food restaurant. In 1985, Americans spent $47.5 billion on fast food. Figure 1 shows how much of this business went to a few national chains of fast-food restaurants. Notice that these numbers do not total $47.5 billion. The remaining amount of money was spent at smaller chains and at independent restaurants.

Is there anything wrong with this trend? Some people say no. Convenience foods save time, and some are very tasty. Fast foods are thought of as inexpensive. Few restaurants can provide a meal for just a few dollars.

Some people are concerned that Americans are trading good nutrition for convenience. Many fast-food restaurants do not serve vegetables or fruits. Some fast-food restaurants have salad bars, but most do not.

APPLYING CRITICAL THINKING SKILLS

1. According to Figure 1, what is the most popular kind of fast food?
2. According to Figure 1, what is the least popular kind of fast food?
3. What kinds of fast foods are not included in Figure 1?
4. Suggest some reasons why salads and vegetables are not more common in fast-food restaurants.
5. Some fast-food restaurants have salad bars. Do you think this is a good substitute for serving vegetables? Why or why not?
6. Suppose you know someone who eats at fast-food restaurants several times each week. What would you suggest that this person do to improve the balance of his or her diet?

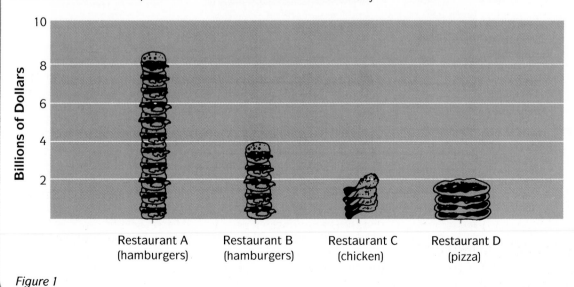

Figure 1

Critics of fast foods say that these foods do not contain enough fiber from fresh fruits, vegetables, and whole grains. They also do not contain enough vitamin A or C, or minerals such as calcium. What nutrients are found in fast foods? These foods are high in sugar, starches, fat, and salt.

The high levels of sugar come mostly from soft drinks, shakes, pies, and ice cream. Hamburger rolls, french fries, pizza crust, and the coating on fried chicken contain starches. Together these carbohydrates contribute to high-Calorie foods.

Most adults require between 1200 and 2000 Calories a day. A deluxe hamburger has over 600 Calories. A serving of french fries contains about 200 Calories. A shake adds another 350 Calories. As you can see, one fast-food meal could use up most of a person's Calorie allotment for the day.

Defenders of fast foods point out that these foods do contain protein. They also contain an adequate amount of B vitamins. Calcium is included in the meal if a person has milk or a shake instead of a soft drink. Iron is provided if a person chooses beef or chicken. The idea is that if people choose wisely, a fast-food meal can be nutritious.

Choosing a piece of chicken for its protein and iron content also means choosing all the fat the chicken is fried in. Nutrition experts say that fat should make up no more than 35 percent of a person's Calories. However, 51 percent of the Calories in an average fast meal comes from fats.

Too much fat in the diet can cause health problems such as atherosclerosis. This is a condition in which fatty deposits form on the inside of arteries. This condition keeps blood from flowing normally and can lead to heart attack.

Fast foods also are high in sodium, a mineral that comes mostly from salt. Too much sodium can contribute to high blood pressure and to obesity. Most doctors recommend that people keep sodium intake between 1100 and 3300 mg per day. Figure 2 shows the fat and sodium content of some fast foods.

APPLYING CRITICAL THINKING SKILLS

1. The body needs between 15 and 25 g of fat each day. What foods listed have more fat than this? Does this fat content cause health problems? Explain your answer.
2. Compare the sodium content in the servings of french fries from restaurants A and B. Each restaurant made its own measurements. What difference in how the measurement was made could account for the difference in sodium?

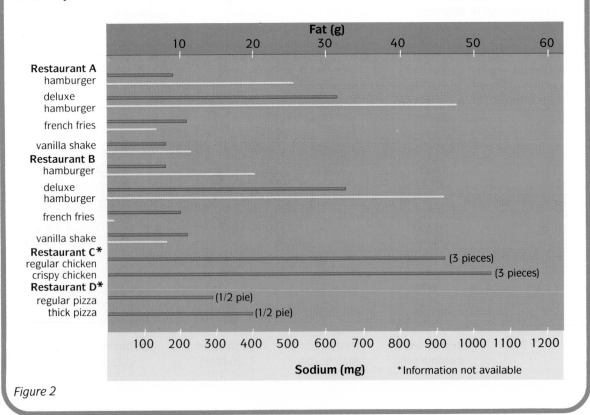

Figure 2

ORANGE DRINK

Nutrition Information Per Serving
Serving Size: 2 Heaping Teaspoons In 4 Fl. Oz. Water
Serving Per Container: 48
Calories 60
Protein 0
Fat 0
Carbohydrate . . . . 15 grams
**Percentage of U.S. Recommended
Daily Allowances (U.S. RDA)**
Vitamin A 20%
Vitamin C 100%
Calcium 6%

Contains Less Than 2% of U.S. RDA Of Protein, Thiamine, Riboflavin, Niacin, And Iron.

INGREDIENTS: SUGAR, CITRIC ACID, DEXTRIN, CALCIUM PHOSPHATE, NATURAL ORANGE FLAVOR, POTASSIUM CITRATE, ASCORBIC ACID (VITAMIN C), VEGETABLE OIL (PARTIALLY HYDROGENATED COTTONSEED OIL AND/OR PARTIALLY HYDROGENATED COCONUT OIL), ARTIFICIAL FLAVOR, XANTHAN GUM, ARTIFICIAL COLOR (FC&C YELLOW #5 AND YELLOW #6) AND VITAMIN A PALMITATE (STABILIZED).

ORANGE JUICE

Nutrition Information Per Serving
Serving Size: 4 Fl. Oz.
Servings Per Container: 16
Calories 55
Protein 1
Fat . . . . less than 1
Carbohydrate . . . . .13 grams
Potassium . . . . .260 mg
**Percentage of U.S. Recommended
Daily Allowances (U.S. RDA)**
Vitamin C 90%
Thiamine 8%

Contains Less Than 2% of the U.S. RDA Of Protein, Vitamin A, Riboflavin, Niacin, Calcium, And Iron.

INGREDIENTS: FRESH ORANGE JUICE

Figure 3

3. A deluxe hamburger usually has twice as much meat as a regular hamburger. It also has about twice the protein and Calories of a regular hamburger. However, the deluxe hamburger has more than twice the fat. Suggest a reason for this difference.

4. The serving of chicken listed is slightly higher in Calories than are the deluxe hamburgers. It also is higher in fat but is lower in carbohydrates. Account for these differences.

5. What could be done to decrease the fat and sodium content in the hamburgers listed? Why, do you think, is this not being done?

One problem with relying heavily on fast foods is that they do not contain as wide a variety of nutrients as a diet that includes fresh foods. To stay healthy the body needs over 40 different nutrients each day. These nutrients include vitamins A, B, C, D, and E, as well as minerals such as calcium, iron, potassium, and iodine.

Both processed convenience foods and fast foods may lack some of these important nutrients. This may be due to the processes used to precook, freeze, or dry foods. For example, much of the vitamin C in foods is destroyed during cooking. Vitamins that are lost in processing can be replaced, but vitamins that are normally present in small amounts usually are not replaced.

Another difference between fresh foods and processed foods is that processed foods often contain added chemicals. Figure 3 compares the nutrients in fresh orange juice with those in orange drink made from a powder.

APPLYING CRITICAL THINKING SKILLS

1. Which has more different nutrients—fresh orange juice or orange drink made from a powder?

2. What nutrients are found in greater amounts in fresh orange juice than in orange drink? What nutrients are found in greater amounts in orange drink than in fresh orange juice?

3. Advertisements for the orange drink say that it is fortified with vitamin C. This means vitamin C has been added. What else has been added to the orange drink? Why, do you think, does the company that makes the orange drink not advertise these ingredients?

4. Notice the difference in Calories and carbohydrates in the two drinks. Which has more Calories? Suggest a reason for this difference.

5. One serving of fresh orange juice costs twice as much as one serving of orange drink. Why is fresh orange juice more expensive? Do you think it is worth the difference in price? Why or why not?

ECOLOGY

*T*he earth is a unique planet among the other planets that orbit the sun. The earth's environment supports a great variety of living things. Humans have changed the environment. Some of the changes have had a harmful effect on living things of the earth. In this unit you will study the environment and how it has been changed by humans. You will also learn what can be done to stop some of the harmful changes. ■

▲ *This African antelope, called a steenbok, lives in an area affected by drought.*

◄ *Strip mining of coal is less expensive than underground mining, but it damages the environment.*

SCRAP METAL CONSERVES NATURAL RESOURCES

▲ *Steel from automobiles is recycled. This helps to conserve iron, an important resource.*

▶ This engraving, made in 1734, shows an early view of Savannah, Georgia. As cities grow, natural areas are often destroyed.

▼ A train of the Santa Fe Railroad going through Colorado. It brought people and industry to the West.

▶ Other animals are the food source of hawks. This sparrow hawk is eating a mouse.

THE ENVIRONMENT

During a storm, you may have seen a flash of lightning like that shown in the photograph. You may have seen lightning between clouds or between the sky and the ground. Lightning affects gases in the air. One gas, nitrogen, is changed by lightning. During a rainstorm, water in the atmosphere changes, too. It collects in the atmosphere and falls to the earth as rain. Gases and water move in cycles on the earth. How do these and other nonliving factors in an environment affect the living things on the earth?

- *How do living and nonliving things in an environment interact with each other?*
- *What is the role of lightning in the cycling of nitrogen? How is water cycled on the earth?*

22-1 THE BIOSPHERE

FACTORS IN THE ENVIRONMENT

Organisms live in and interact with their *environment* (ehn vī ruhn muhnt). The environment includes all of the things, both living and nonliving, that surround an organism. A fish in a pond is an example of an organism in its environment. The pond contains living things, such as other fish, insects, and plants. The pond also contains nonliving things, such as water, minerals, and rocks. The study of the interactions between living things and their environment is called **ecology** (ee KAHL uh jee). What are some interactions that occur between a fish and the water in which it lives?

The living things in an environment are called **biotic** (bī AHT ihk) **factors**. Plants, animals, and fungi are biotic factors. Protists are also biotic factors. The nonliving things in an environment are called **abiotic factors**. Light, temperature, and wind are abiotic factors. Rocks, soil, and minerals are also abiotic factors. What kind of factor is water—biotic or abiotic?

After completing this section, you will be able to

- **distinguish** between biotic factors and abiotic factors.
- **identify** the part of the earth that is the biosphere.
- **describe** and **give an example** of an ecosystem.

The key terms in this section are

abiotic factors	ecology
biosphere	ecosystem
biotic factors	

---

bio- (life)
a- (without)

Figure 22-1

A bird's nest contains both biotic and abiotic factors.

sphaera (ball, globe)

Various kinds of environments exist all over the earth. Think about the birds in their nest, as shown in Figure 22-1. The nest is a small environment that contains many biotic and abiotic factors. For example, organisms such as fungi and insects are often found in birds' nests. These nests are made up of nonliving things such as small twigs, mud, and pieces of dried grass. What other abiotic factors might be in the nest?

THE BIOSPHERE AND ECOSYSTEMS

Living things on the earth are found in a zone called the **biosphere** (BĪ uh sfihr). The biosphere is made up of the land, the oceans, and part of the atmosphere. Figure 22-2 shows the biosphere. Notice that it is a very thin layer, only about 21 km deep. The biosphere stretches from the deepest parts of the oceans to several kilometers into the air.

The biosphere is made up of smaller units called ecosystems (EE kuh sihs tuhmz). An **ecosystem** is an area in which living things and nonliving things interact, exchanging energy and materials. The word *ecosystem* is a short form of the term *ecological system*. An ecosystem is the basic unit of ecology. Ecosystems can be large, like a forest, or small, like a leaf or a drop of water.

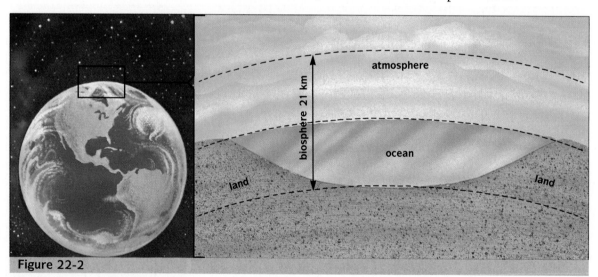

Figure 22-2

The biosphere.

A tree and the space just around it in a forest can be thought of as an ecosystem, as shown in Figure 22-3. Leaves fall from the tree and provide hiding places for small animals on the ground. Acorns also fall to the ground. Some of these acorns become buried in the soil and, over time, grow into trees. Some acorns are gathered by squir-

OBJECTIVE
Determine which factors in different environments are biotic and which are abiotic.

MATERIALS
none

PROCEDURE
A. Examine the area around your school. Note those factors that are biotic and those that are abiotic.
B. Make a data table like the one shown. In the table, list at least ten biotic factors and ten abiotic factors found around your school. If you are not sure about some things, write them in a column marked *Uncertain*.
C. Examine the area inside your science classroom. In the table, list at least ten biotic factors and ten abiotic factors found in the classroom.

Environment	Biotic Factors	Abiotic Factors	Uncertain
School area			
Science classroom			

RESULTS AND CONCLUSIONS
1. How would you describe the environment around your school?
2. In what ways does the environment around your school differ from that inside your science classroom?
3. In each of the environments that you examined, state how the biotic factors and the abiotic factors affect each other.
4. If your school did not exist, what biotic factors might be present in the area?
5. What biotic factors can be found in the area as a direct result of the school being built there?

rels and used for food. Other acorns are used by smaller organisms as places in which to lay eggs. Acorn weevils and some moths lay eggs in acorns. When the eggs hatch, the larvae eat the nuts. In turn, some of the larvae are eaten by insects and other small animals.

A stream running through a forest is also an ecosystem. The stream has specific biotic and abiotic factors. These factors, such as fish and water, are different from those in the forest floor ecosystem. The stream and the forest floor are examples of small ecosystems. These smaller ecosystems are part of a larger ecosystem—the forest. The forest ecosystem includes all the biotic and abiotic factors within the forest.

REVIEW

1. How do biotic factors and abiotic factors differ?
2. Give one example each of a biotic factor and an abiotic factor.
3. What parts of the earth make up the biosphere?
4. What is an ecosystem? Give two examples of ecosystems.

CHALLENGE Describe the changes that would occur in an ecosystem that has been flooded. How would the biotic and abiotic factors change? Explain your answer.

Figure 22-3

A small ecosystem. What are some living things that interact in this type of ecosystem?

22-2 POPULATIONS AND COMMUNITIES

HABITATS AND NICHES

Ecosystems can be divided into habitats. A **habitat** is the kind of place in which an organism lives. Think of an ecosystem as an organism's neighborhood. Think of its habitat as the organism's address. An organism's habitat must supply all the biotic and abiotic factors that the organism needs for survival.

Different species of organisms live in different habitats. Earthworms live in the soil. Starfish live on the ocean bottom. However, different species can also live in the same habitat. Earthworms share their soil habitat with insects and plants. Starfish live on the ocean floor with clams. What organisms live in your habitat?

The organisms in an ecosystem interact with each other in many ways. Each kind of organism has a specific role. The role of an organism in an ecosystem is called its **niche** (nihch). Recall that an organism's habitat is where it lives. An organism's niche can be thought of as what the organism does. The niche of an organism includes all of its behaviors. Hunting, feeding, and reproducing are

SCIENCE & TECHNOLOGY

Since 1950, nearly 400 artificial reefs have been built in waters off the nation's coasts. These reefs provide a habitat for many sea plants and animals. Objects sunk to make reefs include everything from cars and buses to steel ships.

Once an object has been sunk, organisms move in almost at once. Algae begin to grow on the surface of objects in a few days. Algae form the base of the food chain in the new reef. Soon, sponges, corals, mussels, and barnacles also move in.

Larger animals, such as crabs, eels, and small fish, move into the reef later. Bigger fish that prey on these smaller organisms soon follow. In just a few weeks, a sunken wreck can be home to thousands of creatures.

A sunken ship has many nooks in which organisms can hide from predators. These hiding places also give fish a place to rest, out of the strong underwater currents.

Artificial reefs also act as nurseries. These reefs offer shelter for many young fish.

Figure 22-4

The niche of vultures involves eating the body of a dead animal (*A*). The niche of a trap-door spider includes making a trap door (*B*).

part of the niche of a wolf. Look at the vultures shown in Figure 22-4*A*. The niche that a vulture occupies includes eating dead animals. The niche also includes nesting in certain kinds of trees. The niche of a trap-door spider, also shown, includes making a tunnel under a trap door. The spider's victims fall into the tunnel.

ACTIVITY   What Interactions Occur in a Plot of Land?

OBJECTIVE
Identify the interactions of organisms on a small plot of land.

MATERIALS
meterstick, 4 wood stakes, string (4.5 m), garden trowel, plastic bag, white paper towels, hand lens, probe

PROCEDURE

A. Work with a partner or in teams of three. Use a meterstick to measure a square plot of ground that is 1 m long on each side. Push a stake into the ground to mark each corner of the plot. **Caution:** Do not touch any plants that have not been identified as safe. Some plants may irritate your skin.
B. Connect the stakes with a piece of string to form a square.
C. List the kinds of plants and animals found within the square. Count each kind of organism. Record your results.

D. Identify and record the kinds of nonliving things found in the plot.
E. With a garden trowel, take a small amount of soil from the plot and place it in a plastic bag. Take this sample to your classroom.
F. In the classroom, spread the soil sample out on a white paper towel on your desk. Use a hand lens and probe to examine the soil carefully for living and nonliving things. Note if decaying matter is present.
G. After 2 weeks, repeat steps **C** through **F**. Note any changes that may have occurred.

RESULTS AND CONCLUSIONS
1. Describe the plot of land in your study.
2. Describe the soil sample that you obtained.
3. List any interactions that you think may occur between organisms in the plot.
4. List any changes you noted in the plot during the 2-week period.
5. Describe the ecosystem in which the plot is located.

Different species of organisms can have the same habitat. But in a balanced ecosystem, no two species can have the same niche. Each species has its own role. When two species try to have the same niche, they are said to *compete* with one another. In time, the species that is better suited to the environment will fill the niche.

COMMUNITIES AND POPULATIONS

All the organisms living together in an area make up a **community**. A community is the living part of an ecosystem. Nonliving things, such as soil and water, are not part of the community. A desert community might be made up of cacti, shrubs, jack rabbits, snakes, scorpions, and other plants and animals. A tidal pool community might be made up of starfish, worms, mollusks, and some kinds of algae. What organisms might be found in a forest community?

Each community is made up of several populations. A **population** is a group of organisms belonging to one species living in a given area. All the jack rabbits in a desert community make up a population. All the starfish in a tidal pool community make up a population.

Figure 22-5

A water hole in a desert community (*left*); tidal pool community (*right*).

REVIEW

1. How does a habitat differ from a niche?
2. What is the habitat of a squirrel? Give an example of part of a squirrel's niche.
3. What is the difference between a population and a community? What are some populations in your schoolyard?

CHALLENGE Explain how a frog and a tadpole occupy different niches.

22-3 ENERGY FLOW IN THE BIOSPHERE

PRODUCERS, CONSUMERS, DECOMPOSERS

All living things need energy for survival. The main source of energy for most living things is the sun. Some organisms can directly use the sun's energy to make food. For example, you have learned that green plants use sunlight to produce food, in a process called *photosynthesis* (foh tuh SIHN thuh sihs). Green plants are producers. A **producer** is an organism that makes its own food. Plantlike protists and some monerans also are producers.

Many living things cannot make their own food. They must get food by eating plants or other animals. An organism that eats other organisms is called a **consumer**. All animals are consumers. Look at Figure 22-6. Which organisms are producers, and which are consumers?

> After completing this section, you will be able to
>
> - **identify** producers, consumers, and decomposers.
> - **describe** the flow of energy in an ecosystem.
>
> *The key terms in this section are*
>
> | | |
> |---|---|
> | carnivore | omnivore |
> | consumer | predator |
> | decomposer | prey |
> | food chain | producer |
> | food web | scavenger |
> | herbivore | |

Figure 22-6

Producers and consumers.

There are several kinds of consumers. A consumer that is a plant eater is called a **herbivore** (HER buh vawr). Mice, deer, horses, and cows are examples of herbivores. What are some other herbivores?

A consumer that eats other animals is a **carnivore** (KAHR nuh vawr). Lions, vultures, dogs, and cats are ex-

herba- (plant)

carnis (flesh)

praedari (to seize by force)

amples of carnivores. Some carnivores, such as the cougar shown in Figure 22-7, are predators. A **predator** (PREHD-uh tawr) is an animal that hunts and kills other animals for food. The **prey** is the animal that is hunted. A raccoon may be the prey of a cougar. What might be the prey of a shark? You will learn more about predator-prey relationships in Chapter 23.

Figure 22-7

A cougar is a carnivore.

Other carnivores, such as vultures, are scavengers. A **scavenger** (SKAV uhn juhr) is an animal that feeds on dead or dying organisms. A hagfish is a scavenger that feeds on dead or dying fish.

A third kind of consumer eats both plants and other animals. A consumer that eats both plants and animals is called an **omnivore** (AHM nuh vawr). Bears and raccoons are examples of omnivores. Some fish also are omnivores. Are humans herbivores, carnivores, or omnivores?

In addition to producers and consumers, there are organisms in a community called decomposers. A **decomposer** (dee kuhm POH zuhr) is an organism that breaks down the remains of dead plants and animals into simpler substances. Decomposers cause dead plants and animals to decay. Fungi and some bacteria are decomposers. They are important in releasing nutrients from dead organisms into the environment. These nutrients can then be reused.

Figure 22-8

Fungi are decomposers. What material is being decomposed?

FOOD CHAINS AND FOOD WEBS

When one organism eats another, energy is transferred. Consider a field mouse eating grain. Energy is transferred from the grain to the mouse. Energy can be transferred from one organism to another more than once. If the mouse is then eaten by a barn owl, some of the energy from the grain is transferred to the barn owl.

The transfer of energy in the form of food from one organism to another is called a **food chain**. In the food chain just described, energy is transferred from the grain to the mouse to the owl. The first energy source for almost all food chains is the sun. How is the sun the first energy source in the grain–mouse–barn owl food chain?

Most consumers have more than one food source. For example, owls may eat mice, snakes, or rabbits. Thus organisms may be involved in many food chains. These different food chains usually overlap.

Figure 22-9

A food chain that consists of grain, a mouse, and an owl.

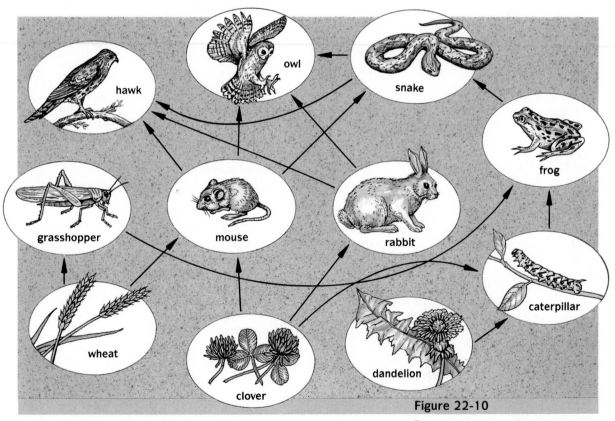

Figure 22-10

The organisms in a food web.

This overlap results in a food web. A food web is an overlapping of food chains in an ecosystem. Figure 22-10 shows a food web involving grain plants, mice, owls, and other organisms. Which organisms are producers? Which are consumers?

ECOLOGICAL PYRAMIDS

Most of the energy from sunlight that is used by producers goes into carrying on life processes. Just a small amount of the energy is stored as food. When a plant is eaten by an animal, most of the food energy is used for the animal's life processes. Much of this energy is lost as heat. Some of the energy is stored in body tissues. There are different levels in a food chain. At each level of a food chain, some energy is transferred but most energy is lost as heat.

The transfer of energy in an ecosystem can be shown by using an *energy pyramid*. An energy pyramid is a drawing that shows the amount of energy available at each level of a food chain. Figure 22-11A shows an energy pyramid. The bottom of the pyramid is made up of producers. The other levels of the pyramid are made up of consumers. Notice that the pyramid shape shows that less energy is available at each higher level of the food chain.

ACTIVITY   How Does Energy Move in a Food Chain?

OBJECTIVE
Trace the path of energy in the food chains that are involved in an organism's diet.

MATERIALS
none

PROCEDURE
A. Make three copies of the data table shown. Copy only the column headings.
B. List all the food that you eat in a day.
C. Trace the energy in the food back to its origin. You may have to look at the ingredients listed on the packages of the foods that you eat. Use only the major ingredients.
D. Two entries are given in the sample table shown. Use these entries as a guide for completing your first data table.
E. Observe two animals other than humans in your ecosystem. Determine what foods they eat. Determine the source of the food. Complete the other two data tables.
F. Draw separate food chains to show your diet and the diets of the animals you chose. Use arrows to show how energy moves from organisms that are eaten to organisms doing the eating.

RESULTS AND CONCLUSIONS
1. In one day, in how many different food chains are you the consumer?
2. Determine whether the animals that you listed in your table are herbivores, carnivores, or omnivores.
3. Which organisms appear in more than one food chain?
4. What is the initial energy source for all of the food chains that you identified in this activity?

Energy Relationships For_____

Food	Source of Food	Source of Food for Organism in Second Column	Source of Food for Organism in Third Column	Energy Source
Hamburger	Cow	Grass		Sun
Pretzels	Wheat			Sun

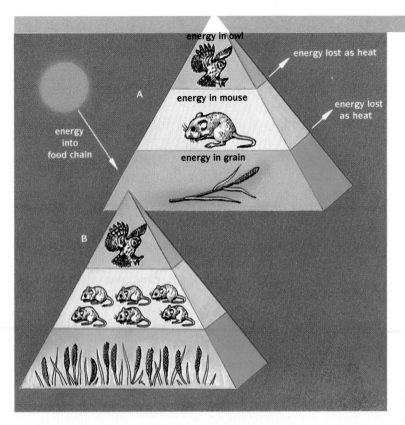

Figure 22-11

An energy pyramid (A); a numbers pyramid (B).

Other types of pyramids can be used to show the relationships between organisms in a food chain. A *numbers pyramid* shows the number of organisms at each level of the food chain. There are more grain plants than mice in a food chain. There are more mice than barn owls in a food chain. Look at the numbers pyramid in Figure 22-11B. Why are there fewer organisms at the top of the pyramid than at the bottom?

REVIEW

1. How do producers, consumers, and decomposers differ?
2. What are the different kinds of consumers?
3. How is a food chain different from a food web?
4. Explain why there is less energy at each higher level of a food chain.

CHALLENGE Think about an ocean food chain. Suppose that the producers get 1000 units of energy a day from photosynthesis. The small fish that eat the producers get only 1 percent of that energy. The large fish that eat the small fish get 10 percent of the energy available at that level. How many units of energy do the large fish get?

SCIENCE PUZZLER

A chemical called DDT was widely used to kill insect pests on crops. Its use was stopped in the early 1970s. DDT caused the eggshells of ospreys to be much thinner than normal. Ospreys are birds that eat fish. The osprey eggs were crushed when the parent birds sat on them. How did the use of DDT affect the number of ospreys? Describe a food chain through which the DDT could have reached the ospreys.

22-4 SYMBIOTIC RELATIONSHIPS

After completing this section, you will be able to

- **define** the term *symbiosis.*
- **identify** three kinds of symbiotic relationships.

The key terms in this section are

commensalism	parasitism
mutualism	symbiosis

sym- (together)
mutuus (exchanged)

Organisms in an ecosystem depend on each other for food. Organisms may also depend on each other for protection, transportation, or shelter. A close, long-term relationship between two organisms is called **symbiosis** (sihm bī OH sihs). There are several kinds of symbiosis.

Mutualism (MYOO chu uh lihz uhm) is a kind of symbiosis in which both organisms benefit. Figure 22-12A shows an example of mutualism. The oxpecker bird spends a lot of time on the back of the rhinoceros. The bird feeds on ticks and other small organisms that live on the skin of the rhinoceros. Both the bird and the rhinoceros benefit from this relationship.

A sea anemone living on the shell of a hermit crab is another example of mutualism. The sea anemone hides the hermit crab and helps to protect it from predators. A sea anemone cannot move from place to place on its own. When the hermit crab moves around, it carries the sea anemone with it. This increases the area in which the anemone can feed. Both organisms benefit.

Figure 22-12

Examples of mutualism: oxpecker birds on the head of a rhinoceros (*A*); sea anemones on the shell of a hermit crab (*B*).

Commensalism (kuh MEHN suh lihz uhm) is a kind of symbiosis in which one organism is helped and the other is neither helped nor harmed. A blue jay living in a tree is an example of commensalism. The blue jay gains protection and a place to live. The tree is not affected by the blue jay. Figure 22-13 shows a fish called a remora. Notice that the remora is attached to a shark. The remora feeds on scraps of the shark's food. It also gets a ride from place to place. The shark is not affected by the remora.

Figure 22-13

The attachment of a remora to a shark is a form of commensalism.

Sometimes, symbiosis is harmful to one of the organisms. **Parasitism** (PAR uh sih tihz uhm) is a symbiotic relationship in which one organism is helped and the other is harmed. The organism that benefits from the relationship is called a *parasite*. The organism that is harmed is called the *host*. A parasite lives in or on the body of a host. The tick shown in Figure 22-14 is a parasite. The dog on which the tick lives is the host. The tick gets nutrients from the blood of the dog. The dog may be weakened by the loss of nutrients from the presence of many ticks.

Many diseases are caused by parasites that are microorganisms. For example, athlete's foot, a skin infection, is caused by a fungus. Some kinds of food poisoning are caused by harmful bacteria in the intestines. Malaria, a serious blood disease, is caused by a parasitic protist. What are some other diseases that are caused by parasites?

Some plants are parasites of other plants. Mistletoe is a plant that attaches itself to trees, as shown in Figure 22-14. The mistletoe can make its own food because it is a plant. But it also gets nutrients from the tree. Too much mistletoe growing on a tree can seriously harm the tree.

REVIEW

1. What is symbiosis?
2. Compare mutualism and commensalism.
3. What is parasitism? Give an example of a parasitic relationship.

CHALLENGE Termites cannot digest the cellulose in the wood that they eat. Certain protozoans that can digest cellulose live in the intestines of termites. The termites get nutrients from the cellulose that the protozoans break down. The protozoans get nutrients from the termite's digestive tract. What kind of symbiosis is described here? Explain your answer.

Figure 22-14

Examples of parasitism: a tick near a dog's ear (*top*); mistletoe on a tree (*bottom*).

22-5 CYCLES IN NATURE

Energy from the sun is transferred through an ecosystem. This energy is not reused or recycled. It is supplied constantly by the sun. Nonliving materials, such as water, carbon, oxygen, and nitrogen, also move through ecosystems. These materials are essential to life. Water makes up much of living tissue. Many cell reactions take place in water. Carbon in the form of carbon dioxide is needed by plants for photosynthesis. Oxygen is needed by most organisms for respiration. Nitrogen is a part of proteins.

Nonliving materials exist in limited amounts. These materials are reused. Water, carbon, oxygen, and nitrogen move in cycles through living and nonliving parts of the environment.

THE WATER CYCLE

The movement of water through an ecosystem is called the **water cycle**. This cycle is shown in Figure 22-15. The sun's energy causes evaporation (ih vap uh RAY shuhn) of some of the water on the earth. *Evaporation* is the process by which water changes from a liquid to a gas. Water evaporates from oceans, rivers, and lakes. It also evaporates from soil. Living things give off water to the air.

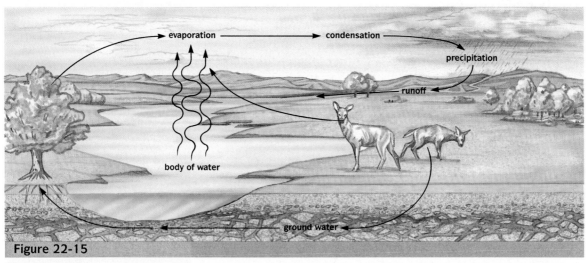

Figure 22-15

The water cycle.

As the water in the air cools, it changes back to a liquid by the process of *condensation* (kahn dehn SAY shuhn). Clouds form due to condensation. At some point, the water in clouds falls to the earth. This process is called *precipitation* (prih sihp uh TAY shuhn). Rain, snow, hail, and sleet are forms of precipitation.

Some water seeps into the soil and moves along as *ground water*. Some water flows along the surface of the ground to oceans or other bodies of water. This water that flows along the surface is called *runoff*. Water on or in the ground is used by living things. Plants absorb water through their roots. Animals drink water and take it in with food. The water in plants and animals is later returned to the ground or to the air. Plants lose water through their leaves. What is this process called? Animals lose water when they excrete wastes. The water cycle is completed when water again evaporates.

THE CARBON DIOXIDE–OXYGEN CYCLE

The movement of carbon dioxide and oxygen through an ecosystem is called the **carbon dioxide–oxygen cycle**. Figure 22-16 shows how these materials are cycled together. Look at the figure as you read about the cycle.

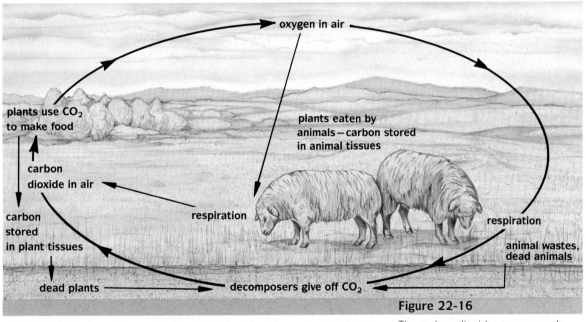

Figure 22-16

The carbon dioxide–oxygen cycle.

Plants take in carbon dioxide gas from the air. They use this gas to make food. What is this process called? During this process, oxygen is given off as a waste product. Oxygen is used by living things for respiration. Respiration is the process by which living things get energy from food. During respiration, carbon dioxide is given off as waste. Carbon dioxide is also given off when once-living things decay and when fuels are burned. The carbon dioxide from these processes can be used by plants in making food, thus completing the cycle.

THE NITROGEN CYCLE

Almost 80 percent of the air is nitrogen gas. But most living things cannot use nitrogen in this form. It must first be changed into nitrogen compounds. Nitrogen that is combined with other elements in a compound is called *fixed nitrogen.* Nitrogen is changed into fixed nitrogen in the nitrogen cycle. The **nitrogen cycle** is the movement of nitrogen through an ecosystem.

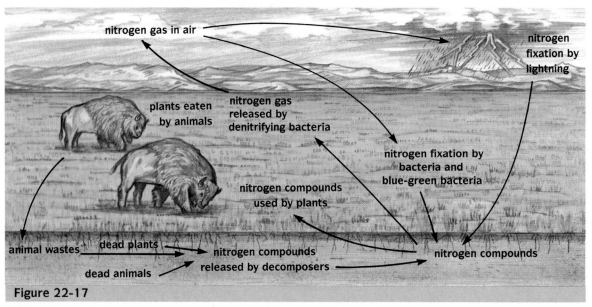

nitrogen gas in air

nitrogen fixation by lightning

plants eaten by animals

nitrogen gas released by denitrifying bacteria

nitrogen fixation by bacteria and blue-green bacteria

nitrogen compounds used by plants

animal wastes   dead plants

dead animals

nitrogen compounds released by decomposers

nitrogen compounds

Figure 22-17

The nitrogen cycle.

Figure 22-18

Soybeans get nitrogen from bacteria that live in their roots.

There are two ways in which nitrogen from the air is fixed into compounds. One way is by lightning. As lightning passes through air, it causes nitrogen to combine with oxygen to form *nitrates.* Lightning also causes nitrogen to combine with hydrogen to form ammonia. These compounds are washed out of the air to the earth by rain. They can then be used by plants or microorganisms.

Nitrogen is also fixed by some microorganisms. Blue-green bacteria that live in soil fix nitrogen. *Nitrogen-fixing bacteria* live on the roots of certain plants, such as soybeans and peas. The nitrogen fixed by the bacteria is used by the plants to make proteins. Animals take in nitrogen by eating the plants. When the animals die, decomposers return the nitrogen in the animals' bodies to the soil. The nitrogen in animal wastes is also released by decomposers.

The nitrogen cycle is completed by *denitrifying (dee-* Nī *truh fī ihng) bacteria.* These bacteria live in the soil. They change nitrogen compounds into nitrogen gas. The nitrogen gas is released into the air. Why are denitrifying bacteria important to the nitrogen cycle?

REVIEW

1. Describe the water cycle.
2. What processes are involved in the carbon dioxide–oxygen cycle?
3. Name two ways in which nitrogen is fixed.

CHALLENGE Fertilizers are often added to plants to help them grow. Fertilizers contain nitrogen compounds. Which of the ecosystem cycles is most affected by adding fertilizers to soil? What step in this cycle is being bypassed?

CHAPTER SUMMARY

The main ideas in this chapter are listed below. Read these statements before you answer the Chapter Review questions.

- The biosphere is the zone in which living things are found on the earth. The biosphere is formed of smaller units called ecosystems. Living and nonliving things in an ecosystem interact, exchanging energy and materials. (22-1)

- A habitat is the specific place in which an organism lives. The role of an organism in its habitat is called its niche. All the organisms living together in an area make up a community. A community is made up of several populations. A population is a group of organisms of one species living together in a given area. (22-2)

- Depending on how they get food, organisms can be grouped as producers, consumers, or decomposers. (22-3)

- The transfer of energy in the form of food is called a food chain. The overlapping of food chains in an ecosystem is called a food web. (22-3)

- An energy pyramid shows the amount of energy available at each level in a food chain. A numbers pyramid shows the number of organisms at each level in a food chain. (22-3)

- A close, long-term relationship between two organisms is called symbiosis. There are three kinds of symbiosis: mutualism, commensalism, and parasitism. (22-4)

- Water, carbon dioxide, oxygen, and nitrogen are nonliving materials cycled through ecosystems. (22-5)

The key terms in this chapter are listed below. Use each term in a sentence that shows the meaning of the term.

abiotic factors	community	habitat	population
biosphere	consumer	herbivore	predator
biotic factors	decomposer	mutualism	prey
carbon dioxide– oxygen cycle	ecology	niche	producer
	ecosystem	nitrogen cycle	scavenger
carnivore	food chain	omnivore	symbiosis
commensalism	food web	parasitism	water cycle

Chapter Review

Use the key terms from this chapter to complete the following sentences correctly.

1. A symbiotic relationship in which both organisms benefit is called _____.
2. A symbiotic relationship in which one organism is harmed while the other benefits is called _____.
3. The zone in which all living things on the earth are found is called the _____.
4. _____ is the study of the relationships between living things and their environment.
5. A/An _____is an area in which living and nonliving things interact, exchanging material and energy.
6. All the living things within an area make up a/an _____.
7. The transfer of energy in the form of food from one organism to another is called a/an _____.
8. An animal that hunts and kills other animals for food is called a/an _____.
9. The movement of water through an ecosystem is called the _____.
10. The role of an organism in an area is called its _____.

CONCEPTS

1. Name some biotic and abiotic factors that you might find in a pond. (22-1)
2. Name two ecosystems that might be found in a forest. (22-1)
3. What is a habitat? (22-2)
4. How does an organism's habitat differ from its niche? (22-2)
5. Give an example of an organism's niche. (22-2)
6. How does a population differ from a community? (22-2)
7. Which of the following organisms are producers and which are consumers: bullfrog, corn plant, rosebush, dog, moss, house wren? (22-3)
8. Organism A eats insects and earthworms, organism B eats fish, organism C eats popcorn, breadcrumbs, and nuts, and organism D eats fish, eggs, and fruits. Determine whether each organism is a herbivore, a carnivore, or an omnivore. (22-3)
9. Determine whether each of the following is a predator-prey relationship: a fox chasing a rabbit; a vulture finding a dead animal; a honeybee collecting nectar from a flower. Explain your answers. (22-3)

10. What is the role of decomposers in an ecosystem? (22-3)
11. Describe the movement of energy in a food chain. (22-3)
12. Name and describe two kinds of food pyramids. (22-3)
13. Explain why all the energy within a level of a food chain is not available to the next higher level. (22-3)
14. How do food webs relate to food chains? (22-3)
15. Certain wasps lay eggs on the tomato horn worm. The relationship harms the tomato horn worm. What kind of symbiosis does this example show? (22-4)
16. A lichen is a special relationship between a fungus and an alga in which both organisms benefit. What kind of symbiosis does this example show? (22-4)
17. Give an example of commensalism. (22-4)
18. What materials cycled in an ecosystem are essential to life? (22-5)
19. What role does evaporation have in the water cycle? (22-5)
20. How does respiration affect the carbon dioxide–oxygen cycle? (22-5)
21. How is nitrogen fixed in the nitrogen cycle? (22-5)
22. What are the roles of different bacteria in the nitrogen cycle? (22-5)

APPLICATION/ CRITICAL THINKING

1. What would happen to an ecosystem in which the number of predators was greatly reduced?
2. Certain bacteria that make vitamins are present in the intestines of humans. What kind of symbiosis is this relationship? How is each organism affected?
3. What is the largest ecosystem? Explain your answer.

EXTENSION

1. Observe organisms in your neighborhood. Report on a food chain you observe.
2. Pick an environment different from the examples used in this chapter and draw a poster to show the food web that exists there.
3. Draw a poster showing how you use water. How is the water you use part of the water cycle?

READINGS

Adams, T. "Pond Life," *Sierra,* March/April 1984, p. 83.

Hair, J.D. "The Manager of a Biosphere." *International Wildlife,* November/December 1984, p. 26.

Postel, S. "The Earth's Forest Systems Are Collapsing." *Natural History,* April 1985, p. 60.

CHANGES IN THE ENVIRONMENT

What has happened to the forest that once covered the mountain shown in the photograph? The area shown is Mount St. Helens in Washington. Mount St. Helens is a volcano that erupted in May 1980. Lava and volcanic ash material covered the area after the eruption. Populations of animals and plants were buried. Over much of the area, the volcanic material was more than 100 m deep. Few living things survived the eruption. But now, living things are beginning to grow in the area. What living things do you see in the picture? How might the area look 50 years after the eruption?

- *How do populations change when the environment changes?*
- *What factors other than major changes in the environment cause populations to change?*
- *What are some of the different regions in which plants and animals live? How do these regions vary?*

23-1 CHANGES IN POPULATIONS

Recall that a *population* is a group of organisms belonging to one species living in a given area. A population may be all of the bald eagles in a national park, all of the people in a town, or all of the bass in a lake.

POPULATION SIZE AND DENSITY

The size of a population is the total number of members in that population. If a lake contains 50 bass, the population size is 50. **Population density** is the number of individuals per unit of space. Suppose an area of 10 square kilometers (km²) contains 100 rabbits. The population density is 100 rabbits in 10 km², or 10 rabbits per square kilometer. How can two populations be the same size but have different densities?

Many factors can change the size of a population. For example, the size increases when new individuals move into an area. A high birth rate also can cause an increase

After completing this section, you will be able to

- **distinguish** between population size and population density.
- **interpret** a graph showing birth rate data.
- **describe** factors that affect the size of a population.

The key terms in this section are
birth rate
death rate
limiting factor
population density

in population size. The **birth rate** is the ratio of the number of births to the number of individuals in a population. The human birth rate in six different areas during 1983 is shown in Figure 23-1. Notice that in 1983 the birth rate in North America was about 16 births per 1000 people. What is the highest birth rate shown? What is the lowest birth rate shown?

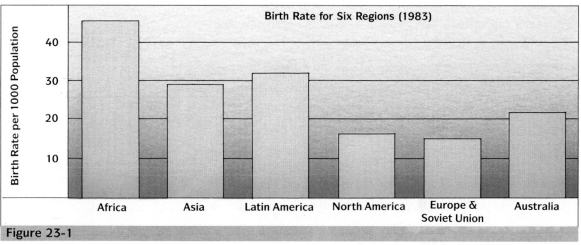

Figure 23-1

The human birth rate varies from one area to another.

The movement of members out of a population decreases its size. Deaths also decrease its size. The **death rate** is the ratio of the number of deaths to the number of individuals in a population. A factor such as disease may increase the death rate.

If conditions are favorable, one bacterium could produce over 200,000 descendants in just 6 hours. Elephants breed very slowly. Yet if conditions are favorable, it is thought that one pair of elephants could produce 19 million descendants in 750 years.

Why is it that bacteria and elephants do not cover the earth? The graph shown in Figure 23-2 can help you answer this question. The graph shows the typical growth pattern of a population. Notice that the population grows slowly at first. Then it grows more rapidly, as shown by the steep part of the curve. At some point in time, the growth levels off, as shown by the straight line at the top of the curve. Thus, the population size becomes stable.

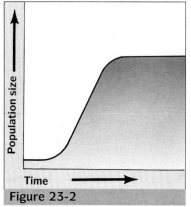

Figure 23-2

Many populations show a growth pattern like this one.

LIMITING FACTORS

When the population size is stable, the birth rate is about equal to the death rate. There may be small increases or decreases during certain years. But in general, the population size stays about the same.

Certain factors in the environment keep a population from increasing in size. A factor that prevents a population from reaching its greatest possible size is called a **limiting factor**. For example, the amounts of food and water that are available may be limiting factors. How does Figure 23-3 show the effects of water as a limiting factor?

Figure 23-3

The effects of limited rainfall remain after an area begins to recover.

Some limiting factors are related to population density. These limiting factors include food, water, disease, predators, and the amount of space available. The greater the population density, the greater the effect that these limiting factors have on a population.

As density increases, members of a population may compete with each other for food. For a herd of deer living in a forest, the amount of plant matter may be a limiting factor. The amount of food available to any one deer depends on the total number of deer in the herd. If the deer population is too dense, there will not be enough food and some deer will starve. Then the deer population will decrease. Later, with fewer deer competing, more food will be available. The deer population may increase again.

Diseases can decrease the size of the deer population. There is a relationship between disease and population density. If the deer population is very dense, a disease will spread quickly. The disease will decrease population size quickly.

Predators also decrease the size of the deer population. Recall that a *predator* is an animal that hunts and kills another animal for food. The prey is the animal that is hunted. As the density of the deer population increases, wolves and other predators can find deer more easily.

ACTIVITY   Does Precipitation Affect a Bird Population?

OBJECTIVE
Analyze data to find the effect of precipitation on the hatching of whooping crane eggs.

MATERIALS
graph paper

PROCEDURE
A. The chart at the bottom of the page shows the number of whooping crane eggs hatched in the wild during a 7-year experiment. The amount of rainfall and snowfall during each of the 7 years was also recorded. Study the data before reading step **B**.

B. Make a data table with headings like those shown. Under each heading in your data table, copy the correct data from the chart.

C. Determine the total precipitation in each year by adding the amount of rainfall and the amount of snowfall. Record the totals in your data table.

D. Find the percent of eggs hatched in each year. To do this, divide the number of eggs hatched by the number of eggs laid, and then multiply by 100. Record the percents in your data table.

E. Make a graph to show how the amount of precipitation relates to the percent of eggs hatched. Use the graph shown as a guide.

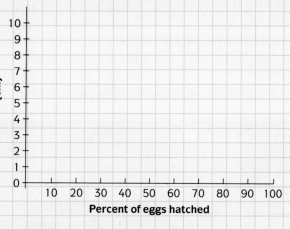

RESULTS AND CONCLUSIONS
1. In which year was the precipitation lowest? Highest?
2. What seems to be the relationship between the amount of precipitation and the number of eggs hatched? Give a reason for your answer.
3. On the basis of the data, does precipitation seem to be a limiting factor for the whooping crane population? Explain your answer.
4. Does the effect of precipitation on the population seem to be dependent on the density of the population? Give a reason for your answer.

Year	Number of Eggs Laid	Number of Eggs Hatched	Rainfall (cm)	Snowfall (cm)	Total Precipitation (cm)	Percent of Eggs Hatched

Whooping Crane Eggs Hatched

Year	Number of Adults	Number of Nests	Number of Eggs Laid	Number of Eggs Hatched	Rainfall (cm)	Snowfall (cm)
1979	21	6	6	4	1.4	1.5
1980	23	4	6	2	2.5	5.6
1981	32	0	0	0	7.6	3.0
1982	26	10	10	7	3.2	0.8
1983	32	10	10	6	2.9	1.0
1984	30	4	4	3	3.5	0.4
1985	32	5	5	4	2.1	0.6

Because of the increased food supply, the number of predators will increase. If more deer are preyed upon, the number of deer will decrease. The graph in Figure 23-4 shows the ways in which predators and their prey interact. You can see that when the number of predators is high, the number of prey is low. What happens to the number of prey when the number of predators is low? Why?

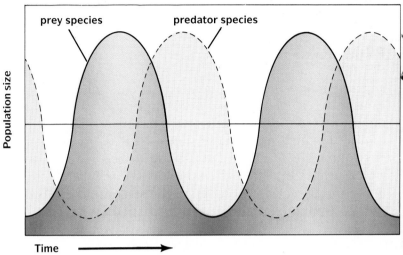

Figure 23-4

Timber wolves (*top*) prey on deer (*bottom*). The populations of predator and prey species often follow a pattern like that shown in the graph (*left*).

Humans do many things that can upset the balance of predator-prey cycles. For example, humans move organisms to environments where there are no natural enemies of these organisms. The new population may increase so quickly that it destroys existing plants and animals in the area.

Limiting factors that do not depend on population density also affect the size of a population. For example, natural disasters and extreme weather can change population size, regardless of the population density. The eruption of a volcano may destroy many different populations. Long periods without rain may have the same effect.

REVIEW

1. A pasture that is 2 km² contains six horses. Find the population size and population density of the horses.
2. What ratios do birth rate and death rate represent?
3. Name four factors that may limit the size of a population.

CHALLENGE Suppose you planted 200 tree seedlings in a box 1 m² in area and 15 cm deep. How would limiting factors relate to the density of the seedling population? Explain your answer.

23-2 SUCCESSION

After completing this section, you will be able to

- **define** and **give examples** of primary succession and secondary succession.
- **describe** a climax community.
- **describe** some possible causes of succession.

The key terms in this section are
climax community
pioneers
succession

succedere (go after)

Suppose you planted a vegetable garden. What would happen if you did not take care of it? Your vegetables would soon be crowded out by other plants. The plot would become covered with weeds. In several years you might find small trees growing there. The orderly sequence of changes that occur in a community over time is called **succession** (suhk SEHSH uhn).

PRIMARY SUCCESSION

There are two major types of succession—primary and secondary. *Primary succession* occurs where no organisms have lived before. For example, it occurs on sand dunes, bare rock, and on lava that has cooled after a volcanic eruption. Primary succession also can occur in aquatic environments. The filling of a pond to become a field is a type of primary succession. Follow the numbered steps in Figure 23-5 as you read about the stages in the succession of a pond community to a field community.

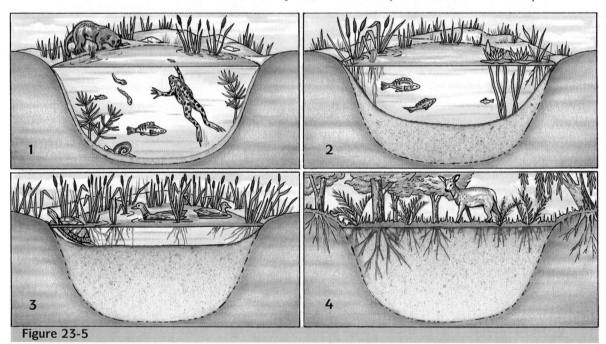

Figure 23-5

Primary succession can change a pond to a field.

1. Many living things live in and around a pond.
2. As organisms die, they sink to the bottom. Over time, the pond begins to fill in.
3. As the pond fills in, a marsh develops.
4. The marsh dries up. Grasses, shrubs, trees and other plants grow in the field that develops.

Primary succession is usually a slow process. For example, it may take hundreds of years for an area covered with bare rock to become forest. The first organisms to grow in an area where primary succession is taking place are called **pioneers**. Lichens (LĪ kuhnz) are often the pioneers on bare rock. Recall that a lichen is made up of an alga and a fungus. You can see lichens on the rock surface in Figure 23-6. Lichens release chemicals that break down rock into small particles. As lichens die, they form a mat of decaying matter. The rock particles, together with the decaying matter, are the beginnings of soil. As the amount of soil increases, small plants such as mosses can grow. In time there is enough soil for shrubs to grow.

The oak and hickory trees in Figure 23-6 are the final stage in the succession of this community. The final community in succession is called the **climax community**. It is usually named for the most numerous or largest plants that grow in the community. The oak-hickory forest shown is a climax community. A climax community will remain unless there is a major change in climate or in the community itself. For example, a forest fire might burn all the trees in the oak-hickory forest. What other things could change this forest?

When the plants in an area change, the animals also change. The plants present during the early stages of succession are food for small animals, such as insects. As the numbers and kinds of plants increase, more species of animals can live in the area. Amphibians, reptiles, birds, and mammals may live in the community.

Figure 23-6

This climax community (*left*) may result from primary succession started by lichens (*right*).

SECONDARY SUCCESSION

Secondary succession occurs where communities used to exist but were destroyed. Plants in a community often are destroyed by human activities. These activities include logging, road building, and plowing to plant crops. Natural disasters, such as fires and earthquakes, also may destroy existing plants. Without plants to hold the soil in place, it may be carried away by running water. But if the soil is not lost by erosion, secondary succession will occur.

Figure 23-7 shows an example of secondary succession. Plants will grow back in an abandoned field after plowing has destroyed the natural community. Plants will also begin to regrow in a wooded area after fire has destroyed that community. During secondary succession, larger plants replace smaller plants. This process continues until the climax community has again developed.

Figure 23-7

How does a cornfield change 1 year (*left*), 10 years (*middle*), and 30 years (*right*) after being abandoned?

FACTORS CAUSING SUCCESSION

Succession is often caused by the living things that make up a community. The community growing at one stage of succession changes the environment. These changes make the environment less favorable for that community to survive. For example, pine seedlings need light to grow. They grow quickly in a sunny field. As they grow larger, they shade the ground beneath them. Conditions no longer favor the growth of pine seedlings. Seedlings of trees such as oaks and hickories grow well in shade. Soon these kinds of trees outnumber the pines. Oaks and hickories become the climax community.

The climax community is more stable than earlier communities that were present. Yet, climax communities can also change over time. Diseases can change a climax

ACTIVITY   What Evidence of Succession Can Be Observed?

OBJECTIVE
Observe succession in a vacant lot.

MATERIALS
field guides or taxonomic keys, notebook, pencil, hand lens, tape measure

PROCEDURE
A. Observe the plants in a vacant lot. Use field guides or taxonomic keys to help you identify the plants. **Caution:** Do not touch any plants that have not been identified as safe. Some plants may irritate your skin.
B. Make a list of the five most common species of woody plants you see. Rank each species according to how numerous it is. Record this information in your notebook.
C. Repeat step **B** for the five most common herbaceous plants on the lot. Herbaceous plants have soft, green stems.
D. Look for animals in the vacant lot. Use field guides or taxonomic keys to help you identify the animals. Make a list of those

you find. Look for evidence of animal species you do not observe directly. Evidence might include feathers, tracks, and fur. Record what you see.
E. Examine the surfaces of rocks for further evidence of plant and animal life. Record what you see.

RESULTS AND CONCLUSIONS
1. Does the lot show primary or secondary succession? Explain.
2. Describe any evidence of primary succession you observed.
3. Describe any evidence of secondary succession you observed.
4. How long do you think it has been since the area was last disturbed? Give reasons for your answer.
5. What species of plants might be growing in the area in 100 years if the area were left undisturbed? Would the climax community be the same as that of other nearby communities? Why or why not?

---

community. For example, chestnut trees once made up many climax communities in the eastern United States. A fungus killed almost all of the chestnut trees. Now other kinds of trees have replaced the chestnut trees.

Nonliving factors can also cause succession. For example, a change in the amount of nutrients in soil may result in major changes in communities. Such a change may occur if a stream or river overflows. The water that overflows may deposit nutrients on the land. How might this affect the species of plants in the community alongside the stream or river?

REVIEW

1. What is succession? Explain the two major types of succession.
2. What is a climax community?
3. Give three examples of events that could start secondary succession.
4. What kinds of factors cause succession to occur?

CHALLENGE   Climax communities are different in different parts of the country. What nonliving factors might affect the kinds of climax communities that will develop in a given area?

Figure 23-8

This chestnut tree is dying from a fungus.

23-3 LAND BIOMES

If you took a car trip across the United States, you would see many different regions. You might pass through forests, through grassy areas, and through deserts. All of these regions look different because they have different climates. **Climate** is the average weather in a region over a long period of time. The two factors that most determine climate are temperature and rainfall. Climate, along with factors such as sunlight, wind, and soil type, affects the types of organisms that can live in a certain region.

A large region that has a distinct climate and combination of plants and animals is called a **biome** (BĪ ohm). There are two major kinds of biomes—land biomes and water biomes. Water biomes will be described later. Many biologists group land biomes into six types. The location of major land biomes is shown in Figure 23-9. Refer to this map as you read about each type of biome.

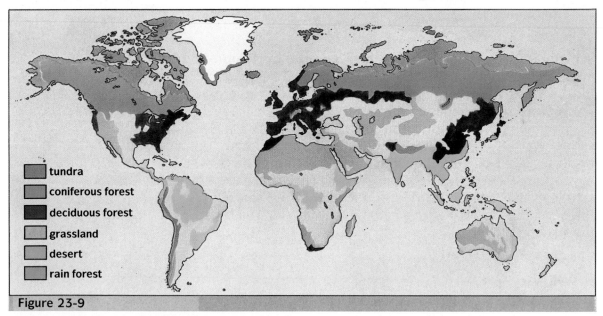

tundra
coniferous forest
deciduous forest
grassland
desert
rain forest

Figure 23-9

The major biomes of the world. Find the biome in which you live.

TUNDRA

The **tundra** (TUHN druh)—the northernmost land biome—is a cold, dry region that has a limited variety of plants. Locate the tundra in Figure 23-9. Parts of which continents are covered by tundra? In winter, the tundra temperatures may drop to −40°C. Summer temperatures rarely rise above 10°C. The average rainfall is only about 37 cm per year.

Winter in the tundra lasts 6 to 9 months. The ground is frozen and covered with snow throughout the winter. There is little daylight. The brief summer growing season lasts about two months. During the summer, only the top 10 cm to 30 cm of soil thaw. Below these depths the earth remains frozen. The layer of permanently frozen soil is called **permafrost**. During the summer, rain collects above the permafrost. The tundra becomes soggy, and many marshes cover the land.

Figure 23-10 shows some of the living things that inhabit the tundra. The variety of plant life is limited. During the summer, mosses and lichens cover the ground. Grasses, and marsh plants called sedges, grow rapidly. In the tundra there are a few small woody plants, such as birch, willow, and alder. There are no tall trees.

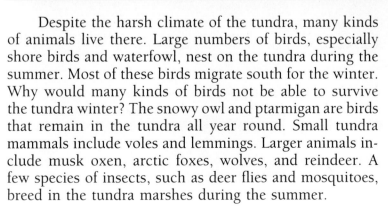

Figure 23-10

Many animals live in the tundra, including the ptarmigan (*top*) and the arctic fox (*bottom*).

Despite the harsh climate of the tundra, many kinds of animals live there. Large numbers of birds, especially shore birds and waterfowl, nest on the tundra during the summer. Most of these birds migrate south for the winter. Why would many kinds of birds not be able to survive the tundra winter? The snowy owl and ptarmigan are birds that remain in the tundra all year round. Small tundra mammals include voles and lemmings. Larger animals include musk oxen, arctic foxes, wolves, and reindeer. A few species of insects, such as deer flies and mosquitoes, breed in the tundra marshes during the summer.

CONIFEROUS FOREST

Look back at Figure 23-9. The wide band of forested area south of the tundra is the coniferous (kuh NIHF uhruhs) forest. The **coniferous forest** is a biome made up mainly of cone-bearing trees, or conifers, such as pines and spruces. The coniferous forest stretches across parts of North America, Europe, and Asia. The northern part of this forest also is called *taiga* (TĪ guh).

The climate of the coniferous forest is less harsh than that of the tundra. Some areas receive as much as 125 cm of rain and snow each year. Temperatures range from −30°C in winter to 20°C in summer.

Most trees in the coniferous forest are conifers with needlelike leaves, such as spruce, fir, and pine. A few broad-leaved trees, such as willow and poplar, grow along stream banks or in open areas in the forest. The top layer of the forest is so dense that little light reaches the forest floor. Ferns and mosses grow beneath the trees. Why would very few shrubs grow in the coniferous forest?

The coniferous forest supports many more species of animals than does the tundra. Some examples can be seen in Figure 23-11. A large number of insects provide food for birds such as woodpeckers and warblers. Hawks, eagles, and owls feed on small mammals such as mice and shrews. Many waterfowl nest in areas near streams and ponds. Mammals such as elk, deer, moose, and squirrels feed on forest plants and plant parts. These animals are food for wolves, foxes, and bears.

Figure 23-11

The woodpecker (*above*) and the moose (*inset right*) live in the coniferous forest.

DECIDUOUS FOREST

The **deciduous** (dih SIHJ yoo uhs) **forest** is a biome made up mainly of broad-leaved trees that lose their leaves in the fall. Locate this kind of biome in Figure 23-9. The deciduous forest has a moderate climate. There are four distinct seasons of about equal length: winter, spring, summer, and fall. Winter temperatures are the coldest, reaching −20°C in some areas. Summers are warm and may reach 30°C. Spring and fall temperatures are mild. The total yearly precipitation ranges from 75 cm to 150 cm.

The climax community in the deciduous forest may vary from place to place. Some areas have maple and beech trees. Others have oaks and hickories. Areas near coasts may have different kinds of trees.

There are a number of layers of plants in a deciduous forest, as shown in Figure 23-12. Notice that the highest layer of trees, called the **canopy** (KAN uh pee), is made up of the major tree species. Below the canopy is a layer of shorter trees and tall shrubs called the **understory**. Short, woody plants that grow beneath the understory make up the *shrub layer*. An *herb layer*, made up of plants with soft, green stems, grows closer to the ground. Decaying plant and animal matter cover the forest floor.

The layers of plants support a wide variety of animal life. Squirrels and birds live in the trees of the canopy and understory. Decaying matter and living plants on the forest floor provide shelter for mice, shrews, lizards, newts, and snakes. Larger animals such as raccoons, deer, foxes, and skunks feed on the smaller animals or on plants.

Figure 23-12

The four layers of a forest.

Figure 23-13

The newt (*inset left*) and skunk (*right*) live in the deciduous forest.

RAIN FORESTS

The **tropical rain forest** is a warm, humid biome that has the greatest variety of living things. It is found near the equator. In what places in Figure 23-9 is this type of biome found? There are no distinct seasons in this biome. Temperatures may vary more from day to night than from one part of the year to another. Most of the tropical rain forest receives up to 220 cm of rain per year.

The climate of the tropical rain forest is ideal for plant growth. The trees that form the canopy may be over 50 m tall. These trees almost completely shade the forest floor. Vines are common. Vines are plants with stems that grow around trees or other supports. Many plants, such as many orchids and mosses, grow far above the ground and are attached to trees. The soil of the tropical rain forest is usually poor. Many nutrients are washed away by the frequent rainfall.

What animals of the tropical rain forest are shown in Figure 23-14? Many of the animals of this biome live in trees. In addition to many bird species, a wide variety of mammals live in the trees. These animals include monkeys, gibbons, and orangutans. Many amphibians and reptiles, such as frogs and snakes, also are tree dwellers. Thousands of insect species thrive in this biome.

Figure 23-14

The macaw (*left*) and tree frog (*inset right*) live in the tropical rain forest.

Since the 1950s tropical rain forests have been cleared at alarming rates. Most of the clearing has been done to provide areas for growing crops and raising cattle. Land that has been cleared is more likely to be eroded. Much of this land has become unproductive and, so, is abandoned.

Tropical rain forests provide habitats for about half of the living species on the earth. When these forests are cleared, millions of plants and animals are killed. Not only are living things lost, but the foods, medicines, fuels, timber, and other products that the forests provide are also lost.

Conserving these forests is vital. Education is needed so people will understand that saving the tropical rain forests will benefit everyone.

Assistance programs from the United States may help some tropical nations conserve their rain forests.

Technology may also help to save tropical rain forests. New farming methods include agroforestry—the science of growing crops *with* forests

rather than *instead* of forests. It is also important for people to learn to raise cattle in areas that have already been cleared but have been abandoned. New ways to manage land may also help to save the tropical rain forests.

Another type of rain forest, called the **temperate** (TEHM-puhr iht) **rain forest**, occurs along the western coast of North America. The temperate rain forest extends from California to Alaska. Temperatures are moderate, and rainfall may be as much as 300 cm per year. Conifers, such as Douglas firs and redwoods, are the main trees in this biome. These conifers are much larger than those of the coniferous forests south of the tundra. Figure 23-15 shows California redwood trees in a temperate rain forest.

GRASSLAND

The **grassland** is a biome in which grasses are the main plants and in which rainfall is moderate. The yearly rainfall in this biome is between 25 cm and 75 cm. This amount of moisture will prevent deserts from forming but is not enough for trees to grow. Locate this biome in Figure 23-9. Note that grasslands usually occur far from coasts. Many species of grasses may be present in this biome.

Many animals live in grasslands. Grouse, meadow-larks, and prairie chickens are birds that nest in grasslands of North America. Gophers, mice, and prairie dogs live in burrows that they dig. Owls, badgers, snakes, and other

Figure 23-15

A temperate rain forest.

Figure 23-16

Bison (*inset left*) and the meadow-lark (*inset right*) live in the grassland.

predators eat these small mammals. Herds of grazing animals, such as antelope and bison, also live in the grassland.

Another name for the grassland is the *prairie*. Prairies like the one shown in Figure 23-16 once covered most of middle North America. Today, only a few patches of prairie remain. Prairies have been replaced by farmland where crops are grown. Prairies also have been used to graze livestock.

DESERT

A **desert** is a biome that occurs in an area that receives less than 25 cm of rainfall per year. The largest desert in the United States is the Great Basin Desert. It is between the Rocky Mountains and the Sierra Nevada Mountains, as shown in Figure 23-17. Refer back to Figure 23-9 to locate other large deserts in Africa and Asia.

There are both hot deserts and cool deserts. Hot deserts have an average yearly temperature of 20°C. In cool deserts the average yearly temperature is 10°C. In a cool desert, temperatures often drop below freezing during the winter. Many deserts have very high daytime temperatures. Summer daytime temperatures of more than 50°C have been recorded in deserts in California. Temperatures in these deserts may be cold at night.

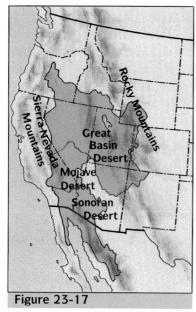

Figure 23-17

North American deserts.

Figure 23-18

The collared lizard (*inset left*) and the roadrunner (*inset right*) live in the desert.

Despite their high temperatures and lack of water, deserts are the home of a wide variety of living things. Some shrubs and small trees can survive in desert areas. Desert plants often have spinelike or hairy leaves. Plants that store water are called succulents. Such plants, which include cactuses, are common in deserts. As in the tundra, there are no tall trees in the desert. Why?

Common animals in deserts of the United States include snakes, lizards, jack rabbits, and armadillos. Mule deer and bighorn sheep feed on the desert plants. Birds, coyotes, and cougars are found in some deserts. Figure 23-18 shows examples of desert animals.

REVIEW

1. What is a biome? What two factors are most important in determining the climate of a biome?
2. What is permafrost? In which biome would you find it?
3. Distinguish between a deciduous forest and a tropical rain forest in terms of climate and variety of organisms.
4. What distinguishes grasslands from deserts?

CHALLENGE Suppose the climate in a grassland changed and 100 cm of rain began to fall each year. Describe the changes that you would expect to see in the grassland over a 15-year period.

23-4 WATER BIOMES

Water biomes cover most of the earth's surface. There are two major types of water biomes—marine and freshwater. The *marine biome* is made up of the oceans. Water in the marine biome contains about 3.5 percent salt. The *freshwater biome* is made up of bodies of water such as lakes and rivers with less than 0.005 percent salt.

THE MARINE BIOME

The marine biome is larger than all of the land and freshwater biomes put together. It covers over 70 percent of the earth. Four limiting factors determine which organisms can live in this biome. These factors are *salinity* (suh LIHN uh tee), light, temperature, and pressure. Salinity is the amount of salt in water. Salinity in different parts of the oceans does not vary much. Light, temperature, and pressure vary more than salinity. Both light and temperature decrease as the depth of the water increases. Pressure increases with depth. Why?

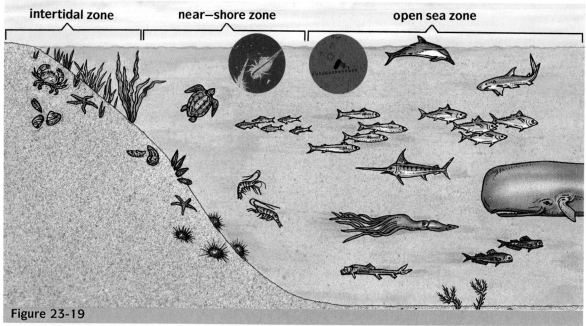

Figure 23-19

The marine biome has a wide variety of organisms. Insets show marine phytoplankton (*left*) and zooplankton (*right*).

Figure 23-19 shows the major zones of the marine biome. Locate the *intertidal zone* along the ocean shore. Organisms in this zone live in a constantly changing environment. They are covered with water at high tide. They are exposed to the air at low tide. They must be able to survive changes in temperature and salinity.

Find the *near-shore zone* over the continental shelf. There is enough light in this zone to support a wide variety of organisms. The many small organisms, some microscopic, that float or swim near the surface of the water are called **plankton**. *Phytoplankton* (fī toh PLANGK tuhn) are small plants that carry on photosynthesis. Almost all the other organisms in the sea depend in some way on phytoplankton for food. The microscopic animals are called *zooplankton* (zō uh PLANGK tuhn). The zooplankton feed on the phytoplankton and on other microscopic animals. Animals such as shrimps, oysters, mussels, and small fish feed on the plankton. Squid and larger fish, such as some sharks, feed on the small animals. A few mammals, such as walruses and seals, may also live in the near-shore zone.

The third zone is the *open-sea zone*. The top 200 m of this part of the ocean provide the greatest amount of food. The phytoplankton are most numerous there. Scientists have counted up to 2 billion organisms per cubic meter of water in this part of the ocean. The phytoplankton support most of the other organisms that live in the open sea.

Below 200 m the marine biome is cold and dark. The temperature is lower and the pressure is greater. Because there is no light, there is almost no plant life. Animals that live there depend on food from the upper water. They feed on other living things or on dead or decaying organisms that drift down from above. Figure 23-20 shows a fish that lives at great depths. This fish has special features for living deep in the ocean.

plarktos (wandering)

THE FRESHWATER BIOME

The freshwater biome includes both standing and running water environments. Ponds, lakes, and swamps are standing water. Streams, rivers, and springs are running water.

Many limiting factors determine which organisms live in fresh water. The most important of these factors are temperature, oxygen, current, dissolved minerals, and *turbidity* (ter BIHD uh tee). Turbidity refers to the number of particles suspended in the water. Often, organisms that live in fresh water can only stand narrow ranges of these limiting factors. A sudden change in one or more of these limiting factors may kill many freshwater organisms.

The freshwater environment can be divided into zones. The zone nearest the shore has a wide variety of life, including rooted plants. The upper layer of the open water receives enough light for photosynthesis. Phytoplankton

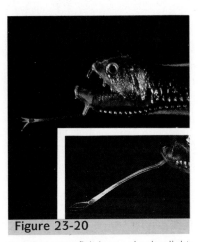

Figure 23-20

This deep-sea fish has a glowing light attached to a thin tube on its lower jaw. The light attracts other fish, which it eats.

make food, and they support many other organisms. Fish and other animals that live at greater depths depend on food sources from the upper levels.

Many kinds of organisms live in a standing freshwater environment such as the one shown in Figure 23-21. Scientists often classify these organisms according to where they live. One group includes mosquitoes and other insects that live near the surface of the water. These organisms visit the water to feed or to reproduce. Plants such as waterlilies float on the surface but are rooted in the bottom. Both zooplankton and phytoplankton float near the surface of the water. Organisms that swim freely in the water, such as fish, water snakes, and turtles, form another group. Worms, crayfish, mussels, clams, and other invertebrates live in or on the bottom.

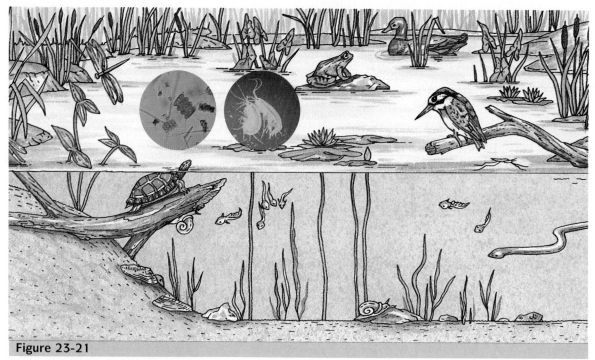

Figure 23-21

The freshwater biome. Insets show freshwater phytoplankton (*left*) and zooplankton (*right*).

Running water is quite different from standing water. Because of the current, running water is constantly mixed. The temperature and the amounts of oxygen and nutrients are usually more stable in running water than in standing water. Organisms that live in running water are adapted to the current. Plants may be firmly attached to rocks by roots or by structures called *holdfasts*. Animals may have hooks or suckers. Some animals burrow into the bottom of the stream or river.

REVIEW

1. What is the main difference between freshwater and marine biomes?
2. What is plankton? What is its importance to other organisms in the water biomes?
3. What are the most important limiting factors in a marine biome? In a freshwater biome?
4. How do scientists usually classify the organisms that live in standing fresh water?
5. What are the two types of freshwater environments? What are the main differences between them?

CHALLENGE Suppose a river were dammed and a lake formed. How would the plant and animal life change?

CHAPTER SUMMARY

The main ideas in this chapter are listed below. Read these statements before you answer the Chapter Review questions.

- Population size is affected by birth rate, death rate, and members moving in or out. Limiting factors prevent a population from reaching its greatest possible size. (23-1)

- Some limiting factors, such as food and disease, are related to population density. Natural disasters are limiting factors that are not related to population density. (23-1)

- Succession is an orderly sequence of changes in a community over time. Primary succession occurs where no organisms have lived before. Secondary succession occurs where communities used to exist but were destroyed. (23-2)

- Succession may occur because one community makes the environment unfavorable to its own survival. A climax community finally results. (23-2)

- Biomes are largely determined by climate. The major land biomes include the tundra, coniferous forest, deciduous forest, tropical and temperate rain forests, grasslands, and deserts. (23-3)

- Water biomes include both marine and freshwater biomes. Organisms in each water biome vary with location and factors such as salinity, light, temperature, oxygen, and current. Freshwater biomes may have standing water or running water. (23-4)

The key terms in this chapter are listed below. Use each term in a sentence that shows the meaning of the term.

biome	death rate	pioneers	tropical
birth rate	deciduous forest	plankton	rain forest
canopy	desert	population density	tundra
climate	grassland	succession	understory
climax community	limiting factor	temperate rain	
coniferous forest	permafrost	forest	

VOCABULARY

Write the letter of the term that best matches the definition. Not all the terms will be used.

1. The ratio of the number of births to the number of individuals in a population
2. A large region with a distinct climate and combination of plants and animals
3. A factor that prevents a population from reaching its greatest possible size
4. A layer of permanently frozen soil
5. The number of individuals per unit of space
6. The highest layer of trees in a forest
7. The final community in succession
8. The layer of tall shrubs and shorter trees beneath the canopy
9. The cold, dry, northernmost land biome that has a limited variety of plants
10. The first organisms to grow in an area where primary succession is taking place

a. biome
b. birth rate
c. canopy
d. climate
e. climax community
f. coniferous forest
g. death rate
h. deciduous forest
i. limiting factor
j. permafrost
k. pioneers
l. plankton
m. population density
n. succession
o. tundra
p. understory

CONCEPTS

1. Distinguish between population size and population density. (23-1)
2. What effect does a limiting factor have on a population? (23-1)
3. Give three examples of factors in the environment that prevent populations from reaching their greatest possible size. (23-1)
4. Describe how the population density of the prey affects the predator population. (23-1)
5. What is the role of pioneers in primary succession? Give an example of a pioneer and describe its effect on an area. (23-2)
6. Distinguish between pioneers and a climax community. (23-2)
7. What is the major difference between primary succession and secondary succession? (23-2)
8. Give an example of how a nonliving factor in the environment might cause succession to occur. (23-2)
9. How do living communities cause succession? (23-2)
10. In which biomes are there few or no trees? For each of these biomes, explain the lack of trees. (23-3)

11. Describe the layers of plants in a deciduous forest. (23-3)
12. What two factors most determine climate? Along with climate, what other factors affect the type of biome that is present in a certain area? (23-3)
13. How does permafrost affect where water is found in the tundra? (23-3)
14. What are two important limiting factors in desert, tundra, and grassland biomes? (23-3)
15. Why might the conifers in the temperate rain forest be much taller than those in the coniferous forest? (23-3)
16. What four limiting factors are most important in a marine biome? (23-4)
17. What are the three major zones of the ocean? (23-4)
18. Where do ocean organisms that live at depths below 200 m get food? (23-4)
19. What factors are more stable in a running water environment than in a standing water environment? (23-4)

APPLICATION/ CRITICAL THINKING

1. Which population would be more likely to be affected by a disease—one that has a density of 5 individuals per km^2 or one that has a density of 30 individuals per km^2? Why?
2. Why is primary succession slower than secondary succession?
3. Construction projects frequently cause the turbidity of the water in streams and lakes to increase because of erosion. How might this increase in turbidity affect the organisms present? Consider effects on both plants and animals.

EXTENSION

1. In what biome is your city or town located? Find out what organisms are considered to be part of the climax community in your biome.
2. Look for examples of primary succession and secondary succession. Take pictures of these processes. Label and display your photographs.
3. Find out if any kinds of plants or animals have become problems in your area. If so, find out how they became problems and how they are being controlled.

READINGS

Begley, S. "The Prairie's Last Stand." *Newsweek*, January 3, 1985, p. 76.

Harrison, G. H. "Life in a Frozen Lake." *Natural Wildlife*, February/March 1985, p. 12.

PRESERVING THE ENVIRONMENT

The wolf shown in the photograph is in its natural environment. This type of wolf lives in certain parts of the western United States. The wolf's environment, however, is becoming smaller. Humans have changed the environment and have killed many wolves.

Recently, there has been an effort by some people to save the wolves. They have suggested that the wolves be brought to Yellowstone National Park. But there is much debate about this plan. A predator has never before been artificially introduced into a national park.

- *How do humans change the environment? How do the changes affect the living things in an environment?*
- *What needs to be done to preserve natural environments?*

24-1 MATTER RESOURCES

Think about how you began your day. How did you use water? You probably drank water or washed with it. What products made from metals did you use this morning? What plant products did you use? The water, metals, and plants you used this morning are examples of natural resources. **Natural resources** are materials from the earth that are needed by humans.

Natural resources are classified as either renewable or nonrenewable. **Renewable resources** are materials that can be replaced through natural cycles. Soil, water, and forests are examples of renewable resources. **Nonrenewable resources** are materials that are used but not replaced. Metals are nonrenewable resources. Most energy sources are also nonrenewable resources.

The amounts of renewable resources are limited by the rate at which natural cycles can replace them. If water is used faster than the water cycle can replace it, the amount of water available for use becomes limited.

After completing this section, you will be able to

- **distinguish** between renewable resources and nonrenewable resources.
- **describe** methods of conserving soil, water, and forest resources.

The key terms in this section are
natural resources
nonrenewable resources
renewable resources

565

An aluminum recycling collection area. Some recycling collection centers pay by weight for glass, aluminum, tin, or paper.

Nonrenewable resources are available in limited amounts. However, many nonrenewable resources can be *recycled.* Recycling is a process in which wastes are used to make new products. In this way the resource being recycled can be reused. Figure 24-1 shows a recycling collection area. Recycling materials is one way to conserve resources. *Conservation* includes all practices that preserve and wisely use natural resources.

SOIL

Soil is one of the most important natural resources. Millions of living things depend on soil for their survival. For example, the fruits and vegetables that you eat come from plants grown in soil.

Although soil is a renewable resource, it takes 200 to 400 years for just 1 cm of topsoil to form. Topsoil is the upper layer of soil. Topsoil is rich in humus (HYOO-muhs). Humus is the decaying remains of dead plants and animals. When humus is formed, materials such as nitrogen, phosphorus, and sulfur are released into the soil. What parts of the nitrogen cycle occur in soil?

Plants growing in the soil remove nutrients from it. Nutrients can be added to the soil by the use of fertilizers. One way to reduce the loss of nutrients in soil is by *crop rotation.* Crop rotation is the practice of growing different kinds of plants in a given area each season. Different kinds of plants need different nutrients. By rotating crops, farmers can reduce the nutrients lost from the soil.

Figure 24-2

Contour plowing of farmland can help to keep topsoil from eroding.

In many places, rich topsoil is being lost by *erosion*. Erosion is the carrying away of topsoil by water or wind. Erosion often occurs where land is cleared to plant crops or to build roads and buildings. The roots of plants hold soil in place. When plants are removed, erosion is likely to occur. Most erosion is caused by water runoff. Dry soil is easily blown away by wind. Severe loss of soil can create bare areas where few plants can grow.

Special farming methods can be used to save soil from erosion. *Contour plowing* is a method of plowing at right angles to the slope of the land. As you can see in Figure 24-2, the furrows keep water from carrying soil downhill. *Strip cropping* is a farming method in which strips of cover crops are planted between strips of other crops. Cover crops are crops that completely cover the soil, as you can see in Figure 24-3. Hay and wheat are cover crops. These plants form a grassy area that holds water and helps to keep soil in place.

Figure 24-3

In strip cropping, cover crops, such as the alfalfa shown, are planted between rows of other crops, such as the corn shown. How does this method reduce erosion?

ACTIVITY   What Is the Composition of Soil?

OBJECTIVE
Identify the parts of soil.

MATERIALS
lab apron, section of soil 15 cm deep, metric ruler, spatula, glass-marking pencil, 6 paper cups, 3 glass jars, alcohol, forceps, spoon, hand lens

PROCEDURE
A. Wear a lab apron during this activity. Obtain a section of soil.
B. Without breaking the soil sample apart, measure the top 5 cm of soil. Use a spatula to cut the top 5 cm of soil away from the rest of the soil. Place the top soil section on a piece of white paper labeled *top*.
C. Repeat step **B** to cut the next 5 cm from the original soil sample. Place this 5-cm soil section on white paper labeled *middle*.
D. Place the bottom 5 cm of soil on a piece of white paper labeled *bottom*.
E. Use a glass-marking pencil to label six paper cups as follows: *top plants, top rocks, middle plants, middle rocks, bottom plants, bottom rocks*. Label three glass jars *top animals, middle animals,* and *bottom animals*. Fill each jar half full of alcohol.

F. Use forceps and a spoon to separate the parts of the soil samples. Begin with the soil sample labeled *top*. Place all the animals and animal parts from this soil sample in the *top animals* jar. Use a hand lens to help you see any small animals or animal parts that may be in the sample.
G. Place all the plants and plant parts from this soil sample in the *top plants* cup.
H. Separate out all the rocks and pebbles from the sample. Place them in the *top rocks* cup.
I. Repeat steps **F** through **H** for the soil samples labeled *middle* and *bottom*.
J. Record observations you make about the amounts and kinds of animals, plants, and rocks in each sample. Draw a soil profile—a diagram showing each layer of soil and its contents.

RESULTS AND CONCLUSIONS
1. Which soil sample has the most plant material? Animal material?
2. Which soil sample has the most rocks and pebbles? Which has the least?
3. Would soil taken from another location be the same? Explain your answer.

Figure 24-4

Grand Coulee Dam. Reservoirs are formed by dams built on lakes or rivers.

WATER

Water is another important renewable resource. Most of the water on the earth is salt water. Only 3 percent of the earth's water is fresh water. Most of this water is frozen in the polar icecaps. A small amount of the earth's fresh water is available for use. Fresh water becomes available when water is recycled in the water cycle. Thus, fresh water is a resource that is limited. It is a resource that must be conserved.

Most of the fresh water used by humans comes from *reservoirs* (REHZ uhr vwahrz) and from underground water. A reservoir is a place where fresh water is stored. Some reservoirs are formed by dams built on lakes or rivers, as shown in Figure 24-4. Water trapped behind the dam can be released when the water is needed. Storing water in reservoirs is an important conservation practice.

Underground water can be conserved by protecting *watersheds*. A watershed is a land area that supplies water to a river or other body of fresh water. Plants in the watershed help hold soil in place. This allows water to seep slowly into the ground. When the plants are removed, as when roads or houses are built, most rain water flows on the surface of the ground. Therefore, the water is not returned to the underground water supply. Runoff in a watershed can be reduced by keeping the ground covered with plants.

ACTIVITY   What Is the Cost of a Leaky Faucet?

OBJECTIVE
Calculate the amount of water lost by a leaky faucet and the cost of this water.

MATERIALS
none

PROCEDURE
A. Suppose a leaky faucet loses 630 drops of water every 10 minutes.
   1. How many drops are lost in 1 hour?
   2. How many drops are lost in 1 day?
B. Every 210 drops of water equals 10 mL.
   3. How many mL are lost each day?
   4. How many L are lost each day?
C. An average month has 30 days.
   5. How many L are lost in an average month?

D. Most water companies in the United States do not sell water in metric volumes. Suppose the price of water is $1.72 per cubic foot, or about $0.06 per L.
   6. What is the monthly cost of the leaky faucet?
E. Look around your home for a leaky faucet. If you find one, repeat steps A through D to determine the monthly cost of the leaky faucet. Report your findings to a parent or other adult in your household.

RESULTS AND CONCLUSIONS
1. From a cost viewpoint, explain why it is important to fix even slow leaks in a faucet.
2. For what reason other than cost is it good to repair leaky faucets?

Figure 24-5

Methods of conserving fresh water. Drip irrigation of citrus tree (*top left*). Not running water while brushing teeth (*bottom left*) and running dishwasher with a full load (*right*).

Water is conserved when wastewater is cleaned and recycled in a water treatment plant. Another way to conserve water is to use less of this resource. Figure 24-5 shows some ways water can be saved. Farmers help to save water by using better methods to water crops. There are many ways that people can conserve water. They can take shorter showers and can repair leaky faucets. What are some other ways that people can use less water?

FORESTS

You have learned that forests provide habitats for many kinds of living things. Forests also help to conserve both soil and water. The recycling of carbon, oxygen, and nitrogen depends greatly on forests. Rainfall and other weather conditions are affected by forests. Trees supply important products, such as lumber for building and wood for fuel and for making paper.

Many hectares of forest area are being destroyed. In the United States and some other countries, fires account for the loss of much forestland. Forest fires are often the result of human carelessness.

The major reason that forests are being destroyed is to clear land for farming and other uses. Most of the forests that are being destroyed are in the tropics. Tropical rain forests are being cleared at the rate of over 40,000 km^2 a year. When these forests are cleared, the places where many animals live are destroyed. Also, the soil in these areas often erodes.

Conservation efforts are being made to save forests. Many forests are being managed so that they can be preserved. Managing forests involves the careful removal of trees for lumber and other uses without harming the environment. The size of the areas in which trees are cut is limited. In this way the surrounding trees can reseed the bare areas and regrowth can occur. Sometimes, cut areas are replanted with young trees. Recycling paper also helps to conserve forests.

Figure 24-6

Conservation of forests includes forest management. What conservation practices are shown?

REVIEW

1. What is the difference between renewable resources and nonrenewable resources?
2. Name two farming methods that can decrease the loss of topsoil by erosion.
3. Describe three ways in which water can be conserved.
4. What is being done to conserve forests?

CHALLENGE In this section, soil is described as a renewable resource. What evidence would support the idea that topsoil should be considered a nonrenewable resource?

24-2 PROTECTING WILDLIFE

Have you ever seen any of the living things in Figure 24-7? Once there were many of each of these kinds of organisms. One kind, the passenger pigeon, is now *extinct* (ehk STIHNKT). When an organism is extinct, it means that there are no members of the species left alive.

Look at the other animal shown in Figure 24-7. This species, and many other species of wildlife, is endangered. An **endangered species** is a species that is in danger of becoming extinct. The California condor and the Florida panther are endangered animals. The Tennessee purple coneflower and the green pitcher plant are endangered plants. More plants than animals are endangered. If action is not taken to preserve these species, they may become extinct in your lifetime.

Extinction is a natural process. In the past, species became extinct at a rate of about one every 1000 years. But in the last 350 years, humans have caused a rapid increase in the rate of extinction.

> *After completing this section, you will be able to*
> - **distinguish** between extinct species and endangered species.
> - **describe** the major causes of extinction.
> - **give examples** of conservation methods that protect wildlife.
>
> *The key term in this section is* **endangered species**

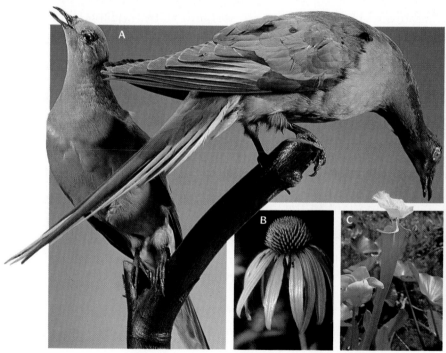

Figure 24-7

Passenger pigeons are extinct animals (*A*). The Tennessee purple coneflower (*B*) and the green pitcher plant (*C*) are endangered plants. The California condor (*D*) is an endangered animal.

Loss of habitat is the main cause of extinction. Recall that a habitat is the place where an organism lives. Most land habitats are made up of large numbers of plants. When the plants in an area are destroyed, the animals that depend on them are also destroyed.

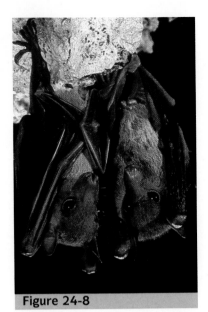

Figure 24-8

These nectar-eating bats, an endangered species, pollinate the durian tree. Durian fruit is an important food source in Southeast Asia.

Most habitat loss is caused by human activities. The clearing of land to plant crops and to build roads destroys many habitats. Chemicals and other wastes that people release into the environment also may destroy habitats.

Another human cause of the extinction of animals is overhunting. Animals may be hunted for food and for animal products. Some animals are hunted for sport. Some plants and animals are collected for hobbies.

Why does it matter if the California condor or the green pitcher plant becomes extinct? Recall from Chapter 22 that each species has a niche, or role, in an ecosystem. If a species becomes extinct, the food chains of which it is a part may be changed. Other organisms may become extinct because of this loss of their food source. People may also be affected. For example, a type of bat found in Southeast Asia is the only species that pollinates an important fruit crop grown there. People have destroyed much of the bat's habitat. They have endangered the animal without understanding its role. Now the fruit crop is threatened by the reduced number of bats.

When a species becomes extinct, its traits are lost forever. The traits that are lost might be valuable. For example, plants are the source of many important medicines. Some kinds of plants may become endangered or extinct before their value is even known.

Many countries are trying to stop the loss of plants and animals. Over 89 countries have signed a treaty to control the trade of rare animals and animal products. The United States has several laws that protect wildlife and plants. One important law is the Endangered Species Act. It protects species that are endangered and those that may soon become endangered. The law also protects the habitats important to the survival of these species.

Wildlife is also protected by laws that control hunting and fishing. Certain areas also are saved as wildlife refuges. A wildlife refuge is an area in which natural habitats are preserved to help species survive.

REVIEW

1. What is the difference between an extinct species and an endangered species?
2. What is the main cause of the extinction of wildlife?
3. What are some ways endangered species are protected?
4. Why should endangered species be protected?

CHALLENGE Suppose an animal species not normally found in your area is released where you live. If that animal has no natural enemies there, what might happen?

24-3 ENERGY RESOURCES

ENERGY FROM FOSSIL FUELS

Think about some of the ways you use energy resources. Have you used an electric light today? Perhaps you came to school in a gasoline-powered car or bus. Energy is used to produce the clothing you wear and other products that you use. Much of the energy needed for human activities comes from the burning of fossil fuels. **Fossil fuels**—coal, oil, and natural gas—are fuels that were formed over millions of years from the remains of once-living things. Long ago, dead organisms were buried by particles of rock, soil, and the remains of other organisms. Pressure and high temperatures over millions of years changed these once-living things to fuels.

Fossil fuels are still being formed. But they are forming at such a slow rate that they are considered to be nonrenewable resources. They are being used more quickly than they are being replaced. And these fuels cannot be recycled. Scientists are trying to find other fuels that can be used in place of fossil fuels.

Because fossil fuels are being used up, people need to conserve these resources. To conserve fossil fuels, people must use energy more efficiently. Many machines and appliances are now designed to get the most power from the least amount of fuel. A lot of cars made today go at least twice as far on the same amount of fuel as did cars made 10 years ago. New appliances, like those shown in Figure 24-9 (*right*), have energy-saving features.

> After completing this section, you will be able to
>
> - **describe** ways in which fossil fuels can be conserved.
> - **explain** why other energy sources must be used in place of fossil fuels and **list** these energy sources.
>
> *The key terms in this section are*
>   biomass energy
>   fossil fuels
>   geothermal energy
>   nuclear energy
>   solar energy

Figure 24-9

The use of mass transit (*left*) and the use of energy-saving appliances (*right*) help to save fossil fuels.

Another way to save fossil fuels is simply to use less. If more people use mass transportation systems instead of driving cars, less energy would be used. Figure 20-9 (*left*) shows a modern system for mass transportation in use in Miami, Florida. Carpooling can also reduce fossil fuel use. Keeping buildings cooler in the winter and warmer in the summer also saves fuel. Much fossil fuel is burned in power plants to produce electricity. What are some ways you can save fuel by using less electricity in your home?

BIOMASS ENERGY

bio- (life)

Fossil fuels come from the remains of once-living things that have changed over a long time. Biomass energy comes from organisms that have recently died or are still living. **Biomass energy** is plant or animal material that can be changed into fuel. The main source of biomass energy is wood. Nearly half of the world's population depends on wood for fuel. But in many parts of the world there is a severe shortage of wood fuel. One reason for this shortage is that forests are cleared for farming and other uses. Another reason is that trees are cut down faster than forests can regrow. Some countries have begun to plant trees on farms. These tree farms have fast-growing trees that can yield many metric tons of wood each year.

Figure 24-10

In many countries, wood is the main source of energy for cooking and heating. Why is wood in short supply in many places?

Other kinds of biomass energy are available. Wastes from living things, such as manure from cows, can be used to make methane gas. Methane gas is a fuel. It can be burned to cook food or to produce electricity. Some kinds of plants, such as sugar cane, can be grown to produce fuel. Sugar cane contains a lot of sugar, which can be changed to alcohol. This alcohol can be used as fuel in cars. One quarter of the cars now sold in Brazil run on alcohol produced from sugar cane.

NUCLEAR ENERGY

In some countries, nuclear (NOO klee uhr) energy is being used in addition to energy from fossil fuels. **Nuclear energy** is energy that is released when the structure of atoms is changed. Energy produced at nuclear power plants comes from *nuclear fission* (FIHSH uhn). Nuclear fission is the splitting of atoms to release energy. The energy released during fission is used to produce electricity.

One problem with nuclear energy is its effects on the environment. Nuclear fission produces wastes that are radioactive. Radioactive materials give off energy and particles that can damage living tissue. The radioactive wastes from nuclear power plants contain some elements that remain dangerous for thousands of years. The safe disposal of radioactive wastes is a major problem that has not yet been solved.

Figure 24-11

Inside a nuclear reactor, the core of a nuclear power plant. In a nuclear power plant, energy is produced by nuclear fission.

SOLAR ENERGY

solaris (sun)

You learned in Chapter 22 that the sun is the source of energy for all ecosystems. Energy from the sun is called **solar energy**. Solar energy can be used to heat and cool buildings and to produce electricity. Buildings like the one shown in Figure 24-12A can be designed to receive much sunlight. Notice the large south-facing windows. How does this design make use of solar energy?

Solar panels, like the one shown in Figure 24-12B, are installed on buildings to absorb the sun's energy. The energy can be used to heat a home. Water for washing may also be heated. Some solar panels have *solar cells.* Solar cells are devices that change sunlight directly to electricity.

Solar energy is a clean source of energy that will not be used up. But solar energy must be stored for use during the night and on cloudy days. Methods for the long-term storage of solar energy have not yet been perfected. Also, the cost of solar devices is still high. As less expensive ways to make these devices are found, their use will no doubt become more widespread.

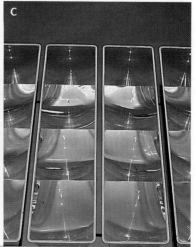

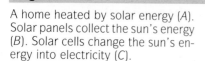

Figure 24-12

A home heated by solar energy (A). Solar panels collect the sun's energy (B). Solar cells change the sun's energy into electricity (C).

ENERGY FROM WIND AND WATER

The wind has been a source of energy for many years. Today, modern windmills are being built in open areas that have steady winds. These devices use *wind energy* to produce electricity. Large numbers of windmills are found on windmill farms, as shown in Figure 24-13. Why is the production of electricity from modern windmills not possible in all areas?

Figure 24-13

In areas where the wind blows steadily, windmill farms can be used to produce electricity.

The energy from falling water also can be used to produce electricity. A natural waterfall, such as Niagara Falls in New York, is one example of falling water. A dam built on a lake or river can also create a waterfall. The number of sites for large dams is limited, but a few new sites have been found. Dams that are no longer in use are being repaired and used again. What environmental factors should be considered before a dam is built?

ENERGY FROM EARTH'S HEAT

Energy that comes from heat beneath the earth's surface is called **geothermal** (gee uh THER muhl) **energy.** You may be familiar with the steam and hot water of *geysers* (GĪ zerz). A geyser is hot underground water that shoots out of the ground through an opening. Old Faithful is a geyser in Yellowstone National Park. Many people come to see this geyser erupt, as shown in Figure 24-14. The steam and hot water from the earth can be tapped by drilling wells. The heat energy can then be used to make electricity. Geothermal energy is available only in certain areas, such as in Iceland.

Figure 24-14

Old Faithful erupts approximately every 66 minutes. The steamy column of hot water that shoots out of the ground may reach heights of 45 m or more.

geo- (earth)
-therm (heat)

REVIEW

1. Why is it necessary to find fuels other than fossil fuels?
2. How can fossil fuels be conserved?
3. What are the advantages of using solar energy?
4. What is geothermal energy?

CHALLENGE Think about the wastes your family produces each day. How could some wastes be used as fuel?

24-4 PROBLEMS OF POLLUTION

As the human population grows, there are greater demands for clean water, air, and land. You have learned that these resources are renewable. But the supplies of these resources have become limited because of pollution (puh LOO shuhn). **Pollution** is the introduction of unwanted, usually harmful materials into an environment. A **pollutant** (puh LOO tuhnt) is a material that harms the environment. Chemicals, metals, and even heat can be pollutants. Almost all pollution of water, air, and land has been caused by humans.

WATER POLLUTION

Most people in the United States take clean water for granted. But in many places in the world, clean water is already in short supply. One reason for the shortage is that fresh water has been polluted. *Water pollution* refers to the presence of harmful materials in water. Pollution makes water unsafe for drinking, washing, and recreation. Water pollution is caused by improper disposal of some substances. It is also caused by certain methods used in industry and farming.

pollutus (soiled, bad-smelling)

Sewage is wastewater from sinks, showers, and toilets. When untreated sewage is dumped into water, the sewage is broken down by bacteria. The bacteria use oxygen in the process. When large amounts of sewage are dumped, the oxygen in water is greatly decreased. As a result, fish and other living things in water may die from lack of oxygen. Many cities and towns have water treatment plants.

Figure 24-15

Not all types of water pollution are as obvious as shown here. How does sewage affect the living things in water?

These plants remove harmful substances from water that contains sewage. Disease-causing organisms are also killed by treatment.

Industries often pollute water supplies with poisonous metals, such as lead and mercury, and with other chemicals. Even small amounts of these substances in water can kill living things. The Clean Water Act and other laws limit the amount of these harmful substances that can be released into water.

Farming activities also cause water pollution. Soil, fertilizers, and pesticides all reach water supplies in runoff. Some fertilizers and pesticides kill certain living things in water. Fertilizers may also cause other living things to increase in numbers very quickly. The increase in certain species can result in the loss of other species. For example, fertilizers can cause a rapid increase in the growth of algae. As large numbers of the algae die, they decay. The decay of algae by bacteria reduces the oxygen content of the water. What effect does less oxygen have on fish? Efforts to decrease erosion and to use fewer chemicals in farming will reduce water pollution.

Figure 24-16

Fertilizers polluting a body of fresh water can cause a rapid increase in the growth of algae.

Oil spills in the ocean are another source of water pollution. Oil spills kill fish, mollusks, water birds, and other marine life. Oil washing up on shore can damage long stretches of beaches. Cleaning up oil spills is difficult and costly. Scientists are studying types of bacteria that use oil as food. How might such bacteria be helpful in cleaning up oil spills?

Some industries release large amounts of heat into lakes and rivers. **Thermal pollution** is pollution caused by the release of waste heat into the environment. Most thermal pollution of water is caused by power plants. These plants use cold water from lakes and rivers to cool heated machines. The heated water is then returned to the lakes and rivers. Even small changes in temperature can kill some living things in water. Hot water does not contain as much oxygen as does cold water. Many species of fish die when the oxygen content of water is reduced.

Some power plants are being built with cooling towers like those shown in Figure 24-17. Heated water is sprayed into the towers, where it is cooled by air. Then the cooled water is returned to the lake or river.

Figure 24-17

Cooling towers are used by power plants to cool hot water before it is released into the environment.

AIR POLLUTION

Air pollution refers to the presence of harmful material in the air. Burning fossil fuels in factories is one source of air pollution. Car exhaust contains many pollutants that come from the burning of fuel in the engine. Some states require that car exhausts be tested for pollutants, as shown in Figure 24-18.

Figure 24-18

New Jersey is one of the states that requires yearly tests of automobile exhausts.

Smog is one form of air pollution that exists in and around many big cities. Smog is a mixture of smoke and fog. A common type of smog forms when sunlight reacts with exhaust pollutants in air.

One of the main air pollutants from burning fossil fuels is a gas called sulfur dioxide. This gas is formed when coal that contains sulfur is burned. The gas is also present in car exhaust. Sulfur dioxide causes much damage to the environment when it forms sulfuric acid. This chemical change occurs when the gas combines with oxygen and water in the air. The mixture of acid and rain water that falls to the earth is called **acid rain.**

Acid rain causes environmental problems. It corrodes metals and dissolves some types of stone, such as marble. How does the statue in Figure 24-19 show the effects of acid rain? Acid rain harms living things. Fish and other water-dwelling organisms die if the water in which they live contains too much acid. Acid rain breaks down soil nutrients. Many plants, especially trees, die if the soil in which they grow is damaged in this way.

One way that acid rain can be reduced is by using coal that has low amounts of sulfur. Washing coal before burning it removes sulfur compounds. It is also possible to remove sulfur gases from exhausts. Many cars are equipped with pollution control devices that do this.

Figure 24-19

A marble statue in 1920, just before it was placed outdoors (*left*). The same statue in 1981 (*right*). Acid rain has discolored and dissolved the marble.

LAND POLLUTION

Wastes that are disposed of on land cause *land pollution*. One kind of land pollution is caused by discarded materials called *litter*. Litter includes trash such as glass bottles, plastic, metal cans, papers, and organic wastes in the form of unused food. Some of these materials, such as paper and organic wastes, will be broken down over time by the action of bacteria. Other materials do not break down. They make the environment ugly and they damage habitats.

Some land pollutants can be recycled. Other land pollutants are buried in areas called *landfills*. The land can then be reclaimed, or made usable again.

ACTIVITY   How Much Pollution Is in Water and Air?

OBJECTIVES
Observe the solid pollutants in water samples.
Observe the solid pollutants in the air.

MATERIALS
lab apron, graduate, samples of pure and polluted water, 4 100-mL beakers, glass-marking pencil, paper towels, 2 pieces of filter paper, 2 funnels, hand lens, 3 cardboard squares (5 cm × 5 cm), wax paper, transparent tape, petroleum jelly

PROCEDURE

A. Wear a lab apron during this activity. Using a graduate, pour 50 mL of pure water into a beaker labeled *pure water.* Use paper towels to dry the graduate.
B. Pour 50 mL of polluted water into a beaker labeled *polluted water.*
C. Fold two pieces of filter paper to form each into a cone. Put each cone in a different funnel. Set each funnel in a dry beaker. Label one beaker *pure* and the other beaker *polluted.*
D. Pour the pure water sample through the filter in the *pure* beaker. Pour the polluted water sample through the other filter. Remove the filter papers and spread each one on a paper towel. With a hand lens, examine each filter paper and the water

that passed through each filter. Record your observations.
E. Label three cardboard squares *A, B,* and *C.* Write your name on each square.
F. Cover one side of each square with wax paper. Use transparent tape to secure the wax paper. Coat the wax-paper side with petroleum jelly.
G. Place the squares so that the jelly side is exposed to the air. Place square *A* near a vent in your classroom. Place square *B* near the classroom door. Place square *C* on your work table. Secure the squares and record the location of each.
H. After 1 week, examine each square with the hand lens. Record your observations.

RESULTS AND CONCLUSIONS
1. Describe the material that you observed on the filter used with the polluted water sample. How did that filter compare with the one used with pure water?
2. Describe the water that passed through each filter. How do you explain how the polluted water looked after it was filtered?
3. Which location in the classroom showed the most material on the cardboard square? How do you explain the result?
4. What kinds of locations outdoors would show the most material in the air?

Some land pollutants called *hazardous wastes* cannot be disposed of easily. Hazardous wastes are wastes that are poisonous, that burn easily, or that react dangerously with other substances. Chemicals used in dry cleaning are examples of such wastes. Radioactive materials also are hazardous wastes. Proper disposal of hazardous wastes is vital to maintain a safe and healthy environment.

REVIEW

1. Describe how sewage harms water supplies.
2. What is thermal pollution?
3. How is acid rain formed? What are its effects?
4. How can water, air, and land pollution be avoided?

CHALLENGE Suppose you are a farmer who wants to grow large healthy crops and also wants to be sure that the environment is not harmed. What methods could you use to avoid polluting the environment?

24-5 A LOOK TO THE FUTURE

The need for energy, fresh water, and other resources is growing. Finding ways to meet this need and maintain a healthy environment is an important challenge of the future. Science and technology have a major role in meeting this challenge.

You have learned that one way to help meet the growing need for resources is to conserve them. Different conservation methods, such as recycling, can help to make resources last longer. Paper, metals, and glass are materials that are commonly recycled. Technology can expand the kinds of materials that are recycled. For example, new methods are being developed to recycle plastic to make fuel or other products.

A few technologies now used in a limited way are being developed for more widespread use. Recall that solar energy is used to heat some buildings. To get more benefit from solar energy, research is being done with *solar power towers*. A tall tower like the one shown in Figure 24-20 is surrounded by mirrors that collect the sun's rays. Solar energy is then used to produce electricity. The main drawbacks to these towers and mirrors are that they take up much space and are useful only when it is sunny.

Figure 24-20

Solar power towers are being investigated as a possible source of clean energy for the future. Notice the many mirrors around the tower.

SCIENCE & TECHNOLOGY

*C*opaifera multijuga (koh PĪ-fuhr uh muhl tee YOO guh) is a kind of Brazilian tree that produces oil. The oil is obtained by drilling a hole in the tree trunk and then inserting a pipe in the hole. The oil drains out through the pipe. About 20 L of oil can be drained from each tree twice a year. The oil obtained is a diesellike fuel that can be used directly in diesel engines. It can also be processed and used in other products, such as in medicines.

Ways to increase the amount of oil produced by these plants are being studied. Genetic engineering is among the techniques being researched. It may be possible to transfer the genes that control oil making to other plants. If the other plants grow faster or can be grown in places besides Brazil, then plant oil production might be increased. Other research is being done to improve the quality as well as the quantity of oil. If oil-making plants could make enough oil, then this oil could become an energy source alternative to fossil fuels.

Another oil-making plant is *Euphorbia lathyris* (yoo-FAWR bee uh LATH uh rihs). This plant is also known as gopher weed. It received this name because the milky liquid it produces irritates the eyes and skin of animals. Gophers will stay away from areas where the plant grows.

The liquid produced by gopher weed, shown in the photograph, is used to produce oil that is very much like petroleum from the earth. This oil can be used as a fuel. It is also used in making plastics.

Solar satellites have been proposed as another possible energy source. The satellites would be in space, above the earth's atmosphere. There the sun's rays could be collected at all times. The satellites would change solar energy to microwave energy. The microwave energy would be sent back to the earth.

Research is also being done to find new sources of energy. For example, tests are being done with magnets. When very hot gases are passed near a magnet, an electric current is produced. In the future it may be possible to produce large amounts of electricity in this way.

Nuclear fusion (FYOO zhuhn) may also be a major source of energy in the future. **Nuclear fusion** is a process in which energy is given off when two atoms are joined. Energy on the sun is produced by this process. Nuclear fusion has advantages over nuclear fission. But a method for controlling the fusion process has not yet been found.

Some countries are trying to get energy from the ocean. Ocean water varies in temperature. Research on the use of heat energy from the ocean to produce electricity is being done. Also, the ocean is in constant motion. **Tidal energy** is energy released by the movement of ocean tides, waves, and currents. Tidal energy may prove to be a useful source of energy. Tidal power plants, such as the one in Figure 24-21, are in use in France and in Canada.

Figure 24-21

A tidal power plant at the Bay of Fundy in Canada. The movement of ocean water can be used to produce energy at a tidal power plant.

REVIEW

1. Describe two ways in which solar energy may become more widely used.
2. What is nuclear fusion?
3. How might the ocean be a source of energy?

CHALLENGE You have learned that fossil fuels are a major energy source today. What advantages do the energy sources described in this section have that fossil fuels do not have?

CHAPTER SUMMARY

The main ideas in this chapter are listed below. Read these statements before you answer the Chapter Review questions.

- Natural resources are classified as renewable and nonrenewable. Renewable resources include soil, water, and forests. Nonrenewable resources include metals and fossil fuels. (24-1)

- Soil, water, and forests are resources that must be conserved. Several methods aid in the conservation of these natural resources. (24-1)

- Species are becoming extinct at an alarming rate. Loss of habitat is the main cause of extinction. Protection of endangered species is vital to their survival. (24-2)

- Fossil fuels, a major energy source, are being used up. Conserving fossil fuels involves using them more efficiently and using less. Biomass energy is plant or animal material that can be changed into fuel.

- Wood is the main source of biomass energy. (24-3)

- Nuclear energy and solar energy are other energy sources. The energy of wind and of falling water are also used to produce electricity. Energy from heat beneath the earth's surface is an energy source used in some areas. (24-3)

- Water, air, and land are among the resources becoming polluted. Pollution can kill living things. Chemicals, metals, and heat are pollutants. Both prevention of pollution and proper cleanup are necessary. (24-4)

- Possible energy sources for the future are being studied and developed. These sources include recycled plastics to make fuel, solar power towers, nuclear fusion, and tidal energy. (24-5)

The key terms in this chapter are listed below. Use each term in a sentence that shows the meaning of the term.

acid rain	natural resources	pollution
biomass energy	nonrenewable resources	renewable resources
endangered species	nuclear energy	solar energy
fossil fuels	nuclear fusion	thermal pollution
geothermal energy	pollutant	tidal energy

VOCABULARY

Write the letter of the term that best matches the definition. Not all the terms will be used.

1. Energy from tides
2. The introduction of unwanted, usually harmful materials into an environment
3. Materials from the earth that are needed by humans
4. Pollution caused by the release of waste heat into the environment
5. Energy that comes from heat beneath the earth's surface
6. The mixture of acid and rain water that falls to the earth
7. A species that is in danger of extinction
8. Fuels formed over millions of years from the remains of once-living things
9. Materials that are used but not replaced
10. Energy released when the structure of atoms is changed
11. A material that harms the environment
12. Materials that can be replaced through natural cycles

a. acid rain
b. biomass energy
c. endangered species
d. fossil fuels
e. geothermal energy
f. natural resources
g. nonrenewable resources
h. nuclear energy
i. nuclear fusion
j. pollutant
k. pollution
l. renewable resources
m. solar energy
n. thermal pollution
o. tidal energy

CONCEPTS

1. What distinguishes renewable resources from nonrenewable resources? (24-1)
2. How can renewable resources become limited? (24-1)
3. How can recycling conserve nonrenewable resources? (24-1)
4. How does strip cropping reduce soil erosion? (24-1)
5. Where does most of the fresh water used come from? (24-1)
6. How can watersheds be protected? (24-1)
7. What are two causes of the destruction of forests? (24-1)
8. Identify two causes of wildlife extinction. (24-2)
9. Give two reasons why it is important that species not become extinct. (24-2)

10. Describe laws to prevent the extinction of species. (24-2)

11. Describe three ways that fossil fuels can be conserved. (24-3)

12. Identify three kinds of energy that can be used in place of fossil fuels. (24-3)

13. What is one problem caused by nuclear fission? (24-3)

14. What are advantages and disadvantages of solar energy? (24-3)

15. How can farming methods result in water pollution? (24-4)

16. How do fertilizers affect algae? How do algae cause reduced oxygen content of water? (24-4)

17. How can thermal pollution harm organisms in water? (24-4)

18. Describe one way to avoid thermal pollution. (24-4)

19. What is smog, and what causes it? (24-4)

20. Describe how acid rain forms and its effects. (24-4)

21. What kind of nuclear energy process is being developed for the future? (24-5)

22. Describe one possible future source of energy from the sun. (24-5)

APPLICATION/ CRITICAL THINKING

1. Describe an ideal life style for someone who wants to reduce pollution. In your description, include that person's home energy source, means of transportation, and daily practices.

2. Explain how a power plant that produces electricity in one area of the country might cause pollution in another area.

3. What limits the widespread use of wind energy, geothermal energy, and tidal energy?

EXTENSION

1. Visit a water treatment plant in your community. Find out what happens to the wastes after they are treated.

2. Study the laws that your state has for the protection of endangered wildlife. Find out if there is a state endangered species list. Report your findings to your class.

3. Contact an organization or company that designs or builds solar homes. Arrange a visit to a model solar home. Write a report about how it is different from other homes.

READINGS

Aiboraiko, A. "Hazardous Wastes: Storing Up Trouble." *National Geographic,* March 1985, p. 320.

Hyde, M. *Energy: The New Look.* New York: McGraw-Hill Book Company, 1981.

Steinhart, P. "Soil: We Can't Grow When It's Gone." *National Wildlife,* February/March 1985, p. 17.

Will city areas become too crowded? What is the pattern of traffic flow? Where should recreation areas be located? These are questions that an urban planner answers.

Urban planners plan and design areas within cities. Their goal is to benefit the city as well as the environment. Urban planning is needed to ensure land conservation. Housing developments and parks are among the areas planned. The planners work with architects and engineers. They also work with people in city government and with individuals who work for private businesses.

Urban planners usually have a four-year-college degree and often have an advanced degree. They study sociology and urban studies. Some also have a background in architecture. If you are interested in this career, you should take courses in biology, sociology, and mathematics in high school.■

Urban Planner

Have you ever gone camping in a state or national park? If you did, you may have noticed the presence of park rangers. Park rangers ensure the safety of the people who use the park.

Park rangers also answer questions about park use and about the wildlife living in the park. They make sure that the wildlife is not harmed as people use the park for recreation. They also check that habitats are not being damaged.

Park rangers usually have a four-year college degree in biology or natural resource management. Often candidates must pass an additional examination before they can work in the park. If you like being outdoors and are interested in a career as a park ranger, you should take courses in biology and earth science in high school.■

Park Ranger

Dr. Eugene P. Odum, Ecologist

Dr. Eugene P. Odum is a pioneer in modern ecology. He is an ecologist who studied succession in abandoned cornfields. Dr. Odum knew that small plants soon grew in these fields. He also knew that larger plants, such as shrubs and finally, trees, would replace the smaller ones that first grew there.

Dr. Odum's special interest, however, was animal populations. He began to collect data on the types of birds that lived in areas that had been abandoned for different lengths of time. He kept careful records of his observations. Dr. Odum was able to show that the bird populations, like the plants, showed succession. Different species of birds would live in the area as the area aged.

Dr. Odum teaches at the University of Georgia. He is also the author of several widely used ecology textbooks. Through his work, Dr. Odum has introduced many students to the basic principles of ecology.■

Issues and Technology

Technology gives people the power to disturb the delicate balance of nature. Water is being brought to deserts. Places that were once underwater are being filled in and turned into farms and cities. Forests are being cut and turned into pastures for cattle.

These changes all seem to be useful developments. But what happens to desert-dwelling animals when the desert becomes a field of crops? What becomes of sea creatures when parts of the sea are filled in? What happens to forest dwellers when trees are cut down? Such drastic changes in habitat make it impossible for some species to survive. Scientists refer to such changes as *habitat loss*. Some scientists think that habitat loss will lead to the extinction of many species.

Habitat loss is a particularly serious problem in tropical forests. These forests are the habitat of a great variety of species. An estimated 25 to 40 percent of the earth's plant and animal species live in tropical forests. Unfortunately, 67 million hectares of these forests are being cleared each year. They are cleared for farms and pastures to raise food for hungry people. The forests are cleared to build roads and towns for growing populations. Scientists have estimated that the rate of extinction in the tropical forests may be as high as one species each day. This rate of extinction could reduce the number of species in the world by one half in the next few decades. Many of the species that have not been identified are probably in the tropical forests.

Tropical forests have been the source of many foods, such as bananas, rice, and sugar cane. Drugs such as quinine have been made from plants of the tropical forest. There may be many more useful species in the tropical forests. If we destroy these species, we may lose some future sources of foods and medicines.

Some scientists have estimated that as many as 1.5 million species will become extinct by the year 2000. Figure 1 shows which portion of these extinctions are expected to take place in tropical forests.

APPLYING CRITICAL THINKING SKILLS

1. In what three areas of the world are tropical forests located? Which of these areas is predicted to have the greatest number of extinctions?
2. How is the habitat changed when forests are turned into farmlands? What kinds of animals would be affected by this change?
3. Many more species are being lost now than ever before. Suggest some reasons for this trend.
4. Do you think that the rate at which species are lost can be decreased? Suggest some ways to accomplish this decrease. Do you think it is important to save these species?

Not all extinctions have been the result of habitat loss. Some species were hunted until their population was small. If a population is very small, there may be too few organisms to breed enough offspring to maintain the species. Some animals were killed for food. Others were killed because parts of their body are valuable.

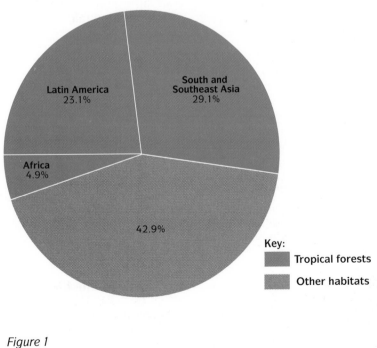

Latin America 23.1%

South and Southeast Asia 29.1%

Africa 4.9%

42.9%

Key:
Tropical forests
Other habitats

Figure 1

For centuries, humans have hunted mammals for their fur. Today some species, such as minks, are bred in captivity. However, many wild animals are still hunted. In South America the chinchilla and the ocelot are hunted extensively. The population of each animal is now very small.

Elephants are killed for their ivory tusks. The tusks are used to make jewelry. Asian elephants are seriously endangered. There may be less than 41,000 of them left in the world.

For centuries, Eskimos have hunted whales. The meat can be eaten, and the fat is used to produce soaps, as well as oil for lamps. Such hunting by Eskimos did not greatly affect whale populations.

In the nineteenth century, whaling became a big business.

In addition to using the oil and meat, people wanted whalebone from the mouth of some kinds of whales. Whalebone is not true bone but a flexible substance that was used to make combs and the stiff ribs of corsets and umbrellas. This commercial whaling greatly reduced the population of many kinds of whales. Figure 2 shows how the population of some whales has been changed by hunting.

The United States has banned the hunting of whales and the importation of whale products. The only exception to the ban on hunting allows Eskimos to take a limited number of whales. The International Whaling Commission (IWC) tries to control the hunting of whales, but some member countries of the IWC are against the total banning of whale hunting.

APPLYING CRITICAL THINKING SKILLS
1. Which kind of whale shown had the largest population before commercial hunting began?
2. Which kind of whale shown has the largest population now? Which has the smallest population now?
3. Do you think whalebone is still needed for any practical uses? Do you think there are any substitutes? Explain your answers.
4. Although Japan and Norway are members of the IWC, both countries continue to hunt whales. People in these countries eat whale meat as well as other products of the sea. Why do these countries depend so heavily on the sea? What could be done to reduce their consumption of whales?

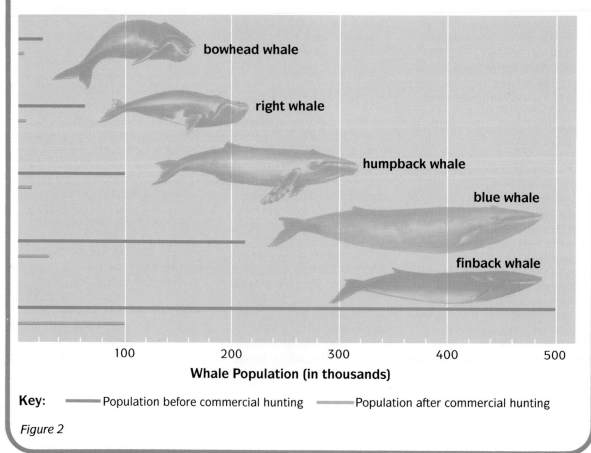

bowhead whale

right whale

humpback whale

blue whale

finback whale

100 200 300 400 500

Whale Population (in thousands)

Key: ——— Population before commercial hunting ——— Population after commercial hunting

Figure 2

590

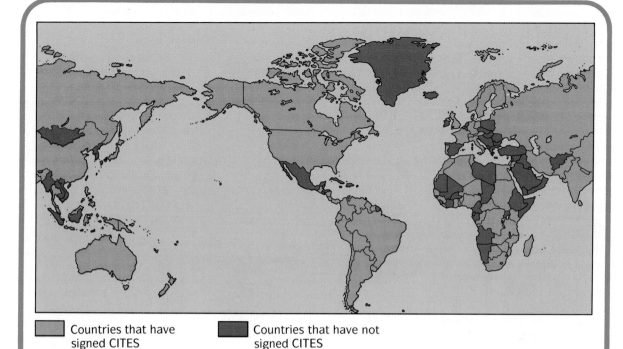

Countries that have
signed CITES

Countries that have not
signed CITES

Figure 3

One of the problems in controlling whale hunting is that many countries are involved. International cooperation is important. The IWC is an example of such cooperation. However, organizing a separate commission to control each endangered species would be difficult.

Instead many countries have developed a more general treaty to control the trade in endangered species. The Convention on International Trade in Endangered Species (CITES) is a treaty that has been signed by 80 countries. This treaty has banned the international trade of about 600 species of plants and animals. An additional 200 species can be exported only if the exporter has a license to do so.

Although CITES is reducing the international trade in endangered species, it cannot stop all such trade. Figure 3 shows the countries that have signed the treaty. As you can see, there are still many countries that have not signed the treaty. CITES cannot control these countries. Some members of CITES break the rules. For example, Japan imports tortoise shells and crocodile skins. Both of these products are banned from international trade.

Another problem with CITES is that it cannot stop individuals from trying to smuggle banned products. Most smuggling is done by people who can make large amounts of money selling products that are in limited supply because of the ban. For example, one coat made of smuggled ocelot skins may be worth as much as $40,000.

Some smuggling is done by tourists who bring home souvenirs made of banned products. When Americans pass through the Customs Service on returning from a foreign country, they may have these souvenirs taken from them. They may also have to pay a fine.

APPLYING CRITICAL THINKING SKILLS

1. Have a majority of the world's nations signed the CITES treaty?
2. Macaws are parrotlike birds found in South America. Chimpanzees are found in Africa. Both of these endangered species are protected by CITES. Why would these animals be valuable for trade?
3. Coral is used to make jewelry. Removing coral from the reef can cause problems for other organisms. What might some of these problems be? Do you think this use of coral is justified? Explain your answer.
4. Large amounts of coral are taken from the Philippines, even though this country has signed CITES. What can be done to enforce the treaty?
5. Do you think all countries should sign the treaty? What reasons might a country give for not signing the treaty?

APPENDIX 1 Taxonomy Tree

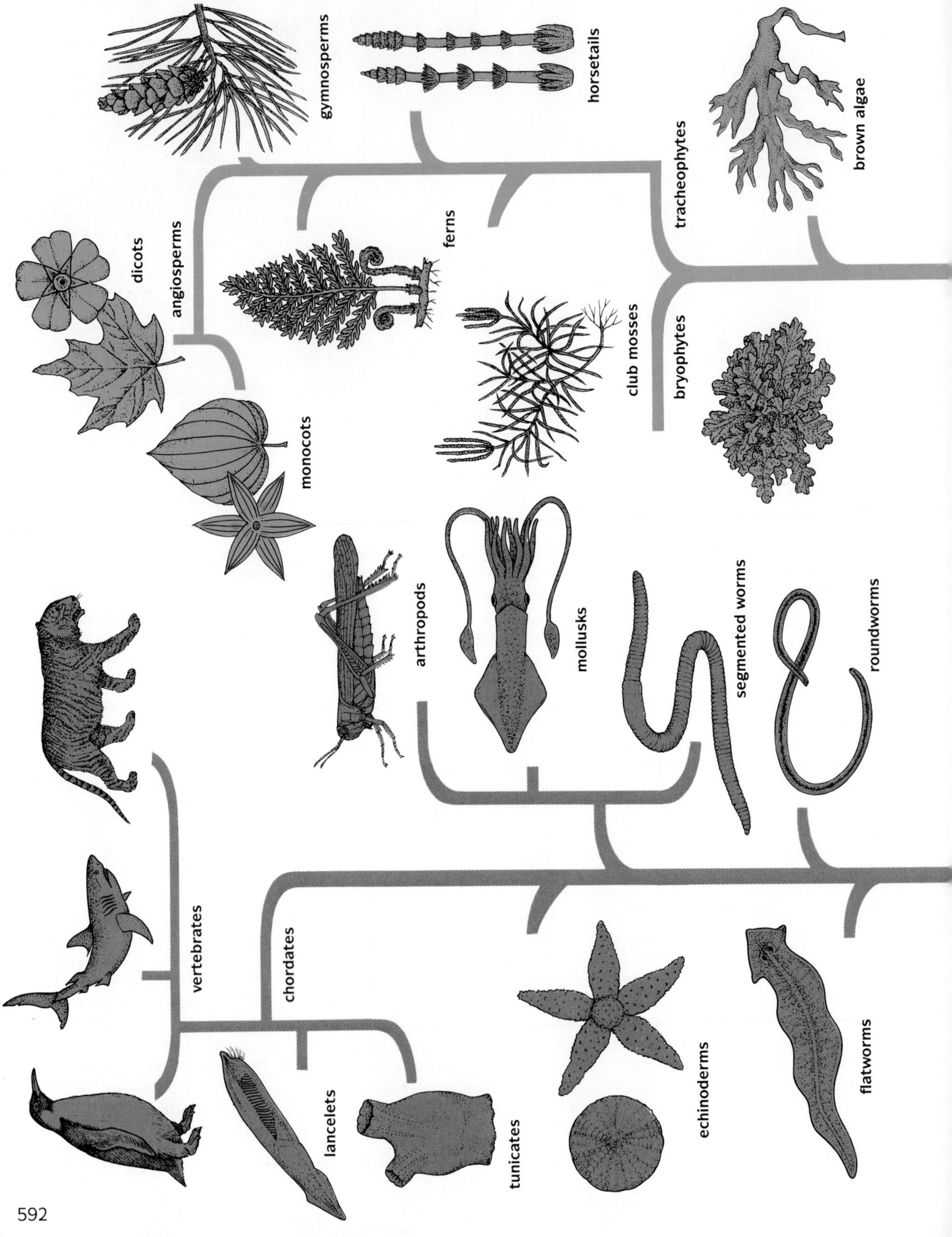
gymnosperms
horsetails
brown algae
tracheophytes
ferns
dicots
angiosperms
club mosses
bryophytes
monocots
arthropods
mollusks
segmented worms
roundworms
vertebrates
chordates
lancelets
tunicates
echinoderms
flatworms

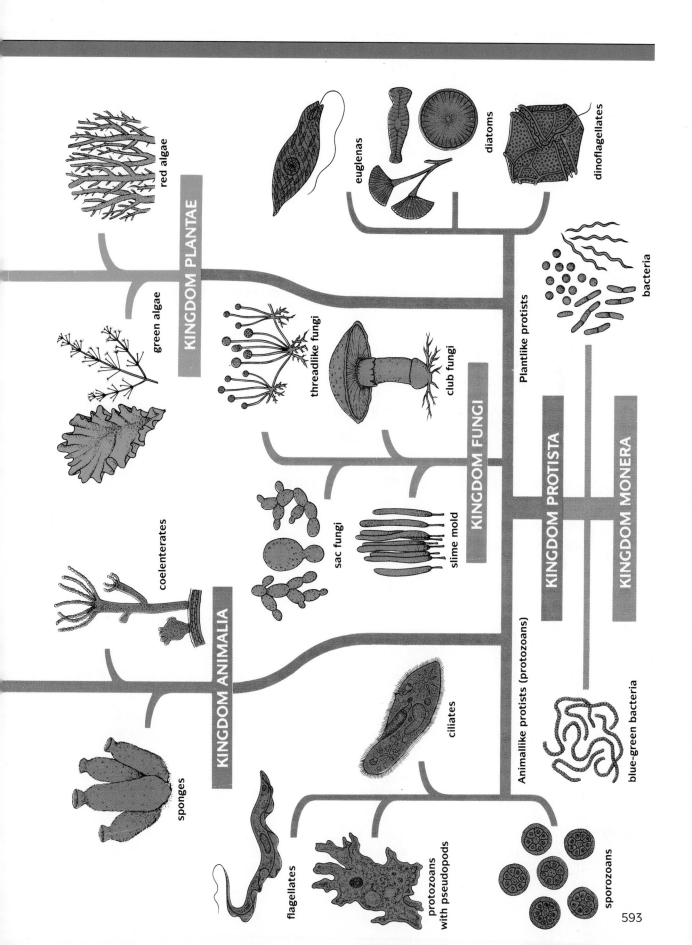

red algae

KINGDOM PLANTAE

euglenas

diatoms

dinoflagellates

green algae

bacteria

threadlike fungi

club fungi

Plantlike protists

KINGDOM FUNGI

coelenterates

sac fungi

slime mold

KINGDOM PROTISTA

KINGDOM MONERA

KINGDOM ANIMALIA

ciliates

Animallike protists (protozoans)

blue-green bacteria

sponges

flagellates

protozoans with pseudopods

sporozoans

APPENDIX 2 *Safety*

An important part of your study of life science will be working on activities. Most of the activity work you will do is quite safe. Yet some equipment, chemicals, and specimens can cause you or a classmate injury if you do not handle them properly.

Within certain activities, safety symbols are included next to the heading PROCEDURE. These safety symbols alert you to specific hazards in the procedure and to safety measures that should be taken to prevent accidents. Read the following guidelines and safety symbol explanations.

Safety Guidelines

- Prepare for every activity by reading through the entire activity before starting.
- Follow all written directions exactly unless your teacher gives you other directions.
- Work in a careful, organized manner. Do not play or fool around.
- Report all spills, accidents, or injuries to your teacher immediately.
- Use only tongs, test-tube holders, or hot pads to hold or move hot glassware.
- Make sure your working area is dry and clutter free. Do not handle electrical equipment with wet hands.
- Do not allow cords from hot plates or microscopes to dangle from work tables.
- Do not use any electrical equipment with frayed cords, loose connections, or exposed wires. Report such equipment to your teacher.
- Do not use glassware that is cracked. If glassware is broken, tell your teacher. Do not pick up broken glass yourself.
- Always place a specimen to be dissected in a pan or on a protected hard surface. Never try to cut the specimen while holding it in your hand.
- Since many plants are poisonous, never place unknown plants, berries, seeds, or fruits into your mouth.
- At the end of every activity, clean up your work area, put everything away, and wash your hands.
- Your teacher may have additional safety guidelines for you to follow.

Safety Symbols

 This symbol will be used when a lab apron should be worn during an activity to protect clothing.

 This symbol will be used when goggles must be worn during an activity to prevent possible eye injury.

 This symbol will be used to remind you that there is a danger of cuts caused by glassware, scalpels, and other equipment.

 This symbol will be used whenever plants that are studied may have sharp edges or thorns, or when outdoor work may expose you to plants that can cause an allergic reaction.

 This symbol will be used when chemicals can possibly cause noxious fumes and when dissecting a preserved specimen. Preservatives used on specimens can be an irritant, so proper ventilation is necessary.

 This symbol will be used to remind you to use care when handling electrical equipment, such as hot plates and electric microscopes.

 This symbol will be used for activities where you may be going outdoors near bodies of water to collect specimens.

 This symbol will be used whenever live animals are studied. It is meant to remind you to be careful and gentle when handling any live animal.

Silver Burdett
LIFE SCIENCE SKILLS HANDBOOK

You have acquired many skills while studying about plants and animals. One of these skills is classifying. The Life Science Skills Handbook will give you an opportunity to put this and other skills into practice.

You will study one family from each of five different classes of living things — mammals, birds, reptiles, angiosperms, and gymnosperms. What makes one species in a family different from the other species in the same family? How can you learn to distinguish among related species? You will find the answers to these questions and others in the next ten pages.

Each lesson consists of a visual display, a brief explanation, and a series of questions. Rather than asking you to simply recall information, the questions require you to compare, hypothesize, infer, and identify cause and effect, as well as interpret diagrams.

CONTENTS

THE PINE FAMILY 596–597
(Correlates with **Units 1, 3, and 7**)
Skills: observing, comparing, inferring, interpreting diagrams

A FAMILY WITH FAVORITE FRUIT TREES 598–599
(Correlates with **Units 1, 3, and 7**)
Skills: observing, comparing, classifying, interpreting diagrams, identifying cause and effect, inferring, hypothesizing

A POISONOUS SNAKE FAMILY 600–601
(Correlates with **Units 1, 4, and 7**)
Skills: observing, comparing, classifying, interpreting diagrams, identifying cause and effect, inferring, hypothesizing

THE WATERFOWL FAMILY 602–603
(Correlates with **Units 1, 4, and 7**)
Skills: observing, comparing, interpreting diagrams, inferring, hypothesizing

THE DEER FAMILY OF NORTH AMERICA 604–605
(Correlates with **Units 1, 4, and 7**)
Skills: observing, comparing, inferring, interpreting diagrams

THE PINE FAMILY

Class: Gymnospermae
Family: Pinaceae

Needles

Single

2

3

5

In rosettes of
10 to 20

In groups of
2, 3, or 5

Red Fir *Abies magnifica*

White Spruce *Picea glauca*

Cone: 20 cm; erect
Needles: Single

Cone: 2.5–5 cm; hanging
Needles: Single

The pine family is one of the six families of conifers, or cone-bearing trees. These trees grow naturally in places that have long, cold winters. Many grow where the minimum annual temperature is between $-45°$ and $-40°C$. Many other kinds of trees would not survive if the temperature dipped so low.

The pine family is the most varied of all the conifer families. All members of the family have woody cones and needlelike leaves, arranged in several different ways: (1) single needles attached on opposite sides of a shoot (firs, spruces, hemlocks); (2) groups of 2, 3, or 5 needles bound in bundles and attached to a shoot (pines); (3) rosettes of 10 to 20 needles attached to a spur shoot (larches — to which the tamarack belongs).

The cones are helpful in tree identification. Shapes of the cones differ, as you can see in the drawings. The cones of spruce, hemlock, and pine hang down, or droop, after pollination occurs. The cones of fir and tamarack remain erect on the branch after pollination. Most cones are deciduous. They fall after releasing their seeds.

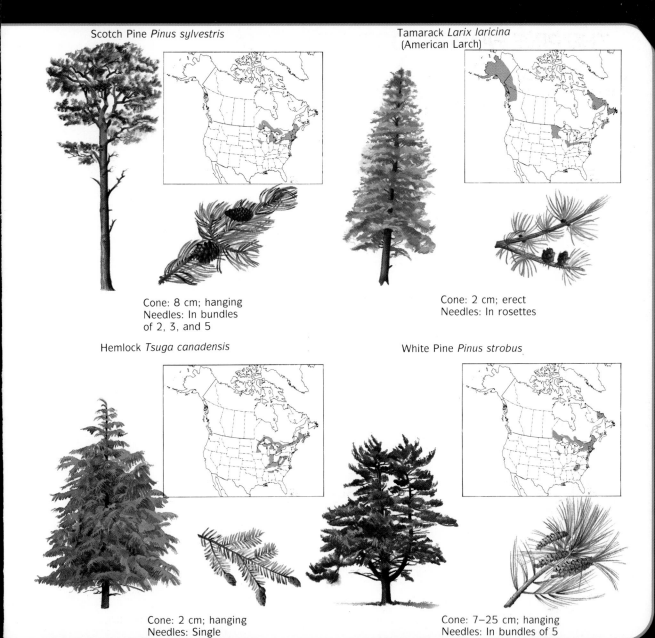

Scotch Pine *Pinus sylvestris*

Cone: 8 cm; hanging
Needles: In bundles
of 2, 3, and 5

Tamarack *Larix laricina*
(American Larch)

Cone: 2 cm; erect
Needles: In rosettes

Hemlock *Tsuga canadensis*

Cone: 2 cm; hanging
Needles: Single

White Pine *Pinus strobus*

Cone: 7–25 cm; hanging
Needles: In bundles of 5

The cones of tamarack trees remain on the tree after the seeds have fallen.

Questions

1. What general characteristics are used to classify the different species of the pine family?
2. Which different species of the pine family might you find growing naturally in the same area?
3. If you found a cone on the ground near a larch and a hemlock, what clue might help you to know which tree the cone came from?
4. Which two species of conifers seem better suited to endure very cold temperatures?
5. If you owned a tree nursery in Alaska would you plant red fir trees to sell as Christmas trees? Explain.
6. In what parts of North America do most of the species of the pine family shown grow naturally?
7. Which tree shown matches this description: A conifer with small, drooping cones and with single needles attached on opposite sides of a shoot?

A FAMILY WITH FAVORITE FRUIT TREES

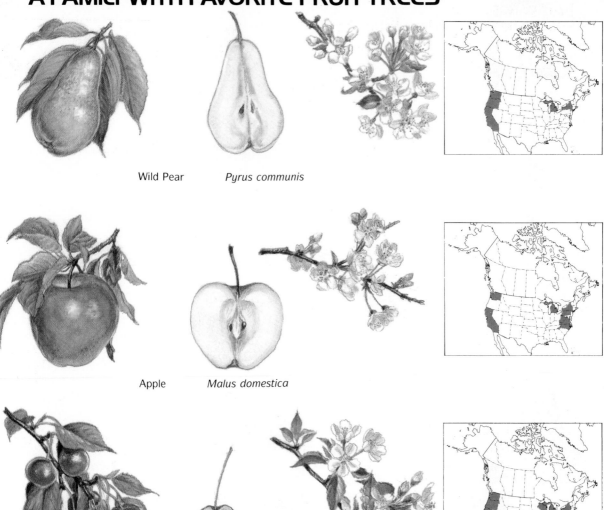

Wild Pear   *Pyrus communis*

Apple   *Malus domestica*

Sweet Cherry   *Prunus avium*

All trees of the rose family have similar flowers: five green sepals, five showy petals, many stamens with golden anthers, and a central green pistil. They all produce nectar and are pollinated by insects. The trees of the family are classified according to the kind of fruit they produce. The trees of the subfamily Pomoidae produce fruits called pomes. A pome has a paperlike core with seeds. The core is surrounded by a fleshy covering. Trees of the subfamily Prunoidae produce fruits called drupes. A drupe has a single seed inside a hard pit. This is surrounded by a fleshy outer covering.

Many fruit trees are not native to this country, but several kinds of cherry trees are. Pear trees were originally grown in southern Europe and Asia. Plum, apricot, and peach trees are native to southwestern Asia.

Certain varieties of fruit trees are produced more than others for the market. Bartlett and Anjou are popular pears. Bing cherries are popular too. Delicious, Golden Delicious, McIntosh, Rome Beauty, and Jonathan are favorite apples enjoyed by many people.

Class: Angiospermae
Family: Rosaceae
Subfamilies: Pomoidae, Prunoidae

Plum   *Prunus domestica*

Apricot   *Prunus armenica*

Peach   *Prunus persica*

Questions

1. What characteristic is used to classify the trees of the rose family?
2. How does a pome differ from a drupe? Classify the fruits shown as pomes or drupes.
3. Which states are large producers of three or more of the fruit trees shown?
4. Only fifteen states produce most of the fruit of the types shown. What might determine which states are the leading producers of these fruits?
5. How could a peach tree be distinguished from an apple tree before the trees had produced fruit?
6. The fruits shown are from trees cultivated for many generations. How might the fruits of these trees compare in size with the fruits of their ancestors that grew in the wild? Explain your answer.
7. Which of the following groups are more closely related: a. apple, cherry; b. peach, plum; c. apple, pear? Explain.

A POISONOUS SNAKE FAMILY

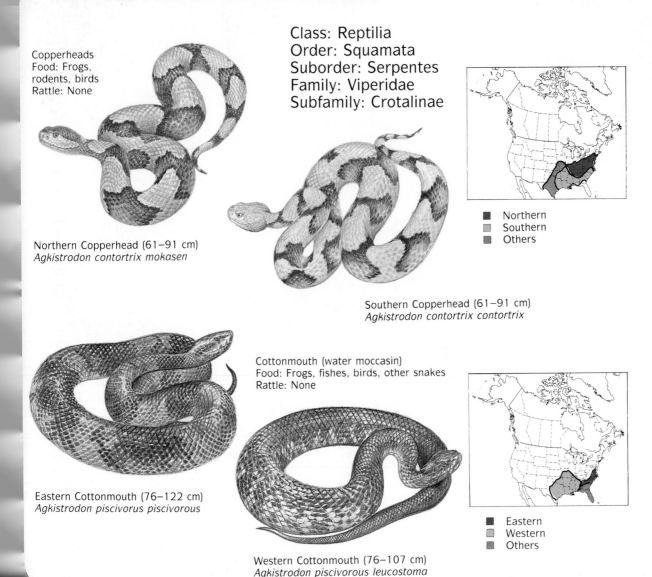

Class: Reptilia
Order: Squamata
Suborder: Serpentes
Family: Viperidae
Subfamily: Crotalinae

Copperheads
Food: Frogs, rodents, birds
Rattle: None

Northern Copperhead (61–91 cm)
Agkistrodon contortrix mokasen

Southern Copperhead (61–91 cm)
Agkistrodon contortrix contortrix

■ Northern
■ Southern
■ Others

Cottonmouth (water moccasin)
Food: Frogs, fishes, birds, other snakes
Rattle: None

Eastern Cottonmouth (76–122 cm)
Agkistrodon piscivorus piscivorous

Western Cottonmouth (76–107 cm)
Agkistrodon piscivorous leucostoma

■ Eastern
■ Western
■ Others

There are two kinds of poisonous snakes in North America: coral snakes and pit vipers. They belong to two different families. The snakes shown above are all pit vipers. Notice that more than one type is shown for some species of snakes.

Pit vipers have a pit organ on each side of the head between the eye and the nostril. By means of the pit organ, a snake can determine the location of its prey by detecting the body heat the prey gives off. The fangs of a pit viper are hollow and are connected to a venom gland.

When not in use, the fangs are retracted. Unlike other reptiles, all pit vipers give birth to living young.

Some pit vipers may have rattles, or hollow segments at the end of their tail. Each time these snakes shed their skin they add one new section to the rattle. So, the rattle can be used to tell a snake's age.

Like all cold-blooded animals, a snake's temperature changes with the temperature of its surroundings. Most snakes are active only when their body temperature is in the range of

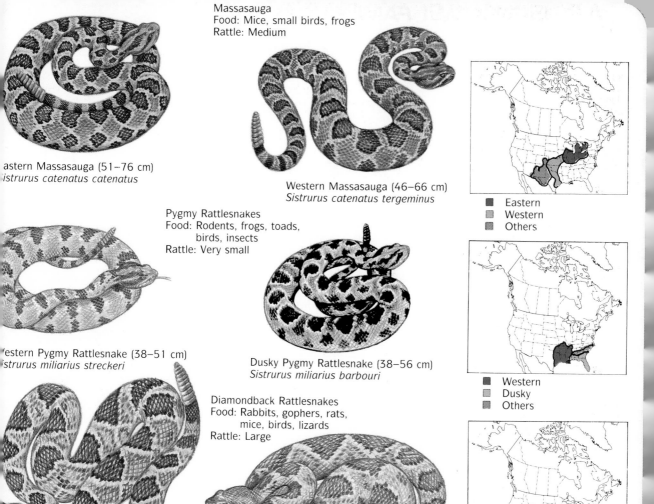

Massasauga
Food: Mice, small birds, frogs
Rattle: Medium

Eastern Massasauga (51–76 cm)
Sistrurus catenatus catenatus

Western Massasauga (46–66 cm)
Sistrurus catenatus tergeminus

- ■ Eastern
- ■ Western
- ■ Others

Pygmy Rattlesnakes
Food: Rodents, frogs, toads,
    birds, insects
Rattle: Very small

Western Pygmy Rattlesnake (38–51 cm)
Sistrurus miliarius streckeri

Dusky Pygmy Rattlesnake (38–56 cm)
Sistrurus miliarius barbouri

- ■ Western
- □ Dusky
- ■ Others

Diamondback Rattlesnakes
Food: Rabbits, gophers, rats,
    mice, birds, lizards
Rattle: Large

Eastern Diamondback Rattlesnake (84–183 cm)
Crotalus adamanteus

Western Diamondback Rattlesnake (76–183 cm)
Crotalus atrox

- ■ Eastern
- ■ Western

20° to 35°C. They may hibernate if the temperature falls below this range.

Questions

1. What physical features distinguish the eastern diamondback rattlesnake from the western diamondback?
2. How does the eastern massasauga differ from the western massasauga?
3. Compare the northern copperhead and the southern copperhead. What indications are there that they belong to the same species?
4. Notice that the list of prey of all the pit vipers shown includes birds or mammals. Explain why you think this is so.
5. Which of the snakes shown ranges farthest north? Describe the range.
6. Why is it unlikely that a copperhead would be found in the northeastern United States in December?
7. Which of the snakes shown might you find in Georgia? in Indiana? Are you likely to find cottonmouths in a lake in Pennsylvania? Explain your answer.

THE WATERFOWL FAMILY

Class: Aves
Order: Anseriformes
Family: Anatidae

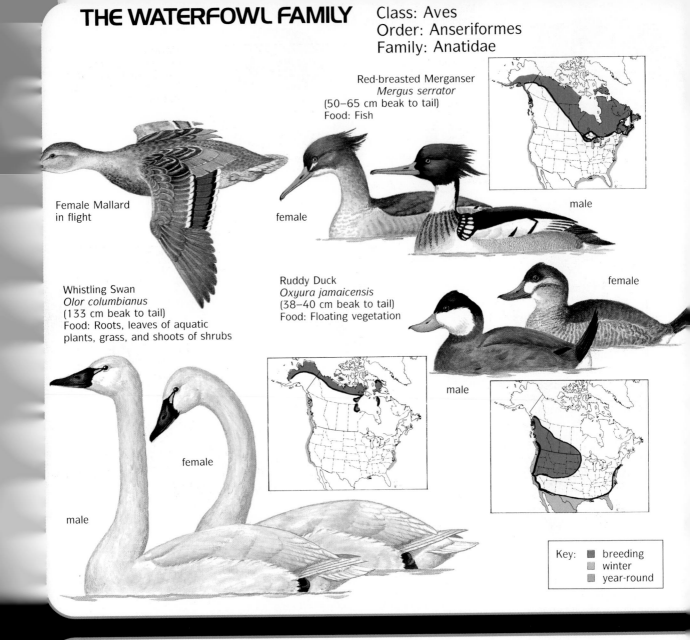

Red-breasted Merganser
Mergus serrator
(50–65 cm beak to tail)
Food: Fish

male

female

Female Mallard in flight

Whistling Swan
Olor columbianus
(133 cm beak to tail)
Food: Roots, leaves of aquatic plants, grass, and shoots of shrubs

Ruddy Duck
Oxyura jamaicensis
(38–40 cm beak to tail)
Food: Floating vegetation

female

male

female

male

male

Key:
- ■ breeding
- ■ winter
- ■ year-round

Swans, geese, and ducks make up the waterfowl family. Members of this family have webbed feet, long necks, and narrow-pointed wings.

Whistling swans are the most common swans in North America. Like all swans, both sexes have similar plumage. They mate for life and have their young in the Arctic.

The Canada goose is the honking wild goose that passes in large groups over many parts of North America. Both males and females have similar plumage.

The mallard is a surface-feeding duck. It is common in ponds and freshwater marshes. The wood duck is also a surface feeder. It has the unusual habit (for ducks) of nesting in trees.

The red-breasted merganser, like most diving birds, has a narrow, saw-toothed bill used in catching and holding fish. It breeds in wooded swamps near fresh water, returning to salt water in autumn.

The ruddy duck has the unusual habit of swimming with its tail held stiffly upward. It is common in summer on lakes and ponds.

Mallard
Anas platyrhynchos
(50–70 cm beak to tail)
Food: Plants, mollusks,
insects, and fish

Canada Goose *Branta canadensis*
(63–108 cm beak to tail)
Food: Grasses, buds, insects,
and water plants

Wood Duck *Aix sponsa*
(43–51 cm beak to tail)
Food: Water and land plants

male
female
male
female
male
female

Questions

1. What features distinguish the males of the mallard from the males of the wood duck and the red-breasted merganser?
2. List some distinctive physical features of the whistling swan. What is the breeding range of this swan?
3. During what time of the year might the wood duck be seen in Florida?
4. Are nests of the Canada goose likely to be found in the southern United States? Explain your answer.
5. Would a duck with a green head seen in Iowa during winter be a mallard, a wood duck, or a red-breasted merganser? Explain why this might be so.
6. How does the female mallard differ in appearance from the male mallard?
7. Suppose a ruddy duckling was reported as seen in eastern Canada. Why might such a report be greeted with skepticism?
8. If you spotted red-breasted mergansers migrating northward, what season of the year would it be?

THE DEER FAMILY OF NORTH AMERICA

Class: Mammalia
Order: Artiodactyla
Suborder: Ruminantia
Family: Cervidae

Food: Tender buds, twigs, leaves, water plants
Antlers: Male

Moose
(height, 152–198 cm)
Alces alces

track:

Food: Grass, flowers, greens, twigs in winter
Antlers: Male

Wapiti
(American Elk)
(height 122–152 cm)
Cervus canadensis

track:

Deer belong to the group of hoofed mammals with an even number of toes. They are all plant eaters, but the types of plants eaten vary from species to species. Male deer have antlers, which they shed yearly.

The moose is the largest member of the deer family. It roams forest lands where there are lakes and swamps. The wapiti, or American elk, is the second largest member of the deer family. The wapiti grazes the higher mountain valleys in the spring and the lower valleys in the winter months.

Caribou are the North American reindeer. They have large feet, which make it easier to travel over snow. Many caribou migrate 800 to 950 km each year in search of food.

White-tailed deer are the most widespread deer in the country. They occur in forests and swamps throughout much of the United States. The mule deer is similar to the white-tailed deer. However, one way the two species differ is in the shape of their antlers. Mule deer are found in forest, mountain, and shrub habitats, where they find plants to feed on.

Caribou
(height 107–122 cm)
Rangifer caribou

Food: Lichens
(reindeer moss)
Antlers: Both sexes

track:

Whitetail
  Deer
(height 91–107 cm)
Odocoileus virginianus

Food: Green shoots, twigs,
        shrubs, grass,
Antlers: Male

track:

Mule Deer
(height 96–110 cm)
Odocoileus hemionus

Food: Grass, lichens, moss,
fallen leaves
Antlers: Male

track:

Questions

1. What physical traits would help you to distinguish a mule deer from a white-tailed deer?
2. How could you distinguish between moose and wapiti? Are large deer tracks found in eastern Canada likely to be those of moose or wapiti? Explain your answer.
3. How might shedding antlers in winter be of survival value to members of the deer family?
4. Which of the North American deer is found farthest north?
5. Of the five kinds of tracks shown, which two would be the most difficult to distinguish in nature?
6. In which states is it possible to see moose?
7. Suppose you come across some deer tracks in north-central Canada. The tracks are rounded on both sides, and each print has an egg-shaped central space. What kind of deer probably made the tracks?

Glossary

abdomen (AB duh muhn)   The last part of the body of an arthropod, containing reproductive and digestive organs.   *p. 246*

abiotic factors   The nonliving things in an environment.   *p. 521*

acid rain   A mixture of acid and rain water that falls to the earth.   *p. 581*

active transport   The process by which a cell uses energy to move molecules of a substance from an area where the molecules are less crowded to an area where they are more crowded.   *p. 86*

adaptation (ad ap TAY shuhn)   A trait that makes an organism better able to survive in an environment.   *pp. 180, 365*

addiction   A condition in which the body requires a drug.   *p. 482*

adult   An animal that has grown and developed enough to reproduce.   *p. 251*

aerobic (air OH bihk) **bacteria**   Bacteria that need oxygen in order to grow.   *p. 109*

air sac   A structure that is connected to the lungs of a bird and that helps to supply oxygen used in respiration.   *p. 294*

albumen (al BYOO muhn)   A watery substance that provides a liquid environment for a bird embryo.   *p. 298*

alga (AL guh)   A simple plant that lacks roots, stems, and leaves.   *p. 147*

alveoli (al VEE uh lī)   Groups of tiny air sacs in the lungs.   *p. 453*

amino (uh MEE noh) **acids**   The building blocks from which proteins are formed.   *p. 68*

amnion (AM nee uhn)   A clear membrane that surrounds a human embryo.   *p. 499*

amoeba (uh MEE buh)   A freshwater protozoan that moves by forming pseudopods.   *p. 125*

amphibian (am FIHB ee uhn)   A cold-blooded vertebrate that usually lives in water after hatching from an egg but as an adult can live on land.   *p. 281*

anaerobic bacteria   Bacteria that can grow only in the absence of oxygen.   *p. 100*

anemia (uh NEE mee uh)   A disorder in which there are too few red blood cells or too little hemoglobin.   *p. 450*

angiosperm (AN jee uh sperm)   A seed plant that produces flowers.   *p. 170*

Animalia   A major classification group; the kingdom that contains all animals.   *p. 36*

antenna   A sense organ found in some arthropods.   *p. 249*

anus (AY nuhs)   An opening at one end of the digestive tract, through which undigested food leaves the body of some animals.   *pp. 233, 316*

arachnid (uh RAK nihd)   An arthropod that has four pairs of jointed legs.   *p. 259*

artery (AHR tuhr ee)   A blood vessel that carries blood away from the heart.   *p. 442*

arthropod (AHR thruh pahd)   An animal that has a body made up of segments, a hard outer covering, and jointed legs.   *p. 245*

asexual (ay SEHK shoo uhl) **reproduction** A form of reproduction that involves only one parent. *p. 61*

atherosclerosis (ath uhr oh skluh ROH sihs) The buildup of fatty materials in the walls of arteries. *p. 449*

atom The smallest unit of matter that can exist and still be recognized as a particular kind of matter. *p. 63*

atrium (AY tree uhm) Each of the two upper chambers of the heart. *p. 445*

auxin (AWK sihn) A hormone that regulates plant growth and development. *p. 208*

bacilli (buh SIHL ī) Rod-shaped bacteria. *p. 107*

bacteria A group of many kinds of monerans. *p. 107*

ball-and-socket joint A joint that allows movement in almost all directions. *p. 398*

biomass energy Plant or animal material from living or recently living things that can be changed into fuel. *p. 574*

biome (BĪ ohm) A large region that has a distinct combination of plants and animals. *p. 550*

biosphere (BĪ uh sfihr) The zone in which living things are found on the earth. *p. 522*

biotic (bī AHT ihk) **factors** The living things in an environment. *p. 521*

bird A warm-blooded vertebrate that has wings and a body covering of feathers. *p. 293*

birth rate The ratio of the number of births to the number of individuals in a population. *p. 542*

bivalve (BĪ valv) A mollusk that has two shells that are hinged together. *p. 239*

bladder A saclike organ that stores urine until it is excreted. *p. 459*

blade The wide, flat portion of a leaf. *p. 185*

blood types Groups into which blood is classified based on its characteristics. *p. 440*

blue-green bacteria Monerans that are able to make their own food by photosynthesis. *p. 104*

bone The hard tissue that makes up most of the skeleton. *p. 272*

bony fish A fish that has an endoskeleton made up mostly of bone. *p. 278*

book lungs A series of flat, air-filled plates that function in respiration in most arachnids. *p. 259*

brain The main control center of the nervous system. *pp. 329, 468*

bronchi (BRAHNG kī) The two branching tubes of the trachea. *p. 453*

brown algae Water-dwelling, multicellular organisms that contain both a green pigment and a brown pigment. *p. 153*

bryophyte (BRĪ uh fīt) A small, green, nonvascular plant that lives on land. *p. 156*

budding A process of asexual reproduction in which a new individual develops from an outgrowth of the parent. *pp. 131, 228*

bulb A short underground stem surrounded by thick leaf bases that store food. *p. 184*

Calorie (KAL uh ree) A measure of the energy available in food. *p. 424*

cambium (KAM bee uhm) A layer of dividing cells that produce new xylem and phloem cells in a stem. *p. 183*

canopy (KAN uh pee) The highest layer of trees in a forest. *p. 553*

capillary (KAP uh lehr ee) A blood vessel whose wall is only one cell thick; the smallest blood vessel. *p. 442*

carbohydrates (kahr boh HĪ drayts) A group of organic compounds; nutrients that are the main source of energy for living things. *pp. 66, 416*

carbon dioxide-oxygen cycle The movement of carbon dioxide and oxygen through an ecosystem. *p. 535*

cardiac (KAHR dee ak) **muscle** The muscle that makes up the heart. *p. 405*

carnivore (KAHR nuh vawr) A consumer that eats other animals. *p. 527*

cartilage (KAHR tuh lihj) A tough, flexible tissue. *p. 272*

cartilage fish Fish that have an endoskeleton composed entirely of cartilage. *p. 277*

cell The smallest unit in which all of the life processes can be carried on. *p. 53*

cell membrane The organelle that controls the movement of substances into and out of a cell. *p. 80*

cell theory A theory that states that all living things are made up of one or more cells, that cells are the basic unit of structure and function of all living things, and that new cells come only from other cells. *p. 76*

cell wall A nonliving structure that surrounds a plant cell. *p. 80*

centipede (SEHN tuh peed) An arthropod that has one pair of jointed legs attached to most of its body segments. *p. 261*

centrioles (SEHN tree ohlz) Organelles that seem to control the spindle during cell division in animal cells. *p. 92*

cephalothorax (sehf uh loh THAWR aks) The fused head and thorax of a crustacean. *p. 257*

cerebellum (sehr uh BEHL uhm) The part of the brain that is involved in muscle coordination and body balance. *p. 469*

cerebrum (suh REE bruhm) The part of the brain that functions in learning, memory, and reasoning. *p. 468*

chemical digestion The process that chemically changes food into simpler substances. *p. 426*

chlorophyll (KLAWR uh fihl) A green pigment inside some of the cells of plants that aids in trapping light energy. *p. 147*

chloroplast (KLAWR uh plast)   An organelle in plant cells and in plantlike protists, in which the food-making processes of the cell take place.   *pp. 81, 150*

chordate (KAWR dayt)   An animal that is a member of phylum Chordata.   *p. 269*

chromosome   A threadlike structure that is made up of DNA and protein; a series of genes.   *pp. 92, 353*

cilia (SIHL ee uh)   Short hairlike structures that extend from a cell and are used in movement.   *p. 125*

circulatory (SER kyuh luh tawr ee) **system**   The organ system made up of the blood, blood vessels, and heart. *p. 437*

class   A group of closely related orders.   *p. 35*

classification (klas uh fuh KAY shuhn)   The grouping or arranging of things according to a system.   *p. 27*

climate   The average weather in a region over a long period of time.   *p. 550*

climax community   The final, stable community in succession.   *p. 547*

closed circulatory system   A transport system in which blood circulates within blood vessels.   *p. 323*

club fungus   A fungus that forms spores on microscopic club-shaped stalks.   *p. 132*

club moss   A small evergreen vascular nonseed plant with tiny, pointed leaves.   *p. 161*

cocci (KAHK sī)   Sphere-shaped bacteria.   *p. 107*

cochlea (KAHK lee uh)   A fluid-filled tube in the ear, containing hairlike receptors for sound.   *p. 475*

coelenterate (sih LEHN tuh rayt)   An invertebrate that has a large central body cavity.   *p. 227*

cold-blooded animal   An animal that has a body temperature that changes with the temperature of the environment.   *p. 272*

colony   A group of animals that live together and that share work and food.   *p. 255*

commensalism (kuh MEHN suh lihz uhm)   A kind of symbiosis in which one organism is helped and the other is neither helped nor harmed.   *p. 532*

community   All the organisms living together in an area. *p. 526*

compound   A substance that contains atoms of two or more elements joined together.   *p. 64*

conclusion   A statement of whether or not the data from an experiment support the hypothesis.   *p. 9*

cone   A woody reproductive structure on which naked seeds develop.   *p. 172*

cones   Receptors in the eye that detect color.   *p. 474*

conifer (KAHN ih fer)   A tree or shrub that bears its seeds in cones.   *p. 172*

coniferous (kuh NIHF uhr uhs) **forest**   A biome made up of cone-bearing trees, or conifers, such as pines and spruces.   *p. 552*

conjugation (kahn juh GAY shuhn)   A type of sexual reproduction in which two organisms join and exchange nuclear materials.   *p. 126*

connective tissue   Tissue that joins and supports different parts of the body.   *p. 394*

consumer   An organism that eats other organisms. *p. 527*

contour (KAHN tawr) **feather**   One of the large feathers that help to give a bird its streamlined shape.   *p. 295*

contractile vacuole (kuhn TRAK tuhl   VAK yoo uhl)   A structure from which extra water and liquid wastes are released from a cell.   *p. 126*

cornea (KAWR nee uh)   The clear area at the front of the eye.   *p. 473*

cotyledon (kaht uh LEE duhn)   A food-storing part of a seed that is used by the developing plant until it can produce its own food.   *p. 175*

cramp   A painful and involuntary contraction of a muscle. *p. 408*

crop   A chamber that stores food in the digestive system of some animals.   *pp. 236, 295, 317*

crustacean (kruhs TAY shuhn)   An arthropod that usually has five pairs of jointed legs.   *p. 257*

cutting   A plant part that has been removed from the parent plant and used to grow a new plant.   *p. 206*

cyst (sihst)   A protozoan with a protective coating. *p. 125*

cytoplasm (sī tuh plaz uhm)   The jellylike substance that surrounds the nucleus of a cell.   *p. 78*

death rate   The ratio of the number of deaths to the number of individuals in a population.   *p. 542*

deciduous (dih SIHJ yoo uhs) **forest**   A biome made up mainly of broad-leaved trees that lose their leaves in the fall.   *p. 553*

deciduous plant   A plant that sheds all of its leaves at one time.   *p. 170*

decomposer (dee kuhm POH zuhr)   An organism that breaks down the remains of dead plants and animals into simpler substances.   *p. 528*

degree Celsius (°C)   A unit used when measuring temperature.   *p. 16*

dermis (DER mihs)   The thicker, inner layer of the skin. *p. 409*

desert   A biome that occurs in an area that receives less than 25 cm of rainfall per year.   *p. 556*

diaphragm (DĪ uh fram)   A sheet of muscle that separates the chest cavity from the other internal organs.   *p. 454*

diatom (DĪ uh tahm)   A plantlike protist that is surrounded by a cell wall.   *p. 121*

dicot (DĪ kaht)   An angiosperm with two cotyledons. *p. 175*

diffusion (dih FYOO zhuhn)   The movement of atoms or molecules from a crowded area to a less crowded area. *p. 84*

digestion (duh JEHS chuhn)   A series of steps in which large complex food substances are broken into smaller, simpler forms that are usable by cells.   *pp. 55, 316*

digestive enzyme   A substance that chemically breaks down a nutrient.   *p. 430*

digestive gland   An organ that produces and releases digestive enzymes.   *pp. 318, 430*

digestive system   An organ system made up of organs that function together to digest, or break down, foods.   *p. 426*

dinoflagellate (dī nuh FLAJ uh layt)   A protist that lives mainly in salt water and that has two flagella used in movement.   *p. 123*

DNA   A nucleic acid that stores all of the information needed for a cell to function.   *p. 68*

dominant (DAHM uh nuhnt) **trait**   A trait that prevents the showing of another trait.   *p. 347*

down feather   A short, fluffy feather found close to a bird's body.   *p. 296*

drug   A chemical that causes physical, chemical, emotional, or behavioral changes in the body.   *p. 482*

eardrum   A circular membrane that vibrates when sound waves strike it.   *p. 475*

echinoderm (ih KĪ nuh derm)   A spiny-skinned invertebrate that lives in the ocean.   *p. 262*

ecology (ee KAHL uh jee)   The study of the interactions between living things and their environment.   *p. 521*

ecosystem (EE kuh sihs tuhm)   An area in which living things and nonliving things interact, exchanging energy and materials.   *p. 522*

ectoderm   The outer tissue layer that forms tissues and organs in some developing animals.   *p. 222*

egg cell   A female reproductive cell.   *p. 158*

electron microscope   A kind of microscope that uses beams of electrons, instead of beams of light, to produce an enlarged image.   *p. 18*

element   A substance that is made up of only one type of atom.   *p. 63*

embryo (EHM bree oh)   A many-celled organism in the early stages of its development; in humans the developing organism from about the third week of development until the end of the second month.   *pp. 200, 298, 498*

endangered species   A species that is in danger of becoming extinct.   *p. 571*

endocrine (EHN doh krihn) **system**   A control system made up of glands.   *p. 478*

endoderm   The inner tissue layer that forms tissues and organs in some developing animals.   *p. 222*

endoplasmic reticulum (ehn doh PLAZ mihk   reh TIHK-yu luhm)   A network of membranes that runs throughout the cytoplasm of a cell.   *p. 79*

endoskeleton (ehn doh SKEHL uh tuhn)   A skeleton that is inside an animal's body.   *pp. 272, 314*

endospore   A structure that contains bacterial DNA and a small amount of cytoplasm surrounded by a tough, protective coat.   *p. 110*

enzyme (EHN zīm)   A protein that controls the rate of chemical changes that occur in living things.   *p. 316*

epidermis (ehp uh DERM uhs)   The outer layer of a leaf; the tough outer layer of the skin.   *pp. 192, 409*

epithelial (ehp uh THEE lee uhl) **tissue**   Tissue made up of sheets of cells that cover and protect the inner and outer surfaces of the body.   *p. 393*

era (IHR uh)   A major division of geologic time.   *p. 375*

esophagus (ee SAHF uh guhs)   A long, muscular tube that connects the throat to the stomach.   *p. 427*

euglena (yoo GLEE nuh)   A plantlike protist that is common in fresh water and in damp soils.   *p. 121*

evergreen   A plant that appears green all year because it does not shed all of its leaves at one time.   *p. 170*

evolution (ehv oh LOO shuhn)   The process of change that occurs over time in species of living things.   *p. 377*

excretion (ehk SKREE shuhn)   The process by which the waste products of metabolism are removed from the cells and body of an organism.   *pp. 56, 326*

excretory system   An organ system that helps in excretion; it is made up of the lungs, skin, and kidneys.   *p. 457*

exoskeleton (ehk soh SKEHL uh tuhn)   A skeleton that covers the outside of an animal's body.   *pp. 246, 313*

experiment   A test of a hypothesis.   *p. 8*

extensor (ehk STEHN suhr)   A muscle that contracts and causes a part of the body to straighten, or move away from the body.   *p. 407*

external fertilization (ehks TER nuhl   fer tuh luh ZAY-shuhn)   The joining of an egg cell and a sperm cell outside the body of an organism.   *p. 331*

extinct (ehk STIHNKT)   Species of organisms of the past that no longer exist.   *p. 372*

family   A group of closely related genera.   *p. 35*

fat   A nutrient that provides energy and building materials for the body.   *p. 416*

fermentation (fer mehn TAY shuhn)   The process in which energy is released from sugar and in which alcohol and carbon dioxide are produced.   *p. 131*

fern   A seedless vascular plant with roots, stems, and leaves.   *p. 162*

fertilization (fer tuh luh ZAY shuhn)   A process in which a sperm cell and an egg cell join.   *pp. 158, 491*

fetus (FEE tuhs)   The developing baby from the beginning of the third month until birth.   *p. 500*

fiber   The part of plants that the human body cannot digest.   *p. 422*

field guide   A book that contains facts about identifying certain groups of living things.   *p. 39*

fins Winglike structures in fish, used for balance and to control movement when swimming. *p. 274*

fish A cold-blooded vertebrate that lives in water and has gills that are used for breathing. *p. 274*

fission (FIHSH uhn) A process of asexual reproduction in which one cell splits into two cells. *p. 109*

flagella (fluh JEHL luh) A whiplike structure that extends out from the cytoplasm of a cell. *pp. 107, 225*

flatworm An invertebrate with a flattened body. *p. 230*

flexor (FLEHK suhr) A muscle that contracts and causes a part of the body to bend toward the body. *p. 407*

flower The reproductive structure of an angiosperm. *p. 201*

food chain The transfer of energy in the form of food from one organism to another. *p. 529*

food vacuole (VAK yoo uhl) An organelle in which food is digested. *p. 125*

food web A complex overlapping of food chains in an ecosystem. *p. 529*

foot A muscular structure that extends from the body of a mollusk and is used in movement. *p. 238*

fossil (FAHS uhl) The preserved remains or a trace of an organism that lived in the past. *p. 369*

fossil fuels Fuels that were formed over millions of years from the remains of once-living things. *p. 573*

fracture (FRAK chuhr) A crack or break in a bone. *p. 407*

fraternal twins Twins formed when two eggs are released at the same time and fertilized by two sperm. *p. 504*

frond The mature leaf of a fern. *p. 162*

fruit A ripened ovary that contains one or more seeds. *p. 204*

Fungi A major classification group; the kingdom that contains living things that are not green and that do not make their own food. *p. 37*

fungus (FUHN guhs) An organism that lacks chlorophyll, produces spores, and absorbs food from living or once-living things. *p. 128*

ganglion (GANG glee on) A mass of nerve cells. *p. 328*

gene Each section of a chromosome carrying the information for a specific trait. *p. 353*

genetic disorders Disorders that are inherited. *p. 506*

genetic engineering The transfer of genes from one organism to another. *p. 359*

genetics (juh NEHT ihks) The scientific study of heredity. *p. 344*

genotype (JEEN uh tīp) The genetic makeup of an organism. *p. 349*

genus A group of closely related species. *p. 35*

geothermal (gee uh THER muhl) **energy** Energy that comes from heat beneath the earth's surface. *p. 577*

germination (jer muh NAY shuhn) The development of a plant embryo into a young plant. *p. 205*

gill cover A bony flap that covers and protects the gill. *p. 279*

gills Organs that absorb oxygen dissolved in water and that allow for exchange of gases in many water-dwelling animals. The many thin sheets on the underside of a mushroom cap. *pp. 132, 274, 320*

gizzard (GIHZ uhrd) A chamber in some animals in which food is broken down into smaller parts by the action of muscles. *pp. 236, 317*

gliding joint A joint that allows sliding movements. *p. 399*

grassland A biome in which grasses are the main plants and in which rainfall is moderate. *p. 555*

green algae Simple organisms with cells that have a rigid cell wall and contain chloroplasts. *p. 150*

growth An increase in the size of an organism. *p. 57*

gymnosperm (JIHM nuh sperm) A vascular plant whose seeds are not enclosed by a special structure such as a fruit. *p. 169*

habitat The specific place in which an organism lives. *p. 524*

half-life The length of time it takes for one half of the atoms of a radioactive element to change. *p. 374*

head The first part of the body, containing sense organs. *p. 246*

hemoglobin (HEE muh gloh buhn) A protein in red blood cells that joins with oxygen. *p. 438*

herbaceous (her BAY shuhs) **stem** A stem that is soft and green and that bends easily. *p. 182*

herbivore (HER buh vawr) A consumer that is a plant eater. *p. 527*

heredity (huh REHD uh tee) The passing of traits from parents to young. *p. 344*

hibernation (hī buhr NAY shuhn) The period of inactivity of some animals during winter months. *p. 283*

hinge joint A joint that allows movement in only one direction. *p. 398*

holdfast A structure that anchors some types of algae to rocks or other objects in water. *p. 153*

hormone (HAWR mohn) A chemical that is produced in one part of an organism and that controls an activity in another part of the organism; a chemical produced by an endocrine gland. *pp. 208, 478*

horsetail A vascular nonseed plant. *p. 161*

hybrid (HĪ brihd) An organism that is produced by a cross of parents that have different forms of a trait. *p. 346*

hyphae (HĪ fee) Threadlike structures of mold and other fungi. *p. 128*

hypothesis (hī PAHTH uh sihs) A proposed answer to a question about nature. *p. 8*

identical twins Twins formed from a single fertilized egg. *p. 504*

impulse The electrical message that travels along a neuron, or nerve cell. *p. 466*

incomplete dominance A condition in which neither trait of a pair is dominant or recessive. *p. 351*

incubation (ihn kyuh BAY shuhn) The warming of a bird egg to a certain temperature over a period of time while the embryo develops. *p. 299*

insect An arthropod that has three pairs of jointed legs. *p. 248*

instinct A complex, inborn pattern of behavior. *p. 301*

internal fertilization (ihn TER nuhl fer tuh luh ZAY-shuhn) The joining of an egg cell and a sperm cell inside the body of an organism. *pp. 285, 332*

invertebrate (ihn VER tuh briht) An animal that does not have a backbone. *p. 221*

involuntary muscle A muscle that is not under conscious control. *p. 404*

iris A ring of muscle in the eye that expands or contracts in response to light. *p. 473*

jawless fish Wormlike fish that have no jaw. *p. 276*

joint A place where two or more bones come together in the skeleton. *pp. 326, 398*

kidneys The main organs of excretion in humans and other vertebrates; the organs that remove wastes from the blood. *p. 457*

kilogram (kg) The SI unit used when measuring mass. *p. 14*

kingdom The largest classification division. *p. 34*

large intestine A short, wide tube in the digestive system that absorbs water from remaining undigested food. *p. 429*

larva (LAHR vuh) An insect in the wormlike stage of development. *p. 252*

leaf A plant organ in which food is made by photosynthesis. *p. 185*

lens A clear, flexible structure in the eye that focuses light. *p. 473*

lichen (LĪ kuhn) A fungus and an alga living together. *p. 135*

life processes The things that organisms do to maintain life. *p. 51*

life science The branch of science that studies living things. *p. 3*

ligaments Strong bands of connective tissue that hold two or more bones together at joints. *p. 398*

limiting factor A factor that prevents a population from reaching its greatest possible size. *p. 543*

lipids (LIH pihds) Organic compounds that store energy. *p. 67*

liter (L) A unit of volume. *p. 15*

liver A large lobed organ that produces bile. *p. 431*

liverwort (LIHV uhr wert) A small nonvascular plant that grows flat along a surface. *p. 157*

lungs The organs through which vertebrates get oxygen from air. *p. 321*

lymph (lihmf) Small amounts of plasma that leak out of capillaries. *p. 444*

mammal A warm-blooded vertebrate that has hair and that feeds milk to its young. *p. 300*

mammary (MAM uh ree) **gland** A structure in female mammals that secretes milk. *p. 300*

mandibles (MAN duh buhlz) A pair of jaws that are used for chewing. *p. 248*

mantle A fleshy tissue that covers and protects the organs of a mollusk. *p. 238*

marrow (MAR oh) A soft tissue inside bone, containing blood vessels and living blood-forming cells. *p. 400*

marsupial (mahr SOO pee uhl) A mammal whose young complete their development in a pouch in the female's body. *p. 304*

mass A measure of the amount of matter in an object. *p. 14*

matter Anything that has mass and takes up space. *p. 63*

mechanical digestion The process that breaks food into small pieces. *p. 426*

medulla (mih DUL uh) The part of the brain that controls many involuntary functions necessary for life. *p. 469*

meiosis (mī OH sihs) Cell division in which sperm or eggs are made. *p. 495*

melanin (MEHL uh nihn) A brown pigment that colors the skin. *p. 409*

menstrual (MEHN stroo uhl) **cycle** The monthly changes in the body of a female that occur with the release of an egg from an ovary. *p. 493*

mesoderm The middle tissue layer that forms tissues and organs in some developing animals. *p. 222*

metabolism (muh TAB uh lihz uhm) The sum of all the chemical processes that occur in an organism. *p. 55*

metamorphosis (meht uh MAWR fuh sihs) A series of distinct changes in form through which an organism passes as it develops from an egg to an adult. *p. 251*

meter (m) The SI unit used when measuring length or distance. *p. 14*

microscope A device used to observe objects that are too small to be seen with the unaided eye. *p. 18*

migration (mī GRAY shuhn) The seasonal movement of animals from one location to another. *p. 297*

millipede (MIHL uh peed) An arthropod that has two pairs of jointed legs attached to most of its body segments. *p. 261*

mineral An element that helps the body to function normally and to use other nutrients. *p. 420*

mitochondria (mī tuh KAHN dree uh) Organelles that release energy from food. *p. 78*

mitosis (mī TOH sihs) Cell division in which daughter cells are formed that are just like the parent cell. *p. 91*

molecule (MAHL uh kyool) The smallest unit of many compounds. *p. 64*

mollusk (MAHL uhsk) An animal that has a soft body, usually covered by a hard shell. *p. 238*

molting The process of shedding the exoskeleton. *p. 247*

Monera (muh NIHR uh) A major classification group; the kingdom containing living things that are made up of a single cell that lacks a nucleus. *p. 37*

monerans (muh NIHR uhnz) Organisms that have the simplest cell structure. *p. 104*

monocot (MAHN uh kaht) An angiosperm with one cotyledon. *p. 175*

monotreme (MAHN uh treem) An egg-laying mammal. *p. 303*

moss A small nonvascular plant that often grows in moist areas in woods or near stream banks. *p. 156*

muscle tissue Tissue made of muscle cells that can contract, or become shorter. *p. 393*

muscles Bundles of muscle tissue that contract, or become shorter. *p. 314*

muscular system An organ system made up of all the muscles in the body; it produces movement of body parts. *p. 403*

mutation (myoo TAY shuhn) A change in the genes or chromosomes of a cell. *p. 367*

mutualism (MYOO chu uh lihz uhm) A kind of symbiosis in which both organisms benefit. *p. 532*

natural resources Materials from the earth that are needed by humans. *p. 565*

natural selection The survival of those organisms best suited to their environment. *p. 379*

nephron (NEF rahn) A structure in the kidney that filters the blood and forms urine. *p. 458*

nerve cell A cell that is specialized for receiving and conducting messages. *p. 328*

nerve tissue Tissues made of long, branched nerve cells that carry messages throughout the body. *p. 394*

nervous system A control system made up of the brain, spinal cord, and nerves. *p. 465*

neuron (NUR ahn) Nerve cells that carry electrical messages. *p. 465*

niche (nihch) The role of an organism in an ecosystem. *p. 524*

nitrogen cycle The movement of nitrogen through an ecosystem. *p. 536*

nitrogen-fixing bacteria Bacteria that combine nitrogen in the air with other elements to form compounds that other living things can use. *p. 113*

nonrenewable resources Materials from the earth that are needed by humans and that are not replaced. *p. 565*

nonvascular plants Plants that lack vascular tissue. *p. 148*

nuclear (NOO klee uhr) **energy** Energy that is released when the structure of atoms is changed. *p. 575*

nuclear fusion (FYOO zhuhn) A process in which energy is given off when two atoms are joined. *p. 584*

nuclear membrane A membrane that surrounds the nucleus and separates it from the other parts of the cell. *p. 78*

nucleic (noo KLEE ihk) **acids** Organic compounds that control the activities of cells. *p. 68*

nucleus (NOO klee uhs) The organelle that controls the activities of a cell. *p. 77*

nutrient (NOO tree uhnt) Any substance that the body needs to live and grow. *p. 415*

nutrition (noo TRIHSH uhn) The process by which organisms obtain and use the nutrients they need. *pp. 54, 415*

nymph (nihmf) A young insect that looks like a small adult. *p. 251*

observation An examination of some part of nature. *p. 7*

omnivore (AHM nuh vawr) A consumer that eats both plants and animals. *p. 528*

open circulatory system A transport system in which blood is not always contained within blood vessels. *p. 322*

order A group of closely related families. *p. 35*

organ A group of two or more different tissues that work together and perform a certain function. *p. 395*

organ system A group of organs that work together and perform one or more specific functions. *p. 395*

organic (awr GAN ihk) **compound** A compound that contains the element carbon. *p. 66*

organism (AWR guh nihz uhm) A complete, individual living thing. *p. 51*

osmosis (ahz MOH sihs) The diffusion of water through a semipermeable membrane. *p. 86*

ovary (OH vuhr ee) A reproductive organ that produces eggs. The enlarged base of a pistil. *pp. 201, 492*

oviduct The tube through which an egg passes from an ovary to the uterus. *p. 492*

ovulation (oh vyuh LAY shuhn) The release of an egg from an ovary. *p. 493*

palisade (pal uh SAYD) **layer** A layer of long, narrow cells below the upper epidermis in a leaf. *p. 192*

pancreas (PAN kree uhs) A digestive gland that produces pancreatic juice. *p. 432*

paramecium (par uh MEE shee uhm) A slipper-shaped protozoan that has cilia. *p. 125*

parasite (PAR uh sīt) An organism that lives in or on another organism and harms it. *pp. 111, 230*

parasitism (PAR uh sih tihz uhm) A symbiotic relationship in which one organism is helped and the other is harmed. *p. 533*

passive transport The movement of a substance through the cell membrane without the use of energy by the cell. *p. 84*

penis The male organ through which semen passes to the outside of the body. *p. 492*

peristalsis (pehr uh STAHL sihs) The squeezing motion that pushes food through the digestive system. *p. 427*

permafrost The layer of permanently frozen soil in the tundra. *p. 551*

petal (PEHT uhl) A brightly colored structure above the sepals of a flower. *p. 201*

petiole (PEHT ee ohl) The stalk that joins the leaf to the stem. *p. 185*

pharynx (FAR ihngks) A tube that joins the mouth to the rest of the digestive tract. *p. 231*

phenotype (FEEN uh tīp) The inherited appearance of an organism. *p. 349*

phloem (FLOH uhm) Vascular tissue that conducts food throughout the plant. *p. 177*

photosynthesis (foh tuh SIHN thuh sihs) A process by which plants use light energy from the sun to make their own food. *pp. 147, 191*

phylum (FĪ luhm) A group of closely related classes. *p. 35*

pioneers The first organisms to grow in an area where primary succession is taking place. *p. 547*

pistil (PIHS tuhl) A female reproductive structure of a flower. *p. 201*

pivot joint A joint that allows rotating movement from side to side. *p. 399*

placenta (pluh SEHN tuh) A structure through which a developing mammal receives food and oxygen from the mother and gives off wastes to the mother. *pp. 304, 498*

placental (pluh SEHN tuhl) **mammal** A mammal whose young are nourished through a placenta as they develop inside the female's body. *p. 304*

plankton The many small organisms, some microscopic, that float or swim near the surface of ocean water. *pp. 152, 559*

Plantae A major classification group; the kingdom that contains all plants. *p. 36*

plasma The pale yellow liquid portion of the blood. *p. 438*

plasmodium (plaz MOH dee uhm) The slimy mass of cytoplasm that is one stage in the life cycle of a slime mold. *p. 134*

platelet A cell fragment that functions in blood clotting. *p. 439*

pollen grain A structure that will form the sperm cell in seed plants. *p. 199*

pollination (pahl uh NAY shuhn) The transfer of pollen from the male reproductive structure to the female. *p. 200*

pollutant (puh LOO tuhnt) A material that harms the environment. *p. 578*

pollution (puh LOO shuhn) The introduction of unwanted, usually harmful materials into an environment. *p. 578*

population A group of organisms belonging to one species living in a given area. *p. 526*

population density The number of individuals per unit of space. *p. 541*

predator (PREHD uh tawr) An animal that hunts and kills other animals for food. *p. 528*

prey The animal that is hunted. *p. 528*

primate A mammal that has a well-developed brain and an opposable thumb. *p. 308*

producer An organism that makes its own food. *p. 527*

proteins (PROH teenz) Nutrients that provide the body with materials for cell growth and repair, and that control body functions. Organic compounds that form the structure and that control the function of living things. *pp. 67, 418*

Protista A major classification group; the kingdom that contains living things that are made up of a single cell that has a nucleus. *p. 37*

protists (PROH tihsts) Mostly single-celled microscopic organisms that are found living in fresh water, salt water, and moist places. *p. 119*

protozoan (proh tuh ZOH uhn) An animallike protist. *p. 120*

pseudopod (SOO duh pahd) A fingerlike extension of the cytoplasm of an amoeba, used in moving and feeding. *p. 124*

pulse The alternate stretching and relaxing of the arteries with each heartbeat. *p. 448*

Punnett (PUHN iht) **square** A chart that shows all the possible combinations of traits among the offspring of a cross. *p. 350*

pupa (PYOO puh) The stage of insect development that follows the larva stage. *p. 252*

pupil The opening in the middle of the iris. *p. 473*

purebred An organism that will show the same form of a trait in all its offspring if the organism is self-pollinated. *p. 345*

radial symmetry (RAY dee uhl SIHM uh tree) The arrangement of body parts around a central area. *p. 263*

radioactive (ray dee oh AK tihv) **dating** The use of radioactive elements to find the age of a fossil. *p. 374*

radioactive (ray dee oh AK tihv) **element** An element whose atoms change to other kinds of atoms, giving off energy and particles in the process. *p. 374*

receptor A structure that receives a stimulus from the environment. *p. 471*

recessive (rih SEHS ihv) **trait** A trait that is hidden by the presence of a dominant trait. *p. 347*

red algae Many-celled algae that live in water and contain green, blue, and red pigments. *p. 154*

red blood cell A cell that transports oxygen. *p. 438*

reflex A quick, automatic response to a stimulus. *p. 470*

regeneration (ree jehn uh RAY shuhn) The regrowth of body parts that have been lost or damaged. *p. 226*

renewable resources Materials from the earth that are used by humans and that can be replaced through natural cycles. *p. 565*

reproductive system The organ system made up of organs that produce sex cells and bring those cells together. *p. 491*

reptile (REHP tíl) A cold-blooded vertebrate that has dry, scaly skin and that lays eggs that have a leathery shell. *p. 285*

respiration (rehs puh RAY shuhn) The process by which food, usually sugar, is broken down and energy is released. *pp. 55, 195, 320*

respiratory (REHS puhr uh tawr ee) **system** An organ system made up of the structures and organs used in breathing. *p. 452*

response The reaction of an organism to a stimulus. *p. 57*

retina (REHT uh nuh) A layer of receptor cells at the back of the eye. *p. 474*

rhizoid (RĪ zoid) A rootlike structure that anchors a bryophyte to the soil and absorbs water and minerals. *p. 156*

rhizome (RĪ zohm) An underground stem that grows parallel to the soil surface. *pp. 162, 183*

ribosomes (RĪ buh sohmz) The organelles on which new proteins are formed. *p. 79*

RNA A nucleic acid that puts into use the information stored in DNA. *p. 68*

rods Receptors in the eye that detect the presence or absence of light. *p. 474*

root An organ that anchors a plant in the ground and absorbs water and minerals from the soil. *p. 177*

root cap Cells that protect the cells of the root tip from being injured as the root grows through the soil. *p. 178*

root hairs The long threadlike extensions of cells on the surface of a root. *p. 178*

roundworm A smooth, cylinder-shaped worm that is pointed at both ends and has a tubelike digestive system. *p. 233*

runner A long, slender stem that grows along the surface of the ground. *p. 184*

sac fungus A fungus that forms reproductive cells, or spores, within sacs. *p. 130*

saliva A liquid that contains the digestive enzyme that begins the chemical digestion of starch. *p. 430*

salivary (SAL uh vehr ee) **glands** The glands that produce saliva. *p. 431*

saprobe An organism that uses the remains of dead plants and animals as food. *p. 113*

scales Overlapping, flat plates that cover an animal's body and that provide protection. *p. 274*

scavenger (SKAV uh juhr) An organism that feeds on dead or dying organisms. *pp. 276, 528*

science A method of obtaining knowledge about nature. *p. 3*

scientific method The special way in which a scientist gathers information and tests ideas. *p. 7*

seed A structure made up of a plant embryo, stored food, and a seed coat. *p. 200*

seed coat A tough outer covering that protects a seed. *p. 200*

seed plant A vascular plant that reproduces by forming seeds. *p. 169*

segmented worm A worm whose body is made up of ringlike sections, or segments. *p. 235*

selective breeding The crossing of plants or animals having the most useful traits to produce offspring that have the combined useful traits of the parents. *p. 359*

semicircular canals Structures in the ear that help the body maintain balance. *p. 475*

sepal (SEE puhl) A leaflike structure found at the base of a flower. *p. 201*

setae (SEE tee) Short bristles that help an earthworm move. *p. 235*

sex chromosomes The two chromosomes that determine sex. *p. 355*

sex-linked trait A trait that results from a gene that is found on the X chromosome but not on the Y chromosome. *p. 356*

sexual reproduction A form of reproduction in which a new living thing is produced by the joining of an egg cell and a sperm cell. *pp. 61, 331*

skeletal muscle A muscle that is attached to and that moves the skeleton. *p. 405*

skeleton The structural framework that supports the body and protects the internal organs. *p. 396*

slime mold A protist that has stages in its life cycle that are similar to those of both protozoans and fungi. *p. 134*

small intestine A long, narrow tube in the digestive system in which food is digested and absorbed. *p. 428*

smooth muscle The muscle that makes up the walls of many organs inside the body. *p. 405*

social insect An insect that lives in a colony. *p. 255*

solar energy Energy from the sun. *p. 576*

sori (SAWR ee) Clusters of spore cases on the underside of a fern frond. *p. 163*

spawning The release of eggs into the water by a female fish. *p. 275*

species A group of living things that can mate with each other and whose young can also mate and produce offspring. *p. 35*

sperm cell A male reproductive cell. *p. 158*

spicule (SPIHK yool) A hard, pointed structure that is found in some sponges and that supports the animal's body. *p. 224*

spinal cord A nerve cord that extends from the brain and is enclosed and protected by a backbone; the structure that carries messages between the brain and other parts of the body. *pp. 329, 468*

spiracle (SPĪ ruh kuhl) A small opening through which air enters the body of some arthropods. *p. 250*

spirilla (spī RIHL uh) Bacteria that are shaped like spirals or corkscrews. *p. 107*

sponge The simplest invertebrate. *p. 224*

spongin A flexible substance that forms a network between cells of some sponges and that helps to support the animal's body. *p. 224*

spongy layer A layer of loosely packed cells below the palisade layer in a leaf. *p. 192*

spore (spawr) An asexual reproductive cell with a hard covering. *p. 158*

sporozoan (spawr uh ZOH uhn) A protozoan that has no means of movement and that sometimes forms spores. *p. 127*

sprain An injury that occurs when a ligament is stretched or torn away from a joint. *p. 407*

stalk The upright part of a mushroom. *p. 132*

stamen (STAY muhn) A male reproductive structure of a flower. *p. 201*

stem An organ that supports the leaves and reproductive organs of a plant and that carries food, water, and minerals to these parts of the plant. *p. 182*

stimulus (STIHM yuh luhs) An event or a condition that causes an organism to react. *p. 57*

stinging cell A cell in coelenterates that has a pointed, threadlike part used in food getting. *p. 227*

stomach A J-shaped, muscular sac that stores food and helps to digest it. *p. 428*

stomate (STOH mayt) An opening in the leaf epidermis through which gases are exchanged with the air. *p. 193*

succession (suhk SEHSH uhn) The orderly sequence of changes that occur in a community over time. *p. 546*

symbiosis (sihm bī OH sihs) A close, long-term relationship between two organisms. *pp. 135, 532*

synapse (sih NAPS) A gap between two neurons. *p. 466*

taxonomic (tak suh NAHM ihk) **key** A guide to identifying living things, based on certain traits. *p. 40*

taxonomy (tak SAHN uh mee) The science of classifying living things. *p. 29*

technology (tehk NAHL uh jee) The use of scientific knowledge in an effort to improve the quality of human life. *p. 5*

temperate (TEHM puhr iht) **rain forest** A biome in which the main trees are conifers, such as redwoods; it occurs along the western coast of North America. *p. 555*

tendons Tough bands of connective tissue that attach skeletal muscles to bones. *p. 406*

tentacles (TEHN tuh kuhlz) Armlike extensions that some animals use in catching food and bringing it into the body cavity. *p. 227*

testes (TEHS teez) The reproductive organs that produce sperm. *p. 491*

theory (THIHR ee) A hypothesis that has been tested many times and that is supported by data. *p. 10*

thermal pollution Pollution caused by the release of waste heat into the environment. *p. 580*

thorax (THAWR aks) The middle body part that joins the head and abdomen. *p. 246*

threadlike fungus A fungus that grows in the form of fine threads that collect to form fluffy, cottony masses. *p. 128*

tidal energy Energy released by the movement of ocean tides, waves, and currents. *p. 584*

tissue A group of cells that are similar in structure and function. *p. 393*

trachea (TRAY kee uh) A tube in the throat that carries air from the larynx toward the lungs. *p. 453*

tracheophyte (TRAY kee uh fīt) A plant that has vascular tissue. *p. 160*

trait A characteristic, or feature, of an organism. *p. 343*

transpiration (trans puh RAY shuhn) The loss of water through the stomates of leaves. *p. 197*

tropical rain forest A warm, humid biome that has the greatest variety of living things. *p. 554*

tropism (TROH pihz uhm) The growth of a plant toward or away from an outside stimulus. *p. 209*

tube feet Hollow, suction-cuplike structures used in movement by echinoderms. *p. 263*

tuber (TOO ber) An enlarged food-storing underground stem or rhizome. *p. 184*

tundra (TUHN druh) The northernmost land biome; a cold, dry region that has a limited variety of plants. *p. 550*

umbilical (uhm BIHL uh kuhl) **cord** A ropelike structure that attaches the embryo to the placenta. *p. 499*

understory A layer of shorter trees and tall shrubs. *p. 553*

univalve (YOO nuh valv) A mollusk that is usually covered with a single shell. *p. 239*

ureters (yu REE tuhrs) The tubes that carry urine out of the kidneys. *p. 459*

urethra (yu REE thruh) The tube that carries urine out of the body. *p. 459*

uterus (YOO tuhr uhs) A hollow, pear-shaped organ with thick muscular walls in which a baby develops. *p. 492*

vaccine A substance that contains viruses or other disease-causing agents that are dead or weakened and can no longer cause disease. *p. 102*

vacuoles (VAK yoo ohlz) Fluid-filled sacs in a cell. *p. 80*

vagina (vuh JĪ nuh) The passageway from the uterus to the outside of the body. *p. 492*

valve A flap of tissue that allows blood to pass in only one direction. *p. 446*

vascular plants Plants with tissue of tubelike cells that carries food, water, and minerals. *p. 148*

vascular tissue A group of tubelike cells that carries food, water, and minerals from one part of a plant to another. *p. 148*

vegetative propagation (VEHJ uh tay tihv prahp uh GAY-shuhn) The development of a new plant from a stem, root, or leaf of the parent plant. *p. 206*

vein A blood vessel that carries blood toward the heart. In vascular plants, a structure that contains vascular tissue that transports materials to and from the leaf. *pp. 185, 443*

ventricle (VEHN truh kuhl) Each of the two lower chambers of the heart. *p. 445*

vertebrate (VER tuh briht) An animal that has a backbone. *p. 269*

villi Millions of tiny fingerlike structures that cover the inner walls of the small intestine. *p. 432*

virus A very small particle made up of a core of nucleic acid with a protein covering, or protein coat. *p. 99*

vitamin An organic substance that helps to control the chemical functions of the body. *p. 419*

volume A measure of the amount of space something occupies. *p. 15*

voluntary muscle A muscle that is under conscious control. *p. 404*

warm-blooded animal An animal that has a constant body temperature that is independent of the external temperature. *p. 273*

water cycle The movement of water through an ecosystem. *p. 534*

white blood cell A cell that helps to defend the body against disease. *p. 438*

woody stem A stem that contains large amounts of xylem cells that have thick cell walls. *p. 182*

X chromosome A sex chromosome found in the cells of both males and females. *p. 355*

xylem (ZĪ luhm) Vascular tissue that conducts water and minerals from the roots to the stems and leaves. *p. 177*

Y chromosome A sex chromosome found only in the cells of males. *p. 355*

yolk Food for the embryo. *p. 298*

zygote (ZĪ goht) A fertilized egg. *pp. 158, 498*

Index

Abdomen, 246
Abiotic factors, 521
Absorption, 432, 432 *ill.*
Acid rain, 581, 581 *ill.*
Acquired characteristic, 377
Acquired Immune Deficiency
    Syndrome (AIDS), 102
Active transport, 86–87, 87 *ill.,*
    198, 198 *ill.*
ADA, 360
Adaptations
    of arthropods, 245
    of birds for flight, 294–295,
      294 *ill.*
    of insects, 253–254
    of leaves, 186, 186 *ill.*
    of reptiles, 285–286
    of roots, 180, 180 *ill.*
    of stems, 183–184, 184 *ill.*
    time and, 365–366, 366 *ill.*
Addiction, 482
Adrenal glands, 479, 479 *ill.*
Adrenaline, 479
Adult, 251, 252
Aerobic bacteria, 109–110, 110
    ill.
African sleeping sickness, 124,
    124 *ill.*
African violet, 206 *ill.,* 207
Afterbirth, 501
Agar, 155, 155 *ill.*
Age of Reptiles, 285
Agroforestry, 555
Air bladder, 153, 280
Air pollution, 580–581,
    580–581 *ill.*
Air sacs, 294, 294 *ill.*
Albino, 367–368, 368 *ill.*
Albumen, 298
Alcohol, 484
Alcoholism, 484
Alder, 551
Alga, 135–136
    See also Algae.
Algae, 106, 147–149, 148 *ill.,*
    579
    brown algae, 153–154,
      153–154 *ill.*

green algae, 150–152,
    150–152 *ill.*
red algae, 154–155, 154–155
    ill.
Algin, 154, 154 *ill.*
Alligators, 287, 287 *ill.*
Alveoli, 453, 453 *ill.*
Amber-preserved fossils, 370,
    370 *ill.*
Amino acids, 68, 68 *ill.,* 418,
    418 *ill.*
Ammonia, 326, 536
Amniocentesis, 510, 510 *ill.*
Amnion, 499
Amoeba, 53 *ill.,* 125, 125 *ill.*
Amoebalike cells, 225
Amoebic dysentery, 125
Amphetamines, 483
Amphibian heart, 324
Amphibians
    circulatory system of,
      324–325, 324 *ill.*
    tailed amphibians, 283–284,
      283–284 *ill.*
    tailless amphibians,
      281–283, 281–282 *ill.*
    traits of, 281
Anaerobic bacteria, 110
Anal pore, 126
Anaphase, 92
Anemia, 450
Angiosperms, 169, 170, 196
    life patterns of, 176, 176 *ill.*
    monocots and dicots, 175,
      175 *tab.*
    reproduction of, 201–205,
      201–205 *ill.*
    traits of, 174, 174 *ill.*
Animal cells, 77–80, 77–78 *ill.*
Animal kingdom, 221–223,
    222–223 *ill.*
Animalia, 34, 36
Animal-pollinated flowers, 202
Annelid, 235
Annual rings, 183, 183 *ill.*
Annuals, 176, 176 *ill.,* 182
Anteaters, 307
Antelope, 556

Antennae, 257
Anther, 201, 202
Antibiotics, 111, 111 *ill.*
Antibodies, 102
Antigens, 440
Ants, 255
Anus, 233, 316, 429
Aorta, 446
Appendicitis, 428
Appendix, 428
Apple trees, 170
Aquatic mammals, 306–307,
    307 *ill.*
Arachnids, 259–260, 259–260 *ill.*
Arctic fox, 551
Aristotle, 30
Armadillos, 307, 307 *ill.,* 557
Artery, 442, 442 *ill.*
Arthropods
    arachnids, 259–260, 259–260
      ill.
    centipedes and millipedes,
      261, 261 *ill.*
    crustaceans, 257–258,
      257–258 *ill.*
    echinoderms, 262–264,
      262–264 *ill.*
    insects, 248–256, 248–249
      ill., 251–253 *ill.,*
      255–256 *ill.*
    nervous system of, 329, 329
      ill.
    traits of, 245–247, 246–247
      ill., 313, 315
Artificial pacemakers, 322
Artificial red blood cells, 441
Artificial reefs, 524
Artificial skin, 410
Asexual reproduction, 61, 61
    ill., 206, 222, 226
Ash, 174, 174 *ill.*
Asio otus, 31, 31 *ill.*
Association neurons, 467
Asthma, 455
Atherosclerosis, 449, 449 *ill.*
Athlete's foot, 130, 533
Atom, 63
ATP, 88, 194–195

Atrium, 300, 324, 445
Auditory nerve, 475
Auxin, 208, 209, 209 *ill.*
Axon, 466

Bacilli, 107
Backbone, 269, 272, 396
Bacteria, 37, 37 *ill.*, 107–108,
    107 *ill.*
  in genetic research, 360
  growth of, 109–110, 110 *ill.*
  harmful bacteria, 111–113,
    111 *ill.*, 113 *ill.*
  helpful bacteria, 113–114,
    113–114 *ill.*
  in pollution control, 579
  reproduction of, 109, 109 *ill.*
  See also Blue-green bacte-
    ria; Monerans.
Bacteria-infecting virus, 100
  ill., 101 *ill.*
Badgers, 555
Balance (instrument), 14, 15 *ill.*
Balance (sense of), 475
Balanced diet, 424, 424 *ill.*
Bald cypress, 170
Ball-and-socket joint, 398
Barbiturates, 485
Bark, 182
Barnacles, 257
Bases (in DNA), 93–94, 93 *ill.*
Bass, 275
Bats, 306, 306 *ill.*, 572, 572 *ill.*
Beak (bird), 296, 296 *ill.*
Bean seed
  effect of water on growth, 210
  germination of, 205, 205 *ill.*
Bears, 552
Beaver, 306 *ill.*
Beech, 553
Bees, 254–256, 255–256 *ill.*
Behavior
  of mammals, 301–302, 302 *ill.*
  of plants, 209–210, 209–210
    ill.
Biceps muscle, 406
Biennials, 176
Bile, 319, 431
Binoculars, 21
Biologist, 3–4
Biology, 3

Bioluminescence, 90
Biomass energy, 574–575, 574
  ill.
Biomes
  land, 550–557, 550–557 *ill.*
  water, 558–560, 558–560 *ill.*
Biosphere, 522, 522 *ill.*
  ecological pyramids,
    530–531, 531 *ill.*
  food chains and food webs,
    529, 529 *ill.*
  producers, consumers, and
    decomposers, 527–528,
    527–528 *ill.*
  See also Environment; Pol-
    lution.
Biotic factors, 521
Birch, 551
Bird egg, 298, 298 *ill.*
Birds, 557
  excretion in, 327
  reproduction of, 298–299,
    298–299 *ill.*
  traits of, 293–297, 294–296
    ill.
Birth, 500–501, 501 *ill.*
Birth rate, 542, 542 *ill.*
Bison, 556
Bivalve, 239, 239 *ill.*
Black bread mold, 128–129,
  128 *ill.*
Bladder, 327, 459
Blade, 153, 185
Blood
  composition of, 438–439,
    438–439 *ill.*
  functions of, 437
  types of, 440–441, 440–441
    ill.
Blood vessels, 442–443,
  442–443 *ill.*
Blue whale, 307 *ill.*
Blue-green bacteria, 104–106,
  104–106 *ill.*, 536
  See also Monerans.
Bobolink, 297, 297 *ill.*
Body cells, 354
Body movement, 314–315,
  314–315 *ill.*, 406–407, 406
  ill.
Bone, 272, 396–398, 396–398 *ill.*

disorders of, 407, 408 *ill.*
  structure and growth of,
    400–402, 400–401 *ill.*
Bone cells, 400
Bony fish, 278–280, 278–279 *ill.*
Bony layer, 400
Book lungs, 259, 259 *ill.*, 320,
  320 *ill.*
Botanist, 4, 4 *ill.*
Botany, 4
Botulism, 111–112
Brain, 301, 329, 329 *ill.*,
  468–469, 468–469 *ill.*
Breastbone, 396
Breathing process, 452, 452 *ill.*,
  454–455, 454 *ill.*
Bristlecone pine, 172, 172 *ill.*
Brittle stars, 262, 262 *ill.*
Broad-leaved plants, 185
Bronchi, 453
Bronchioles, 453
Brown algae, 153–154,
  153–154 *ill.*
Bryophytes, 149
  mosses and liverworts,
    156–157, 157 *ill.*
  reproduction of, 158, 158 *ill.*
  traits of, 156
  uses of, 159
Budding, 131, 131 *ill.*, 226,
  228, 331, 331 *ill.*
Buds, 184, 207
Bulb, 184, 184 *ill.*
Butterfly, 221, 222 *ill.*,
  253–254, 253 *ill.*
Bypass surgery, 450, 450 *ill.*

Cactuses, 174, 186, 365, 366
  ill., 557
Caffeine, 483
Calcium, 257, 396, 400, 401,
  480
California condor, 571
Calories, 424–425
Cambium, 183, 208
Camouflage, 366, 366 *ill.*
Canines (teeth), 301
Canopy, 553
Cap (mushroom), 132
Capillaries, 274, 442–443
Capillary bed, 442–443, 443 *ill.*

Capsule, 107, 158
Carbohydrates, 66, 88, 416, 416 *ill.*
Carbon, 68, 69
Carbon compounds, 195
Carbon dioxide, 88, 89, 194, 195, 320–321, 326, 446, 452, 535
Carbon dioxide-oxygen cycle, 535, 535 *ill.*
Carbon-14, 374, 374 *ill.*
Carbon monoxide, 486
Cardiac muscle, 405, 405 *ill.*
Cardinal, 296 *ill.*
Carnivore, 527, 528 *ill.*
Carrier, 508
Carrier molecules, 86–87, 87 *ill.*
Cartilage, 272, 272 *ill.*, 398, 398 *ill.*, 400, 401
Cartilage fish, 277, 277 *ill.*
Cast, 408
Cast fossils, 370, 370 *ill.*
Celery, 186
Cell body, 465
Cell membrane, 80, 83, 83 *ill.*
Cell theory, 75–76
Cell wall, 80–81, 106
Cells, 33, 53, 53 *ill.*, 393
   active transport in, 86–87, 87 *ill.*
   animal cells, 77–80, 77–78 *ill.*
   cell division, 91–92, 91–92 *ill.*
   energy for, 88–90, 88–89 *ill.*
   passive transport in, 84–85, 84–85 *ill.*
   plant cells, 80–81, 81 *ill.*
   variations among, 82, 82 *ill.*
Cenozoic Era, 376
Centipedes, 261, 261 *ill.*
Central nervous system, 468–469, 468–469 *ill.*
Centrioles, 92
Cephalothorax, 257
Cerebellum, 469, 469 *ill.*
Cerebrospinal fluid, 469
Cerebrum, 468
Cervix, 492, 500
Chemical change, 65, 65 *ill.*
Chemical digestion, 426
Chemical equation, 65
Chemical formula, 64

Chemical symbols, 64, 64 *tab.*
Chestnut tree, 549, 549 *ill.*
Chitons, 238
Chlorella, 150, 150 *ill.*
Chlorophyll, 81, 89, 105, 123, 147, 194
Chloroplast, 81, 81 *ill.*, 89, 89 *ill.*, 150, 194
Cholesterol, 449
Chondrus, 154, 154 *ill.*
Chordates
   subphyla, 270–271, 271 *ill.*
   traits of, 269–270, 270 *ill.*
Chromosomes, 78, 92, 353–354, 353–354 *ill.*
   sex chromosomes, 355–356, 355 *ill.*, 506, 506 *ill.*
Cilia, 125
Circulation, 445–447, 446 *ill.*
   in amphibians, 324–325, 324 *ill.*
   in earthworms, 236, 236 *ill.*
   in fish, 274, 275 *ill.*
Circulatory system, 321
   blood, 437–441, 438–441 *ill.*
   blood vessels, 442–443, 442–443 *ill.*
   disorders of, 449–451, 449–451 *ill.*
   heart and circulation, 445–448, 445–448 *ill.*
   lymphatic system, 444, 444 *ill.*
   types of, 322–325, 322–324 *ill.*
Cirrhosis, 484
Clams, 238, 239 *ill.*, 560
Class, 35
Classification
   five-kingdom system, 36–38, 36–37 *ill.*, 38 *tab.*
   identification of living things, 39–41
   Linnaeus's system, 30–32, 30–31 *ill.*
   modern system, 33–35, 33–35 *ill.*
   need for, 27–29, 28 *ill.*
Clean Water Act, 579
Climate, 550
Climax community, 547–548, 547 *ill.*
Clitellum, 235

Cloaca, 319
Closed circulatory system, 236, 236 *ill.*, 272, 322–323 *ill.*, 323
Cloth, 171
Clotting (blood), 439, 439 *ill.*
Club fungi, 132, 132 *ill.*
Club mosses, 160–161, 161 *ill.*
Coal, 573
Cocaine, 483
Cocci, 107
Cochlea, 475
Cocoon, 252
Coelenterates, 223, 313
   traits of, 227–228, 227–228 *ill.*
   types of, 228–229, 228–229 *ill.*
Cold-blooded animal, 272–273
Cold-blooded vertebrates
   amphibians, 281–284, 281–284 *ill.*
   fish, 274–280, 274–279 *ill.*
   reptiles, 285–288, 285–288 *ill.*
   See also Warm-blooded vertebrates.
Coleus, 208 *ill.*
Collar cells, 225
Collared lizards, 557 *ill.*
Colonies, 104, 104 *ill.*, 119, 150, 255
Color blindness, 357–358, 357–358 *ill.*
Commensalism, 532, 533 *ill.*
Community, 526, 526 *ill.*
Complete metamorphosis, 251–252, 252 *ill.*
Complex sugars, 416
Compound eyes, 249, 257
Compound leaf, 185–186, 186 *ill.*
Compound light microscope, 18, 19 *ill.*, 75, 76 *ill.*
Compounds, 64, 64 *ill.*
   inorganic, 66
   organic, 66–68, 66–68 *ill.*
Computers, 21–22, 21 *ill.*
Conception, 498
Conclusion, 9
Condensation, 534
Cone, 169–170, 170 *ill.*, 172, 199
Cones (eye), 474
Coniferous forest, 552, 552 *ill.*

Conifers, 172, 172 *ill.*, 186, 199, 552

Conjugation, 126, 127 *ill.*, 151, 151 *ill.*

Connective tissue, 394

Conservation, 566, 570, 570 *ill.*

Consumer, 527, 527 *ill.*

Contour feathers, 295–296, 296 *ill.*

Contour plowing, 566 *ill.*, 567

Contractile vacuole, 126

Contracting muscle, 406, 406 *ill.*

Control group, 8

Copaifera multijuga, 584

Coral reef, 229, 229 *ill.*

Corals, 229, 313

Cordgrass, 366, 367 *ill.*

Corm, 207

Corn, 170, 180, 180 *ill.*

Cornea, 473

Cotyledon, 175, 204

Cougars, 557

Cover crops, 567

Coyotes, 557

Crabgrass, 184

Crabs, 257–258

Crack (drug), 483

Cramp, 408

Cranium, 396

Crayfish, 257–258, 257 *ill.*, 321 *ill.*, 560

  digestive system of, 317–318, 317 *ill.*

Crocodiles, 287, 287 *ill.*

Crop (digestive organ), 236, 295, 317

Crop rotation, 566

Crops (12 most important), 171 *ill.*

Cross, 344

Cross-pollination, 345

Crustaceans, 257–258, 257–258 *ill.*

Cucumbers, 204

Culturing, 22

Cuticle, 192

Cutin, 156

Cutting (of plant), 206, 206 *ill.*

Cuttlefish, 239–240, 240 *ill.*

Cycads, 173, 173 *ill.*

Cyst, 125, 135

Cystic fibrosis, 508

Cytoplasm, 78

Daddy longlegs, 260, 260 *ill.*

Daisies, 174, 175

Dams, 577

Dandelions, 170, 174, 179, 182

Dark reactions, 194, 194 *ill.*

Darwin, Charles, 32, 378–381, 378–379 *ill.*

Data, 9

Daughter cell, 91–95

DDT, 531

Death rate, 542

Deciduous forest, 553, 553 *ill.*

Deciduous plant, 170, 170 *ill.*

Decomposer, 528, 528 *ill.*

Deep-sea red algae, 155

Deer, 552, 553

Deer flies, 551

Degree Celsius, 16, 17 *ill.*

Dendrites, 466

Denitrifying bacteria, 536

Depressants, 483–485, 483 *tab.*, 484–485 *ill.*

Dermis, 409

Deserts, 556–557, 556–557 *ill.*

Development (human), 498–500, 499 *ill.*

Diabetes, 480 *ill.*, 481

Diaphragm, 454, 454 *ill.*

Diatom, 121–122, 122 *ill.*

Diatomaceous earth, 122, 122 *ill.*

Dicots, 175, 175 *tab.*

Diet

  calories, 424–425

  food groups, 422–424, 422–424 *ill.*

Diffusion, 84–85, 84–85 *ill.*, 196

Digestion, 55, 55 *ill.*

  absorption, 430–432, 430–432 *ill.*

  in coelenterates, 316, 316 *ill.*

  in crayfish, 317–318, 317 *ill.*

  in earthworms, 236, 236 *ill.*

  in roundworms, 233, 233 *ill.*

  types of, 426

Digestive enzyme, 430

Digestive glands, 318, 430

Digestive system, 316

  of frog, 318–319, 319 *ill.*

  organs of, 427–429, 427–429 *ill.*

  types of digestion, 426

Dinoflagellate, 123

Dinosaurs, 285, 285 *ill.*, 372–373

Disease

  caused by bacteria, 111–113

  caused by viruses, 102–103, 102 *ill.*

Disinfectants, 112

Dissection, 22, 22 *ill.*

DNA, 68, 77, 91

  in moneran cell, 104

  role of, 93–95, 93–94 *ill.*

Dolphin, 300 *ill.*, 306

Dominant trait, 347, 502

Double-pan balance, 14, 14 *ill.*

Douglas fir, 555

Down feathers, 295–296, 296 *ill.*

Down's syndrome, 506 *ill.*, 507

Downy mildews, 129, 129 *ill.*

Dragonfly, 246 *ill.*, 250

Drones, 255–256, 255 *ill.*

Drug abuse, 482

Drugs, 482, 482 *ill.*

  depressants, 483–485, 483 *tab.*, 484–485 *ill.*

  hallucinogens, 486

  narcotics, 485

  smoking, 486, 486 *ill.*

  stimulants, 483, 483 *tab.*

Drunk driving, 485, 485 *ill.*

Duck, 296 *ill.*

Duckbilled platypus, 303, 303 *ill.*

Dutch elm disease, 130

Dyes, 171

Eagles, 552

Ear, 475, 475 *ill.*

Eardrum, 475

Earthworms, 221, 222 *ill.*, 235–237, 236 *ill.*

  body movement of, 314, 314 *ill.*

  circulatory system of, 323, 323 *ill.*

  digestive system of, 317, 317 *ill.*

Echinoderms, 262–264, 262–264 *ill.*

Ecological pyramids, 530–531, 531 *ill.*
Ecology, 4, 5 *ill.*, 521
Ecosystem, 522–523, 523 *ill.*
Ectoderm, 222
Eelgrass, 174
Egg (insect), 251
Egg cells, 200, 202
Eggs (sex cells), 354, 495–497, 497 *ill.*
Element, 63–64, 63 *ill.*
Elephants, 308, 308 *ill.*
Elk, 552
Embryo, 200, 298
Emphysema, 456, 456 *ill.*, 486
Endangered species, 571, 571 *ill.*
Endangered Species Act, 572
Endocrine glands, 478–481, 478 *ill.*
Endocrine system, 478–481, 478 *ill.*
Endoderm, 222
Endoplasmic reticulum (ER), 79
Endoskeleton, 262, 272, 314
Endosperm, 204
Endospore, 110, 110 *ill.*
Energy, 54–55, 416
    for cells, 88–90, 88–89 *ill.*
    for plants, 195, 198
Energy pyramid, 530, 531 *ill.*
Energy resources
    biomass energy, 574–575, 574 *ill.*
    fossil fuels, 573–574, 573 *ill.*
    nuclear energy, 575, 575 *ill.*
    solar energy, 576, 576 *ill.*
    wind, water, and heat energy, 576–577, 577 *ill.*
English ivy, 180
Environment, 57–58, 505
    biosphere and ecosystems, 522–523, 522–523 *ill.*
    communities and populations, 526, 526 *ill.*
    factors in, 521–522, 522 *ill.*
    habitats and niches, 524–526, 525 *ill.*
    preservation of, 565–577, 566–577 *ill.*
    See also Biosphere; Pollution.

Enzymes, 67, 128, 316, 418
Epidermis, 192, 409
Epiglottis, 427, 453
Epithelial tissue, 393, 409
Era, 375
Erosion, 567
Escherichia coli, 107
Esophagus, 236, 317, 427
Euglena, 36, 36 *ill.*, 121, 121 *ill.*
Evaporation, 534
Evergreen, 170, 170 *ill.*, 172
Evolution
    genetics, 381–382, 381 *ill.*
    patterns of change, 382, 382 *ill.*
    Darwin's theory, 378–379, 378–379 *ill.*
    Lamarck's theory, 377, 377 *ill.*
Excretion, 56, 56 *ill.*, 326–327, 326–327 *ill.*, 457, 457 *ill.*
Excretory system
    disorders of, 460
    excretion process, 457–459, 457–458 *ill.*
    of mammals, 327, 327 *ill.*
    of planarians, 326, 326 *ill.*
Exoskeleton, 246–247, 247 *ill.*, 257, 313–314, 315 *ill.*
Experiment, 8, 9 *ill.*
Experimental group, 8
Extensor muscle, 407
External fertilization, 275, 331
Extinct species, 372, 571, 571 *ill.*
Extinction, 571
Eye (human), 473–474, 473 *ill.*
Eyes (potato), 207

Fallopian tube, 492
Family, 35
Fat cells, 425
Fats, 416–417, 417 *ill.*
Fatty acids, 417, 426
Feces, 429
Feedback control, 480, 481 *ill.*
Felis concolor, 28–29, 28 *ill.*
Female reproductive system, 492–494, 493–494 *ill.*
Fermentation, 132
Ferns, 160, 162, 196, 552
    life cycle of, 163–164, 163–164 *ill.*

structure of, 162 *ill.*, 163
Fertilization, 158, 200, 204, 491, 498, 498 *ill.*
Fertilizers, 579, 579 *ill.*
Fetus, 500, 500 *ill.*
Fiber, 422
Fibrous root system, 179, 179 *ill.*
Field guide, 39
Field marks, 39
Filaments, 150, 201
Filaria worm, 234
Filter feeders, 224, 239, 316
Fins, 274
Fir, 5, 172, 552
First offspring generation, 346, 346 *ill.*
Fish
    bony fish, 278–280, 278–279 *ill.*
    cartilage fish, 277, 277 *ill.*
    excretion in, 326
    jawless fish, 276, 276 *ill.*
    traits of, 274–275, 274–275 *ill.*, 559, 560
Fish heart, 324
Fission, 109, 109 *ill.*, 120, 120 *ill.*
Five-kingdom system, 36–38, 38 *tab.*
Fixed joint, 398
Fixed nitrogen, 536
Flagella, 107–108, 121, 123, 225
Flagellates, 124
Flame cells, 326, 326 *ill.*
Flatworms, 222, 230–231, 230–231 *ill.*
Flexor muscle, 407
Flight, 254
Florida panther, 571
Flower, 174, 174 *ill.*
    pollination in, 202–203, 202–203 *ill.*
    structure of, 201–202, 201 *ill.*
Flu virus, 102 *ill.*
Flukes, 232
Foam-nesting frog, 284
Food, 171
    need for, 54, 54 *ill.*
    from plants, 191–195, 192–195 *ill.*
    use of, 55, 55 *ill.*

Food chain, 529, 529 *ill.*
Food groups, 422–424,
    422–424 *ill.*
Food poisoning, 111–112
Food vacuole, 125
Food web, 529, 529 *ill.*
Forebrain, 329
Forests, 569–570, 570 *ill.*
Fossil fuels, 160, 573–574, 573
    ill.
Fossils, 33, 33 *ill.*
    determining age of, 374–375,
        374 *ill.*
    evidence of change, 372–373,
        372 *ill.*
    formation of, 369–371,
        369–371 *ill.*
Foxes, 552, 553
Fracture, 407
Fraternal twins, 504, 504 *ill.*
Free-living worm, 230
Freshwater biome, 559–560,
    560 *ill.*
Frogs, 221, 281–283, 282 *ill.*, 554
    digestive system of,
        318–319, 319 *ill.*
    muscular system of, 315, 315
        ill.
    reproductive system of, 332,
        332 *ill.*
    skeleton of, 314, 314 *ill.*
Fruit, 170, 174, 204, 204 *ill.*
Fruit and vegetable group, 422,
    423 *ill.*
Fruit flies (eye color), 356, 356
    ill.
Fucus, 153, 153 *ill.*
Fungi, 37
    club fungi, 132, 132 *ill.*
    relatives of, 134–136,
        134–136 *ill.*
    sac fungi, 130–131, 130–131
        ill.
    structure of, 133
    threadlike fungi, 128–129,
        128–129 *ill.*
    traits of, 128

Galápagos Islands, 378
Gall bladder, 319, 431, 431 *ill.*
Ganglion, 328

Gas exchange, 193, 236, 258,
    320, 453
Gastric glands, 431
Gastric juice, 431
Gene, 353, 353 *ill.*
Genetic code, 94
Genetic counselor, 508 *ill.*, 509
Genetic engineering, 114, 584
Genetics, 344–347, 345–346 *ill.*
    applications of, 359–360,
        359–360 *ill.*
    chromosomes, genes, and he-
        redity, 353–354,
        353–354 *ill.*
    and evolution, 381–382, 381
        ill.
    genetic disorders, 506–510,
        506–510 *ill.*
    incomplete dominance,
        351–352, 351 *ill.*
    inheritance of traits,
        502–505, 502–504 *ill.*
    Mendel's results, 348–349,
        348–349 *ill.*
    Punnett squares, 350–351,
        350 *ill.*
    sex chromosomes, 355–358,
        355–358 *ill.*
Genotype, 349, 349 *ill.*, 502
Genus, 30, 35
Geologic time, 375–376, 375 *tab.*
Geologists, 369
Geothermal energy, 577, 577 *ill.*
Geotropism, 209 *ill.*, 210
Germination, 205, 205 *ill.*
Geysers, 577, 577 *ill.*
Gibbons, 554
Gill cover, 279
Gill slits, 270
Gills, 132, 132 *ill.*, 258, 274,
    320, 321 *ill.*
Ginkgo, 169, 173, 173 *ill.*
Giraffes, 377, 377 *ill.*
Gizzard, 236, 317
Gladiolus, 207
Gliding joint, 399
Glucose, 88, 89, 194–195, 195
    ill., 416, 480
Glycerol, 417, 426
Gophers, 555
Graduated cylinder, 15

Grafting, 206, 207 *ill.*
Grain group, 423, 423 *ill.*
Grapes, 184, 184 *ill.*
Grasses, 170, 174, 175, 551, 555
Grasshopper, 248–250, 249 *ill.*
    circulatory system of, 323,
        323 *ill.*
    nervous system of, 329, 329 *ill.*
Grasslands, 555–556, 556 *ill.*
Great Basin Desert, 556
Green algae, 150–152, 150–152
    ill.
Ground water, 535
Grouse, 555
Growth, 57, 57 *ill.*
    of bacteria, 109–110, 110 *ill.*
    of plants, 208, 209 *ill.*
Growth hormone, 479
Growth pattern, 542, 542 *ill.*
Guard cells, 193, 193 *ill.*
Gymnosperms, 169–170, 196
    conifers, 172, 172 *ill.*
    cycads, 173, 173 *ill.*
    ginkgoes, 173, 173 *ill.*
    reproduction of, 199–200,
        199–200 *ill.*

Habitat, 524, 571
Hagfish, 276, 276 *ill.*
Hair follicles, 410
Half-life, 374
Hallucinogens, 486
Hamsters, 306
Hares, 306
Hatchet-footed mollusks, 238
Hawks, 552
Hazardous wastes, 582
Head (arthropod), 246
Head-footed mollusks, 238, 240
    ill.
Hearing, 474–475, 475 *ill.*
Heart (human)
    circulation, 445–447, 446 *ill.*
    heartbeat and pulse,
        447–448, 447–448 *ill.*
    structure of, 445, 445 *ill.*
Heart attack, 449
Heartbeat, 447
Hedgehogs, 305
Hemlock, 172
Hemoglobin, 438

Hemophilia, 358
Hepatitis B, 130
Hepatitis virus, 100 *ill.*
Herb layer, 553
Herbaceous stem, 182
Herbivore, 527
Heredity
    human heredity, 502–505,
       502–504 *ill.*
    Mendel's experiments,
       344–347, 345–346 *ill.*
    traits, 343–344, 344 *ill.*
Hermit crab, 532, 532 *ill.*
Hibernation, 283, 302
Hickory trees, 174, 547, 547
    ill., 553
Hindbrain, 329
Hinge joint, 398
Hog-nosed snake, 30, 30 *ill.*
Holdfast, 153, 560
Honeybees, 255–256, 255–256 *ill.*
Hoofed animals, 308
Hooke, Robert, 75
Hookworm, 233–234, 234 *ill.*
Hormones (human), 437,
    478–481
Hormones (plant), 208, 209 *ill.*
Horses, 372, 372 *ill.*, 380
Horsetails, 160–162, 161 *ill.*
Host, 111, 533
Housefly, 253, 253 *ill.*
Humans, 221
Humus, 566
Huntington's disease, 508
Hyacinths, 184
Hybrid, 346
Hydra, 61 *ill.*, 227–228 *ill.*,
    228–229
    digestion in, 316
    nervous system of, 328, 328
       ill.
    reproduction in, 331, 331 *ill.*
Hydrogen, 68
Hydrotropism, 210
Hypertension, 449
Hyphae, 128–129
Hypothesis, 8, 10

Iceland, 577
Identical twins, 504, 504 *ill.*
Impulse, 466

Incisors, 301
Incomplete dominance,
    351–352, 351 *ill.*
Incomplete metamorphosis, 251
Inner ear, 475
Inorganic compound, 66
Insect eaters, 305
Insect-eating bat, 300 *ill.*
Insect-pollinated flowers, 202
Insects
    adaptations of, 253–256, 253
       ill., 255–256 *ill.*
    reproduction of, 250–252,
       251–252 *ill.*
    respiration in, 320
    traits of, 248–250, 248–249 *ill.*
Instinct, 301
Insulin, 114, 480
Interferon, 103, 114
Internal fertilization, 286, 332
International System of Mea-
    surement (SI), 13–17, 13 *tab.*
Interphase, 91, 92 *ill.*
Intertidal zone, 558
Intestinal juice, 432
Intestine, 236
Invertebrates
    arthropods, 248–264,
       248–249 *ill.*, 251–253
       ill., 255–258 *ill.*,
       260–264 *ill.*
    coelenterates, 227–229,
       227–229 *ill.*
    flatworms, 230–231,
       230–231 *ill.*
    flukes and tapeworms, 232,
       232 *ill.*
    mollusks, 238–240, 238–240
       ill.
    roundworms, 233–234,
       233–234 *ill.*
    segmented worms, 235–237,
       235–236 *ill.*
    sponges, 224–226, 224–226 *ill.*
    traits of, 221–223, 222–223 *ill.*
Involuntary muscle, 404
Iridium, 373
Iris (eye), 473
Iris (flower), 175, 183
Irish moss, 154
Iron, 438, 450

Jack rabbits, 557
Japanese salamanders, 283
Jellyfish, 221, 222 *ill.*, 227 *ill.*,
    229, 313
Jointed legs, 247
Joints (arthropod), 246, 315
Joints (human), 398–399, 399 *ill.*
Juniper, 169

Kalanchöe, 207, 207 *ill.*
Kangaroo, 304, 304 *ill.*
Karyotype, 506
Kelps, 153–154, 153 *ill.*
Keratin, 409
Kidney failure, 460
Kidney machine, 6, 6 *ill.*, 460,
    460 *ill.*
Kidney stones, 460
Kidneys, 326, 457, 457 *ill.*
Kilogram (kg), 13, 14
Kingdom, 34
Koala, 304, 304 *ill.*

Labor, 500–501, 500 *ill.*
Ladybugs, 256 *ill.*
Lamarck, Jean B., 377, 377 *ill.*
Lamprey, 276, 276 *ill.*
Lancelets, 271, 271 *ill.*
Land biomes
    coniferous forest, 552, 552 *ill.*
    deciduous forest, 553, 553 *ill.*
    desert, 556–557, 556–557 *ill.*
    grasslands, 555–556, 556 *ill.*
    rain forests, 554–555,
       554–555 *ill.*
    tundra, 550–551, 551 *ill.*
    See also Water biomes.
Land pollution, 581–582
Landfills, 581
Larch, 170, 170 *ill.*, 172
Large intestine, 319, 429, 429 *ill.*
Larva, 252
Larynx, 452
Latent virus, 101–102
Lateral line, 279
Lateral roots, 179
Latin, 32
Learned behavior, 302, 302 *ill.*
Learning, 471–472
Leaves
    adaptations of, 186, 186 *ill.*

kinds of, 185–186, 186 *ill.*
structure of, 185, 185 *ill.*,
192–193, 192–193 *ill.*
Leech, 235, 235 *ill.*
Leeuwenhoek, Anton van, 76,
76 *ill.*, 119
Legumes, 422
Lemmings, 551
Lemon shark, 277 *ill.*
Lens, 249, 473
Leopard frog, 282 *ill.*
Leukemia, 451
Lichens, 135–136, 135–136 *ill.*,
547, 547 *ill.*, 551
Life cycle
of ferns, 163–164, 163–164 *ill.*
of grasshopper, 251, 251 *ill.*
of moss, 158, 158 *ill.*
of moth, 252, 252 *ill.*
of pine tree, 199–200,
199–200 *ill.*
of slime mold, 134–135, 134
ill.
Life science, 3–6
Life scientist, 3–4
Ligaments, 398
Light energy, 191, 194
Light microscope, 18
Light reactions, 194, 194 *ill.*
Lightning, 528 *ill.*
Lilies, 174, 175, 183
Lima beans, 175
Limiting factors, 542–545, 543
ill.
Linnaeus, Carolus, 30–33
Lionfish, 278 *ill.*
Lions, 528 *ill.*
Lipids, 67, 67 *ill.*, 88, 417
Liter (L), 13, 15
Litter, 581
Live young, 332
Liver, 319, 431, 431 *ill.*, 447
Liver-fluke disease, 232
Liverworts, 149, 157, 157 *ill.*
Living things
cells, 53, 53 *ill.*
chemicals of life, 66–68,
66–68 *ill.*
growth and response, 57–59,
57–58 *ill.*
life processes, 51–53

needs of, 53, 53 *tab.*
nutrition and metabolism,
54–56, 54–56 *ill.*
origin of life, 69–70, 70 *ill.*
reproduction of, 60–62,
60–62 *ill.*
Lizards, 272, 273 *ill.*, 288, 288
ill., 553, 557
Lobsters, 222, 222 *ill.*, 257
Long bones, 397, 397 *ill.*
LSD, 486
Lumber, 5, 171, 172
Lung cancer, 456, 456 *ill.*, 486
Lungs, 281, 321
Lymph, 444
Lymphatic system, 444, 444 *ill.*

Macaws, 554 *ill.*
Malaria, 127, 127 *ill.*, 533
Mammal heart, 300–301, 300 *ill.*
Mammals
excretory system of, 327, 327
ill.
marsupials, 304, 304 *ill.*
monotremes, 303, 303 *ill.*
placentals, 304–308,
305–308 *ill.*
traits of, 300–302, 300–302 *ill.*
Mammary gland, 300
Mandibles, 248, 257
Mantle, 238
Maple trees, 553
Marigolds, 174, 176 *ill.*, 182
Marijuana, 486
Marine biome, 558–559, 558 *ill.*
Marrow, 396, 400–401
Marsh plants, 551
Marsupials, 304, 304 *ill.*
Mass, 14–15
Master gland, 479
Matching (of blood), 440–441,
441 *ill.*
Matter, 63–65, 63–65 *ill.*, 64 *tab.*
Meadowlark, 555, 556 *ill.*
Measurement, 11–12
Meat eaters, 308, 308 *ill.*
Meat group, 422, 422 *ill.*
Mechanical digestion, 426
Medicines, 171
Medulla, 469
Megapode, 299

Meiosis, 354, 495–497, 495 *ill.*,
497 *ill.*
Melanin, 409, 410
Memory, 472
Mendel, Gregor, 344–347
Meniscus, 15
Menopause, 494
Menstrual cycle, 493–494, 494 *ill.*
Menstruation, 493–494
Mental retardation, 507
Mesoderm, 222
Mesozoic Era, 376, 376 *ill.*
Metabolism, 55–56, 55–56 *ill.*,
479
Metamorphosis, 251–252,
251–252 *ill.*, 282, 282 *ill.*
Metaphase, 92
Meter (m), 14
Methane gas, 575
Metric system, 13
Mice, 306, 553, 555
Microbiology, 4
Microscope, 18–20, 18–19 *ill.*,
75–76, 76 *ill.*
Microscopic, 18
Midbrain, 329
Middle ear, 475
Migration, 297, 297 *ill.*
Milk group, 422, 422 *ill.*
Millipedes, 261, 261 *ill.*
Minerals, 198, 420, 420 *tab.*
Mistletoe, 174, 533, 533 *ill.*
Mites, 260
Mitochondria, 78, 78 *ill.*, 82, 82
ill.
Mitosis, 91–92, 91–92 *ill.*, 495,
498
Model, 63
Modern classification system,
33–35, 33–35 *ill.*
Molars, 301
Mold (fossil), 370, 370 *ill.*
Molecule, 64
Moles, 305, 305 *ill.*
Mollusks, 223, 313
traits of, 238, 238 *ill.*
types of, 239–240, 239–240 *ill.*
Molting, 247, 247 *ill.*, 288, 288
ill.
Monera, 37
Monerans, 37, 37 *ill.*, 119

bacteria, 107–114, 107 *ill.,*
    109–111 *ill.,* 113–114 *ill.*
  blue-green bacteria,
    104–106, 104–106 *ill.*
Monkeys, 365, 366 *ill.,* 554
Monocots, 175–176, 175 *tab.*
Monotremes, 303, 303 *ill.*
Moose, 552, 552 *ill.*
Morels, 130
Mosquito, 253, 253 *ill.,* 551, 560
Mosses, 149, 156–157, 157 *ill.,*
    551, 552, 554
  life cycle of, 158, 158 *ill.*
  structure of, 159
Moth, 252, 252 *ill.*
Moth larva, 254, 255 *ill.*
Motor neurons, 467
Mound builders, 299
Mouth parts (insects), 253, 253
    ill.
Movable joint, 398
Mud puppy, 283–284, 283 *ill.*
Mule deer, 557
Multicellular organism, 120
Mums (hypothesis on flowering
    of), 8–10, 8 *ill.*
Muscle tissue, 393–394
Muscles, 314–315, 314–315 *ill.*
  disorders of, 408
  structure of, 403–405,
    403–405 *ill.*
Muscular system, 403, 403 *ill.*
  of frogs, 315, 315 *ill.*
Mushrooms, 54 *ill.,* 132, 132 *ill.*
Musk oxen, 366, 367 *ill.,* 551
Mussels, 238–239, 239 *ill.,* 559,
    560
Mutants, 367
Mutations, 366–368, 368 *ill.*
Mutualism, 532, 532 *ill.*

Narcotics, 485
Natural gas, 573
Natural resources, 565
  energy resources, 573–577,
    573–577 *ill.*
  forests, 569–570, 570 *ill.*
  soil, 566–567, 566–567 *ill.*
  water, 568–569, 568–569 *ill.*
  wildlife, 571–572, 571–572 *ill.*
Natural selection, 379

Nautilus, 239–240, 240 *ill.*
Near-shore zone, 559
Nectar, 203, 256
Needle-leaved plants, 185–186,
    186 *ill.*
Nephritis, 460
Nephron, 458–459, 458 *ill.*
Nerve cell, 82 *ill.,* 328
Nerve cord, 270
Nerve net, 328
Nerve tissue, 394
Nervous system
  central nervous system,
    468–469, 468–469 *ill.*
  of earthworm, 236, 236 *ill.*
  of grasshopper, 329, 329 *ill.*
  and learning, 471–472, 472 *ill.*
  of mammals, 301
  peripheral nervous system,
    470–471, 470 *ill.*
  of planarian, 231, 231 *ill.,*
    328, 328 *ill.*
  senses, 473–477, 473 *ill.,*
    475–477 *ill.*
  of vertebrates, 272
Neurons, 465–467, 466 *ill.*
Newts, 284, 284 *ill.*
Niagara Falls, 577
Niche, 524–526, 525 *ill.*
Nicotine, 483, 486
Nitrates, 536
Nitrogen, 68, 534, 536
Nitrogen cycle, 536, 536 *ill.*
Nitrogen-containing com-
    pounds, 326
Nitrogen-fixing bacteria, 113–114,
    114 *ill.,* 536, 536 *ill.*
Nodes (lymph), 444
Nodules, 114
Nonrenewable resources, 565
Nonseed plants (traits of),
    147–149, 148–149 *ill.*
Nonvascular plants, 148–149,
    149 *ill.,* 156
Nose, 452
Nostoc (blue-green bacterium),
    104 *ill.*
Notochord, 269, 272
Nuclear energy, 575, 575 *ill.*
Nuclear fission, 575, 575 *ill.*
Nuclear fusion, 584

Nuclear membrane, 78
Nucleic acids, 68
Nucleus, 33, 37, 77
Numbers pyramid, 531, 531 *ill.*
Nutrient, 415
Nutrition, 54, 54 *ill.,* 415
  carbohydrates, 416, 416 *ill.*
  fats, 416–417, 417 *ill.*
  minerals, 420, 420 *tab.,* 421 *ill.*
  proteins, 418, 418 *ill.*
  vitamins, 419–420, 419 *tab.*
  water, 421, 421 *ill.*
Nymph, 251

Oak, 174, 174 *ill.,* 547, 547 *ill.,*
    548, 553
Obesity, 425
Observation, 7–8
Octopus, 238, 239, 240 *ill.*
Odor, 330
Offspring, 344
Oil (as fossil fuel), 573
Oil glands, 410
Oil spills, 579
Omnivore, 528
Onions, 184
Open circulatory system,
    322–323, 322–323 *ill.*
Open-sea zone, 559
Opossum, 304, 304 *ill.*
Opposable thumb, 308
Optic nerve, 474
Oral groove, 126
Orangutans, 554
Orb-weaver spider, 58, 58 *ill.*
Orchid, 180, 180 *ill.,* 554
Order, 35
Organ, 177, 230, 395
Organ systems, 230, 394–395
    tab., 395
Organelles, 77, 119
Organic compound, 66
Origin of life, 69–70, 70 *ill.*
Origin of Species, The, 378
Osmosis, 86, 86 *ill.,* 197
Ospreys, 531
Outer membrane (of bone), 400
Ovaries, 331, 481, 492
Overhunting, 572
Overproduction, 379, 379 *ill.*
Oviducts, 332, 492

Ovulation, 493
Ovules, 200, 202, 204
Owls, 31, 31 *ill.*, 552, 555
Oxpecker bird, 532, 532 *ill.*
Oxygen, 68, 109, 152, 194, 294,
    295, 438, 452
  in carbon dioxide-oxygen
      cycle, 534–535, 535 *ill.*
  in circulation, 446–447
  in respiration, 88–90, 320–321
Oysters, 238, 239 *ill.*, 559

Paleozoic Era, 376
Palisade layer, 192
Pancreas, 319, 431 *ill.*, 432,
    480, 480 *ill.*
Pancreatic juice, 432
Paramecium, 125–126, 125 *ill.*,
    127 *ill.*
Parasite, 111, 230, 233, 235,
    276, 276 *ill.*, 533, 533 *ill.*
Parasitism, 533, 533 *ill.*
Parathyroid glands, 480
Parent cell, 91, 95
Parent generation, 346
Passive transport, 84–85,
    84–85 *ill.*, 87 *ill.*
Pasteurization, 113, 113 *ill.*
PCP, 486
Peanuts, 175
Pea plants (heredity of),
    344–347, 345–346 *ill.*
Peat, 159, 159 *ill.*
Pedigree, 509, 509 *ill.*
Pelvis, 397
Penicillin, 111, 130
Penis, 492
Perch, 278, 279 *ill.*, 280
Perennials, 176, 182
Peripheral nervous system,
    470–471, 470 *ill.*
Peristalsis, 427, 427 *ill.*
Permafrost, 551
Permeable, 83
Petal, 201, 203
Petiole, 185
Pharynx, 231, 317, 452
Phenotype, 349, 349 *ill.*, 503
Phenylketonuria (PKU), 507,
    507 *ill.*
Phloem, 177, 182–183, 185,

192, 196, 196 *ill.*, 198
Phosphorus, 396, 401, 480
Photosynthesis, 81, 121, 147,
    150, 182, 185, 527
  process of, 191–195,
      194–195 *ill.*
  compared with respiration,
      89–90, 89 *ill.*, 89 *tab.*
Phototropism, 209, 209 *ill.*
Phycocyanin, 105
Phylum, 35, 221–222
Physiology, 5
Phytoplankton, 559, 560
Pigeon, 294 *ill.*
Pika, 306, 306 *ill.*
Pill bugs, 257, 258, 258 *ill.*
Pine, 169, 172
  as biome type, 552
  life cycle of, 199–200,
      199–200 *ill.*
Pineapple, 206
Pioneers, 547
Pistil, 201
Pituitary gland, 479
Pivot joint, 399
Placenta, 304, 498–499, 499 *ill.*
Placentals, 304
  aquatic mammals, 306–307,
      307 *ill.*
  bats, 306, 306 *ill.*
  elephants, 308, 308 *ill.*
  hoofed mammals, 308, 308 *ill.*
  insect eaters, 305, 305 *ill.*
  meat eaters, 308, 308 *ill.*
  primates, 308, 308 *ill.*
  rodentlike mammals, 306,
      306 *ill.*
  rodents, 306, 306 *ill.*
  toothless mammals, 307, 307
      ill.
Planarians, 230–231, 230–231 *ill.*
  excretory system of, 326, 326
      ill.
  nervous system of, 328, 328 *ill.*
Plankton, 152, 559
Plant cells, 80–81, 80–81 *ill.*
Plantae, 36
Plants
  life processes of, 191–210
  nonseed plants, 147–164
  seed plants, 169–186

Plasma, 438, 438 *ill.*
Plasmodium, 134–135
Plastid, 81
Platelet, 439
Pollen, 170
Pollen grain, 199–200, 200 *ill.*,
    202–203, 203 *ill.*
Pollen tube, 200, 204, 204 *ill.*
Pollination, 200, 202–203,
    202–203 *ill.*, 345
Pollution
  air pollution, 580–581,
      580–581 *ill.*
  land pollution, 581–582
  water pollution, 578–580,
      578–580 *ill.*
Population, 526
  limiting factors, 542–545,
      543 *ill.*, 545 *ill.*
  size and density, 541–542,
      542 *ill.*
Population density, 541
Porcupine fish, 279 *ill.*
Pores
  of skin, 410
  of sponge, 224
Porpoises, 306
Potassium-40, 375
Powdery mildews, 130
Practicing (and learning), 472,
    472 *ill.*
Prairie, 556
Prairie chicken, 555
Prairie dogs, 555
Precambrian Era, 376
Precipitation, 534
Predator, 528, 543, 545, 545 *ill.*
Predator-prey cycle, 543, 545,
    545 *ill.*
Pregnancy, 498
Premolars, 301
Prey, 528
Primary succession, 546–547,
    546–547 *ill.*
Primates, 308, 308 *ill.*
Producer, 527, 527 *ill.*
Prop roots, 180, 180 *ill.*
Prophase, 92
Proteins, 67–68, 68 *ill.*, 418,
    418 *ill.*
Protista, 37, 119

Protists, 37
  animallike protists, 124–127, 124–125 ill., 127 ill.
  plantlike protists, 121–123, 121–123 ill.
  traits of, 119–120, 120 ill.
Protococcus, 150, 150 ill.
Protozoan, 120
Pseudopod, 124–125. 125 ill.
Ptarmigan, 551
Pterosaur, 373
Puberty, 493
Puffballs, 132
Pulpwood, 172
Pulse, 448, 448 ill.
Punnett squares, 350–351, 350 ill., 502
Pupa, 251–252
Pupil (of eye), 473
Purebred, 345, 345 ill.

Queen bee, 255, 255 ill.

Rabbits, 306
Rabies virus, 100
Raccoons, 553
Radial symmetry, 263, 263 ill.
Radiation, 367
Radioactive dating, 374
Radioactive element, 374
Radioactive wastes, 575
Radioactivity, 374
Rain forests, 554–555, 554–555 ill.
Ratio, 350
Rats, 306, 553
Rays (fish), 277, 277 ill.
Receptor, 471
Recessive trait, 347, 502
Rectum, 429
Recycling, 566, 583
Red algae, 154–155, 154–155 ill.
Red blood cell, 438, 438 ill.
Red marrow, 401
Red tide, 123
Red wolf, 571
Redi, Francesco, 60–61, 60 ill.
Reduction division, 495
Redwood trees, 172, 172 ill., 555
Reflex, 470–471
Reflex arc, 470

Regeneration, 226, 231, 231 ill., 264, 331, 331 ill.
Reindeer moss, 136, 157
Relaxation, of muscle, 406
Remora, 532, 533 ill.
Renewable resources, 565
Reproduction, 60
  in algae, 151, 151 ill.
  in amphibians, 332, 332 ill.
  in angiosperms, 201–205, 201–205 ill.
  asexual, 61, 61 ill.
  in bacteria, 109, 109 ill.
  in birds, 298–299, 298–299 ill.
  in bryophytes, 158, 158 ill.
  in coelenterates, 228, 331, 331 ill.
  female reproductive system, 492–494, 493–494 ill.
  fertilization and development, 498–501, 498–501 ill.
  in fish, 275, 275 ill.
  in flatworms, 231, 231 ill.
  in gymnosperms, 199–200, 199–200 ill.
  in insects, 250–252, 251–252 ill.
  male reproductive system, 491–492, 492 ill.
  in protists, 120, 120 ill.
  sex cell production, 495–497, 495 ill., 497 ill.
  sexual, 62, 62 ill.
  in sponges, 225–226
  in viruses, 101, 101 ill.
Reptiles, 285–286, 285–286 ill.
Reservoirs, 568, 568 ill.
Respiration, 55, 88–90, 88 ill., 89 tab., 320–321, 320–321 ill., 535
  in humans, 452, 452 ill.
  in plants, 195
Respiration rate (cold-blooded animals), 273
Respiratory system
  breathing, 454–455, 454 ill.
  disorders of, 455–456, 456 ill.
  parts of, 452–454, 453 ill.
Response, 57–59, 57–58 ill.
Retina, 474
Rh factor, 440

Rhea darwinii, 32
Rhinoceros, 532, 532 ill.
Rhizoids, 156, 157
Rhizome, 162, 183–184, 184 ill.
Rhubarb, 186
Ribosomes, 79
Ringworm, 130
Road runners, 557 ill.
Rocky Mountain spotted fever, 260
Rodentlike mammals, 306, 306 ill.
Rodents, 306, 306 ill.
Rods, 474
Root cap, 178
Root hairs, 178, 178 ill., 181, 197–198, 198 ill.
Root zones, 178, 178 ill.
Roots
  adaptations of, 180, 180 ill.
  kinds of, 179, 179 ill.
  reproduction from, 207
  structure and function of, 177–178, 177–178 ill.
Roses, 174
Roundworms, 233–234, 233–234 ill.
Royal jelly, 255–256
Rubber, 171
Runner, 184
Running water, 559, 560
Runoff, 535

Saber-toothed tiger (fossil), 371 ill.
Sac fungi, 130–131, 130–131 ill.
Salamanders, 283–284, 283 ill.
Salinity, 558
Saliva, 427, 430–431
Salivary glands, 431, 431 ill.
Salmonella, 112
Salts, 326, 457
Sand boa, 270 ill.
Sand dollar, 262, 262 ill.
Sandworm, 235, 235 ill.
Saprobe, 113, 113 ill., 128, 129, 174
Scales (fish), 274, 274 ill.
Scallops, 239, 239 ill.
Scanning electron microscope (SEM), 19, 19 ill., 21, 21 ill.
Scavengers, 276, 528
Schleiden, Matthew, 76

Schwann, Theodor, 76
Science, 3
Scientific method, 7–10, 7–10 *ill.*
Scientists, 3
Scorpionfish, 278 *ill.*
Scorpions, 260, 260 *ill.*
Scrotum, 491
Sea anemones, 223, 229, 532, 532 *ill.*
Sea cucumbers, 262 *ill.*
Sea horse, 278 *ill.*
Sea lilies, 262
Sea squirt, 271, 271 *ill.*
Sea turtles, 287, 287 *ill.*
Sea urchins, 262 *ill.*
Seals, 559
Second offspring generation, 346, 346 *ill.*
Secondary succession, 548, 548 *ill.*
Sedimentary rock, 369–370, 369 *ill.*
Seed coat, 200
Seed dispersal, 204
Seed plants
   angiosperms, 174–176, 174 *ill.*, 175 *tab.*, 176 *ill.*
   gymnosperms, 172–173, 172–173 *ill.*
   leaves of, 185–186, 185–186 *ill.*
   roots of, 177–181, 177–180 *ill.*
   stems of, 182–184, 182–184 *ill.*
   traits of, 169–170, 170 *ill.*
   uses of, 171, 171 *ill.*
      See also Nonseed plants.
Seeds, 200, 204, 204 *ill.*
Segmented worms, 235–237, 235–236 *ill.*
Selection (Darwin's theory), 379
Selective breeding, 359, 359 *ill.*
Self-pollination, 345
Semen, 492
Semicircular canals, 475
Semipermeable, 83
Sense organs, 410, 473
Senses
   hearing and balance, 474–475, 475 *ill.*
   sight, 473–474, 473 *ill.*
   smell, 476, 476 *ill.*
   taste, 477

touch, 477, 477 *ill.*
Sensory neurons, 467
Sepal, 201
Setae, 235
Sex cells, 354, 354 *ill.*, 495–497, 495 *ill.*, 497 *ill.*
Sex chromosomes, 355–356, 355 *ill.*
Sex determination, 355–356, 356 *ill.*
Sex hormones, 481, 493
Sex linkage, 356–358, 356–358 *ill.*
Sex-linked trait, 356
Sexual reproduction, 61–62, 222, 331–332, 332 *ill.*
Shaft (feather), 296
Sharks, 277, 277 *ill.*, 559
Shell membrane, 298
Shellfish, 258
Shrew, 305, 305 *ill.*, 553
Shrimp, 257, 258, 559
Shrub layer, 553
Sickle cell disease, 451, 451 *ill.*
Sight, 473–474, 473 *ill.*
Silica, 162
Simple eyes, 249, 259
Simple leaf, 185, 186 *ill.*
Simple microscope, 18, 18 *ill.*
Simple sugars, 416, 416 *ill.*
Skeletal muscle, 405, 405 *ill.*
Skeletal system, 396–399, 397–399 *ill.*
Skeleton, 313
   bones of, 396–398, 397–398 *ill.*
   joints of, 398–399, 399 *ill.*
Skin, 409–410, 409 *ill.*, 477, 477 *ill.*
Skull, 396
Skunks, 553, 553 *ill.*
Slime molds, 134–135, 134 *ill.*
Small intestine, 319, 428, 429 *ill.*, 431–432, 432 *ill.*
Smell (sense of), 476, 476 *ill.*
Smog, 580
Smoking, 456, 486, 486 *ill.*
Smooth muscle, 405, 405 *ill.*
Snails, 238, 239 *ill.*
Snakes, 288, 288 *ill.*, 553–555, 557

Snowy owl, 551
Social insects, 255–256, 255–256 *ill.*
Soil, 566–567, 566–567 *ill.*
Solar cells, 576, 576 *ill.*
Solar energy, 576, 576 *ill.*
Solar panels, 576, 576 *ill.*
Solar power towers, 583, 583 *ill.*
Solar satellites, 584
Sori, 163
Spanish moss, 157
Spawning, 275, 275 *ill.*
Species, 35
Sperm cells
   genetics and, 354
   in humans, 491–492, 495–497, 497 *ill.*
   in plants, 158, 202, 204
Sperm duct, 491
Sphagnum moss, 159
Sphincter muscle, 428
Spices, 171
Spicules, 224, 313
Spider web, 259–260, 260 *ill.*
Spiders, 222, 222 *ill.*, 259–260, 259–260 *ill.*, 320, 320 *ill.*
Spinal column, 396
Spinal cord, 329, 468, 468 *ill.*
Spindle, 92
Spinnerets, 260
Spiny anteater, 303, 303 *ill.*
Spiracles, 250, 320, 320 *ill.*
Spirilla, 107
Spirogyra, 151, 151 *ill.*
Sponges, 222–226, 222 *ill.*, 224–226 *ill.*, 314, 316
Spongin, 224
Spongy bone, 400
Spongy layer, 192
Spore, 127, 158, 163–164, 163 *ill.*
Spore cases, 129
Sporozoan, 127
Sprain, 407–408
Spring wood, 183, 183 *ill.*
Spruce, 169, 172, 552
Squid, 238–240, 240 *ill.*, 559
Squirrels, 306, 552, 553
Stalk, 132
Stamen, 201
Standards, 12
Standing water, 559–560

Starch granules, 121

Starches, 66, 66 *ill.*, 195, 195 *ill.*, 416, 416 *ill.*

Starfish, 222 *ill.*, 262–264, 263–264 *ill.*

Stem cuttings, 206

Stems
adaptations of, 183–184, 184 *ill.*
structure and function of, 182–183, 182–183 *ill.*

Sternum, 396–397

Stethoscope, 447, 447 *ill.*

Stigma, 201, 204

Stimulants, 483, 483 *tab.*

Stimulus, 57–58, 58 *ill.*, 328, 465

Sting ray, 277, 277 *ill.*

Stinging cell, 227

Stipe, 153

Stomach, 317, 428, 429 *ill.*

Stomach-footed mollusks, 238

Stomates, 185, 193, 193 *ill.*

Stonefish, 278 *ill.*

Strawberry plants, 184

Striations, 405

Strip cropping, 567, 567 *ill.*

Stroke, 449

Style, 201

Subphyla, 270

Successful adaptation, 245, 253–256, 253–256 *ill.*

Succession
factors causing, 548–549, 549 *ill.*
primary succession, 546–547, 546–547 *ill.*
secondary succession, 548, 548 *ill.*

Succulents, 186, 186 *ill.*, 557

Sugar cane, 206, 575

Sugar maple, 170 *ill.*

Sugars, 66, 66 *ill.*, 195, 320, 416, 416 *ill.*

Sulfur dioxide, 581

Summer wood, 183, 183 *ill.*

Sunfish, 278 *ill.*

Sunflowers, 174

Supercomputers, 22, 103

Support, 313–314, 314 *ill.*

Surgeonfish, 278 *ill.*

Survival of the fittest, 379

Swallowing process, 427–428, 427 *ill.*

Sweat glands, 409–410

Sweet potatoes, 207

Swimmerets, 258

Symbiosis, 135–136, 532–533, 532–533 *ill.*

Synapse, 466–467, 467 *ill.*

Synthesis, 55–56, 55 *ill.*

Table sugar, 416, 416 *ill.*

Tadpoles, 282, 282 *ill.*

Taiga, 552

Tailed amphibians, 283–284, 283–284 *ill.*

Tailless amphibians, 281–283, 281–282 *ill.*

Tapeworms, 232, 232 *ill.*

Taproot system, 179, 179 *ill.*

Tar, 486

Tar pit, 370

Taste (sense of), 477

Taste buds, 477

Taxonomic key, 40–41

Taxonomist, 29

Taxonomy, 29

Tay-Sachs disease, 507

Techniques (scientific), 22, 22 *ill.*

Technology, 5–6

Teeth, 301, 301 *ill.*

Telophase, 92

Temperate rain forest, 555, 555 *ill.*

Temperature, 16–17

Tendons, 406

Tendrils, 184, 184 *ill.*

Tennessee purple coneflower, 571

Tentacles, 227

Termites, 251, 255

Testes, 331, 481, 491

Theory, 10

Theory of evolution by inheritance of acquired characteristics, 377

Theory of evolution by natural selection, 380

Thermal pollution, 580, 580 *ill.*

Thigmotropism, 210, 210 *ill.*

Thorax, 246

Thorn mimic, 255 *ill.*

Threadlike fungi, 128–129, 128–129 *ill.*

Thyroid gland, 479

Ticks, 260, 533, 533 *ill.*

Tidal energy, 584, 584 *ill.*

Timber wolves, 545 *ill.*

Tissue, 148, 177, 222, 223 *ill.*, 393–395, 394 *tab.*

Toads, 281, 281 *ill.*

Tobacco mosaic virus, 100 *ill.*

Tomato, 204, 204 *ill.*

Tools (scientific), 18–21, 18–19 *ill.*, 21 *ill.*

Toothless mammals, 307, 307 *ill.*

Topsoil, 566

Tortoises, 287, 287 *ill.*

Touch (sense of), 477, 477 *ill.*

Toxins, 111–112

Trachea, 453

Tracheal tubes, 320, 320 *ill.*

Tracheophytes, 148
club mosses and horsetails, 161–162, 161 *ill.*
ferns, 162–164, 162–164 *ill.*
traits of, 160, 160 *ill.*

Traits (inherited), 343–344, 344 *ill.*, 348–352, 348–351 *ill.*, 502–504, 502–503 *ill.*

Transfusion, 440–441, 440 *ill.*

Transmission electron microscope (TEM), 18–19, 19 *ill.*, 21, 21 *ill.*

Transpiration, 197, 197 *ill.*

Transport (cellular), 83, 83 *ill.*
active, 86–87, 87 *ill.*
passive, 84–86, 84–86 *ill.*
in plants, 196–198, 196–198 *ill.*

Trap-door spider, 525, 525 *ill.*

Tree frog, 270 *ill.*

Tree sloth, 307

Triceps muscle, 406, 406 *ill.*

Trichina worms, 234, 234 *ill.*

Trichinosis, 234

Tropical rain forest, 554, 554 *ill.*, 570

Tropisms, 209–210, 209–210 *ill.*

Trypanosome, 124

Tuataras, 285, 285 *ill.*

Tube feet, 263–264, 264 *ill.*

Tuber, 184, 184 *ill.*, 207

Tulips, 184
Tundra, 550–551, 551 *ill.*
Tunicates, 270–271, 271 *ill.*
Turbidity, 559
Turtles, 287, 287 *ill.*, 560
Twins, 504–505, 504 *ill.*
Tyto alba, 31, 31 *ill.*

Ultraviolet rays, 367
Ulva, 152, 152 *ill.*
Umbilical cord, 499, 501
Understory, 553
Univalves, 239
Urea, 326, 327, 457
Ureters, 327, 458–459
Urethra, 327, 459, 492
Uric acid, 326, 327
Urine, 327, 457, 458
Uterus, 492

Vaccine, 102, 102 *ill.*
Vacuoles, 80
Vagina, 492–493
Valves, 300, 446
Vane (feather), 296
Variation (Darwin's theory), 379
Vascular bundle, 182
Vascular plants, 148, 149 *ill.*, 169, 196
Vascular tissue, 148, 156, 160, 177
Vegetative propagation, 206–207, 206–207 *ill.*
Vein, 185, 442 *ill.*, 443
Vena cava, 445–446
Ventricles, 300, 324, 445
Vertebrae, 396
Vertebrata, 271
Vertebrates
    amphibians, 281–284, 281–284 *ill.*
    birds, 293–299, 294–299 *ill.*
    fish, 274–280, 274–279 *ill.*
    mammals, 300–308, 300–308 *ill.*
    nervous system of, 329, 329 *ill.*
    phylum chordata, 269–271, 270–271 *ill.*
    reptiles, 285–288, 285–288 *ill.*

    traits of, 272–273, 272–273 *ill.*
    See also Invertebrates.
Villi, 432, 432 *ill.*
Vinegar eel, 233
Vines, 184, 184 *ill.*, 554
Virchow, Rudolf, 76
Viruses
    diseases caused by, 102–103, 102 *ill.*
    reproduction of, 101, 101 *ill.*
    traits of, 99–100, 100 *ill.*
Vitamins, 419–420, 419 *tab.*
Vocal cords, 452
Voles, 551
Volume, 15, 15 *ill.*
Volume of a solid (formula), 16, 16 *ill.*
Voluntary muscle, 404, 404 *ill.*
Volvox, 150 *ill.*, 151
Vulture, 525, 525 *ill.*

Walking stick, 255 *ill.*
Wallace, Alfred, 380
Walruses, 559
Warbler, 552
Warm-blooded animals, 273
Warm-blooded vertebrates
    birds, 293–299, 294–299 *ill.*
    mammals, 300–308, 300–308 *ill.*
    See also Cold-blooded vertebrates; Vertebrates.
Wasps, 255
Wastes, 326–327, 437, 447, 457–459, 575
Water, 197, 326, 400, 421, 421 *ill.*, 568–569, 568–569 *ill.*
Water biomes
    freshwater biome, 559–560, 560 *ill.*
    marine biome, 558–559, 558 *ill.*
    See also Land biomes.
Water cycle, 534–535, 534 *ill.*
Water energy, 577
Water flea, 257
Water hyacinths, 174
Water lilies, 174, 560
Water pollution, 578–580, 578–580 *ill.*

Water snakes, 560
Waterfalls, 577
Waterfowl, 552
Watershed, 568
Wax, 256
Weight, 14
Whales, 306, 307 *ill.*
Whelks, 239
White blood cells, 438–439, 439 *ill.*
White potato, 184, 184 *ill.*, 195, 195 *ill.*, 207
Whooping cranes, 544
Wildlife, 571–572, 571–572 *ill.*
Wildlife refuge, 572
Willow, 551
Wilting, 197, 197 *ill.*
Wind energy, 576, 577 *ill.*
Windbreaks, 172
Windmills, 576, 577 *ill.*
Windpipe, 427
Wind-pollinated flowers, 203, 203 *ill.*
Wine, 131
Wolves, 551, 552
Wood, 171, 574, 574 *ill.*
Woodpecker, 296, 296 *ill.*, 552, 552 *ill.*
Wood-thrush chicks, 299 *ill.*
Woody stem, 182, 182 *ill.*
Woolly mammoth (fossil), 371 *ill.*
Worker bees, 255–256, 255–256 *ill.*
Worms, 560

X chromosome, 355–358, 355 *ill.*
X rays, 367
Xylem, 177–178, 182–183, 185, 192, 196–198, 196 *ill.*

Y chromosome, 355–358, 355 *ill.*
Yeasts, 130–131, 131 *ill.*
Yellow marrow, 401
Yolk, 298

Zamia, 173 *ill.*
Zinnias, 176 *ill.*
Zoologist, 4 *ill.*
Zoology, 4
Zooplankton, 559, 560

Credits

l. Arthur M. Siegelman. r. © Biophoto Associates/Photo Researchers, Inc. 235: l. E.R. Degginger; r. Breck Kent. 236: Dwight Kuhn. 238: Z. Leszczynski/Breck Kent. 239: t. Breck Kent; t.m.l. © Steinhart Aquarium/Tom McHugh/Photo Researchers, Inc.; t.m.m. © Robert C. Hermes/Photo Researchers, Inc.; t.m.r. Breck Kent; b.m. © Gilbert Grant/Photo Researchers, Inc.; b. C. Allan Morgan. 240: t. Z. Leszczynski/Animals, Animals; b.l. © Steinhart Aquarium/Tom McHugh/Photo Researchers, Inc.; b.m. Phil Degginger; b.t.r. © Steinhart Aquarium/Tom McHugh/Photo Researchers, Inc.; b.b.r. E.R. Degginger.

Chapter 11 244: Jane Burton/Bruce Coleman. 246: r. Robert and Linda Mitchell. 247: Ron Dillon/Tom Stack & Associates. 250: © Stephen Dalton/Photo Researchers, Inc. 255: t.l. Robert and Linda Mitchell; t.m. © James L. Castner; t.r. Breck Kent; b. © Treat Davidson/Photo Researchers, Inc. 256: t. D. Wilder/Tom Stack & Associates; b. Robert and Linda Mitchell. 258: Robert and Linda Mitchell. 260: t.l., t.r. Robert and Linda Mitchell; b. Ron Goor/Bruce Coleman. 261: l. Hans Reinhard/Bruce Coleman; r. Breck Kent; inset Robert and Linda Mitchell. 262: l. Carl Roessler/Tom Stack & Associates; t.m. Breck Kent; t.r. E.R. Degginger; b. Bill Ward/Bruce Coleman. 264: Gary Millburn/Tom Stack & Associates.

Chapter 12 268: © Robert C. Hermes/Photo Researchers, Inc. 270: E.R. Degginger. 271: t. © Tom McHugh/Photo Researchers; b. Heather Angel/Biofotos. 272: Robert Pearcy/Animals, Animals. 273: E.R. Degginger. 275: Mark Stouffer/Animals, Animals. 276: t. © Steinhart Aquarium/Tom McHugh/Photo Researchers, Inc.; b.l. Heather Angel/Biofotos; b.r. Tom Stack/Tom Stack & Associates. 277: t. Doug Wechsler; m. © Richard Ellis/Photo Researches, Inc.; b. © Mike Neumann/Photo Researchers, Inc. 278: t.l. Breck Kent; t.m., t.r., b.l. E.R. Degginger; b.m. Z. Leszczynski/Animals, Animals; b.r. © Tom McHugh/Photo Researchers, Inc. 279: Jane Burton/Bruce Coleman. 281: © Steinhart Aquarium/Tom McHugh/Photo Researchers, Inc. 282: t. John H. Gerard; b. Lynn M. Stone/Bruce Coleman. 283: E.R. Degginger. 284: t. Michael Fogden/Animals, Animals; m. Jack Dermid/Bruce Coleman; b. Imagery. 285: r. Heather Angel/Biofotos. 286: Alan Blank/Bruce Coleman. 287: l. © Russ Kinne/Photo Researchers, Inc.; r. Tui A. DeRoy/Bruce Coleman. 288: t.l. E.R. Degginger; t.r. © Larry Miller/Photo Researchers, Inc.; b. Jen and Des Bartlett/Bruce Coleman.

Chapter 13 292: Michael Fogden/Animals, Animals. 294: G.I. Bernhard/Oxford Scientific Films/Animals, Animals. 297: John Gerlach/Tom Stack & Associates. 299: t. Warren Garst/Tom Stack & Associates; m. John F. O'Connor, M.D./Photo Nats; b. Margot Conte/Animals, Animals. 300: l. E.R. Degginger; m. © Merlin D. Tuttle/Photo Researchers, Inc.; r. © William Curtsinger/Photo Researchers, Inc. 302: Phil Degginger. 303: l. © Tom McHugh, Taronga Zoo/Photo Researchers, Inc.; r. © Tom McHugh/Photo Researchers, Inc. 304: t.l. Breck Kent; t.r. E.R. Degginger; b. Imagery. 305: t. © John Dommers/Photo Researchers, Inc.; b. © Howard E. Uible/Photo Researchers, Inc. 306: t. © Merlin Tuttle/Photo Researchers, Inc.; b.l. inset © Leonard Lee Rue III/Photo Researchers, Inc.; m. © Pat and Tom Leeson/Photo Researchers, Inc.; b.r. Rod Planck/Tom Stack & Associates. 307: t.l. © Tom McHugh/Photo Researchers, Inc.; t.r. © Richard Ellis/Photo Researchers, Inc.; b. Warren Garst/Tom Stack & Associates. 308: l. Gerald Corsi/Tom Stack & Associates; t.m. Warren and Jenny Garst/Tom Stack & Associates; t.r. Charles E. Schmidt/Taurus Photos; b. E.R. Degginger.

Chapter 14 312: Z. Leszczynski; l. inset Breck Kent/Animals, Animals; t.m. inset E.R. Degginger; b.m. inset Runk-Schoenberger/Grant Heilman Photography; t.r. inset Stephen Dalton/Animals, Animals; b.r. inset E.R. Degginger/Animals, Animals. 316: Paul L. Janosi/Valan Photos; 321: © Steinhart Aquarium/Tom McHugh/Photo Researchers, Inc. 322: t. Dr. Eugene Musselman; inset Silver Burdett & Ginn. 331: Kjell B. Sandved. 336: t. Silver Burdett & Ginn; m. Mike Malyszko/Stock, Boston.

Unit Five 340: t. The Granger Collection; b. Nancy Adams/Tom Stack & Associates. 341: t.l., t.r. Breck Kent; m. UPI/Bettmann Newsphotos; b. E.R. Degginger.

Chapter 15 342: Dan De Wilde for Silver Burdett & Ginn. 344: l., m. Breck Kent; t.r. © M. Abbey/Photo Researchers, Inc.; b.r. © Eric Grave/Photo Researchers, Inc. 347: Larry Lefever/Grant Heilman Photography. 355: l. Grace Moore/Taurus Photos; r. © Photo Researchers, Inc. 359: l. © Mary M. Thatcher/Photo Researchers, Inc.; b.m. Breck Kent; t.r. E.R. Degginger; b.r. Jon and Sue Hacking/Earth Images.

Chapter 16 364: John Pawloski/Tom Stack & Associates. 366: t. Lou Jacobs, Jr./Grant Heilman Photography; b.l. Stephen J. Krasemann/DRK Photos; b.r. Heather Angel/Biofoto. 367: l. © Darwin Dale/Photo Researchers, Inc.; r. Runk-Schoenberger/Grant Heilman Photography. 368: l. John Shaw/Tom Stack & Associates; r. Runk-Schoenberger/Grant Heilman Photography. 369: inset E.R. Degginger. 370: t.l. E.R. Degginger; t.r. Runk-Schoenberger/Grant Heilman Photography; b. E.R. Degginger. 371: l. Tass/Sovfoto; r. Tom McHugh/Photo Researchers, Inc. 373: James Collison. 378: t, m.l. E.R. Degginger; m.r. M. Austerman/Animals, Animals; b. Leonard Lee Rue III/Tom Stack & Associates. 379: Z. Leszczynski/Animals, Animals.380: Breck Kent. 381: Oxford Scientific Films/Animals, Animals. 386 t. Ralph Barrera/Texastock; m. Grace Moore.

Unit Six 390: l. The Granger Collection; t.r. Martin M. Rotker/Taurus Photos; b.r. © Lennart Nilsson, *Behold Man*, Little, Brown & Co., Inc. 391: t.l. The Granger Collection; b.l. E.R. Degginger; r. Phil Degginger.

Chapter 17 392: Peter Menzel/Stock, Boston. 394: t.l. Ed Reschke/Peter Arnold, Inc.; b.l. Tom Stack & Associates; m. Martin M. Rotker/Taurus Photos; r. Tom Stack &

Associates. 396: The Bettmann Archive. 398: Arthur Sirdofsky/The Stock Shop. 399: Dick Walker/Taurus Photos. 401: t., b. Imagery. 404: Silver Burdett & Ginn. 405: Manfred Kage/Peter Arnold, Inc. 408: David Madison/Bruce Coleman. 410: Dan Mc-Coy/Rainbow.

Chapter 18 414: Dan De Wilde for Silver Burdett & Ginn. 416, 417: Silver Burdett & Ginn. 418: Grant Heilman. 421: Silver Burdett & Ginn. 422: l. Barry L. Runk/Grant Heilman Photography; r. Imagery. 423: l. Alan Pitcairn/Grant Heilman Photography; r. Imagery. 424: Silver Burdett & Ginn. 428: NASA. 432: © Biophoto Associates/Science Source/Photo Researchers, Inc.

Chapter 19 436: Ken Lax/The Stock Shop. 438: l. © Biophoto Associates/Science Source/Photo Researchers, Inc.; r. © Dr. Tony Brain/Science Photo Library/Photo Researchers, Inc. 439: t. © Keith Porter/Science Source/Photo Researchers, Inc.; m. © Dr. D.J. McLaren/Photo Researchers, Inc.; b. © Dr. Anderjs Liepins/Photo Researchers, Inc. 440: Lester V. Bergman & Associates. 442: © Biophoto Associates/Science Source/Photo Researchers, Inc. 443: © Lennart Nilsson, *Behold Man*, Little, Brown & Co., Inc., 447: l. Somso Biological Works, Coburg, West Germany, available through Carolina Biological Supply Company; b. Victoria Beller-Smith/E.R. Degginger. 448: Silver Burdett & Ginn. 449: Lester V. Bergman & Associates. 451: l. © K.R. Porter/Photo Researchers, Inc.; r. © Photo Researchers, Inc. 456: Runk-Schoenberger/Grant Heilman Photography. 460: Terry Newfarmer/University of Utah.

Chapter 20 © Lennart Nilsson, *Behold Man*, Little, Brown & Co., Inc. 466: l. Ed Reschke/Peter Arnold, Inc. 469: l. Michal Heron; r. Breck Kent. 472: Silver Burdett & Ginn. 474: Michael Alexander. 475: Vic Cox/Peter Arnold, Inc. 477: Barry Fernald. 479: Terry Dominico/Earth Images. 480: t. © Biophoto Associates/Photo Researchers, Inc.; b. Grace Moore. 482: Silver Burdett & Ginn. 484: t.l., b.l. © Photo Researchers, Inc.; r. © A. Glauberman/Photo Researchers, Inc. 485: l. Imagery; r. © Van Bucher/Photo Researchers, Inc. 486: t. Silver Burdett & Ginn; b. Martin M. Rotker/Taurus Photos.

Chapter 21 490: Silver Burdett & Ginn; inset Jan Burgess. 492: Ed Reschke/Peter Arnold, Inc. 493: Manfred Kage/Peter Arnold, Inc. 497: t. David Scharf/Peter Arnold, Inc.; b. © John Giannicchi/Science Source/Photo Researchers, Inc. 498: © D.W. Fawcett/Science Source/Photo Researchers, Inc. 502, 504: Silver Burdett & Ginn. 505: l. The Bettmann Archive; r. The Granger Collection. 506: l. Brian Parker/Tom Stack & Associates; r. Martin M. Rotker/Taurus Photos. 507: l. Mead Johnson; r. Erika Stone. 508: b. Grace Moore/Taurus Photos. 514: t. Grace Moore; m. © Hank Morgan/Photo Researchers, Inc.

Unit Seven 518: l. Terry Dominico/Earth Images; t.r. E.R. Degginger; b.r. Tom Stack/Tom Stack & Associates. 519: t. The Granger Collection; b.l. The Bettmann Archive; b.r. Breck Kent.

Chapter 22 520: Spencer Swanger/Tom Stack & Associates. 522: John Gerlach/Tom Stack & Associates. 524: M. Timothy O'Keefe/Tom Stack & Associates. 525: l. Breck Kent; r. Sean Morris/Oxford Scientific Films/Animals, Animals. 526: l. Michael Fogden/Animals, Animals.; r. Runk-Schoenberger/Grant Heilman Photography. 527: t.l. Patti Murray/Animals, Animals; t.r. G.R. Roberts; b.l. Breck Kent; b.r. Imagery. 528: t. C.C. Lockwood/Bruce Coleman; b. Richard Thom/Tom Stack & Associates. 531: Jerry Via. 532: l. © M. Reardon/Photo Researchers, Inc.; r. E.R. Degginger. 533: t. Howard Hall/Earth Images; m. Leonard Lee Rue III/Bruce Coleman; b. Stephen J. Krasemann/DRK Photos. 536: Grant Heilman.

Chapter 23 540, 543: E.R. Degginger. 545: t. Breck Kent; b. Stephen J. Krasemann/DRK Photos. 547: l. Phil Degginger; r. Ken Davis/Tom Stack & Associates. 548: Breck Kent. 549: Leonard Lee Rue III/Click, Chicago. 551: l. Jean Kepler/Rainbow; t.r. Budd Titlow/Tom Stack & Associates; b.r. Bruce Richardson. 552: t. Breck Kent; b.l., b.r., inset E.R. Degginger. 553: l. E.R. Degginger; r. Breck Kent; inset Imagery. 554: l., r. E.R. Degginger; inset Breck Kent. 555: t. L.L.T. Rhodes/Earth Scenes; b. Dale Jorgensen/Tom Stack & Associates. 556: t. Imagery; l. inset Breck Kent; r. inset Luke Wade/Taurus Photos. 557: t. Imagery; l. inset © Pat and Tom Leesòn/Photo Researchers, Inc.; r. inset Imagery. 558: l. Lester V. Bergman & Associates; r. Runk-Schoenberger/Grant Heilman Photography. 559: Oxford Scientific Films/Animals, Animals. 560: l. Runk-Schoenberger/Grant Heilman Photography; r. Lester V. Bergman & Associates.

Chapter 24 564: © Stephen J. Krasemann/Photo Researchers, Inc. 566: t. S.L.O.T.S./Taurus Photos; b. Grant Heilman. 567: Tim McCabe/Taurus Photos. 568: Grant Heilman. 569: t.l. John Colwell/Grant Heilman Photography; b.l., r. Imagery. 570: l. Ron Seymour/Click, Chicago; r. Breck Kent. 571: l. Runk-Schoenberger/Grant Heilman Photography; l. inset © James R. Fisher/Photo Researchers, Inc.; r. inset © Patricia Caulfield/Photo Researchers, Inc.; r. © Kenneth W. Fink/Photo Researchers, Inc. 572: © Merlin Tuttle/Photo Researchers, Inc. 573: l. MDTA Public Affairs; r. Silver Burdett & Ginn. 574: James R. Holland/Stock, Boston. 575: t. Tass/Sovfoto; b. Wisconsin Public Service Company. 576: l. Alec Duncan/Taurus Photos; m. Gary Millburn/Tom Stack & Associates; r. Dick George/Tom Stack & Associates. 577: t. Kevin Schafer/Tom Stack & Associates; b. Grant Heilman. 578: Tom Stack/Tom Stack & Associates. 579: Breck Kent. 580: t. Milton Rand/Tom Stack & Associates; b. Silver Burdett & Ginn. 581: Field Museum of Natural History, Chicago. 583: © Georg Gerster/Photo Researchers, Inc. 584: t. © Georg Gerster/Photo Researchers, Inc.; b. Peter Britton. 588: t. Laimute Druskis/Taurus Photos; m. Fred Whitehead/Animals, Animals.

3 4 5 6 7 8 9 10—RRD—95 94 93 92 91 90 89 88